MW00773752

Die
Manufacturing and Distribution

Current Good Manufacturing Practice,
Labeling, and Premarket Notification

Concise Reference

Second Edition

DIETARY SUPPLEMENTS MANUFACTURING AND DISTRIBUTION

CURRENT GOOD MANUFACTURING PRACTICE, LABELING, AND PREMARKET NOTIFICATION

SECOND EDITION

DR. KIRSTIN A. COUNTS
MINDY J. ALLPORT-SETTLE

Pharma
Logika
Books

Dietary Supplements Manufacturing and Distribution: Current Good Manufacturing Practice, Labeling, and Premarket Notification, Concise Reference, Second Edition

ISBN-13: 978-1-937258-19-1

Authors: Dr. Kirstin A. Counts & Mindy J. Allport-Settle
Published by PharmaLogika Books.
Printed in the United States of America.

Please direct all inquiries to

info@PharmaLogika.com

For information on our other available titles and services, visit us

www.PharmaLogika.com

Table of Contents

Regulations

Legislative Acts & Significant Amendments

Guidance & Associated Documents

Chapter 11
Labeling of Dietary Supplements: Guidance for Industry

Combined Glossary & Index

Preface

About this Book

This book is designed to be a unified reference source for the U.S. Food and Drug Adminstration's Dietary Supplements regulations, guidance, and associated documents.

The included FDA Overview and Orientation provides a foundation for understanding the background of the FDA, its guidelines, its relationship with other countries and its relationship with manufacturers and distributors.

This book is designed to be used both as a reference for experienced industry representatives and as a training resource for those new to the industry.

Included Documents and Features

- ➲ FDA Overview and Orientation
- ➲ Introduction to Dietary Supplements
- ➲ Part 1: General Enforcement Regulations
- ➲ Part 101: Food Labeling
- ➲ Part 111: Current Good Manufacturing Practice in Manufacturing, Packaging, Labeling, or Holding Operations for Dietary Supplements
- ➲ Part 119: Dietary Supplements that Present a Significant or Unreasonable Risk
- ➲ Part 190: Dietary Supplements
- ➲ Dietary Supplement Health and Education Act of 1994
- ➲ Dietary Supplement and Nonprescription Drug Consumer Protection Act
- ➲ Guidance Documents
- ➲ Sample Warning Letters
- ➲ Combined Glossary and Index

About the Reference Tools

FDA Overview and Orientation and the Introduction to Dietary Supplements

The FDA overview provides the reader with a brief history of the Food and Drug Administration (FDA) and explains not only what good manufacturing practice is, but why it exists and how it came to be. The Introduction to Dietary Supplements provides the basic background for regulatory management and a guide to the FDA's approach to dietary supplements commercial manufacture and distribution.

Combined Glossary

The Combined Glossary includes all of the glossaries from each regulation and guidance listed alphabetically rather than by document.

When a word or term appears multiple times in the regulation and guidance documents, the word will appear multiple times in the Combined Glossary if there is a variation in the definition. Each duplicate entry is indented to highlight that it is a duplicate and the earliest reference to the entry is listed first. The source for each entry is bracketed (i.e., [21 CFR § 50]) for ease of reference. While the definitions are similar from one regulatory or guidance document to the next, they are not always identical.

Combined Index for all Regulations

The index is composed of a list of both words and terms specific to the Dietary Supplements regulations and includes selected entries relative to Good Manufacturing Practice.

Like pharmaceutical, biotechnology, and medical device companies, the dietary supplements industry uses terminology that combines scientific and technical jargon with legal phrases and concepts.

The index provides keywords and terminology as a tool to easily locate specific references across all documents rather than having to rely on memory or paging through each document individually.

Chapter 1

FDA Overview and Orientation

The Food and Drug Administration (FDA)

The United States Food and Drug Administration (FDA) is responsible for protecting and promoting the nation's public health.

The programs for safety regulation vary widely by the type of product, its potential risks, and the regulatory powers granted to the agency. For example, the FDA regulates almost every facet of prescription drugs, including testing, manufacturing, labeling, advertising, marketing, efficacy and safety. FDA regulation of cosmetics, however, is focused primarily on labeling and safety. The FDA regulates most products with a set of published standards enforced by a combination of facility inspections, voluntary company reporting standards, and public and consumer watchdog activity.

The FDA frequently works in conjunction with other Federal agencies including the Department of Agriculture, Drug Enforcement Administration, Customs and Border Protection, and Consumer Product Safety Commission.

Historical Origins of Federal Food and Drug Regulation

Prior to the 20th century, there were few federal laws regulating the contents and sale of domestically produced food and pharmaceuticals before the 20th century (with one exception being the short-lived Vaccine Act of 1813). Some state laws provided varying degrees of protection against unethical sales practices, such as misrepresenting the ingredients of food products or therapeutic substances.

The history of the FDA can be traced to the latter part of the 19th century and the U.S. Department of Agriculture's Division of Chemistry (later Bureau of Chemistry). Under Harvey Washington Wiley, appointed chief chemist in 1883, the Division began conducting research into the adulteration and misbranding of food and drugs on the American market. Although they had no regulatory powers, the Division published its findings from 1887 to 1902 in a ten-part series entitled Foods and Food Adulterants. Wiley used these findings, and alliances with diverse organizations (such as state regulators, the General Federation of Women's Clubs, and national associations of physicians and pharmacists) to lobby for a new federal law to set uniform standards for food and drugs to enter into interstate commerce.

Wiley's advocacy came at a time when the public had become alert to hazards in the marketplace by journalists and became part of a general trend for increased federal regulation in matters pertinent to public safety during the Progressive Era.[1] The 1902 Biologics Control Act was put in place after diphtheria antitoxin was collected from a horse named Jim who also had tetanus, resulting in several deaths.[2]

The 1906 Food and Drug Act and creation of the FDA

In June 1906, President Theodore Roosevelt signed into law the Food and Drug Act, also known as the "Wiley Act" after its chief advocate.[3] The Act prohibited, under penalty of seizure of goods, the interstate transport of food which had been "adulterated," with that term referring to the addition of fillers of reduced "quality or strength," coloring to conceal "damage or inferiority," formulation with additives "injurious to health," or the use of "filthy, decomposed, or putrid" substances. The act applied similar penalties to the interstate marketing of "adulterated" drugs, in which the "standard of strength, quality, or purity" of the active ingredient was not either stated clearly on the label or listed in the United States Pharmacopoeia or the National Formulary. The act also banned "misbranding" of food and drugs.[4] The responsibility for examining food and drugs for such "adulteration" or "misbranding" was given to Wiley's USDA Bureau of Chemistry.[5] Strength, quality, identity, potency, and purity (SQuIPP) are currently the key product safety standards, with only two measures added since 1906 Act.

Wiley used these new regulatory powers to pursue an aggressive campaign against the manufacturers of foods with chemical additives, but the Chemistry Bureau's authority was soon checked by judicial decisions, as well as by the creation of the Board of Food and Drug Inspection and the Referee Board of Consulting Scientific Experts as separate organizations within the USDA in 1907 and 1908 respectively. A 1911 Supreme Court decision ruled that the 1906 act did not apply to false claims of therapeutic efficacy,[6] in response to which a 1912 amendment added "false and fraudulent" claims of "curative or therapeutic effect" to the Act's definition of "misbranded." However, these powers continued to be narrowly defined by the courts, which set high standards for proof of fraudulent intent.[7] In 1927, the Bureau of Chemistry's regulatory powers were reorganized under a new USDA body, the Food, Drug, and Insecticide organization. This name was shortened to the Food and Drug Administration (FDA) three years later.[8]

---

1   "Background: Research Tools on FDA History." U S Food and Drug Administration (database online); Available from www.fda.gov/AboutFDA/WhatWeDo/History/ResearchTeaching/ResearchTools/ucm2007259.htm.
2   Bren, Linda. "The Road to the Biotech Revolution - Highlights of 100 Years of Biologics Regulation." FDA Consumer Magazine (2006); Available from www.fda.gov/downloads/AboutFDA/WhatWeDo/History/ProductRegulation/UCM593490.pdf.
3   Meadows, Michelle. "Promoting Safe & Effective Drugs for 100 Years." FDA Consumer Magazine (2006); Available from www.fda.gov/AboutFDA/WhatWeDo/History/ProductRegulation/ucm2017809.htm.
4   Text in quotation marks is the original text of the 1906 Food and Drugs Act and Amendments. United States Congress. "Pure Food and Drug Act of 1906." Wikisource, 11 December 2016. Available from https://en.wikisource.org/wiki/Pure_Food_and_Drug_Act_of_1906.
5   Meadows, Michelle. "A Century of Ensuring Safe Foods and Cosmetics." FDA Consumer Magazine (2006), www.fda.gov/AboutFDA/WhatWeDo/History/ProductRegulation/ucm083863.htm.
6   United States v. Johnson (31 S. Ct. 627 May 29, 1911, decided).
7   "Background: Research Tools on FDA History." US Food and Drug Administration (database online); www.fda.gov/AboutFDA/WhatWeDo/History/ResearchTeaching/ResearchTools/ucm2007259.htm.
8   "Milestones in U.S. Food and Drug Law History." US Food and Drug Administration (database online); www.fda.gov/aboutfda/whatwedo/history/forgshistory/evolvingpowers/ucm2007256.htm.

The 1938 Food, Drug, and Cosmetic Act

By the 1930s, muckraking journalists, consumer protection organizations, and federal regulators began mounting a campaign for stronger regulatory authority by publicizing a list of injurious products which had been ruled permissible under the 1906 law, including radioactive beverages, cosmetics which caused blindness, and worthless "cures" for diabetes and tuberculosis. The resulting proposed law was unable to get through the Congress of the United States for five years but was rapidly enacted into law following the public outcry over the 1937 Elixir Sulfanilamide tragedy, in which over 100 people died after using a drug formulated with a toxic, untested solvent. The only way that the FDA could even seize the product was due to a misbranding problem: an "Elixir" was defined as a medication dissolved in ethanol, not the diethylene glycol used in the Elixir Sulfanilamide.

President Franklin Delano Roosevelt signed the new Food, Drug, and Cosmetic Act (FD&C Act) into law on June 24, 1938. The new law significantly increased federal regulatory authority over drugs by mandating a pre-market review of the safety of all new drugs, as well as banning false therapeutic claims in drug labeling without requiring that the FDA prove fraudulent intent. The law also authorized factory inspections and expanded enforcement powers, set new regulatory standards for foods, and brought cosmetics and therapeutic devices under federal regulatory authority. This law, though extensively amended in subsequent years, remains the central foundation of FDA regulatory authority to the present day.[9]

Early FD&C Act amendments: 1938-1958

Soon after passage of the 1938 Act, the FDA began to designate certain drugs as safe for use only under the supervision of a medical professional, and the category of 'prescription-only' drugs was securely codified into law by the 1951 Durham-Humphrey Amendment.[10] While pre-market testing of drug efficacy was not authorized under the 1938 FD&C Act, subsequent amendments such as the Insulin Amendment and Penicillin Amendment did mandate potency testing for formulations of specific lifesaving pharmaceuticals.[11] The FDA began enforcing its new powers against drug manufacturers who could not substantiate the efficacy claims made for their drugs, and the United States Court of Appeals for the Ninth Circuit ruling in Alberty Food Products Co. v. United States (1950) found that drug manufacturers could not evade the "false therapeutic claims" provision of the 1938 act by simply omitting the intended use of a drug from the drug's label. These developments confirmed extensive powers for the FDA to enforce post-marketing recalls of ineffective drugs.[12] Much of the FDA's regulatory attentions in this era were directed

9   Young, James Harvey. "Long Struggle for the Law." US Food and Drug Administration (database online); www.fda.gov/AboutFDA/WhatWeDo/History/FOrgsHistory/EvolvingPowers/ucm2007264.htm.
10   Swann, PhD, John P. "FDA's Origins. Part III: Drugs and Foods Under the 1938 Act and Its Amendments." FDA History Office. US Food and Drug Administration (database online); www.fda.gov/AboutFDA/WhatWeDo/History/FOrgsHistory/EvolvingPowers/ucm055118.htm.
11   "Milestones in U.S. Food and Drug Law History." US Food and Drug Administration (database online); www.fda.gov/aboutfda/whatwedo/history/forgshistory/evolvingpowers/ucm2007256.htm.
12   Swann, Ph.D., John P. "FDA's Origins. Part II: 1938, Food, Drug, Cosmetic Act." FDA History Office. US Food and Drug Administration (database online); www.fda.gov/AboutFDA/WhatWeDo/History/FOrgsHistory/EvolvingPowers/ucm054826.htm.

towards abuse of amphetamines and barbiturates, but the agency also reviewed some 13,000 new drug applications between 1938 and 1962. While the science of toxicology was in its infancy at the start of this era, rapid advances in experimental assays for food additive and drug safety testing were made during this period by FDA regulators and others.[13]

Good Manufacturing Practices vs. Current Good Manufacturing Practices

The terms "Good Manufacturing Practices (GMPs)" and "Current Good Manufacturing Practices (CGMPs or cGMPs[14])" are often used interchangeably both in industry and by FDA inspectors.

"Good Manufacturing Practices" generally refers to the legal mandates detailed in Title 21 of the Code of Federal Regulations (21CFR). "Current Good Manufacturing Practices" refers not only to the legal requirements, but to the guidance provided by the FDA and the standards practiced in industry that are not memorialized as law.

Organizational Structure

The FDA is an agency within the United States Department of Health and Human Services responsible for protecting and promoting the nation's public health. It is organized into the following major subdivisions, each focused on a major area of regulatory responsibility:

- The Office of the Commissioner (OC)
- The Center for Drug Evaluation and Research (CDER)
- The Center for Biologics Evaluation and Research (CBER)
- The Center for Food Safety and Applied Nutrition (CFSAN)
- The Center for Devices and Radiological Health (CDRH)
- The Center for Veterinary Medicine (CVM)
- The National Center for Toxicological Research (NCTR)
- The Office of Regulatory Affairs (ORA)
- The Office of Criminal Investigations (OCI)

---

13   Swann, PhD, John P. "FDA's Origins. Part III: Drugs and Foods Under the 1938 Act and Its Amendments." FDA History Office. US Food and Drug Administration (database online); www.fda.gov/AboutFDA/WhatWeDo/History/FOrgsHistory/EvolvingPowers/ucm055118.htm.
14   The lower case "c" was coined in industry to differentiate between the law, emphasized with capital letters, and the current accepted industry practice not mandated by law.

How does the FDA communicate with Industry?

Code of Federal Regulations

The Code of Federal Regulations (CFR)[15] is the codification of the general and permanent rules and regulations (sometimes called administrative law) published in the Federal Register by the executive departments and agencies of the Federal Government of the United States. The CFR is published by the Office of the Federal Register, an agency of the National Archives and Records Administration (NARA).

The CFR is divided into 50 titles that represent broad areas subject to Federal regulation. Title 21 is the portion of the Code of Federal Regulations that governs food and drugs within the United States for the Food and Drug Administration (FDA), the Drug Enforcement Administration (DEA), and the Office of National Drug Control Policy (ONDCP).

It is divided into three chapters:

- Chapter I — Food and Drug Administration
- Chapter II — Drug Enforcement Administration
- Chapter III — Office of National Drug Control Policy

Guidance Documents

Guidance documents represent the Agency's current thinking on a particular subject. They do not create or confer any rights for or on any person and do not operate to bind FDA or the public. An alternative approach may be used if such approach satisfies the requirements of the applicable statute, regulations, or both. For information on a specific guidance document, please contact the originating office. Another method of obtaining guidance documents is through the Division of Drug Information.

Federal Register

The Federal Register (since March 14, 1936), abbreviated FR, or sometimes Fed. Reg.) is the official journal of the federal government of the United States that contains most routine publications and public notices of government agencies. It is a daily (except holidays) publication.

The Federal Register is compiled by the Office of the Federal Register (within the National Archives and Records Administration) and is printed by the Government Printing Office.

There are no copyright restrictions on the Federal Register as it is a work of the U.S. government. It is in the public domain.[16]

Citations from the Federal Register are [volume] FR [page number] ([date]), e.g., 65 FR 741 (2000-10-01).

---

15   The Code of Federal Regulations (CFR) annual edition is available through the U.S. Government Publishing Office (GOP) at www.gpo.gov/fdsys/bulkdata/CFR.
16   The Federal Register from 1960 to present is available through the GPO www.gpo.gov/fdsys/browse/collection. action?collectionCode=FR

Direct Communication and Letters

The FDA interacts with consumers, health professionals, and industry representatives through letters, meetings (requested by either the FDA or the industry representatives), and telephone calls.

While not all questions can be answered over the phone, the FDA prefers telephone interactions over physical meetings (when a teleconference can reasonably replace a face-to-face meeting).

www.FDA.gov

The FDA maintains a website at www.fda.gov that is focused on three key audiences:

- consumers
- health professionals
- industry representatives

Through collaboration with users in testing site-wide designs, FDA.gov provides online access to its guidance documents, communication with industry, consumers, and health professionals. Information is categorized by topic, with related subjects consolidated in sections on the site.

Additionally, FDA.gov provides a search engine for Title 21 of the CFR that makes finding keyword references throughout the title more accessible.

Conferences

The FDA routinely sends speakers to industry conferences where they are available to answer questions on their particular area of expertise.

False Statement to a Federal Agency

The U.S. Code of Federal Regulations (CFR) makes it a federal crime for anyone willfully and knowingly to make a false or fraudulent statement to a department or agency of the United States. The false statement must be related to a material matter, and the defendant must have acted willfully and with knowledge of the falsity. It is not necessary to show that the government agency was in fact deceived or misled. The issue of materiality is one of law for the courts. The maximum penalty is five years' imprisonment and a $10,000 fine.

A person may be guilty of a violation without proof that he or she had knowledge that the matter was within the jurisdiction of a federal agency. A businessperson may violate this law by making a false statement to another firm or person with knowledge that the information will be submitted to a government agency. Businesses must take care to avoid exaggerations in the context of any matter that may come within the jurisdiction of a federal agency.

CFR Title 21
Food and Drugs: Parts 1 to 1499[1]

Chapter I — Food and Drug Administration, Department of Health and Human Services

Subchapter A- General

(1) General enforcement regulations

(2) General administrative rulings and decisions

(3) Product jurisdiction

(4) Regulation of Combination Products

(5) Organization

(7) Enforcement policy

(10) Administrative practices and procedures

(11) Electronic records; electronic signatures

(12) Formal evidentiary public hearing

(13) Public hearing before a public board of inquiry

(14) Public hearing before a public advisory committee

(15) Public hearing before the commissioner

(16) Regulatory hearing before the food and drug administration

(17) Civil money penalties hearings

(19) Standards of conduct and conflicts of interest

(20) Public information

(21) Protection of privacy

(25) Environmental impact considerations

(26) Mutual recognition of pharmaceutical good manufacturing practice reports, medical device quality system audit reports, and certain medical device product evaluation reports: United States and the European community

(50) Protection of human subjects

(54) Financial disclosure by clinical investigators

(56) Institutional review boards

(58) Good laboratory practice for nonclinical laboratory studies

(60) Patent term restoration

(70) Color additives

---

1   All of the 21CFR regulations can be searched online for no charge at http://www.accessdata.fda.gov/scripts/cdrh/cfdocs/cfcfr/cfrsearch.cfm

(71) Color additive petitions

(73) Listing of color additives exempt from certification

(74) Listing of color additives subject to certification

(80) Color additive certification

(81) General specifications and general restrictions for provisional color additives for use in foods, drugs, and cosmetics

(82) Listing of certified provisionally listed colors and specifications

(83-98) [reserved]

(99) Dissemination of information on unapproved/new uses for marketed drugs, biologics, and devices

Subchapter B – Food for Human Consumption

(100) General

(101) Food labeling

(102) Common or usual name for nonstandardized foods

(104) Nutritional quality guidelines for foods

(105) Foods for special dietary use

(106) Infant formula requirements pertaining to current good manufacturing practice, quality control procedures, quality factors, records and reports, and notifications

(107) Infant formula

(108) Emergency permit control

(109) Unavoidable contaminants in food for human consumption and food-packaging material

(110) Current good manufacturing practice in manufacturing, packing, or holding human food

(111) Current good manufacturing practice in manufacturing, packaging, labeling, or holding operations for dietary supplements

(112) Standards for the growing, harvesting, packing, and holding of produce for human consumption

(113) Thermally processed low-acid foods packaged in hermetically sealed containers

(114) Acidified foods

(115) Shell eggs

(117) Current good manufacturing practice, hazard analysis, and risk-based preventive controls for human food

(118) Production, storage, and transportation of shell eggs

(119) Dietary supplements that present a significant or unreasonable risk

(120) Hazard analysis and critical control point (HACCP) systems

(121) Mitigation strategies to protect food against intentional adulteration

(123) Fish and fishery products

(129) Processing and bottling of bottled drinking water

(130) Food standards: general

(131) Milk and cream

(133) Cheeses and related cheese products

(135) Frozen desserts

(136) Bakery products

(137) Cereal flours and related products

(139) Macaroni and noodle products

(145) Canned fruits

(146) Canned fruit juices

(150) Fruit butters, jellies, preserves, and related products

(152) Fruit pies

(155) Canned vegetables

(156) Vegetable juices

(158) Frozen vegetables

(160) Eggs and egg products

(161) Fish and shellfish

(163) Cacao products

(164) Tree nut and peanut products

(165) Beverages

(166) Margarine

(168) Sweeteners and table syrups

(169) Food dressings and flavorings

(170) Food additives

(171) Food additive petitions

(172) Food additives permitted for direct addition to food for human consumption

(173) Secondary direct food additives permitted in food for human consumption

(174) Indirect food additives: general

(175) Indirect food additives: adhesives and components of coatings

(176) Indirect food additives: paper and paperboard components

(177) Indirect food additives: polymers

(178) Indirect food additives: adjuvants, production aids, and sanitizers

(179) Irradiation in the production, processing and handling of food

Subchapter D - New Drugs and Over-the-Counter Drug Products/Drugs for Human Use

(300) General

(310) New drugs

(312) Investigational new drug application

(314) Applications for FDA approval to market a new drug

(315) Diagnostic radiopharmaceuticals

(316) Orphan drugs

(317) Qualifying pathogens

(320) Bioavailability and bioequivalence requirements

(328) Over-the-counter drug products intended for oral ingestion that contain alcohol

(329) Nonprescription human drug products subject to section 760 of the Federal Food, Drug, and Cosmetic Act

(330) Over-the-counter (OTC) human drugs which are generally recognized as safe and effective and not misbranded

(331) Antacid products for over-the-counter (OTC) human use

(332) Antiflatulent products for over-the-counter human use

(333) Topical antimicrobial drug products for over-the-counter recognized as safe and effective and not misbranded

(335) Antidiarrheal drug products for over-the-counter human use

(336) Antiemetic drug products for over-the-counter human use

(338) Nighttime sleep-aid drug products for over-the-counter human use

(340) Stimulant drug products for over-the-counter human use

(341) Cold, cough, allergy, bronchodilator, and antiasthmatic drug products for over-the-counter human use

(343) Internal analgesic, antipyretic, and antirheumatic drug products for over-the-counter human use

(344) Topical OTIC drug products for over-the-counter human use

(346) Anorectal drug products for over-the-counter human use

(347) Skin protectant drug products for over-the-counter human use

(348) External analgesic drug products for over-the-counter human use

(349) Ophthalmic drug products for over-the-counter human use

(350) Antiperspirant drug products for over-the-counter human use

(352) Sunscreen drug products for over-the-counter human use [stayed indefinitely]

(355) Anticaries drug products for over-the-counter human use

(357) Miscellaneous internal drug products for over-the-counter human use

(358) Miscellaneous external drug products for over-the-counter human use

(361) Prescription drugs for human use generally recognized as safe and effective and not misbranded: drugs used in research

(369) Interpretative statements re warnings on drugs and devices for over-the-counter sale

(370-499) [reserved]

Subchapter E - Veterinary Products/Animal Drugs, Feeds, and Related Products

(500) General

(501) Animal food labeling

(502) Common or usual names for nonstandardized animal foods

(507) Current good manufacturing practice, hazard analysis, and risk-based preventive controls for food for animals

(509) Unavoidable contaminants in animal food and food-packaging material

(510) New animal drugs

(511) New animal drugs for investigational use

(514) New animal drug applications

(515) Medicated feed mill license

(516) New animal drugs for minor use and minor species

(520) Oral dosage form new animal drugs

(522) Implantation or injectable dosage form new animal drugs

(524) Ophthalmic and topical dosage form new animal drugs

(526) Intramammary dosage form new animal drugs

(528) New animal drugs in genetically engineered animals

(529) Certain other dosage form new animal drugs

(530) Extralabel drug use in animals

(556) Tolerances for residues of new animal drugs in food

(558) New animal drugs for use in animal feeds

(564) [reserved]

(570) Food additives

(571) Food additive petitions

(573) Food additives permitted in feed and drinking water of animals

(579) Irradiation in the production, processing, and handling of animal feed and pet food

(582) Substances generally recognized as safe

(584) Food substances affirmed as generally recognized as safe in feed and drinking water of animals

(589) Substances prohibited from use in animal food or feed

(590-599) [reserved]

Subchapter F - Biologics

(600) Biological products: general

(601) Licensing

(606) Current good manufacturing practice for blood and blood components

(607) Establishment registration and product listing for manufacturers of human blood and blood products

(610) General biological products standards

(630) Requirements for blood and blood components intended for transfusion or for further manufacturing use

(640) Additional standards for human blood and blood products

(660) Additional standards for diagnostic substances for laboratory tests

(680) Additional standards for miscellaneous products

Subchapter G – Cosmetics

(700) General

(701) Cosmetic labeling

(710) Voluntary registration of cosmetic product establishments

(720) Voluntary filing of cosmetic product ingredient composition statements

(740) Cosmetic product warning statements

(741-799) [reserved]

Subchapter H - Medical Devices

(800) General

(801) Labeling

(803) Medical device reporting

(806) Medical devices; reports of corrections and removals

(807) Establishment registration and device listing for manufacturers and initial importers of devices

(808) Exemptions from federal preemption of state and local medical device requirements

(809) In vitro diagnostic products for human use

(810) Medical device recall authority

(812) Investigational device exemptions

(813) [reserved]

(814) Premarket approval of medical devices

(820) Quality system regulation

(821) Medical device tracking requirements

(822) Postmarket surveillance

(830) Unique device identification

(860) Medical device classification procedures

(861) Procedures for performance standards development

(862) Clinical chemistry and clinical toxicology devices

(864) Hematology and pathology devices

(866) Immunology and microbiology devices

(868) Anesthesiology devices

(870) Cardiovascular devices

(872) Dental devices

(874) Ear, nose, and throat devices

(876) Gastroenterology-urology devices

(878) General and plastic surgery devices

(880) General hospital and personal use devices

(882) Neurological devices

(884) Obstetrical and gynecological devices

(886) Ophthalmic devices

(888) Orthopedic devices

(890) Physical medicine devices

(892) Radiology devices

(895) Banned devices

(898) Performance standard for electrode lead wires and patient cables

Subchapter I - Mammography Quality Standard Act

(900) Mammography

Subchapter J - Radiological Health

(1000) General

(1002) Records and reports

(1003) Notification of defects or failure to comply

(1004) Repurchase, repairs, or replacement of electronic products

(1005) Importation of electronic products

(1010) Performance standards for electronic products: general

(1020) Performance standards for ionizing radiation emitting products

(1030) Performance standards for microwave and radio frequency emitting products

(1040) Performance standards for light-emitting products

(1050) Performance standards for sonic, infrasonic, and ultrasonic radiation-emitting products

Chapter II Drug Enforcement Administration, Department of Justice

Chapter III Office of National Drug Control Policy

Chapter 2

Introduction to Dietary Supplements

FDA and Dietary Supplements

FDA regulates dietary supplements under a different set of regulations than those covering "conventional" foods and drug products (prescription and Over-the-Counter).[1] Under the Dietary Supplement Health and Education Act of 1994 (DSHEA), the dietary supplement manufacturer is responsible for ensuring that a dietary supplement is safe before it is marketed. FDA is responsible for taking action against any unsafe dietary supplement product after it reaches the market. Generally, manufacturers do not need to register their products with FDA nor get FDA approval before producing or selling dietary supplements.[2] Manufacturers must make sure that product label information is truthful and not misleading.

FDA's post-marketing responsibilities include monitoring safety, e.g. voluntary dietary supplement adverse event reporting, and product information, such as labeling, claims, package inserts, and accompanying literature. The Federal Trade Commission regulates dietary supplement advertising.

> ✦ **IMPORTANT NOTE** ✦
>
> *ALL* dietary supplement manufacturers are responsible for compliance with current good manufacturing practice.

---

1   Available on the FDA website at http://www.fda.gov/Food/ DietarySupplements/default.htm
2   Domestic and foreign facilities that manufacture/process, pack, or hold food for human or animal consumption in the United States are required to register their facility with the FDA. For more information, see Registration of Food Facilities on the FDA website.

Backgrounder on the Final Rule for CGMPs for Dietary Supplements[3]

Overview

Under the Dietary Supplement Health and Education Act of 1994 (DSHEA), dietary supplement manufacturers have the essential responsibility to substantiate the safety of the dietary ingredients used in manufacturing a product. Manufacturers are also responsible for determining that any representations or claims made about their products are substantiated by adequate evidence to show that they are not false or misleading. FDA is responsible for taking action against any unsafe dietary supplement product after it reaches the market. FDA accomplishes its responsibilities through monitoring safety literature; dietary supplement adverse event reports; and product information, such as labeling, claims, package inserts, and accompanying literature.

As part of DSHEA, Congress gave the Secretary of Health and Human Services and the FDA by delegation, the express authority to issue regulations establishing current good manufacturing practice requirements (CGMPs) for dietary supplements. The FDA has issued a final rule establishing requirements for the production of dietary supplements.

Specifically this rule:

- Requires certain activities in manufacturing, packaging, labeling and holding of dietary supplements to ensure that a dietary supplement contains what it is labeled to contain and is not contaminated with harmful or undesirable substances such as pesticides, heavy metals, or other impurities.

- Requires certain activities that will ensure the identity, purity, quality, strength, and composition of dietary supplements, which is a significant step in assuring consumers they are purchasing the type and amount of ingredients declared.

History

1994 - Dietary Supplement Health and Education Act is passed by Congress.

1997 - The FDA issued an advance notice of proposed rulemaking that contained CGMPs submitted by representatives of the dietary supplement industry as well as nine specific questions from FDA. Approximately 100 comments were received

1999 - FDA conducted numerous outreach activities to include public meetings to ascertain the best approach to rulemaking for dietary supplements.

2003 - The FDA issued a proposed rule to establish CGMPs for dietary supplements and dietary supplement ingredients. There were approximately 400 comments submitted in response to the proposal. The comments came from trade associations, government organizations and officials, health care professionals, consumer groups, manufacturers of

---

3   U.S. Food and Drug Administration, June 22, 2007. https://www.fda.gov/food/guidanceregulation/cgmp/ ucm110863.htm

dietary supplement and dietary ingredients, and individuals. The dietary supplement CGMP final rule and interim final rule (IFR), issued today are based on the comments received and FDA's expertise.

2007 - Today the FDA took action to help Americans get accurately labeled and properly manufactured dietary supplements, through its final rule establishing dietary supplement CGMPs. An IFR has also been issued to allow the manufacturer to petition the FDA for an exemption to the 100 percent testing requirement for the identity of dietary ingredients to be used in dietary supplements. The manufacturer would have to provide data demonstrating that less than 100 percent identity testing does not materially diminish assurance that the dietary ingredient is the correct dietary ingredient.

Science-Based Consumer Protection

FDA has found that manufacturing problems have been associated with dietary supplements. Products have been recalled because of microbiological, pesticide, and heavy metal contamination and because they do not contain the dietary ingredients they are represented to contain or they contain more or less than the amount of the dietary ingredient claimed on the label.

In the past, several private sector laboratories analyses found that a substantial number of dietary supplement products analyzed did not contain the amount of dietary ingredients claimed in their product labels.

FDA has taken enforcement actions against dietary supplements due to undeclared ingredients, subpotency and contamination. Some examples include:

- 2006 - FDA warned several firms after FDA analysis of dietary supplements found undeclared active ingredients used in prescription drugs for erectile dysfunction and their analogs in several dietary supplement products.

- 2005 - FDA issued a Warning Letter to a firm after FDA analysis of two of the firm's products were found to be significantly subpotent in several components, such as Vitamin A, Folic Acid, and Vitamin C.

- 2004 - FDA issued a Warning Letter to a firm after FDA analysis found the firm's tablets to be underweight, such that the weight of the tablets could not contain the amount of nutrients declared on the label. Also, FDA initiated a seizure action against ginseng because analysis found the product to contain illegal pesticide residues

Questions and Answers[4]

Dietary Supplements

What is a dietary supplement?

Congress defined the term "dietary supplement" in the Dietary Supplement Health and Education Act (DSHEA) of 1994. A dietary supplement is a product taken by mouth that contains a "dietary ingredient" intended to supplement the diet. The "dietary ingredients" in these products may include: vitamins, minerals, herbs or other botanicals, amino acids, and substances such as enzymes, organ tissues, glandulars, and metabolites. Dietary supplements can also be extracts or concentrates, and may be found in many forms such as tablets, capsules, softgels, gelcaps, liquids, or powders. They can also be in other forms, such as a bar, but if they are, information on their label must not represent the product as a conventional food or a sole item of a meal or diet. Whatever their form may be, DSHEA places dietary supplements in a special category under the general umbrella of "foods," not drugs, and requires that every supplement be labeled a dietary supplement.

What is a "new dietary ingredient" in a dietary supplement?

The Dietary Supplement Health and Education Act (DSHEA) of 1994 defined both of the terms "dietary ingredient" and "new dietary ingredient" as components of dietary supplements. In order for an ingredient of a dietary supplement to be a "dietary ingredient," it must be one or any combination of the following substances:

- a vitamin,
- a mineral,
- an herb or other botanical,
- an amino acid,
- a dietary substance for use by man to supplement the diet by increasing the total dietary intake (e.g., enzymes or tissues from organs or glands), or
- a concentrate, metabolite, constituent or extract.

A "new dietary ingredient" is one that meets the above definition for a "dietary ingredient" and was not sold in the U.S. in a dietary supplement before October 15, 1994.

---

4   U.S. Food and Drug Administration, updated 29, 2017 https://www.fda.gov/Food/DietarySupplements/UsingDietarySupplements/ucm480069.htm

Regulatory Responsibility and Oversight

What is FDA's role in regulating dietary supplements versus the manufacturer's responsibility for marketing them?

In October 1994, the Dietary Supplement Health and Education Act (DSHEA) was signed into law by President Clinton. Before this time, dietary supplements were subject to the same regulatory requirements as were other foods. This new law, which amended the Federal Food, Drug, and Cosmetic Act, created a new regulatory framework for the safety and labeling of dietary supplements.Under DSHEA, a firm is responsible for determining that the dietary supplements it manufactures or distributes are safe and that any representations or claims made about them are substantiated by adequate evidence to show that they are not false or misleading. This means that dietary supplements do not need approval from FDA before they are marketed. Except in the case of a new dietary ingredient, where pre-market review for safety data and other information is required by law, a firm does not have to provide FDA with the evidence it relies on to substantiate safety or effectiveness before or after it markets its products.Also, manufacturers need to register themselves pursuant to the Bioterrorism Act with FDA before producing or selling supplements. In June, 2007, FDA published comprehensive regulations for Current Good Manufacturing Practices for those who manufacture, package or hold dietary supplement products. These regulations focus on practices that ensure the identity, purity, quality, strength and composition of dietary supplements.

When must a manufacturer or distributor notify FDA about a dietary supplement it intends to market in the U.S.?

The Dietary Supplement Health and Education Act (DSHEA) requires that a manufacturer or distributor notify FDA if it intends to market a dietary supplement in the U.S. that contains a "new dietary ingredient." The manufacturer (and distributor) must demonstrate to FDA why the ingredient is reasonably expected to be safe for use in a dietary supplement, unless it has been recognized as a food substance and is present in the food supply.There is no authoritative list of dietary ingredients that were marketed before October 15, 1994. Therefore, manufacturers and distributors are responsible for determining if a dietary ingredient is "new", and if it is not, for documenting that the dietary supplements its sells, containing the dietary ingredient, were marketed before October 15, 1994. For more detailed information, see new dietary ingredients.

What is FDA's oversight responsibility for dietary supplements?

Because dietary supplements are under the "umbrella" of foods, FDA's Center for Food Safety and Applied Nutrition (CFSAN) is responsible for the agency's oversight of these products. FDA's efforts to monitor the marketplace for potential illegal products (that is, products that may be unsafe or make false or misleading claims) include obtaining information from inspections of dietary supplement manufacturers and distributors, the Internet, consumer and trade complaints, occasional laboratory analyses of selected products, and adverse events associated with the use of supplements that are reported to the agency.

Does FDA routinely analyze the content of dietary supplements?

In that FDA has limited resources to analyze the composition of food products, including dietary supplements, it focuses these resources first on public health emergencies and products that may have caused injury or illness. Enforcement priorities then go to products thought to be unsafe or fraudulent or in violation of the law. The remaining funds are used for routine monitoring of products pulled from store shelves or collected during inspections of manufacturing firms. The agency does not analyze dietary supplements before they are sold to consumers. The manufacturer is responsible for ensuring that the "Supplement Facts" label and ingredient list are accurate, that the dietary ingredients are safe, and that the content matches the amount declared on the label. FDA does not have resources to analyze dietary supplements sent to the agency by consumers who want to know their content. Instead, consumers may contact the manufacturer or a commercial laboratory for an analysis of the content.

Is it legal to market a dietary supplement product as a treatment or cure for a specific disease or condition?

No, a product sold as a dietary supplement and promoted on its label or in labeling[5] as a treatment, prevention or cure for a specific disease or condition would be considered an unapproved--and thus illegal--drug. To maintain the product's status as a dietary supplement, the label and labeling must be consistent with the provisions in the Dietary Supplement Health and Education Act (DSHEA) of 1994.

How are advertisements for dietary supplements regulated?

The Federal Trade Commission (FTC) regulates advertising, including infomercials, for dietary supplements and most other products sold to consumers. FDA works closely with FTC in this area, but FTC's work is directed by different laws. For more information on FTC, go to the FTC web site . Advertising and promotional material received in the mail are also regulated under different laws and are subject to regulation by the U.S. Postal Inspection Service.

Safety and Claims

Who has the responsibility for ensuring that a dietary supplement is safe?

By law (DSHEA), the manufacturer is responsible for ensuring that its dietary supplement products are safe before they are marketed. Unlike drug products that must be proven safe and effective for their intended use before marketing, there are no provisions in the law for FDA to "approve" dietary supplements for safety or effectiveness before they reach

---

5   Labeling refers to the label as well as accompanying material that is used by a manufacturer to promote and market a specific product.

the consumer. Under DSHEA, once the product is marketed, FDA has the responsibility for showing that a dietary supplement is "unsafe," before it can take action to restrict the product's use or removal from the marketplace. However, manufacturers and distributors of dietary supplements must record, investigate and forward to FDA any reports they receive of serious adverse events associated with the use of their products that are reported to them directly. FDA is able to evaluate these reports and any other adverse event information reported directly to us by healthcare providers or consumers to identify early signals that a product may present safety risks to consumers. You can find more information on reporting adverse events associated with the use of dietary supplements at Dietary Supplements - Adverse Event Reporting.

Who validates claims and what kinds of claims can be made on dietary supplement labels?

FDA receives many consumer inquiries about the validity of claims for dietary supplements, including product labels, advertisements, media, and printed materials. The responsibility for ensuring the validity of these claims rests with the manufacturer, FDA, and, in the case of advertising, with the Federal Trade Commission.By law, manufacturers may make three types of claims for their dietary supplement products: health claims, structure/function claims, and nutrient content claims. Some of these claims describe: the link between a food substance and disease or a health-related condition; the intended benefits of using the product; or the amount of a nutrient or dietary substance in a product. Different requirements generally apply to each type of claim, and are described in more detail.

Do manufacturers or distributors of dietary supplements have to tell FDA or consumers what evidence they have about their product's safety or what evidence they have to back up the claims they are making for them?

No, except for rules described above that govern "new dietary ingredients," there is no provision under any law or regulation that FDA enforces that requires a firm to disclose to FDA or consumers the information they have about the safety or purported benefits of their dietary supplement products. Likewise, there is no prohibition against them making this information available either to FDA or to their customers. It is up to each firm to set its own policy on disclosure of such information. For more information, see claims that can be made for dietary supplements

Labeling

What information must the manufacturer disclose on the label of a dietary supplement?

FDA regulations require that certain information appear on dietary supplement labels. Information that must be on a dietary supplement label includes: a descriptive name of the product stating that it is a "supplement;" the name and place of business of the manufacturer, packer, or distributor; a complete list of ingredients; and the net contents of the product.In addition, each dietary supplement (except for some small volume products or those produced by eligible small businesses) must have nutrition labeling in the form of a"Supplement Facts" panel. This label must identify each dietary ingredient contained in the product.

Must all ingredients be declared on the label of a dietary supplement?

Yes, ingredients not listed on the "Supplement Facts" panel must be listed in the "other ingredient" statement beneath the panel. The types of ingredients listed there could include the source of dietary ingredients, if not identified in the "Supplement Facts" panel (e.g., rose hips as the source of vitamin C), other food ingredients (e.g., water and sugar), and technical additives or processing aids (e.g., gelatin, starch, colors, stabilizers, preservatives, and flavors). For more details, see: Federal Register Final Rule - 62 FR 49826 September 23, 1997.

Are dietary supplement serving sizes standardized or are there restrictions on the amount of a nutrient that can be in one serving?

Other than the manufacturer's responsibility to ensure safety, there are no rules that limit a serving size or the amount of a nutrient in any form of dietary supplements. This decision is made by the manufacturer and does not require FDA review or approval.

Why do some supplements have wording (a disclaimer) that says: "This statement has not been evaluated by the FDA. This product is not intended to diagnose, treat, cure, or prevent any disease"?

This statement or "disclaimer" is required by law (DSHEA) when a manufacturer makes a structure/function claim on a dietary supplement label. In general, these claims describe the role of a nutrient or dietary ingredient intended to affect the structure or function of the body. The manufacturer is responsible for ensuring the accuracy and truthfulness of these claims; they are not approved by FDA. For this reason, the law says that if a dietary supplement label includes such a claim, it must state in a "disclaimer" that FDA has not evaluated this claim. The disclaimer must also state that this product is not intended to "diagnose, treat, cure or prevent any disease," because only a drug can legally make such a claim.

Consumer Information

Where can I get information about a specific dietary supplement?

Manufacturers and distributors do not need FDA approval to sell their dietary supplements. This means that FDA does not keep a list of manufacturers, distributors or the dietary supplement products they sell. If you want more detailed information than the label tells you about a specific product, you may contact the manufacturer of that brand directly. The name and address of the manufacturer or distributor can be found on the label of the dietary supplement.

How can consumers inform themselves about safety and other issues related to dietary supplements?

It is important to be well informed about products before purchasing them. Because it is often difficult to know what information is reliable and what is questionable, consumers may first want to contact the manufacturer about the product they intend to purchase (see previous question "Where can I get information about a specific dietary supplement?"). In addition, to help consumers in their search to be better informed, FDA is providing the following sites: Tips For The Savvy Supplement User: Making Informed Decisions And Evaluating Information (includes information on how to evaluate research findings and health information on-line) and Claims That Can Be Made for Conventional Foods and Dietary Supplements, (provides information on what types of claims can be made for dietary supplements).

How do I, my health care provider, or any informed individual report a problem or illness caused by a dietary supplement to FDA?

If you think you have suffered a serious harmful effect or illness from a dietary supplement, the first thing you should do is contact or see your healthcare provider immediately. Then, you or your health care provider can report this by submitting a report through the Safety Reporting Portal. If you do not have access to the internet, you may submit a report by calling FDA's MedWatch hotline at 1-800-FDA-1088.

FDA would like to know when a dietary supplement causes a problem even if you are unsure the product caused the problem or even if you do not visit a doctor or clinic. Anyone may report a serious adverse event or illness thought to be related to a dietary supplement directly to FDA by accessing the SRP mentioned above.

Consumers are also encouraged to report instances of product problems using the Safety Reporting Portal . Examples of product problems are foreign objects in the packaging or other apparent quality defects.

In addition to communicating with FDA on-line or by phone, you may use the postage-paid MedWatch form available from the FDA Web site.

NOTE: The identity of the reporter and/or patient is kept confidential.

REGULATIONS

[Code of Federal Regulations]
[Title 21, Volume 1]
[Revised as of April 1, 2017]
[CITE: 21CFR1]

Title 21–Food and Drugs
Chapter I–Food and Drug Administration
Department of Health and Human Services
Subchapter A–General
Part 1 General Enforcement Regulations[1]

Subpart H—Registration of Food Facilities

General Provisions

Sec. 1.225 Who must register under this subpart?

(a) You must register your facility under this subpart if you are the owner, operator, or agent in charge of either a domestic or foreign facility, as defined in this subpart, and your facility is engaged in the manufacturing/processing, packing, or holding of food for consumption in the United States, unless your facility qualifies for one of the exemptions in 1.226.

(b) If you are an owner, operator, or agent in charge of a domestic facility, you must register your facility whether or not the food from the facility enters interstate commerce.

(c) If you are the owner, operator, or agent in charge of a facility, you may authorize an individual to register your facility on your behalf.

Sec. 1.226 Who does not have to register under this subpart?

This subpart does not apply to the following facilities:

(a) A foreign facility, if food from such facility undergoes further manufacturing/processing (including packaging) by another facility outside the United States. A facility is not exempt

---

1   21CFR§1 is available on the FDA website at https://www.accessdata.fda.gov/scripts/cdrh/cfdocs/cfcfr/CFRSearch.cfm?CFRPart=1

under this provision if the further manufacturing/processing (including packaging) conducted by the subsequent facility consists of adding labeling or any similar activity of a de minimis nature;

(b) Farms;

(c) Retail food establishments;

(d) Restaurants;

(e) Nonprofit food establishments in which food is prepared for, or served directly to, the consumer;

(f) Fishing vessels, including those that not only harvest and transport fish but also engage in practices such as heading, eviscerating, or freezing intended solely to prepare fish for holding on board a harvest vessel. However, those fishing vessels otherwise engaged in processing fish are subject to this subpart. For the purposes of this section, "processing" means handling, storing, preparing, shucking, changing into different market forms, manufacturing, preserving, packing, labeling, dockside unloading, holding, or heading, eviscerating, or freezing other than solely to prepare fish for holding on board a harvest vessel;

(g) Facilities that are regulated exclusively, throughout the entire facility, by the U.S. Department of Agriculture under the Federal Meat Inspection Act (21 U.S.C. 601 et seq.), the Poultry Products Inspection Act (21 U.S.C. 451 et seq.), or the Egg Products Inspection Act (21 U.S.C. 1031 et seq.);

Sec. 1.227 What definitions apply to this subpart?

The definitions of terms in section 201 of the Federal Food, Drug, and Cosmetic Act apply to such terms when used in this subpart. In addition, for the purposes of this subpart:

Calendar day means every day shown on the calendar.

Facility means any establishment, structure, or structures under one ownership at one general physical location, or, in the case of a mobile facility, traveling to multiple locations, that manufactures/processes, packs, or holds food for consumption in the United States. Transport vehicles are not facilities if they hold food only in the usual course of business as carriers. A facility may consist of one or more contiguous structures, and a single building may house more than one distinct facility if the facilities are under separate ownership. The private residence of an individual is not a facility. Nonbottled water drinking water collection and distribution establishments and their structures are not facilities.

(1) *Domestic facility* means any facility located in any State or Territory of the United States, the District of Columbia, or the Commonwealth of Puerto Rico that manufactures/processes, packs, or holds food for consumption in the United States.

(2) *Foreign facility* means a facility other than a domestic facility that manufactures/processes, packs, or holds food for consumption in the United States.

Farm means:

(1) *Primary production farm.* A primary production farm is an operation under one management in one general (but not necessarily contiguous) physical location devoted to the growing of crops, the harvesting of crops, the raising of animals (including seafood), or any combination of these activities. The term "farm" includes operations that, in addition to these activities:

(i) Pack or hold raw agricultural commodities;

(ii) Pack or hold processed food, provided that all processed food used in such activities is either consumed on that farm or another farm under the same management, or is processed food identified in paragraph (1)(iii)(B)(1) of this definition; and

(iii) Manufacture/process food, provided that:

(A) All food used in such activities is consumed on that farm or another farm under the same management; or

(B) Any manufacturing/processing of food that is not consumed on that farm or another farm under the same management consists only of:

(1) Drying/dehydrating raw agricultural commodities to create a distinct commodity (such as drying/dehydrating grapes to produce raisins), and packaging and labeling such commodities, without additional manufacturing/processing (an example of additional manufacturing/ processing is slicing);

(2) Treatment to manipulate the ripening of raw agricultural commodities (such as by treating produce with ethylene gas), and packaging and labeling treated raw agricultural commodities, without additional manufacturing/processing; and

(3) Packaging and labeling raw agricultural commodities, when these activities do not involve additional manufacturing/processing (an example of additional manufacturing/processing is irradiation); or

(2) *Secondary activities farm.* A secondary activities farm is an operation, not located on a primary production farm, devoted to harvesting (such as hulling or shelling), packing, and/or holding of raw agricultural commodities, provided that the primary production farm(s) that grows, harvests, and/or raises the majority of the raw agricultural commodities harvested, packed, and/or held by the secondary activities farm owns, or jointly owns, a majority interest in the secondary activities farm. A secondary activities farm may also conduct those additional activities allowed on a primary production farm as described in paragraphs (1)(ii) and (iii) of this definition.

Food has the meaning given in section 201(f) of the Federal Food, Drug, and Cosmetic Act:

(1) Except for purposes of this subpart, it does not include:

(i) Food contact substances as defined in section 409(h)(6) of the Federal Food, Drug, and Cosmetic Act; or

(ii) Pesticides as defined in 7 U.S.C. 136(u).

(2) Examples of food include: Fruits, vegetables, fish, dairy products, eggs, raw agricultural commodities for use as food or as components of food, animal feed (including pet food), food and feed ingredients, food and feed additives, dietary supplements and dietary ingredients, infant formula, beverages (including alcoholic beverages and bottled water), live food animals, bakery goods, snack foods, candy, and canned foods.

Harvesting applies to farms and farm mixed-type facilities and means activities that are traditionally performed on farms for the purpose of removing raw agricultural commodities from the place they were grown or raised and preparing them for use as food. Harvesting is limited to activities performed on raw agricultural commodities, or on processed foods created by drying/dehydrating a raw agricultural commodity without additional manufacturing/processing, on a farm. Harvesting does not include activities that transform a raw agricultural commodity into a processed food as defined in section 201(gg) of the Federal Food, Drug, and Cosmetic Act. Examples of harvesting include cutting (or otherwise separating) the edible portion of the raw agricultural commodity from the crop plant and removing or trimming part of the raw agricultural commodity (e.g., foliage, husks, roots or stems). Examples of harvesting also include cooling, field coring, filtering, gathering, hulling, shelling, sifting, threshing, trimming of outer leaves of, and washing raw agricultural commodities grown on a farm.

Holding means storage of food and also includes activities performed incidental to storage of a food (e.g., activities performed for the safe or effective storage of that food, such as fumigating food during storage, and drying/dehydrating raw agricultural commodities when the drying/dehydrating does not create a distinct commodity (such as drying/dehydrating hay or alfalfa)). Holding also includes activities performed as a practical necessity for the distribution of that food (such as blending of the same raw agricultural commodity and breaking down pallets), but does not include activities that transform a raw agricultural commodity into a processed food as defined in section 201(gg) of the Federal Food, Drug, and Cosmetic Act. Holding facilities could include warehouses, cold storage facilities, storage silos, grain elevators, and liquid storage tanks.

Manufacturing/processing means making food from one or more ingredients, or synthesizing, preparing, treating, modifying or manipulating food, including food crops or ingredients. Examples of manufacturing/processing activities include: Baking, boiling, bottling, canning, cooking, cooling, cutting, distilling, drying/dehydrating raw agricultural commodities to create a distinct commodity (such as drying/dehydrating grapes to produce raisins), evaporating, eviscerating, extracting juice, formulating, freezing, grinding, homogenizing, irradiating, labeling, milling, mixing, packaging (including modified atmosphere packaging), pasteurizing, peeling, rendering, treating to manipulate ripening, trimming, washing, or waxing. For farms and farm mixed-type facilities, manufacturing/processing does not include activities that are part of harvesting, packing, or holding.

Mixed-type facility means an establishment that engages in both activities that are exempt from registration under section 415 of the Federal Food, Drug, and Cosmetic Act and activities that require the establishment to be registered. An example of such a facility is a "farm mixed-type facility," which is an establishment that is a farm, but also conducts activities outside the farm definition that require the establishment to be registered.

Nonprofit food establishment means a charitable entity that prepares or serves food directly to the consumer or otherwise provides food or meals for consumption by humans or animals in the United States. The term includes central food banks, soup kitchens, and nonprofit food delivery services. To be considered a nonprofit food establishment, the establishment must meet the terms of section 501(c)(3) of the U.S. Internal Revenue Code (26 U.S.C. 501(c)(3)).

Packaging (when used as a verb) means placing food into a container that directly contacts the food and that the consumer receives.

Packing means placing food into a container other than packaging the food and also includes re-packing and activities performed incidental to packing or re-packing a food (e.g., activities performed for the safe or effective packing or re-packing of that food (such as sorting, culling, grading, and weighing or conveying incidental to packing or re-packing)), but does not include activities that transform a raw agricultural commodity, as defined in section 201(r) of the Federal Food, Drug, and Cosmetic Act, into a processed food as defined in section 201(gg) of the Federal Food, Drug, and Cosmetic Act.

Restaurant means a facility that prepares and sells food directly to consumers for immediate consumption. "Restaurant" does not include facilities that provide food to interstate conveyances, central kitchens, and other similar facilities that do not prepare and serve food directly to consumers.

(1) Entities in which food is provided to humans, such as cafeterias, lunchrooms, cafes, bistros, fast food establishments, food stands, saloons, taverns, bars, lounges, catering facilities, hospital kitchens, day care kitchens, and nursing home kitchens are restaurants; and

(2) Pet shelters, kennels, and veterinary facilities in which food is provided to animals are restaurants.

Retail food establishment means an establishment that sells food products directly to consumers as its primary function. The term "retail food establishment" includes facilities that manufacture, process, pack, or hold food if the establishment's primary function is to sell from that establishment food, including food that it manufactures, processes, packs, or holds, directly to consumers. A retail food establishment's primary function is to sell food directly to consumers if the annual monetary value of sales of food products directly to consumers exceeds the annual monetary value of sales of food products to all other buyers. The term "consumers" does not include businesses. A "retail food establishment" includes grocery stores, convenience stores, and vending machine locations. A "retail food establishment" also includes certain farm-operated businesses selling food directly to consumers as their primary function.

(1) Sale of food directly to consumers from an establishment located on a farm includes sales by that establishment directly to consumers:

(i) At a roadside stand (a stand situated on the side of or near a road or thoroughfare at which a farmer sells food from his or her farm directly to consumers) or farmers' market (a location where one or more local farmers assemble to sell food from their farms directly to consumers);

(ii) Through a community supported agriculture program. Community supported agriculture (CSA) program means a program under which a farmer or group of farmers grows food for a group of shareholders (or subscribers) who pledge to buy a portion of the farmer's crop(s) for that season. This includes CSA programs in which a group of farmers consolidate their crops at a central location for distribution to shareholders or subscribers; and

(iii) At other such direct-to-consumer sales platforms, including door-to-door sales; mail, catalog and Internet order, including online farmers markets and online grocery delivery; religious or other organization bazaars; and State and local fairs.

(2) Sale of food directly to consumers by a farm-operated business includes the sale of food by that farm-operated business directly to consumers:

(i) At a roadside stand (a stand situated on the side of or near a road or thoroughfare at which a farmer sells food from his or her farm directly to consumers) or farmers' market (a location where one or more local farmers assemble to sell food from their farms directly to consumers);

(ii) Through a community supported agriculture program. Community supported agriculture (CSA) program means a program under which a farmer or group of farmers grows food for a group of shareholders (or subscribers) who pledge to buy a portion of the farmer's crop(s) for that season. This includes CSA programs in which a group of farmers consolidate their crops at a central location for distribution to shareholders or subscribers; and

(iii) At other such direct-to-consumer sales platforms, including door-to-door sales; mail, catalog and Internet order, including online farmers markets and online grocery delivery; religious or other organization bazaars; and State and local fairs.

(3) For the purposes of this definition, "farm-operated business" means a business that is managed by one or more farms and conducts manufacturing/processing not on the farm(s).

Trade name means the name or names under which the facility conducts business, or additional names by which the facility is known. A trade name is associated with a facility, and a brand name is associated with a product.

U.S. agent means a person (as defined in section 201(e) of the Federal Food, Drug, and Cosmetic Act (21 U.S.C. 321(e))) residing or maintaining a place of business in the United

States whom a foreign facility designates as its agent for purposes of this subpart. A U.S. agent may not be in the form of a mailbox, answering machine or service, or other place where an individual acting as the foreign facility's agent is not physically present.

(1) The U.S. agent acts as a communications link between FDA and the foreign facility for both emergency and routine communications. The U.S. agent will be the person FDA contacts when an emergency occurs, unless the registration specifies another emergency contact.

(2) FDA will treat representations by the U.S. agent as those of the foreign facility, and will consider information or documents provided to the U.S. agent the equivalent of providing the information or documents to the foreign facility. FDA will consider the U.S. agent the equivalent of the registrant for purposes of sharing information and communications. The U.S. agent of a foreign facility may view the information submitted in the foreign facility's registration.

(3) Having a single U.S. agent for the purposes of this subpart does not preclude facilities from having multiple agents (such as foreign suppliers) for other business purposes. A firm's commercial business in the United States need not be conducted through the U.S. agent designated for purposes of this subpart.

You or registrant means the owner, operator, or agent in charge of a facility that manufactures/processes, packs, or holds food for consumption in the United States.

[80 FR 56141, Sept. 17, 2015, as amended at 81 FR 3715, Jan. 22, 2016; 81 FR 45950, July 14, 2016]

Procedures for Registration of Food Facilities

Sec. 1.230 When must you register or renew your registration?

(a) Registration. You must register before your facility begins to manufacture, process, pack, or hold food for consumption in the United States. You may authorize an individual to register the facility on your behalf.

(b) Registration renewal. You must submit a registration renewal containing the information required under 1.232 every other year, during the period beginning on October 1 and ending on December 31 of each even-numbered year. You may authorize an individual to renew a facility's registration on your behalf. If the individual submitting the registration renewal is not the owner, operator, or agent in charge of the facility, the registration renewal must also include a statement in which the individual certifies that the information submitted is true and accurate, certifies that he/she is authorized to submit the registration renewal, and identifies by name, address, and telephone number, the individual who authorized submission of the registration renewal. In addition, the registration renewal must also identify the individual who authorized submission of the registration renewal by email address, unless FDA has granted a waiver under 1.245. Each registration renewal must include the name of the individual submitting the registration renewal, and the individual's signature (for the paper option). Each electronic registration renewal must include the name of the individual submitting the renewal.

(c) Abbreviated registration renewal process. If you do not have any changes to the information required under 1.232 since you submitted the preceding registration, registration renewal, or update for your facility, you may use the abbreviated registration renewal process. If you use the abbreviated registration renewal process, you must confirm that no changes have been made to the information required under 1.232 since you submitted the preceding registration, registration renewal or update, and you must certify that the information submitted is truthful and accurate. Each abbreviated registration renewal must include the name of the individual submitting the abbreviated renewal, and the individual's signature (for the paper option). Each electronic abbreviated registration renewal must include the name of the individual submitting the abbreviated renewal. For abbreviated registration renewals not submitted by the owner, operator, or agent in charge of the facility, the abbreviated renewal must provide the email address of the individual who authorized submission of the abbreviated renewal, unless FDA has granted a waiver under 1.245. You must use Form FDA 3537 to submit abbreviated registration renewals to FDA.

[81 FR 45950, July 14, 2016]

Sec. 1.231 How and where do you register or renew your registration?

(a) Electronic registration and registration renewal.

(1) To register or renew a registration electronically, you must go to http://www.fda.gov/furls, which is available for registration 24 hours a day, 7 days a week. This Web site is available from wherever the Internet is accessible, including libraries, copy centers, schools, and Internet cafes. An individual authorized by the owner, operator, or agent in charge of a facility may also register a facility electronically.

(2) Beginning on January 4, 2020, you must submit your registration or registration renewal to FDA electronically, unless FDA has granted you a waiver under 1.245.

(3) After you submit your electronic registration, FDA will verify the accuracy of your unique facility identifier (UFI) recognized as acceptable by FDA and will also verify that the facility-specific address associated with the UFI is the same address associated with your registration. FDA will not confirm your registration or provide you with a registration number until FDA verifies the accuracy of your facility's UFI and verifies that the facility-specific address associated with the UFI is the same address associated with your registration. With respect to electronic registration renewals, after you submit your electronic registration renewal, FDA will provide you with an electronic confirmation of your registration renewal. When you update your facility's UFI as part of your electronic registration renewal, FDA will verify the accuracy of your facility's UFI and will also verify that the facility-specific address associated with the UFI is the same address associated with your registration. FDA will not provide you with a confirmation of your registration renewal until

FDA verifies the accuracy of your UFI and verifies that the facility-specific address associated with the UFI is the same address associated with your registration.

(4) For electronic registrations not submitted by the owner, operator, or agent in charge of the facility, after submission of the registration, FDA will verify that the individual identified as having authorized submission of the registration in fact authorized the submission on behalf of the facility. FDA will not confirm the registration or provide a registration number until that individual confirms that he or she authorized the submission. With respect to electronic registration renewals, after completion of the electronic registration renewal, FDA will provide an electronic confirmation of the registration renewal. For electronic registration renewals not submitted by the owner, operator, or agent in charge of the facility, FDA will verify that the individual identified as having authorized submission of the registration renewal in fact authorized the submission on behalf of the facility. FDA will not provide an electronic confirmation of the registration renewal until that individual confirms that he or she authorized the submission.

(5) For a foreign facility, after you submit your electronic registration, FDA will verify that the person identified as the U.S. agent for your foreign facility has agreed to serve as your U.S. agent. FDA will not confirm your registration or provide you with a registration number until that person confirms that the person agreed to serve as your U.S. agent. With respect to electronic registration renewals, after you complete your electronic registration renewal, FDA will provide you with an electronic confirmation of your registration renewal. When you update information about your U.S. agent as part of your electronic registration renewal, FDA will verify that the person identified as the U.S. agent for your foreign facility has agreed to serve as your U.S. agent. FDA will not provide you with an electronic confirmation of your registration renewal until that person confirms that the person agreed to serve as your U.S. agent.

(6) If any information you previously submitted was incorrect at the time of submission, you must immediately update your facility's registration as specified in 1.234.

(7) You will be considered registered once FDA electronically sends you your confirmation and registration number.

(b) Registration or registration renewal by mail or fax. Beginning January 4, 2020, you must submit your registration or registration renewal to FDA electronically, unless FDA has granted you a waiver under 1.245. If FDA has granted you a waiver under 1.245, you may register or renew a registration by mail or by fax.

(1) You must register or renew a registration (including abbreviated registration renewals) using Form FDA 3537. You may obtain a copy of this form by writing to the U.S. Food and Drug Administration, Center for Food Safety and Applied Nutrition, 5001 Campus Dr. (HFS-681), College Park, MD 20740 or by requesting the form by phone at 1-800-216-7331 or 301-575-0156.

(2) When you receive the form, you must fill it out completely and legibly and either mail it to the address in paragraph (b)(1) of this section or fax it to 301-436-2804.

(3) If any required information on the form is incomplete or illegible when FDA receives it, FDA will return the form to you for revision, provided that your mailing address or fax number is legible and valid. When returning a registration form for revision, FDA will use the means by which the form was received by the Agency (i.e., by mail or fax).

(4) FDA will enter complete and legible mailed and faxed registration submissions into its registration system, as soon as practicable, in the order FDA receives them.

(5) After you submit your registration, FDA will verify the accuracy of your facility's UFI and will also verify that the facility-specific address associated with the UFI is the same address associated with your registration. FDA will not confirm your registration or provide you with a registration number until FDA verifies the accuracy of your facility's UFI and verifies that the facility-specific address associated with the UFI is the same address associated with your registration. With respect to registration renewals, after you submit your registration renewal by mail or fax, FDA will provide you with a confirmation of your registration renewal. When you update your facility's UFI as part of your registration renewal, FDA will verify the accuracy of your facility's UFI and will also verify that the facility-specific address associated with the UFI is the same address associated with your registration. FDA will not provide you with a confirmation of your registration renewal until FDA verifies the accuracy of your UFI and verifies that the facility-specific address associated with the UFI is the same address associated with your registration.

(6) For registrations not submitted by the owner, operator, or agent in charge of the facility, after submission of the registration by mail or fax, FDA will verify that the individual identified as having authorized submission of the registration in fact authorized the submission on behalf of the facility. FDA will not confirm the registration or provide a registration number until that individual confirms that he or she authorized the submission. With respect to registration renewals, after completion of the registration renewal by mail or fax, FDA will provide a confirmation of the registration renewal. For registration renewals not submitted by the owner, operator, or agent in charge of the facility, FDA will verify that the individual identified as having authorized submission of the registration renewal in fact authorized the submission on behalf of the facility. FDA will not provide a confirmation of the registration renewal until that individual confirms that he or she authorized the submission.

(7) For a foreign facility, after you submit your registration by mail or fax, FDA will verify that the person identified as the U.S. agent for your foreign facility has agreed to serve as your U.S. agent. FDA will not confirm your registration or provide you with a registration number until that person confirms that the person agreed to serve as your U.S. agent. With respect to registration renewals, after you complete your registration renewal by mail or fax, FDA will provide you with a confirmation of your

registration renewal. When you update information about your U.S. agent as part of your registration renewal, FDA will verify that the person identified as the U.S. agent for your foreign facility has agreed to serve as your U.S. agent. FDA will not provide you with a confirmation of your registration renewal until that person confirms that the person agreed to serve as your U.S. agent.

(8) FDA will mail or fax you a copy of the registration as entered, confirmation of registration, and your registration number. When responding to a registration submission, FDA will use the means by which the registration was received by the Agency (i.e., by mail or fax).

(9) If any information you previously submitted was incorrect at the time of submission, you must immediately update your facility's registration as specified in 1.234.

(10) Your facility is considered registered once FDA enters your facility's registration data into the registration system and the system generates a registration number.

(c) Fees. No registration fee is required.

(d) Language. You must submit all registration information in the English language except an individual's name, the name of a company, the name of a street, and a trade name may be submitted in a foreign language. All information, including these items, must be submitted using the Latin (Roman) alphabet.

[81 FR 45950, July 14, 2016]

Sec. 1.232 What information is required in the registration?

(a) For a domestic and foreign facility, the following information is required:

(1) The name, full address, and phone number of the facility;

(2) Beginning October 1, 2020, the facility's UFI recognized as acceptable by FDA;

(3) The preferred mailing address, if different from that of the facility;

(4) The name, full address, and phone number of the parent company, if the facility is a subsidiary of the parent company;

(5) All trade names the facility uses;

(6) The name, full address, and phone number of the owner, operator, or agent in charge of the facility. In addition, the email address of the owner, operator, or agent in charge is required, unless FDA has granted you a waiver under 1.245;

(7) The applicable food product categories of any food manufactured/processed, packed, or held at the facility as identified on Form FDA 3537;

(8) The type of activity conducted at the facility for each food product category identified. You may select more than one activity type for each food product category identified. The activity type options are as follows:

(i) Ambient human food storage warehouse/holding facility;

(ii) Refrigerated human food warehouse/holding facility;

(iii) Frozen human food warehouse/holding facility;

(iv) Interstate conveyance caterer/catering point;

(v) Contract sterilizer;

(vi) Labeler/relabeler;

(vii) Manufacturer/processor;

(viii) Acidified food processor;

(ix) Low-acid food processor;

(x) Farm mixed-type facility;

(xi) Packer/repacker;

(xii) Salvage operator (reconditioner);

(xiii) Animal food warehouse/holding facility;

(xiv) Other activity.

(9) A statement in which the owner, operator, or agent in charge provides an assurance that FDA will be permitted to inspect the facility at the times and in the manner permitted by the Federal Food, Drug, and Cosmetic Act;

(10) A statement in which the owner, operator, or agent in charge certifies that the information submitted is true and accurate. If the individual submitting the form is not the owner, operator, or agent in charge of the facility, the registration must also include a statement in which the individual certifies that the information submitted is true and accurate, certifies that he/she is authorized to submit the registration, and identifies by name, address, and telephone number, the individual who authorized submission of the registration. In addition, the registration must identify the individual who authorized submission of the registration by email address, unless FDA has granted a waiver under 1.245. Each registration must include the name of the individual submitting the registration, and the individual's signature (for the paper option).

(b) For a domestic facility, the following additional information is required:

(1) The email address for the contact person of the facility;

(2) An emergency contact phone number and email address if different from the email address for the contact person in paragraph (b)(1) of this section.

(c) For a foreign facility, the following additional information is required:

(1) The name, full address, phone number, and email address of the foreign facility's U.S. agent;

(2) An emergency contact phone number and email address.

[81 FR 45951, July 14, 2016]

Sec. 1.233 Are there optional items included in the registration form?

Yes. FDA encourages, but does not require, you to submit items that are indicated as optional on the Form FDA 3537 that you submit.

[81 FR 45952, July 14, 2016]

Sec. 1.234 How and when do you update your facility's registration information?

(a) Update requirements. You must update a facility's registration within 60 calendar days of any change to any of the information previously submitted under 1.232 (e.g., change of operator, agent in charge, or U.S. agent), except a change of the owner. You may authorize an individual to update a facility's registration on your behalf. For updates not submitted by the owner, operator, or agent in charge of the facility, the update must provide the email address of the individual who authorized submission of the update, unless FDA has granted a waiver under 1.245.

(b) Cancellation due to ownership changes. If the reason for the update is that the facility has a new owner, the former owner must cancel the facility's registration as specified in 1.235 within 60 calendar days of the change and the new owner must submit a new registration for the facility as specified in 1.231. The former owner may authorize an individual to cancel a facility's registration.

(c) Electronic update.

    (1) To update your registration electronically, you must update at http://www.fda.gov/furls.

    (2) After you submit your electronic update, FDA will provide you with an electronic confirmation of your update. When updating UFI information, FDA will verify the accuracy of your facility's UFI and will also verify that the facility-specific address associated with the UFI is the same address associated with your registration. FDA will not provide you with an electronic confirmation of your registration update until FDA verifies the accuracy of your facility's UFI and verifies that the facility-specific address associated with the UFI is the same address associated with your registration. For foreign facilities, when updating information about your U.S. agent, FDA will verify that the person identified as the U.S. agent for your foreign facility has agreed to serve as your U.S. agent. FDA will not provide you with an electronic confirmation of your registration update until that person confirms that the person agreed to serve as your U.S. agent.

    (3) For electronic updates not submitted by the owner, operator, or agent in charge of the facility, after submission of the electronic update, FDA will verify that the individual identified as having authorized submission of the update in fact authorized the submission on behalf of the facility. FDA will not confirm the update to the registration until that individual confirms that he or she authorized the submission.

(4) Your registration will be considered updated once FDA sends you your update confirmation, unless notified otherwise.

(d) Update by mail or fax. Beginning January 4, 2020, you must submit your update electronically, unless FDA has granted you a waiver under 1.245. If FDA has granted you a waiver under 1.245, you may update your facility's registration by mail or by fax.

(1) You must update your registration using Form FDA 3537. You may obtain a copy of this form by writing to the U.S. Food and Drug Administration, Center for Food Safety and Applied Nutrition, 5001 Campus Dr. (HFS-681), College Park, MD 20740 or by requesting the form by phone at 1-800-216-7331 or 301-575-0156.

(2) When you receive the form, you must legibly fill out the sections of the form reflecting your updated information and either mail it to the address in paragraph (d) (1) of this section or fax it to 301-436-2804.

(3) If the information on the form is incomplete or illegible when FDA receives it, FDA will return the form to you for revision, provided that your mailing address or fax number is legible and valid. When returning a registration form for revision, FDA will use the means by which the registration was received by the Agency (i.e., by mail or fax).

(4) FDA will enter complete and legible updates into its registration system as soon as practicable, in the order FDA receives them.

(5) FDA will then mail to the address or fax to the fax number on the registration form a copy of the update as entered and confirmation of the update. When responding to an update submission, FDA will use the means by which the form was received by the Agency (i.e., by mail or fax). After you submit your update by mail or fax, FDA will verify the accuracy of your facility's UFI and will also verify that the facility-specific address associated with the UFI is the same address associated with your registration. FDA will not provide a confirmation of your registration update until FDA verifies the accuracy of your facility's UFI and verifies that the facility-specific address associated with the UFI is the same address associated with your registration. For foreign facilities, when updating information about your U.S. agent, FDA will verify that the person identified as the U.S. agent for your foreign facility has agreed to serve as your U.S. agent. FDA will not provide you with a confirmation of your registration update until that person confirms that the person agreed to serve as your U.S. agent.

(6) For registration updates not submitted by the owner, operator, or agent in charge of the facility, after submission of the registration update by mail or fax, FDA will verify that the individual identified as having authorized submission of the update in fact authorized the submission on behalf of the facility. FDA will not confirm the registration update until that individual confirms that he or she authorized the update.

(7) If any update information you previously submitted was incorrect at the time of submission, you must immediately resubmit your update.

(8) Your registration will be considered updated once FDA enters your facility's update data into the registration system and the system generates an update confirmation.

[81 FR 45952, July 14, 2016]

Sec. 1.235 How and when do you cancel your facility's registration information?

(a) Notification of registration cancellation. You must cancel a registration within 60 calendar days of the reason for cancellation (e.g., your facility ceases operations, ceases providing food for consumption in the United States, or is sold to a new owner).

(b) Cancellation requirements. The cancellation of a facility's registration must include the following information:

(1) The facility's registration number;

(2) Whether the facility is domestic or foreign;

(3) The facility name and address;

(4) The name, address, and email address (if available) of the individual submitting the cancellation;

(5) For registration cancellations not submitted by the owner, operator, or agent in charge of the facility, the email address of the individual who authorized submission of the registration cancellation, unless FDA has granted a waiver under 1.245; and

(6) A statement certifying that the information submitted is true and accurate, and that the person submitting the cancellation is authorized by the facility to cancel its registration.

(c) Electronic cancellation.

(1) To cancel your registration electronically, you must cancel at http://www.fda.gov/furls.

(2) Once you complete your electronic cancellation, FDA will provide you with an electronic confirmation of your cancellation.

(3) For registration cancellations not submitted by the owner, operator, or agent in charge of the facility, after submission of the registration cancellation, FDA will verify that the individual identified as having authorized submission of the cancellation in fact authorized the submission on behalf of the facility. FDA will not confirm the registration cancellation until that individual confirms that he or she authorized the registration cancellation.

(4) Your registration will be considered cancelled once FDA sends you your cancellation confirmation.

(d) Cancellation by mail or fax. Beginning January 4, 2020, you must cancel your registration electronically, unless FDA has granted you a waiver under 1.245. If FDA has granted a waiver under 1.245, you may cancel your facility's registration by mail or fax.

(1) You must cancel your registration using Form FDA 3537a. You may obtain a copy of this form by writing to the U.S. Food and Drug Administration, Center for Food Safety and Applied Nutrition, 5001 Campus Dr. (HFS-681), College Park, MD 20740 or by requesting the form by phone at 1-800-216-7331 or 301-575-0156.

(2) When you receive the form, you must completely and legibly fill out the form and either mail it to the address in paragraph (d)(1) of this section or fax it to 301-436-2804.

(3) If the information on the form is incomplete or illegible when FDA receives it, FDA will return the form to you for revision, provided that your mailing address or fax number is legible and valid. When returning a cancellation form for revision, FDA will use the means by which the cancellation was received by the Agency (i.e., by mail or fax).

(4) FDA will enter complete and legible mailed and faxed cancellations into its registration system as soon as practicable, in the order FDA receives them.

(5) FDA will mail to the address or fax to the fax number on the cancellation form a copy of the cancellation as entered and confirmation of the cancellation. When responding to a cancellation, FDA will use the means by which the form was received by the Agency (i.e., by mail or fax).

(6) For registration cancellations not submitted by the owner, operator, or agent in charge of the facility, after submission of the registration cancellation by mail or fax, FDA will verify that the individual identified as having authorized submission of the cancellation in fact authorized the submission on behalf of the facility. FDA will not confirm the registration cancellation until that individual confirms that he or she authorized the registration cancellation.

(7) Your registration will be considered cancelled once FDA enters your facility's cancellation data into the registration system. FDA will send you your cancellation confirmation.

[81 FR 45952, July 14, 2016]

Additional Provisions

Sec. 1.240 What other registration requirements apply?

In addition to the requirements of this subpart, you must comply with the registration regulations found in part 108 of this chapter, related to emergency permit control, and any other Federal, State, or local registration requirements that apply to your facility.

Sec. 1.241 What are the consequences of failing to register, update, renew, or cancel your registration?

(a) Section 301 of the Federal Food, Drug, and Cosmetic Act (21 U.S.C. 331) prohibits the doing of certain acts or causing such acts to be done. Under section 302 of the Federal Food, Drug, and Cosmetic Act (21 U.S.C. 332), the United States can bring a civil action in Federal court to enjoin a person who commits a prohibited act. Under section 303 of the Federal Food, Drug, and Cosmetic Act (21 U.S.C. 333), the United States can bring a criminal action in Federal court to prosecute a person who is responsible for the commission of a prohibited act. Under section 306 of the Federal Food, Drug, and Cosmetic Act (21 U.S.C. 335a), FDA can seek debarment of any person who has been convicted of a felony relating to importation of food into the United States. Failure of an owner, operator, or agent in charge of a domestic or foreign facility to register its facility, renew the registration of its facility, update required elements of its facility's registration, or cancel its registration in accordance with the requirements of this subpart is a prohibited act under section 301(dd) of the Federal Food, Drug, and Cosmetic Act.

(b) FDA will consider a registration for a food facility to be expired if the registration is not renewed, as required by 1.230(b). Thus, if you previously submitted a registration to FDA, but do not submit a registration renewal to FDA during the period beginning on October 1 and ending on December 31 of each even-numbered year, FDA will consider the registration for the facility to be expired. FDA will consider a food facility with an expired registration to have failed to register in accordance with section 415 of the Federal Food, Drug, and Cosmetic Act.

(c) FDA will cancel a registration if FDA independently verifies that the facility is no longer in business or has changed owners, and the owner, operator, or agent in charge of the facility fails to cancel the registration, or if FDA determines that the registration is for a facility that does not exist, is not required to register, or where the information about the facility's address was not updated in a timely manner in accordance with 1.234(a) or the registration was submitted by a person not authorized to submit the registration under 1.225. Also, FDA will cancel a registration if the facility's registration has expired because the facility has failed to renew its registration in accordance with 1.230(b). If FDA cancels a facility's registration, FDA will send a confirmation of the cancellation using contact information submitted by the facility in the registration database.

(d) If an article of food is imported or offered for import into the United States and a foreign facility that manufactured/processed, packed, or held that article of food has not registered in accordance with this subpart, the disposition of the article of food shall be governed by the procedures set out in subpart I of this part.

[81 FR 45953, July 14, 2016]

Sec. 1.242 What does assignment of a registration number mean?

Assignment of a registration number to a facility means that the facility is registered with FDA. Assignment of a registration number does not in any way convey FDA's approval or endorsement of a facility or its products.

Sec. 1.243 Is food registration information available to the public?

(a) The list of registered facilities and registration documents submitted under this subpart are not subject to disclosure under 5 U.S.C. 552 (the Freedom of Information Act). In addition, any information derived from such list or registration documents that would disclose the identity or location of a specific registered person, is not subject to disclosure under 5 U.S.C. 552 (the Freedom of Information Act).

(b) Paragraph (a) of this section does not apply to any information obtained by other means or that has previously been disclosed to the public as defined in 20.81 of this chapter.

Sec. 1.245 Waiver request.

Under 1.231(a)(2) and (b), 1.234(d), and 1.235(d), beginning January 4, 2020, you must submit your registration, registration renewal, updates, and cancellations to FDA electronically unless FDA has granted a waiver from such requirement. Under 1.232(a)(6), you must provide the email address of the owner, operator, or agent in charge of the facility unless FDA has granted a waiver from such requirement. In addition, under 1.230(b) and (c), 1.232(a)(10), 1.234(a), and 1.235(b)(5), registration renewals, abbreviated registration renewals, registrations, updates, and cancellations not submitted by the owner, operator, or agent in charge must include the email address for the individual who authorized the submission, unless FDA has granted a waiver. To request a waiver from these requirements, you must submit a written request to FDA that explains why it is not reasonable for you to submit your registration, registration renewal, update, or cancellation to FDA electronically or to provide the email address of the owner, operator, or agent in charge of the facility. You must submit your request to: U.S. Food and Drug Administration, Center for Food Safety and Applied Nutrition, 5001 Campus Dr. (HFS-681), College Park, MD 20740.

[81 FR 45953, July 14, 2016]

Subpart I—Prior Notice of Imported Food

General Provisions

Sec. 1.276 What definitions apply to this subpart?

(a) The act means the Federal Food, Drug, and Cosmetic Act.

(b) The definitions of terms in section 201 of the act (21 U.S.C. 321) apply when the terms are used in this subpart, unless defined in this section.

   (1) *Calendar day* means every day shown on the calendar.

   (2) *Country from which the article originates* means FDA Country of Production.

   (3) *Country from which the article is shipped* means the country in which the article of food is loaded onto the conveyance that brings it to the United States or, in the case of food sent by international mail, the country from which the article is mailed.

(4) **FDA Country of Production** means:

(i) For an article of food that is in its natural state, the country where the article of food was grown, including harvested or collected and readied for shipment to the United States. If an article of food is wild fish, including seafood that was caught or harvested outside the waters of the United States by a vessel that is not registered in the United States, the FDA Country of Production is the country in which the vessel is registered. If an article of food that is in its natural state was grown, including harvested or collected and readied for shipment, in a Territory, the FDA Country of Production is the United States.

(ii) For an article of food that is no longer in its natural state, the country where the article was made; except that, if an article of food is made from wild fish, including seafood, aboard a vessel, the FDA Country of Production is the country in which the vessel is registered. If an article of food that is no longer in its natural state was made in a Territory, the FDA Country of Production is the United States.

(5) **Food** has the meaning given in section 201(f) of the act, except as provided in paragraph (b)(5)(i) of this section.

(i) For purposes of this subpart, food does not include:

(A) Food contact substances as defined in section 409(h)(6) of the act (21 U.S.C. 348(h)(6)); or

(B) Pesticides as defined in 7 U.S.C. 136(u).

(ii) Examples of food include fruits, vegetables, fish, including seafood, dairy products, eggs, raw agricultural commodities for use as food or as components of food, animal feed (including pet food), food and feed ingredients, food and feed additives, dietary supplements and dietary ingredients, infant formula, beverages (including alcoholic beverages and bottled water), live food animals, bakery goods, snack foods, candy, and canned foods.

(6) **Full address** means the facility's street name and number; suite/unit number, as appropriate; city; Province or State as appropriate; mail code as appropriate; and country.

(7) **Grower** means a person who engages in growing and harvesting or collecting crops (including botanicals), raising animals (including fish, which includes seafood), or both.

(8) **International mail** means foreign national mail services. International mail does not include express consignment operators or carriers or other private delivery services unless such service is operating under contract as an agent or extension of a foreign mail service.

(9) **Manufacturer** means the last facility, as that word is defined in 1.227, that manufactured/processed the food. A facility is considered the last facility even

if the food undergoes further manufacturing/processing that consists of adding labeling or any similar activity of a de minimis nature. If the food undergoes further manufacturing/processing that exceeds an activity of a de minimis nature, then the subsequent facility that performed the additional manufacturing/processing is considered the manufacturer.

(10) *No longer in its natural state* means that an article of food has been made from one or more ingredients or synthesized, prepared, treated, modified, or manipulated. Examples of activities that render food no longer in its natural state are cutting, peeling, trimming, washing, waxing, eviscerating, rendering, cooking, baking, freezing, cooling, pasteurizing, homogenizing, mixing, formulating, bottling, milling, grinding, extracting juice, distilling, labeling, or packaging. Crops that have been cleaned (e.g., dusted, washed), trimmed, or cooled attendant to harvest or collection or treated against pests, or polished are still in their natural state for purposes of this subpart. Whole fish headed, eviscerated, or frozen attendant to harvest are still in their natural state for purposes of this subpart.

(11) *Port of arrival* means the water, air, or land port at which the article of food is imported or offered for import into the United States. For an article of food arriving by water or air, this is the port of unloading. For an article of food arriving by land, this is the port where the article of food first crosses the border into the United States. The port of arrival may be different than the port where consumption or warehouse entry or foreign trade zone admission documentation is presented to the U.S. Customs and Border Protection (CBP).

(12) *Port of entry* , in section 801(m) and (l) of the act (21 U.S.C. 381(m) and (l)), means the port of entry as defined in 19 CFR 101.1.

(13) *Registration number* means the registration number assigned to a facility by FDA under section 415 of the act (21 U.S.C. 350d) and subpart H of this part.

(14) *Shipper* means the owner or exporter of the article of food who consigns and ships the article from a foreign country or the person who sends an article of food by international mail or express consignment operators or carriers or other private delivery service to the United States.

(15) *United States* means the Customs territory of the United States (i.e., the 50 States, the District of Columbia, and the Commonwealth of Puerto Rico), but not the Territories.

(16) *You* means the person submitting the prior notice, i.e., the submitter or the transmitter, if any.

[73 FR 66402, Nov. 7, 2008, as amended at 80 FR 56143, Sept. 17, 2015]

Sec. 1.277 What is the scope of this subpart?

(a) This subpart applies to all food for humans and other animals that is imported or offered for import into the United States for use, storage, or distribution in the United States, including food for gifts and trade and quality assurance/quality control samples, food for transshipment through the United States to another country, food for future export, and food for use in a U.S. Foreign Trade Zone.

(b) Notwithstanding paragraph (a) of this section, this subpart does not apply to:

(1) Food for an individual's personal use when it is carried by or otherwise accompanies the individual when arriving in the United States;

(2) Food that was made by an individual in his/her personal residence and sent by that individual as a personal gift (i.e., for nonbusiness reasons) to an individual in the United States;

(3) Food that is imported then exported without leaving the port of arrival until export;

(4) Meat food products that at the time of importation are subject to the exclusive jurisdiction of the U.S. Department of Agriculture (USDA) under the Federal Meat Inspection Act (21 U.S.C. 601 et seq.);

(5) Poultry products that at the time of importation are subject to the exclusive jurisdiction of USDA under the Poultry Products Inspection Act (21 U.S.C. 451 et seq.);

(6) Egg products that at the time of importation are subject to the exclusive jurisdiction of USDA under the Egg Products Inspection Act (21 U.S.C. 1031 et seq.); and

(7) Articles of food subject to Article 27(3) of The Vienna Convention on Diplomatic Relations (1961), i.e., shipped as baggage or cargo constituting the diplomatic bag.

Requirements To Submit Prior Notice of Imported Food

Sec. 1.278 Who is authorized to submit prior notice?

A prior notice for an article of food may be submitted by any person with knowledge of the required information. This person is the submitter. The submitter also may use another person to transmit the required information on his/her behalf. The person who transmits the information is the transmitter. The submitter and transmitter may be the same person.

Sec. 1.279 When must prior notice be submitted to FDA?

(a) Except as provided in paragraph (c) of this section, you must submit the prior notice to FDA and the prior notice submission must be confirmed by FDA for review as follows:

(1) If the article of food is arriving by land by road, no less than 2 hours before arriving at the port of arrival;

(2) If the article of food is arriving by land by rail, no less than 4 hours before arriving at the port of arrival;

(3) If the article of food is arriving by air, no less than 4 hours before arriving at the port of arrival; or

(4) If the article of food is arriving by water, no less than 8 hours before arriving at the port of arrival.

(b) Except in the case of an article of food imported or offered for import by international mail:

(1) If prior notice is submitted via the Automated Broker Interface/Automated Commercial Environment/International Trade Data System (ABI/ACE/ITDS), you may not submit prior notice more than 30-calendar days before the anticipated date of arrival.

(2) If prior notice is submitted via the FDA Prior Notice System Interface (FDA PNSI), you may not submit prior notice more than 15-calendar days before the anticipated date of arrival.

(c) Notwithstanding paragraphs (a) and (b) of this section, if the article of food is arriving by international mail, you must submit the prior notice before the article of food is sent to the United States.

(d) FDA will notify you that your prior notice has been confirmed for review with a reply message that contains a Prior Notice (PN) Confirmation Number. Your prior notice will be considered submitted and the prior notice time will start when FDA has confirmed your prior notice for review.

(e) The PN Confirmation Number must accompany any article of food arriving by international mail. The PN Confirmation Number must appear on the Customs Declaration (e.g., CN22 or CN23 or U.S. equivalent) that accompanies the package.

(f) A copy of the confirmation, including the PN Confirmation Number, must accompany any article of food that is subject to this subpart when it is carried by or otherwise accompanies an individual when arriving in the United States. The copy of the confirmation must be provided to U.S. Customs and Border Protection (CBP) or FDA upon arrival.

(g) The PN Confirmation Number must accompany any article of food for which the prior notice was submitted through the FDA PNSI when the article arrives in the United States and must be provided to CBP or FDA upon arrival.

[73 FR 66402, Nov. 7, 2008, as amended at 82 FR 15629, Mar. 30, 2017]

Sec. 1.280 How must you submit prior notice?

(a) You must submit the prior notice electronically to FDA. You must submit all prior notice information in the English language, except that an individual's name, the name of a company, and the name of a street may be submitted in a foreign language. All information, including the items listed in the previous sentence, must be submitted using the Latin (Roman) alphabet. Unless paragraph (c) of this section applies, you must submit prior notice through:

(1) The U.S. Customs and Border Protection (CBP) Automated Broker Interface/ Automated Commercial Environment/International Trade Data System (ABI/ACE/ ITDS); or

(2) The FDA PNSI at https://www.access.fda.gov/. You must submit prior notice through the FDA Prior Notice System Interface (FDA PNSI) for articles of food imported or offered for import by international mail, and other transaction types that cannot be made through ABI/ACE/ITDS.

(b) If a customhouse broker's or self-filer's system is not working or if the ABI/ACE/ITDS interface is not working, prior notice must be submitted through the FDA PNSI.

(c) If FDA determines that FDA PNSI or the Operational and Administration System for Import Support (OASIS) is not working, FDA will post prominent notification and instructions at http://www.fda.gov. FDA will accept prior notice submissions in the format it deems appropriate during the system(s) outage.

[73 FR 66402, Nov. 7, 2008, as amended at 82 FR 15629, Mar. 30, 2017]

Sec. 1.281 What information must be in a prior notice?

(a) General. For each article of food that is imported or offered for import into the United States, except by international mail, you must submit the information for the article that is required in paragraphs (a)(1) through (18) of this section:

(1) The name of the individual submitting the prior notice and his/her business address, phone number, and e-mail address, and the name and address of the submitting firm, if applicable. If the business address of the individual submitting the prior notice is a registered facility, then the facility's registration number, city, and country may be provided instead of the facility's full address;

(2) If different from the submitter, the name of the individual and firm, if applicable, transmitting the prior notice on behalf of the submitter and his/her business address, phone number, and e-mail address. If the business address of the individual transmitting the prior notice is a registered facility, then the facility's registration number, city, and country may be provided instead of the facility's full address;

(3) The entry type;

(4) The U.S. Customs and Border Protection (CBP) entry identifier (e.g., CBP entry number or in-bond number), if available;

(5) The identity of the article of food being imported or offered for import, as follows:

(i) The complete FDA product code;

(ii) The common or usual name or market name;

(iii) The estimated quantity of food that will be shipped, described from largest container to smallest package size; and

(iv) The lot or code numbers or other identifier of the food if required by the act or FDA regulations, e.g., low-acid canned foods, by 113.60(c) of this chapter; acidified foods, by 114.80(b) of this chapter; and infant formula, by 106.90 of this chapter;

(6) For an article of food that is no longer in its natural state, the identity of the manufacturer, as follows:

(i) The name of the manufacturer; and

(ii) Either the registration number, city, and country of the manufacturer or both the full address of the manufacturer and the reason the registration number is not provided;

(7) For an article of food that is in its natural state, the name and growing location address of the grower, if known. If the submitter does not know the identity of the grower or, if the article has been consolidated and the submitter does not know the identity of any of the growers, you may provide the name and address of the firm that has consolidated the articles of food from different growers or different growing locations;

(8) The FDA Country of Production;

(9) If the shipper is different from the manufacturer, the identity of the shipper, as follows:

(i) The name of the shipper; and

(ii) The full address of the shipper. If the address of the shipper is a registered facility, you also may submit the registration number of the shipper's registered facility;

(10) The country from which the article is shipped;

(11) Anticipated arrival information about the article of food being imported or offered for import, as follows:

(i) The anticipated port of arrival;

(ii) The anticipated date on which the article of food will arrive at the anticipated port of arrival;

(iii) The anticipated time of that arrival; and

(iv) Notwithstanding paragraphs (a)(11) introductory text and (a)(11)(i) through (iii) of this section, if the article of food is arriving by express consignment operator or carrier, the express consignment operator or carrier tracking number may be submitted in lieu of the information required in paragraphs (a)(11) introductory text and (a)(11)(i) through (iii) of this section.

(12) The name and full address of the importer. If the business address of the importer is a registered facility, you also may submit the registration number of the importer's registered facility. The identity of the importer is not required for an article of food that is imported or offered for import for transshipment through the United States under a Transportation and Exportation entry;

(13) The name and full address of the owner if different from the importer or ultimate consignee. If the business address of the owner is a registered facility, you also may

submit the registration number of the owner's registered facility. The identity of the owner is not required for an article of food that is imported or offered for import for transshipment through the United States under a Transportation and Exportation entry;

(14) The name and full address of the ultimate consignee. If the business address of the ultimate consignee is a registered facility, you also may submit the registration number of the ultimate consignee's registered facility. The identity of the ultimate consignee is not required for an article of food that is imported or offered for import for transshipment through the United States under a Transportation and Exportation entry;

(15) The mode of transportation;

(16) The Standard Carrier Abbreviation Code (SCAC) or International Air Transportation Association (IATA) code of the carrier which is, or will be, carrying the article of food from the country from which the article is shipped to the United States to the port of arrival, or if this code is not applicable, then the name of the carrier. If the carrier is a privately owned vehicle, the license plate number of the vehicle and the State or Province that issued the license plate number;

(17) Planned shipment information, as applicable to the mode of transportation and when it exists:

(i) The Airway Bill number(s) or Bill of Lading number(s), as applicable. This information is not required for an article of food when carried by or otherwise accompanying an individual when entering the United States. If the article of food is arriving by express consignment operator or carrier, the express consignment operator or carrier tracking number may by submitted in lieu of the Airway Bill number(s) or Bill of Lading number(s), as applicable;

(ii) For food arriving by ocean vessel, the vessel name and voyage number;

(iii) For food arriving by air carrier, the flight number. If the article of food is arriving by express consignment operator or carrier, the express consignment operator or carrier tracking number may be submitted in lieu of the flight number;

(iv) For food arriving by truck, bus, or rail, the trip number;

(v) For food arriving as containerized cargo by water, air, or land, the container number(s). This information is not required for an article of food when carried by or otherwise accompanying an individual when entering the United States; and

(vi) For food arriving by rail, the car number. This information is not required for an article of food when carried by or otherwise accompanying an individual.

(18) Any country to which the article has been refused entry.

(b) Articles arriving by international mail. For each article of food that is imported or offered for import into the United States by international mail, you must submit the information for the article that is required in paragraphs (b)(1) through (12) of this section:

(1) The name of the individual submitting the prior notice and his/her business address, phone number, and e-mail address, and the name and address of the submitting firm, if applicable. If the business address of the individual submitting the prior notice is a registered facility, then the facility's registration number, city, and country may be provided instead of the facility's full address;

(2) If different from the submitter, the name of the individual and firm, if applicable, transmitting the prior notice on behalf of the submitter and his/her business address, phone number, and e-mail address. If the business address of the individual transmitting the prior notice is a registered facility, then the facility's registration number, city, and country may be provided instead of the facility's full address;

(3) The entry type (which will be a mail entry);

(4) The identity of the article of food being imported or offered for import, as follows:

(i) The complete FDA product code;

(ii) The common or usual name or market name;

(iii) The estimated quantity of food that will be shipped, described from largest container to smallest package size; and

(iv) The lot or code numbers or other identifier of the food if required by the act or FDA regulations, e.g., low-acid canned foods, by 113.60(c) of this chapter; acidified foods, by 114.80(b) of this chapter; and infant formula, 106.90 of this chapter;

(5) For an article of food that is no longer in its natural state, the identity of the manufacturer, as follows:

(i) The name of the manufacturer; and

(ii) Either the registration number, city, and country of the manufacturer or both the full address of the manufacturer and the reason the registration number is not provided;

(6) For an article of food that is in its natural state, the name and growing location address of the grower, if known. If the submitter does not know the identity of the grower or, if the article has been consolidated and the submitter does not know the identity of any of the growers, you may provide the name and address of the firm that has consolidated the articles of food from different growers or different growing locations;

(7) The FDA Country of Production;

(8) If the shipper is different from the manufacturer, the identity of the shipper, as follows:

(i) The name of the shipper; and

(ii) The full address of the shipper. If the address of the shipper is a registered facility, you also may submit the registration number of the shipper's registered facility;

(9) The country from which the article is shipped (i.e., mailed);

(10) The anticipated date of mailing; and

(11) The name and address of the U.S. recipient.

(12) Any country to which the article has been refused entry.

(c) Refused articles. If the article of food has been refused under section 801(m)(1) of the act and under this subpart, you must submit the information for the article that is required in paragraphs (c)(1) through (19) of this section. However, if the refusal is based on 1.283(a)(1)(iii) (Untimely Prior Notice), you do not have to resubmit any information previously submitted unless it has changed or the article has been exported and the original prior notice was submitted through ABI/ACE/ITDS. If the refusal is based on 1.283(a)(1)(ii), you should cancel the previous submission per 1.282(b) and (c).

(1) The name of the individual submitting the prior notice and his/her business address, phone number, and e-mail address, and the name and address of the submitting firm, if applicable. If the business address of the individual submitting the prior notice is a registered facility, then the facility's registration number, city, and country may be provided instead of the facility's full address;

(2) If different from the submitter, the name of the individual and firm, if applicable, transmitting the prior notice on behalf of the submitter and his/her business address, phone number, and e-mail address. If the business address of the individual transmitting the prior notice is a registered facility, then the facility's registration number, city, and country may be provided instead of the facility's full address;

(3) The entry type;

(4) The CBP entry identifier (e.g., CBP entry number or in-bond number), if available;

(5) The identity of the article of food being imported or offered for import, as follows:

(i) The complete FDA product code;

(ii) The common or usual name or market name;

(iii) The quantity of food that was shipped, described from largest container to smallest package size; and

(iv) The lot or code numbers or other identifier of the food if required by the act or FDA regulations, e.g., low-acid canned foods, by 113.60(c) of this chapter; acidified foods, by 114.80(b) of this chapter; and infant formula, by 106.90 of this chapter;

(6) For an article of food that is no longer in its natural state, the identity of the manufacturer, as follows:

(i) The name of the manufacturer; and

(ii) Either the registration number, city, and country of the manufacturer or both the full address of the manufacturer and the reason the registration number is not provided;

(7) For an article of food that is in its natural state, the name and growing location address of the grower, if known. If the submitter does not know the identity of the grower or, if the article has been consolidated and the submitter does not know any of the growers, you may provide the name and address of the firm that has consolidated the articles of food from different growers or different growing locations;

(8) The FDA Country of Production;

(9) If the shipper is different from the manufacturer, the identity of the shipper, as follows:

(i) The name of the shipper; and

(ii) The full address of the shipper. If the address of the shipper is a registered facility, you also may submit the registration number of the shipper's registered facility;

(10) The country from which the article is shipped;

(11) Arrival information about the article of food being imported or offered for import, as follows:

(i) The port of arrival; and

(ii) The date on which the article of food arrived at the port of arrival.

(iii) Notwithstanding paragraphs (c)(11) introductory text and (c)(11)(i) and (ii) of this section, if the article of food arrived by express consignment operator or carrier, the express consignment operator or carrier tracking number may be submitted in lieu of the information required in paragraphs (c)(11) introductory text and (c)(11)(i) and (ii) of this section.

(12) The name and full address of the importer. If the business address of the importer is a registered facility, you also may submit the registration number of the importer's registered facility. The identity of the importer is not required for an article of food that is imported or offered for import for transshipment through the United States under a Transportation and Exportation entry;

(13) The name and full address of the owner, if different from the importer or ultimate consignee. If the business address of the owner is a registered facility, you also may submit the registration number of the importer's registered facility. The identity of the owner is not required for an article of food that is imported or offered for import for transshipment through the United States under a Transportation and Exportation entry;

(14) The name and full address of the ultimate consignee. If the business address of the ultimate consignee is a registered facility, you also may submit the registration number of the ultimate consignee's registered facility. The identity of the ultimate consignee is not required for an article of food that is imported or offered for import for transshipment through the United States under a Transportation and Exportation entry;

(15) The mode of transportation;

(16) The SCAC or IATA code of the carrier which carried the article of food from the country from which the article is shipped to the United States to the port of arrival, or if this code is not applicable, then the name of the carrier. If the carrier is a privately owned vehicle, the license plate number of the vehicle and the State or Province that issued the license plate number;

(17) Shipment information, as applicable to the mode of transportation and when it exists:

(i) The Airway Bill number(s) or Bill of Lading number(s), as applicable; however, this information is not required for an article of food when carried by or otherwise accompanying an individual when entering the United States. If the article of food arrived by express consignment operator or carrier, the express consignment operator or carrier tracking number may be submitted in lieu of the Airway Bill number(s) or Bill of Lading number(s), as applicable;

(ii) For food that arrived by ocean vessel, the vessel name and voyage number;

(iii) For food that arrived by air carrier, the flight number. If the article of food arrived by express consignment operator or carrier, the express consignment operator or carrier tracking number may be submitted in lieu of the flight number;

(iv) For food that arrived by truck, bus, or rail, the trip number;

(v) For food that arrived as containerized cargo by water, air, or land, the container number(s); however, this information is not required for an article of food when carried by or otherwise accompanying an individual when entering the United States; and

(vi) For food that arrived by rail, the car number; however, this information is not required for an article of food when carried by or otherwise accompanying an individual;

(18) The location and address where the article of refused food will be or is being held, the date the article has arrived or will arrive at that location, and identification of a contact at that location.

(19) Any country to which the article has been refused entry.

[73 FR 66402, Nov. 7, 2008, as amended at 76 FR 25545, May 5, 2011; 82 FR 15629, Mar. 30, 2017]

Sec. 1.282 What must you do if information changes after you have received confirmation of a prior notice from FDA?

(a)(1) If any of the information required in 1.281(a), except the information required in:

(i) Section 1.281(a)(5)(iii) (quantity),

(ii) Section 1.281(a)(11) (anticipated arrival information), or

(iii) Section 1.281(a)(17) (planned shipment information), changes after you receive notice that FDA has confirmed your prior notice submission for review, you must resubmit prior notice in accordance with this subpart unless the article of food will not be offered for import or imported into the United States.

(2) If any of the information required in 1.281(b), except the information required in 1.281(b)(10) (the anticipated date of mailing), changes after you receive notice that FDA has confirmed your prior notice submission for review, you must resubmit prior notice in accordance with this subpart, unless the article of food will not be offered for import or imported into the United States.

(b) If you submitted the prior notice via the FDA PNSI, you should cancel the prior notice via the FDA PNSI.

(c) If you submitted the prior notice via ABI/ACE/ITDS, you should cancel the prior notice via ACE by requesting that CBP cancel the entry.

[73 FR 66402, Nov. 7, 2008, as amended at 82 FR 15629, Mar. 30, 2017]

Consequences

Sec. 1.283 What happens to food that is imported or offered for import without adequate prior notice?

(a) For each article of food that is imported or offered for import into the United States, except for food arriving by international mail or food carried by or otherwise accompanying an individual, the consequences are:

(1) Inadequate prior notice –

(i) No prior notice. If an article of food arrives at the port of arrival and no prior notice has been submitted and confirmed by FDA for review, the food is subject to refusal of admission under section 801(m)(1) of the act (21 U.S.C. 381(m)(1)). If an article of food is refused for lack of prior notice, unless U.S. Customs and Border Protection (CBP) concurrence is obtained for export and the article is immediately exported from the port of arrival under CBP supervision, it must be held within the port of entry for the article unless directed by CBP or FDA.

(ii) Inaccurate prior notice. If prior notice has been submitted and confirmed by FDA for review, but upon review of the notice or examination of the article of food, the notice is determined to be inaccurate, the food is subject to refusal of admission under section 801(m)(1) of the act. If the article of food is refused due to inaccurate prior notice, unless CBP concurrence is obtained for export and the article is immediately exported from the port of arrival under CBP supervision, it must be held within the port of entry for the article unless directed by CBP or FDA.

(iii) Untimely prior notice. If prior notice has been submitted and confirmed by FDA for review, but the full time that applies under 1.279 for prior notice has not elapsed when the article of food arrives, the food is subject to refusal of admission under section 801(m)(1) of the act, unless FDA has already reviewed the prior notice, determined its response to the prior notice, and advised CBP of that response. If the article of food is refused due to untimely prior notice, unless CBP concurrence is obtained for export and the article is immediately exported from the port of arrival under CBP supervision, it must be held within the port of entry for the article unless directed by CBP or FDA.

(2) Status and movement of refused food.

    (i) An article of food that has been refused under section 801(m)(1) of the act and paragraph (a) of this section shall be considered general order merchandise as described in section 490 of the Tariff Act of 1930, as amended (19 U.S.C. 1490).

    (ii) Refused food must be moved under appropriate custodial bond unless immediately exported under CBP supervision. If the food is to be held at the port, FDA must be notified of the location where the food is held at that port before the food is moved there. If the food is to be held at a secure facility outside the port, FDA must be notified of the location of the secure facility before the food is moved there. The refused food shall not be entered and shall not be delivered to any importer, owner, or ultimate consignee. If the food is to be held at a secure facility outside a port, the food must be taken directly to that secure facility.

(3) Segregation of refused foods. If an article of food that is refused is part of a shipment that contains articles of food that have not been placed under hold or other merchandise not subject to this subpart, the refused article of food may be segregated from the rest of the shipment. This segregation must take place where the article is held. FDA or CBP may supervise segregation. If FDA or CBP determines that supervision is necessary, segregation must not take place without supervision.

(4) Costs. Neither FDA nor CBP are liable for transportation, storage, or other expenses resulting from refusal.

(5) Export after refusal. An article of food that has been refused under paragraph (a) of this section may be exported with CBP concurrence and under CBP supervision unless it is seized or administratively detained by FDA or CBP under other authority. If an article of food that has been refused admission under paragraph (a) of this section is exported, the prior notice should be cancelled within 5-business days of exportation.

(6) No post-refusal submission or request for review. If an article of food is refused under section 801(m)(1) of the act and no prior notice is submitted or resubmitted, no request for FDA review is submitted in accordance with paragraph (d) of this section, or export has not occurred in accordance with paragraph (a)(5) of this section, the article of food shall be dealt with as set forth in CBP regulations relating to general order merchandise (19 CFR part 127), except that, unless otherwise agreed to by CBP and FDA, the article may only be sold for export or destroyed.

(b) Food carried by or otherwise accompanying an individual. If food carried by or otherwise accompanying an individual arriving in the United States is not for personal use and does not have adequate prior notice or the individual cannot provide FDA or CBP with a copy of the prior notice (PN) confirmation, the food is subject to refusal of admission under section 801(m)(1) of the act. If before leaving the port, the individual does not arrange to have the food held at the port or exported, FDA or CBP may destroy the article of food.

(c) Post-Refusal prior notice submissions.

(1) If an article of food is refused under paragraph (a)(1)(i) of this section (no prior notice) and the food is not exported, prior notice must be submitted in accordance with 1.280 and 1.281(c).

(2) If an article of food is refused under paragraph (a)(1)(ii) of this section (inaccurate prior notice) and the food is not exported, the prior notice should be canceled in accordance with 1.282 and you must resubmit prior notice in accordance with 1.280 and 1.281(c).

(3) Once the prior notice has been submitted or resubmitted and confirmed by FDA for review, FDA will endeavor to review and respond to the prior notice submission within the timeframes set out in 1.279.

(d) FDA review after refusal.

(1) If an article of food has been refused admission under section 801(m)(1) of the act, a request may be submitted asking FDA to review whether the article is subject to the requirements of this subpart under 1.277, or whether the information submitted in a prior notice is complete and accurate. A request for review may not be used to submit prior notice or to resubmit an inaccurate prior notice.

(2) A request may be submitted only by the carrier, submitter, importer, owner, or ultimate consignee. A request must identify which one the requester is.

(3) A request must be submitted in writing to FDA and delivered by fax or e-mail. The location for receipt of a request is listed at http://www.fda.gov —see Prior Notice. A request must include all factual and legal information necessary for FDA to conduct its review. Only one request for review may be submitted for each refused article.

(4) The request must be submitted within 5-calendar days of the refusal. FDA will review and respond within 5-calendar days of receiving the request.

(5) If FDA determines that the article is not subject to the requirements of this subpart under 1.277 or that the prior notice submission is complete and accurate, it will notify the requester, the transmitter, and CBP that the food is no longer subject to refusal under section 801(m)(1) of the act.

(e) International mail. If an article of food arrives by international mail with inadequate prior notice or the PN confirmation number is not affixed as required, the parcel will be held by CBP for 72 hours for FDA inspection and disposition. If FDA refuses the article under section 801(m)(1) of the act and there is a return address, the parcel may be returned to sender marked "No Prior Notice—FDA Refused." If the article is refused and there is no return address or FDA determines that the article of food in the parcel appears to present a hazard, FDA may dispose of or destroy the parcel at its expense. If FDA does not respond within 72 hours of the CBP hold, CBP may return the parcel to the sender or, if there is no return address, destroy the parcel, at FDA expense.

(f) Prohibitions on delivery and transfer.

   (1) Notwithstanding section 801(b) of the act, an article of food refused under section 801(m)(1) of the act may not be delivered to the importer, owner, or ultimate consignee until prior notice is submitted to FDA in accordance with this subpart, FDA has examined the prior notice, FDA has determined that the prior notice is adequate, and FDA has notified CBP and the transmitter that the article of food is no longer refused admission under section 801(m)(1) of the act.

   (2) During the time an article of food that has been refused under section 801(m)(1) of the act is held, the article may not be transferred by any person from the port or other designated secure facility until prior notice is submitted to FDA in accordance with this subpart, FDA has examined the prior notice, FDA has determined that the prior notice is adequate, and FDA has notified CBP and the transmitter that the article of food no longer is refused admission under section 801(m)(1) of the act. After this notification by FDA to CBP and transmitter, entry may be made in accordance with law and regulation.

(g) Relationship to other admissibility decisions. A determination that an article of food is no longer refused under section 801(m)(1) of the act is different than, and may come before, determinations of admissibility under other provisions of the act or other U.S. laws. A determination that an article of food is no longer refused under section 801(m)(1) of the act does not mean that it will be granted admission under other provisions of the act or other U.S. laws.

Sec. 1.284 What are the other consequences of failing to submit adequate prior notice or otherwise failing to comply with this subpart?

(a) The importing or offering for import into the United States of an article of food in violation of the requirements of section 801(m) of the act, including the requirements of this subpart, is a prohibited act under section 301(ee) of the act (21 U.S.C. 331(ee)).

(b) Section 301 of the act prohibits the doing of certain acts or causing such acts to be done.

   (1) Under section 302 of the act (21 U.S.C. 332), the United States can bring a civil action in Federal court to enjoin persons who commit a prohibited act.

   (2) Under sections 301 and 303 of the act (21 U.S.C. 331 and 333), the United States can bring a criminal action in Federal court to prosecute persons who are responsible for the commission of a prohibited act.

(c) Under section 306 of the act (21 U.S.C. 335a), FDA can seek debarment of any person who has been convicted of a felony relating to importation of food into the United States or any person who has engaged in a pattern of importing or offering for import adulterated food that presents a threat of serious adverse health consequences or death to humans or animals.

Sec. 1.285 What happens to food that is imported or offered for import from unregistered facilities that are required to register under subpart H of this part?

(a) Consequences. If an article of food from a foreign facility that is not registered as required under section 415 of the act (21 U.S.C. 350d) and subpart H of this part is imported or offered for import into the United States, the food is subject to being held under section 801(l) of the act (21 U.S.C. 381(l)).

(b) Hold. Unless CBP concurrence is obtained for export and the article is immediately exported from the port of arrival, if an article of food has been placed under hold under section 801(l) of the act, it must be held within the port of entry for the article unless directed by CBP or FDA.

(c) Status and movement of held food.

(1) An article of food that has been placed under hold under section 801(l) of the act shall be considered general order merchandise as described in section 490 of the Tariff Act of 1930, as amended (19 U.S.C. 1490).

(2) Food under hold under section 801(l) of the act must be moved under appropriate custodial bond unless immediately exported under CBP supervision. If the food is to be held at the port, FDA must be notified of the location where the food is held at the port before the food is moved there. If the food is to be held at a secure facility outside the port, FDA must be notified of the location of the secure facility before the food is moved there. The food subject to hold shall not be entered and shall not be delivered to any importer, owner, or ultimate consignee. If the food is to be held at a secure facility outside a port, the food must be taken directly to that secure facility.

(d) Segregation of held foods. If an article of food that has been placed under hold under section 801(l) of the act is part of a shipment that contains articles that have not been placed under hold, the food under hold may be segregated from the rest of the shipment. This segregation must take place where the article is held. FDA or CBP may supervise segregation. If FDA or CBP determine that supervision is necessary, segregation must not take place without supervision.

(e) Costs. Neither FDA nor CBP will be liable for transportation, storage, or other expenses resulting from any hold.

(f) Export after hold. An article of food that has been placed under hold under section 801(l) of the act may be exported with CBP concurrence and under CBP supervision unless it is seized or administratively detained by FDA or CBP under other authority.

(g) No registration or request for review. If an article of food is placed under hold under section 801(l) of the act and no registration number or request for FDA review is submitted in accordance with paragraph (j) of this section or export has not occurred in accordance with paragraph (f) of this section, the food shall be dealt with as set forth in CBP regulations relating to general order merchandise, except that, unless otherwise agreed to by CBP and FDA, the article may only be sold for export or destroyed.

(h) Food carried by or otherwise accompanying an individual. If an article of food carried by or otherwise accompanying an individual arriving in the United States is not for personal use and is placed under hold under section 801(l) of the act because it is from a foreign facility that is not registered as required under section 415 of the act and subpart H of this part, the individual may arrange to have the food held at the port or exported. If such arrangements cannot be made, the article of food may be destroyed.

(i) Post-hold submissions.

(1) To resolve a hold, if an article of food is held under paragraph (b) of this section because it is from a foreign facility that is not registered, the facility must be registered and a registration number must be obtained.

(2) The FDA Division of Food Defense Targeting must be notified of the applicable registration number in writing. The notification must provide the name and contact information for the person submitting the information. The notification may be delivered to FDA by fax or e-mail. The contact information for these delivery methods is listed at http://www.fda.gov —see Prior Notice. The notification should include the applicable CBP entry identifier.

(3) If FDA determines that the article is no longer subject to hold, it will notify the person who provided the registration information and CBP that the food is no longer subject to hold under section 801(l) of the act.

(j) FDA review after hold.

(1) If an article of food has been placed under hold under section 801(l) of the act, a request may be submitted asking FDA to review whether the facility associated with the article is subject to the requirements of section 415 of the act. A request for review may not be submitted to obtain a registration number.

(2) A request may be submitted only by the carrier, submitter, importer, owner, or ultimate consignee of the article. A request must identify which one the requestor is.

(3) A request must be submitted in writing to FDA and delivered by fax or e-mail. The location for receipt of a request is listed at http://www.fda.gov —see Prior Notice. A request must include all factual and legal information necessary for FDA to conduct its review. Only one request for review may be submitted for each article under hold.

(4) The request must be submitted within 5-calendar days of the hold. FDA will review and respond within 5-calendar days of receiving the request.

(5) If FDA determines that the article is not from a facility subject to the requirements of section 415 of the act, it will notify the requestor and CBP that the food is no longer subject to hold under section 801(l) of the act.

(k) International mail. If an article of food that arrives by international mail is from a foreign facility that is not registered as required under section 415 of the act and subpart H of this part, the parcel will be held by CBP for 72 hours for FDA inspection and disposition. If the article is placed under hold under section 801(l) of the act and there is a return address, the parcel may be returned to sender marked "No Registration—No Admission Permitted." If the article is under hold and there is no return address or FDA determines that the article of food in the parcel appears to present a hazard, FDA may dispose of or destroy the parcel at its expense. If FDA does not respond within 72 hours of the CBP hold, CBP may return the parcel to the sender marked "No Registration—No Admission Permitted" or, if there is no return address, destroy the parcel, at FDA expense.

(l) Prohibitions on delivery and transfer. Notwithstanding section 801(b) of the act, while an article of food is under hold under section 801(l) of the act, it may not be delivered to the importer, owner, or ultimate consignee. If an article of food is no longer subject to hold under section 801(l) of the act, entry may be made in accordance with law and regulation.

(m) Relationship to other admissibility provisions. A determination that an article of food is no longer subject to hold under section 801(l) of the act is different than, and may come before, determinations of admissibility under other provisions of the act or other U.S. laws. A determination that an article of food is no longer under hold under section 801(l) of the act does not mean that it will be granted admission under other provisions of the act or other U.S. laws.

[73 FR 66402, Nov. 7, 2008, as amended at 82 FR 15629, Mar. 30, 2017]

Subpart J—Establishment, Maintenance, and Availability of Records

General Provisions

Sec. 1.326 Who is subject to this subpart?

(a) Persons who manufacture, process, pack, transport, distribute, receive, hold, or import food in the United States are subject to the regulations in this subpart, unless you qualify for one of the exclusions in 1.327. If you conduct more than one type of activity at a location, you are required to keep records with respect to those activities covered by this subpart, but are not required by this subpart to keep records with respect to activities that fall within one of the exclusions in 1.327.

(b) Persons subject to the regulations in this subpart must keep records whether or not the food is being offered for or enters interstate commerce.

Sec. 1.327 Who is excluded from all or part of the regulations in this subpart?

(a) Farms are excluded from all of the requirements in this subpart.

(b) Restaurants are excluded from all of the requirements in this subpart. A restaurant/retail facility is excluded from all of the requirements in this subpart if its sales of food it prepares and sells to consumers for immediate consumption are more than 90 percent of its total food sales.

(c) Fishing vessels, including those that not only harvest and transport fish but also engage in practices such as heading, eviscerating, or freezing intended solely to prepare fish for holding on board a harvest vessel, are excluded from all of the requirements in this subpart, except 1.361 and 1.363. However, those fishing vessels otherwise engaged in processing fish are subject to all of the requirements in this subpart. For the purposes of this section, "processing" means handling, storing, preparing, shucking, changing into different market forms, manufacturing, preserving, packing, labeling, dockside unloading, holding or heading, eviscerating, or freezing other than solely to prepare fish for holding on board a harvest vessel.

(d) Persons who distribute food directly to consumers are excluded from the requirements in 1.345 to establish and maintain records to identify the nontransporter and transporter immediate subsequent recipients as to those transactions. The term "consumers" does not include businesses.

(e) Persons who operate retail food establishments that distribute food to persons who are not consumers are subject to all of the requirements in this subpart. However, the requirements in 1.345 to establish and maintain records to identify the nontransporter and transporter immediate subsequent recipients that are not consumers applies as to those transactions only to the extent the information is reasonably available.

(1) For purposes of this section, retail food establishment is defined to mean an establishment that sells food products directly to consumers as its primary function. The term "consumers" does not include businesses.

(2) A retail food establishment may manufacture/process, pack, or hold food if the establishment's primary function is to sell from that establishment food, including food that it manufactures/processes, packs, or holds, directly to consumers.

(3) A retail food establishment's primary function is to sell food directly to consumers if the annual monetary value of sales of food products directly to consumers exceeds the annual monetary value of sales of food products to all other buyers.

(4) A "retail food establishment" includes grocery stores, convenience stores, and vending machine locations.

(f) Retail food establishments that employ 10 or fewer full-time equivalent employees are excluded from all of the requirements in this subpart, except 1.361 and 1.363. The exclusion is based on the number of full-time equivalent employees at each retail food establishment and not the entire business, which may own numerous retail stores.

(g) Persons who manufacture, process, pack, transport, distribute, receive, hold, or import food in the United States that is within the exclusive jurisdiction of the U.S. Department of Agriculture (USDA) under the Federal Meat Inspection Act (21 U.S.C. 601 et seq.), the Poultry Products Inspection Act (21 U.S.C. 451 et seq.), or the Egg Products Inspection Act (21 U.S.C. 1031 et seq.) are excluded from all of the requirements in this subpart with respect to that food while it is under the exclusive jurisdiction of USDA.

(h) Foreign persons, except for foreign persons who transport food in the United States, are excluded from all of the requirements of this subpart.

(i) Persons who manufacture, process, pack, transport, distribute, receive, hold, or import food are subject to 1.361 and 1.363 with respect to its packaging (the outer packaging of food that bears the label and does not contact the food). All other persons who manufacture, process, pack, transport, distribute, receive, hold, or import packaging are excluded from all of the requirements of this subpart.

(j) Persons who manufacture, process, pack, transport, distribute, receive, hold, or import food contact substances other than the finished container that directly contacts food are excluded from all of the requirements of this subpart, except 1.361 and 1.363.

(k) Persons who place food directly in contact with its finished container are subject to all of the requirements of this subpart as to the finished container that directly contacts that food. All other persons who manufacture, process, pack, transport, distribute, receive, hold, or import the finished container that directly contacts the food are excluded from the requirements of this subpart as to the finished container, except 1.361 and 1.363.

(l) Nonprofit food establishments are excluded from all of the requirements in this subpart, except 1.361 and 1.363.

(m) Persons who manufacture, process, pack, transport, distribute, receive, hold, or import food for personal consumption are excluded from all of the requirements of this subpart.

(n) Persons who receive or hold food on behalf of specific individual consumers and who are not also parties to the transaction and who are not in the business of distributing food are excluded from all of the requirements of this subpart.

Sec. 1.328 What definitions apply to this subpart?

The definitions of terms in section 201 of the Federal Food, Drug, and Cosmetic Act (the act) (21 U.S.C. 321) apply to such terms when used in this subpart. In addition, for the purposes of this subpart:

Farm means:

(1) *Primary production farm*. A primary production farm is an operation under one management in one general (but not necessarily contiguous) physical location devoted to the growing of crops, the harvesting of crops, the raising of animals (including seafood), or any combination of these activities. The term "farm" includes operations that, in addition to these activities:

(i) Pack or hold raw agricultural commodities;

(ii) Pack or hold processed food, provided that all processed food used in such activities is either consumed on that farm or another farm under the same management, or is processed food identified in paragraph (1)(iii)(B)(1) of this definition; and

      (iii) Manufacture/process food, provided that:

          (A) All food used in such activities is consumed on that farm or another farm under the same management; or

          (B) Any manufacturing/processing of food that is not consumed on that farm or another farm under the same management consists only of:

              (1) Drying/dehydrating raw agricultural commodities to create a distinct commodity (such as drying/dehydrating grapes to produce raisins), and packaging and labeling such commodities, without additional manufacturing/processing (an example of additional manufacturing/ processing is slicing);

              (2) Treatment to manipulate the ripening of raw agricultural commodities (such as by treating produce with ethylene gas), and packaging and labeling treated raw agricultural commodities, without additional manufacturing/processing; and

              (3) Packaging and labeling raw agricultural commodities, when these activities do not involve additional manufacturing/processing (an example of additional manufacturing/processing is irradiation); or

    (2) *Secondary activities farm*. A secondary activities farm is an operation, not located on a primary production farm, devoted to harvesting (such as hulling or shelling), packing, and/or holding of raw agricultural commodities, provided that the primary production farm(s) that grows, harvests, and/or raises the majority of the raw agricultural commodities harvested, packed, and/or held by the secondary activities farm owns, or jointly owns, a majority interest in the secondary activities farm. A secondary activities farm may also conduct those additional activities allowed on a primary production farm as described in paragraphs (1)(ii) and (iii) of this definition.

Food has the meaning given in section 201(f) of the Federal Food, Drug, and Cosmetic Act. Examples of food include, but are not limited to fruits; vegetables; fish; dairy products; eggs; raw agricultural commodities for use as food or as components of food; animal feed, including pet food; food and feed ingredients and additives, including substances that migrate into food from the finished container and other articles that contact food; dietary supplements and dietary ingredients; infant formula; beverages, including alcoholic beverages and bottled water; live food animals; bakery goods; snack foods; candy; and canned foods.

Full-time equivalent employee means all individuals employed by the person claiming the exemption. The number of full-time equivalent employees is determined by dividing the total number of hours of salary or wages paid directly to employees of the person and of all of its affiliates by the number of hours of work in 1 year, 2,080 hours (i.e., 40 hours * 52 weeks).

Harvesting applies to farms and farm mixed-type facilities and means activities that are traditionally performed on farms for the purpose of removing raw agricultural commodities from the place they were grown or raised and preparing them for use as food. Harvesting is limited to activities performed on raw agricultural commodities, or on processed foods created by drying/dehydrating a raw agricultural commodity without additional manufacturing/processing, on a farm. Harvesting does not include activities that transform a raw agricultural commodity into a processed food as defined in section 201(gg) of the Federal Food, Drug, and Cosmetic Act. Examples of harvesting include cutting (or otherwise separating) the edible portion of the raw agricultural commodity from the crop plant and removing or trimming part of the raw agricultural commodity (e.g., foliage, husks, roots, or stems). Examples of harvesting also include cooling, field coring, filtering, gathering, hulling, shelling, sifting, threshing, trimming of outer leaves of, and washing raw agricultural commodities grown on a farm.

Holding means storage of food and also includes activities performed incidental to storage of a food (e.g., activities performed for the safe or effective storage of that food, such as fumigating food during storage, and drying/dehydrating raw agricultural commodities when the drying/dehydrating does not create a distinct commodity (such as drying/dehydrating hay or alfalfa)). Holding also includes activities performed as a practical necessity for the distribution of that food (such as blending of the same raw agricultural commodity and breaking down pallets), but does not include activities that transform a raw agricultural commodity into a processed food as defined in section 201(gg) of the Federal Food, Drug, and Cosmetic Act. Holding facilities could include warehouses, cold storage facilities, storage silos, grain elevators, and liquid storage tanks.

Manufacturing/processing means making food from one or more ingredients, or synthesizing, preparing, treating, modifying or manipulating food, including food crops or ingredients. Examples of manufacturing/processing activities include: Baking, boiling, bottling, canning, cooking, cooling, cutting, distilling, drying/dehydrating raw agricultural commodities to create a distinct commodity (such as drying/dehydrating grapes to produce raisins), evaporating, eviscerating, extracting juice, formulating, freezing, grinding, homogenizing, irradiating, labeling, milling, mixing, packaging (including modified atmosphere packaging), pasteurizing, peeling, rendering, treating to manipulate ripening, trimming, washing, or waxing. For farms and farm mixed-type facilities, manufacturing/processing does not include activities that are part of harvesting, packing, or holding.

Mixed-type facility means an establishment that engages in both activities that are exempt from registration under section 415 of the Federal Food, Drug, and Cosmetic Act and activities that require the establishment to be registered. An example of such a facility is a "farm mixed-type facility," which is an establishment that is a farm, but also conducts activities outside the farm definition that require the establishment to be registered.

Nonprofit food establishment means a charitable entity that prepares or serves food directly to the consumer or otherwise provides food or meals for consumption by humans or animals in the United States. The term includes central food banks, soup kitchens, and nonprofit food delivery services. To be considered a nonprofit food establishment, the establishment must meet the terms of section 501(c)(3) of the U.S. Internal Revenue Code (26 U.S.C. 501(c)(3)).

Nontransporter means a person who owns food or who holds, manufactures, processes, packs, imports, receives, or distributes food for purposes other than transportation.

Nontransporter immediate previous source means a person that last had food before transferring it to another nontransporter.

Nontransporter immediate subsequent recipient means a nontransporter that acquires food from another nontransporter.

Packaging (when used as a noun) means the outer packaging of food that bears the label and does not contact the food. Packaging does not include food contact substances as they are defined in section 409(h)(6) of the Federal Food, Drug, and Cosmetic Act.

Packaging (when used as a verb) means placing food into a container that directly contacts the food and that the consumer receives.

Packing means placing food into a container other than packaging the food and also includes re-packing and activities performed incidental to packing or re-packing a food (e.g., activities performed for the safe or effective packing or re-packing of that food (such as sorting, culling, grading, and weighing or conveying incidental to packing or re-packing)), but does not include activities that transform a raw agricultural commodity, as defined in section 201(r) of the Federal Food, Drug, and Cosmetic Act, into a processed food as defined in section 201(gg) of the Federal Food, Drug, and Cosmetic Act.

Person includes individual, partnership, corporation, and association.

Recipe means the formula, including ingredients, quantities, and instructions, necessary to manufacture a food product. Because a recipe must have all three elements, a list of the ingredients used to manufacture a product without quantity information and manufacturing instructions is not a recipe.

Restaurant means a facility that prepares and sells food directly to consumers for immediate consumption. "Restaurant" does not include facilities that provide food to interstate conveyances, central kitchens, and other similar facilities that do not prepare and serve food directly to consumers.

(1) Facilities in which food is directly provided to humans, such as cafeterias, lunchrooms, cafes, bistros, fast food establishments, food stands, saloons, taverns, bars, lounges, catering facilities, hospital kitchens, day care kitchens, and nursing home kitchens, are restaurants.

(2) Pet shelters, kennels, and veterinary facilities in which food is directly provided to animals are restaurants.

Transporter means a person who has possession, custody, or control of an article of food in the United States for the sole purpose of transporting the food, whether by road, rail, water, or air. Transporter also includes a foreign person that transports food in the United States, regardless of whether that foreign person has possession, custody, or control of that food for the sole purpose of transporting that food.

Transporter's immediate previous source means a person from whom a transporter received food. This source can be either another transporter or a nontransporter.

Transporter's immediate subsequent recipient means a person to whom a transporter delivered food. This recipient can be either another transporter or a nontransporter.

You means a person subject to this subpart under 1.326.

[69 FR 71651, Dec. 9, 2004, as amended at 80 FR 56143, Sept. 17, 2015; 81 FR 3715, Jan. 22, 2016]

Sec. 1.329 Do other statutory provisions and regulations apply?

(a) In addition to the regulations in this subpart, you must comply with all other applicable statutory provisions and regulations related to the establishment and maintenance of records for foods except as described in paragraph (b) of this section. For example, the regulations in this subpart are in addition to existing recordkeeping regulations for low acid canned foods, juice, seafood, infant formula, color additives, bottled water, animal feed, and medicated animal feed.

(b) Records established or maintained to satisfy the requirements of this subpart that meet the definition of electronic records in 11.3(b)(6) (21 CFR 11.3 (b)(6)) of this chapter are exempt from the requirements of part 11 of this chapter. Records that satisfy the requirements of this subpart but that are also required under other applicable statutory provisions or regulations remain subject to part 11 of this chapter.

Sec. 1.330 Can existing records satisfy the requirements of this subpart?

The regulations in this subpart do not require duplication of existing records if those records contain all of the information required by this subpart. If a covered person keeps records of all of the information as required by this subpart to comply with other Federal, State, or local regulations, or for any other reason, then those records may be used to meet these requirements. Moreover, persons do not have to keep all of the information required by this rule in one set of records. If they have records containing some of the required information, they may keep those existing records and keep, either separately or in a combined form, any new information required by this rule. There is no obligation to create an entirely new record or compilation of records containing both existing and new information, even if the records containing some of the required information were not created at the time the food was received or released.

Requirements for Nontransporters To Establish and Maintain Records To Identify the Nontransporter and Transporter Immediate Previous Sources of Food

Sec. 1.337 What information must nontransporters establish and maintain to identify the nontransporter and transporter immediate previous sources of food?

(a) If you are a nontransporter, you must establish and maintain the following records for all food you receive:

(1) The name of the firm, address, telephone number and, if available, the fax number and e-mail address of the nontransporter immediate previous source, whether domestic or foreign;

(2) An adequate description of the type of food received, to include brand name and specific variety (e.g., brand x cheddar cheese, not just cheese; or romaine lettuce, not just lettuce);

(3) The date you received the food;

(4) For persons who manufacture, process, or pack food, the lot or code number or other identifier of the food (to the extent this information exists);

(5) The quantity and how the food is packaged (e.g., 6 count bunches, 25 pound (lb) carton, 12 ounce (oz) bottle, 100 gallon (gal) tank); and

(6) The name of the firm, address, telephone number, and, if available, the fax number and e-mail address of the transporter immediate previous source (the transporter who transported the food to you).

Requirements for Nontransporters To Establish and Maintain Records To Identify the Nontransporter and Transporter Immediate Subsequent Recipients of Food

Sec. 1.345 What information must nontransporters establish and maintain to identify the nontransporter and transporter immediate subsequent recipients of food?

(a) If you are a nontransporter, you must establish and maintain the following records for food you release:

(1) The name of the firm, address, telephone number, and, if available, the fax number and e-mail address of the nontransporter immediate subsequent recipient, whether domestic or foreign;

(2) An adequate description of the type of food released, to include brand name and specific variety (e.g., brand x cheddar cheese, not just cheese; or romaine lettuce, not just lettuce);

(3) The date you released the food;

(4) For persons who manufacture, process, or pack food, the lot or code number or other identifier of the food (to the extent this information exists);

(5) The quantity and how the food is packaged (e.g., 6 count bunches, 25 lb carton, 12 oz bottle, 100 gal tank);

(6) The name of the firm, address, telephone number, and, if available, the fax number and e-mail address of the transporter immediate subsequent recipient (the transporter who transported the food from you); and

(b) Your records must include information reasonably available to you to identify the specific source of each ingredient used to make every lot of finished product.

Requirements for Transporters To Establish and Maintain Records

Sec. 1.352 What information must transporters establish and maintain?

If you are a transporter, you must establish and maintain the following records for each food you transport in the United States. You may fulfill this requirement by either:

(a) Establishing and maintaining the following records:

(1) Names of the transporter's immediate previous source and transporter's immediate subsequent recipient;

(2) Origin and destination points;

(3) Date shipment received and date released;

(4) Number of packages;

(5) Description of freight;

(6) Route of movement during the time you transported the food; and

(7) Transfer point(s) through which shipment moved; or

(b) Establishing and maintaining records containing the following information currently required by the Department of Transportation's Federal Motor Carrier Safety Administration (of roadway interstate transporters (49 CFR 373.101 and 373.103) as of December 9, 2004:

(1) Names of consignor and consignee;

(2) Origin and destination points;

(3) Date of shipment;

(4) Number of packages;

(5) Description of freight;

(6) Route of movement and name of each carrier participating in the transportation; and

(7) Transfer points through which shipment moved; or

(c) Establishing and maintaining records containing the following information currently required by the Department of Transportation's Surface Transportation Board of rail and water interstate transporters (49 CFR 1035.1 and 1035.2) as of December 9, 2004:

(1) Date received;

(2) Received from;

(3) Consigned to;

(4) Destination;

(5) State of;

(6) County of;

(7) Route;

(8) Delivering carrier;

(9) Car initial;

(10) Car no;

(11) Trailer initials/number;

(12) Container initials/number;

(13) No. packages; and

(14) Description of articles; or

(d) Establishing and maintaining records containing the following information currently required by the Warsaw Convention of international air transporters on air waybills:

(1) Shipper's name and address;

(2) Consignee's name and address;

(3) Customs reference/status;

(4) Airport of departure and destination;

(5) First carrier; and

(6) Description of goods; or

(e) Entering into an agreement with the nontransporter immediate previous source located in the United States and/or the nontransporter immediate subsequent recipient located in the United States to establish, maintain, or establish and maintain, the information in 1.352(a), (b), (c), or (d). The agreement must contain the following elements:

(1) Effective date;

(2) Printed names and signatures of authorized officials;

(3) Description of the records to be established and/or maintained;

(4) Provision for the records to be maintained in compliance with 1.360, if the agreement provides for maintenance of records;

(5) Provision for the records to be available to FDA as required by 1.361, if the agreement provides for maintenance of records;

(6) Acknowledgement that the nontransporter assumes legal responsibility under 1.363 for establishing and/or maintaining the records as required by this subpart; and

(7) Provision that if the agreement is terminated in writing by either party, responsibility for compliance with the applicable establishment, maintenance, and access provisions of this subpart reverts to the transporter as of the date of termination.

General Requirements

Sec. 1.360 What are the record retention requirements?

(a) You must create the required records when you receive and release food, except to the extent that the information is contained in existing records.

(b) If you are a nontransporter, you must retain for 6 months after the dates you receive and release the food all required records for any food having a significant risk of spoilage, loss of value, or loss of palatability within 60 days after the date you receive or release the food.

(c) If you are a nontransporter, you must retain for 1 year after the dates you receive and release the food all required records for any food for which a significant risk of spoilage, loss of value, or loss of palatability occurs only after a minimum of 60 days, but within 6 months, after the date you receive or release the food.

(d) If you are a nontransporter, you must retain for 2 years after the dates you receive and release the food all required records for any food for which a significant risk of spoilage, loss of value, or loss of palatability does not occur sooner than 6 months after the date you receive or release the food, including foods preserved by freezing, dehydrating, or being placed in a hermetically sealed container.

(e) If you are a nontransporter, you must retain for 1 year after the dates you receive and release the food all required records for animal food, including pet food.

(f) If you are a transporter or nontransporter retaining records on behalf of a transporter, you must retain for 6 months after the dates you receive and release the food all required records for any food having a significant risk of spoilage, loss of value, or loss of palatability within 60 days after the date the transporter receives or releases the food. If you are a transporter, or nontransporter retaining records on behalf of a transporter, you must retain for 1 year after the dates you receive and release the food, all required records for any food for which a significant risk of spoilage, loss of value, or loss of palatability occurs only after a minimum of 60 days after the date the transporter receives or releases the food.

(g) You must retain all records at the establishment where the covered activities described in the records occurred (onsite) or at a reasonably accessible location.

(h) The maintenance of electronic records is acceptable. Electronic records are considered to be onsite if they are accessible from an onsite location.

Sec. 1.361 What are the record availability requirements?

When FDA has a reasonable belief that an article of food, and any other article of food that FDA reasonably believes is likely to be affected in a similar manner, is adulterated and presents a threat of serious adverse health consequences or death to humans or animals, or when FDA believes that there is a reasonable probability that the use of or exposure to an article of food, and any other article of food that FDA reasonably believes is likely to be affected in a similar manner, will cause serious adverse health consequences or death to humans or animals, any records and other information accessible to FDA under section 414 or 704(a) of the Federal Food, Drug, and Cosmetic Act (21 U.S.C. 350c and 374(a)) must be made readily available for inspection and photocopying or other means of reproduction. Such records and other information must be made available as soon as possible, not to exceed 24 hours from the time of receipt of the official request, from an officer or employee duly designated by the Secretary of Health and Human Services who presents appropriate credentials and a written notice.

[77 FR 10662, Feb. 23, 2012]

Sec. 1.362 What records are excluded from this subpart?

The establishment and maintenance of records as required by this subpart does not extend to recipes for food as defined in 1.328; financial data, pricing data, personnel data, research data, or sales data (other than shipment data regarding sales).

Sec. 1.363 What are the consequences of failing to establish or maintain records or make them available to FDA as required by this subpart?

(a) The failure to establish or maintain records as required by section 414(b) of the Federal Food, Drug, and Cosmetic Act and this regulation or the refusal to permit access to or verification or copying of any such required record is a prohibited act under section 301 of the Federal Food, Drug, and Cosmetic Act.

(b) The failure of a nontransporter immediate previous source or a nontransporter immediate subsequent recipient who enters an agreement under 1.352(e) to establish, maintain, or establish and maintain, records required under 1.352(a), (b), (c), or (d), or the refusal to permit access to or verification or copying of any such required record, is a prohibited act under section 301 of the Federal Food, Drug, and Cosmetic Act.

(c) The failure of any person to make records or other information available to FDA as required by section 414 or 704(a) of the Federal Food, Drug, and Cosmetic Act and this regulation is a prohibited act under section 301 of the Federal Food, Drug, and Cosmetic Act.

[80 FR 56144, Sept. 17, 2015]

Compliance Dates

Sec. 1.368 What are the compliance dates for this subpart?

The compliance date for the requirements in this subpart is December 9, 2005. However, the compliance dates for small and very small businesses are contained in paragraphs (a) and (b) of this section. The size of the business is determined using the total number of full-time equivalent employees in the entire business, not each individual location or establishment. A full-time employee counts as one full-time equivalent employee. Two part-time employees, each working half time, count as one full-time equivalent employee.

(a) The compliance date for the requirements in this subpart is June 9, 2006, for small businesses employing fewer that 500, but more than 10 full-time equivalent employees.

(b) The compliance date for the requirements in this subpart is December 11, 2006, for very small businesses that employ 10 or fewer full-time equivalent employees.

[69 FR 71651, Dec. 9, 2004, as amended at 70 FR 8727, Feb. 23, 2005]

Subpart K—Administrative Detention of Food for Human or Animal Consumption

General Provisions

Sec. 1.377 What definitions apply to this subpart?

The definitions of terms that appear in section 201 of the act (21 U.S.C. 321) apply when the terms are used in this subpart. In addition, for the purposes of this subpart:

Act means the Federal Food, Drug, and Cosmetic Act.

Authorized FDA representative means an FDA District Director in whose district the article of food involved is located or an FDA official senior to such director.

Calendar day means every day shown on the calendar.

Food has the meaning given in section 201(f) of the act (21 U.S.C. 321(f)). Examples of food include, but are not limited to, fruits, vegetables, fish, dairy products, eggs, raw agricultural commodities for use as food or components of food, animal feed, including pet food, food and feed ingredients and additives, including substances that migrate into food from food packaging and other articles that contact food, dietary supplements and dietary ingredients, infant formula, beverages, including alcoholic beverages and bottled water, live food animals, bakery goods, snack foods, candy, and canned foods.

Perishable food means food that is not heat-treated; not frozen; and not otherwise preserved in a manner so as to prevent the quality of the food from being adversely affected if held longer than 7 calendar days under normal shipping and storage conditions.

We means the U.S. Food and Drug Administration (FDA).

Working day means any day from Monday through Friday, excluding Federal holidays.

You means any person who received the detention order or that person's representative.

Sec. 1.378 What criteria does FDA use to order a detention?

An officer or qualified employee of FDA may order the detention of any article of food that is found during an inspection, examination, or investigation under the act if the officer or qualified employee has reason to believe that the article of food is adulterated or misbranded.

[76 FR 25541, May 5, 2011]

Sec. 1.379 How long may FDA detain an article of food?

(a) FDA may detain an article of food for a reasonable period that may not exceed 20 calendar days after the detention order is issued. However, an article may be detained for 10 additional calendar days if a greater period of time is required to institute a seizure or injunction action. The authorized FDA representative may approve the additional 10-calendar day detention period at the time the detention order is issued, or at any time within the 20-calendar day period by amending the detention order.

(b) The entire detention period may not exceed 30 calendar days.

(c) An authorized FDA representative may, in accordance with 1.384, terminate a detention order before the expiration of the detention period.

Sec. 1.380 Where and under what conditions must the detained article of food be held?

(a) You must hold the detained article of food in the location and under the conditions specified by FDA in the detention order.

(b) If FDA determines that removal to a secure facility is appropriate, the article of food must be removed to a secure facility. A detained article of food remains under detention before, during, and after movement to a secure facility. FDA will also state in the detention order any conditions of transportation applicable to the detained article.

(c) If FDA directs you to move the detained article of food to a secure facility, you must receive a modification of the detention order under 1.381(c) before you move the detained article of food to a secure facility.

(d) You must ensure that any required tags or labels under 1.382 accompany the detained article during and after movement. The tags or labels must remain with the article of food until FDA terminates the detention order or the detention period expires, whichever occurs first, unless otherwise permitted by the authorized FDA representative.

(e) The movement of an article of food in violation of a detention order issued under 1.393 is a prohibited act under section 301 of the act (21 U.S.C. 331).

Sec. 1.381 May a detained article of food be delivered to another entity or transferred to another location?

(a) An article of food subject to a detention order under this subpart may not be delivered under the execution of a bond. Notwithstanding section 801(b) of the act (21 U.S.C. 381(b)), while any article of food is subject to a detention order under section 304(h) of the act (21 U.S.C. 334(h)), it may not be delivered to any of its importers, owners, or consignees. This section does not preclude movement at FDA's direction of imported food to a secure facility under an appropriate Customs' bond when that bond is required by Customs' law and regulation.

(b) Except as provided in paragraph (c) of this section, no person may transfer a detained article of food within or from the place where it has been ordered detained, or from the place to which it was removed, until an authorized FDA representative releases the article of food under 1.384 or the detention period expires under 1.379, whichever occurs first.

(c) The authorized FDA representative may approve, in writing, a request to modify a detention order to permit movement of a detained article of food for any of the following purposes:

(1) To destroy the article of food,

(2) To move the detained article of food to a secure facility under the terms of a detention order,

(3) To maintain or preserve the integrity or quality of the article of food, or

(4) For any other purpose that the authorized FDA representative believes is appropriate in the case.

(d) You must submit your request for modification of the detention order in writing to the authorized FDA representative who approved the detention order. You must state in your request the reasons for movement; the exact address of and location in the new facility (or the new location within the same facility) where the detained article of food will be transferred; an explanation of how the new address and location will be secure, if FDA has directed that the article be detained in a secure facility; and how the article will be held under any applicable conditions described in the detention order. If you are requesting modification of a detention order for the purpose of destroying the detained article of food, you also must submit a verified statement identifying the ownership or proprietary interest you have in the detained article of food, in accordance with Supplemental Rule C to the "Federal Rules of Civil Procedure."

(e) If FDA approves a request for modification of a detention order, the article may be transferred but remains under detention before, during, and after the transfer. FDA will state any conditions of transportation applicable to the detained article. You may not transfer a detained article of food without FDA supervision unless FDA has declined in writing to supervise the transfer. If FDA has declined in writing to supervise the transfer of a detained article, you must immediately notify in writing the authorized FDA representative who approved the modification of the detention order that the article of food has reached its new location, and the specific location of the detained article within the new location. Such written notification may be in the form of a fax, e-mail, or other form as agreed to by the authorized FDA representative.

(f) You must ensure that any required tags or labels under 1.382 accompany the detained article during and after movement. The tags or labels must remain with the article of food until FDA terminates the detention order or the detention period expires, whichever occurs first, unless otherwise permitted by the authorized FDA representative who approves the modification of a detention order under this section.

(g) The transfer of an article of food in violation of a detention order issued under 1.393 is a prohibited act under section 301 of the act.

Sec. 1.382 What labeling or marking requirements apply to a detained article of food?

The officer or qualified employee of FDA issuing a detention order under 1.393 may label or mark the detained article of food with official FDA tags or labels that include the following information:

(a) A statement that the article of food is detained by FDA in accordance with section 304(h) of the act;

(b) A statement that the article of food must not be consumed, moved, altered, or tampered with in any manner for the period shown, without the written permission of an authorized FDA representative;

(c) A statement that the violation of a detention order or the removal or alteration of the tag or label is a prohibited act, punishable by fine or imprisonment or both; and

(d) The detention order number, the date and hour of the detention order, the detention period, and the name of the officer or qualified employee of FDA who issued the detention order.

Sec. 1.383 What expedited procedures apply when FDA initiates a seizure action against a detained perishable food?

If FDA initiates a seizure action under section 304(a) of the act against a perishable food subject to a detention order under this subpart, FDA will send the seizure recommendation to the Department of Justice (DOJ) within 4 calendar days after the detention order is issued, unless extenuating circumstances exist. If the fourth calendar day is not a working day, FDA will advise the DOJ of its plans to recommend a seizure action on the last working day before the fourth calendar day and send the recommendation as soon as practicable on the first working day that follows. For purposes of this section, an extenuating circumstance includes, but is not limited to, instances when the results of confirmatory testing or other evidentiary development requires more than 4 calendar days to complete.

Sec. 1.384 When does a detention order terminate?

If FDA terminates a detention order or the detention period expires, an authorized FDA representative will issue a detention termination notice releasing the article of food to any person who received the detention order or that person's representative and will remove, or authorize in writing the removal of, the required labels or tags. If FDA fails to issue a detention termination notice and the detention period expires, the detention is deemed to be terminated.

How Does FDA Order a Detention?

Sec. 1.391 Who approves a detention order?

An authorized FDA representative, i.e. , the FDA District Director in whose district the article of food involved is located or an FDA official senior to such director, must approve a detention order. If prior written approval is not feasible, prior oral approval must be obtained and confirmed in writing as soon as possible.

Sec. 1.392 Who receives a copy of the detention order?

(a) FDA must issue the detention order to the owner, operator, or agent in charge of the place where the article of food is located. If the owner of the article of food is different from the owner, operator, or agent in charge of the place where the article is detained, FDA must provide a copy of the detention order to the owner of the article of food if the owner's identity can be determined readily.

(b) If FDA issues a detention order for an article of food located in a vehicle or other carrier used to transport the detained article of food, FDA also must provide a copy of the detention order to the shipper of record and the owner and operator of the vehicle or other carrier, if their identities can be determined readily.

Sec. 1.393 What information must FDA include in the detention order?

(a) FDA must issue the detention order in writing, in the form of a detention notice, signed and dated by the officer or qualified employee of FDA who has reason to believe that such article of food is adulterated or misbranded.

(b) The detention order must include the following information:

(1) The detention order number;

(2) The date and hour of the detention order;

(3) Identification of the detained article of food;

(4) The period of the detention;

(5) A statement that the article of food identified in the order is detained for the period shown;

(6) A brief, general statement of the reasons for the detention;

(7) The address and location where the article of food is to be detained and the appropriate storage conditions;

(8) Any applicable conditions of transportation of the detained article of food;

(9) A statement that the article of food is not to be consumed, moved, altered, or tampered with in any manner during the detention period, unless the detention order is first modified under 1.381(c);

(10) The text of section 304(h) of the act and 1.401 and 1.402;

(11) A statement that any informal hearing on an appeal of a detention order must be conducted as a regulatory hearing under part 16 of this chapter, with certain exceptions described in 1.403;

(12) The mailing address, telephone number, e-mail address, and fax number of the FDA district office and the name of the FDA District Director in whose district the detained article of food is located;

(13) A statement indicating the manner in which approval of the detention order was obtained, i.e. , verbally or in writing; and

(14) The name and the title of the authorized FDA representative who approved the detention order.

[69 FR 31701, June 4, 2004, as amended at 76 FR 25541, May 5, 2011]

What Is the Appeal Process for a Detention Order?

Sec. 1.401 Who is entitled to appeal?

Any person who would be entitled to be a claimant for the article of food, if seized under section 304(a) of the act, may appeal a detention order as specified in 1.402. Procedures for establishing entitlement to be a claimant for purposes of section 304(a) of the act are governed by Supplemental Rule C to the "Federal Rules of Civil Procedure."

Sec. 1.402 What are the requirements for submitting an appeal?

(a) If you want to appeal a detention order, you must submit your appeal in writing to the FDA District Director, in whose district the detained article of food is located, at the mailing address, e-mail address, or fax number identified in the detention order according to the following applicable timeframes:

   (1) Perishable food: If the detained article is a perishable food, as defined in 1.377, you must file an appeal within 2 calendar days of receipt of the detention order.

   (2) Nonperishable food: If the detained article is not a perishable food, as defined in 1.377, you must file a notice of an intent to request a hearing within 4 calendar days of receipt of the detention order. If the notice of intent is not filed within 4 calendar days, you will not be granted a hearing. If you have not filed a timely notice of intent to request a hearing, you may file an appeal without a hearing request. Whether or not it includes a request for hearing, your appeal must be filed within 10 calendar days of receipt of the detention order.

(b) Your request for appeal must include a verified statement identifying your ownership or proprietary interest in the detained article of food, in accordance with Supplemental Rule C to the "Federal Rules of Civil Procedure."

(c) The process for the appeal of a detention order under this section terminates if FDA institutes either a seizure action under section 304(a) of the act or an injunction under section 302 of the act (21 U.S.C. 276) regarding the article of food involved in the detention order.

(d) As part of the appeals process, you may request an informal hearing. Your request for a hearing must be in writing and must be included in your request for an appeal specified in paragraph (a) of this section. If you request an informal hearing, and FDA grants your request, the hearing will be held within 2 calendar days after the date the appeal is filed.

Sec. 1.403 What requirements apply to an informal hearing?

If FDA grants a request for an informal hearing on an appeal of a detention order, FDA must conduct the hearing in accordance with part 16 of this chapter, except that:

(a) The detention order under 1.393, rather than the notice under 16.22(a) of this chapter, provides notice of opportunity for a hearing under this section and is part of the administrative record of the regulatory hearing under 16.80(a) of this chapter;

(b) A request for a hearing under this section must be addressed to the FDA District Director in whose district the article of food involved is located;

(c) The provision in 16.22(b) of this chapter, providing that a person not be given less than 3 working days after receipt of notice to request a hearing, does not apply to a hearing under this subpart;

(d) The provision in 16.24(e) of this chapter, stating that a hearing may not be required to be held at a time less than 2 working days after receipt of the request for a hearing, does not apply to a hearing under this subpart;

(e) Section 1.406, rather than 16.24(f) of this chapter, describes the statement that will be provided to an appellant where a detention order is based on classified information;

(f) Section 1.404, rather than 16.42(a) of this chapter, describes the FDA employees, i.e., Office of Regulatory Affairs Program Directors or other officials senior to a District Director, who preside at hearings under this subpart;

(g) The presiding officer may require that a hearing conducted under this section be completed within 1 calendar day, as appropriate;

(h) Section 16.60(e) and (f) of this chapter does not apply to a hearing under this subpart. The presiding officer must prepare a written report of the hearing. All written material presented at the hearing will be attached to the report. The presiding officer must include as part of the report of the hearing a finding on the credibility of witnesses (other than expert witnesses) whenever credibility is a material issue, and must include a proposed decision, with a statement of reasons. The hearing participant may review and comment on the presiding officer's report within 4 hours of issuance of the report. The presiding officer will then issue the final agency decision.

(i) Section 16.80(a)(4) of this chapter does not apply to a regulatory hearing under this subpart. The presiding officer's report of the hearing and any comments on the report by the hearing participant under 1.403(h) are part of the administrative record.

(j) No party shall have the right, under 16.119 of this chapter to petition the Commissioner of Food and Drugs for reconsideration or a stay of the presiding officer's final agency decision.

(k) If FDA grants a request for an informal hearing on an appeal of a detention order, the hearing must be conducted as a regulatory hearing pursuant to regulation in accordance with part 16 of this chapter, except that 16.95(b) does not apply to a hearing under this subpart. With respect to a regulatory hearing under this subpart, the administrative record of the hearing specified in 16.80(a)(1), (a)(2), (a)(3), and (a)(5), and 1.403(i) constitutes the exclusive record for the presiding officer's final decision on an administrative detention. For purposes of judicial review under 10.45 of this chapter, the record of the administrative proceeding consists of the record of the hearing and the presiding officer's final decision.

[69 FR 31701, June 4, 2004, as amended at 82 FR 14144, Mar. 17, 2017]

Sec. 1.404 Who serves as the presiding officer for an appeal and for an informal hearing?

The presiding officer for an appeal, and for an informal hearing, must be an Office of Regulatory Affairs Program Director or another FDA official senior to an FDA District Director.

[82 FR 14144, Mar. 17, 2017]

Sec. 1.405 When does FDA have to issue a decision on an appeal?

(a) The presiding officer must issue a written report that includes a proposed decision confirming or revoking the detention by noon on the fifth calendar day after the appeal is filed; after your 4 hour opportunity for submitting comments under 1.403(h), the presiding officer must issue a final decision within the 5-calendar day period after the appeal is filed. If FDA either fails to provide you with an opportunity to request an informal hearing, or fails to confirm or terminate the detention order within the 5-calendar day period, the detention order is deemed terminated.

(b) If you appeal the detention order, but do not request an informal hearing, the presiding officer must issue a decision on the appeal confirming or revoking the detention within 5 calendar days after the date the appeal is filed. If the presiding officer fails to confirm or terminate the detention order during such 5-calendar day period, the detention order is deemed terminated.

(c) If you appeal the detention order and request an informal hearing and your hearing request is denied, the presiding officer must issue a decision on the appeal confirming or revoking the detention within 5 calendar days after the date the appeal is filed. If the presiding officer fails to confirm or terminate the detention order during such 5-calendar day period, the detention order is deemed terminated.

(d) If the presiding officer confirms a detention order, the article of food continues to be detained until we terminate the detention under 1.384 or the detention period expires under 1.379, whichever occurs first.

(e) If the presiding officer terminates a detention order, or the detention period expires, FDA must terminate the detention order as specified under 1.384.

(f) Confirmation of a detention order by the presiding officer is considered a final agency action for purposes of 5 U.S.C. 702.

Sec. 1.406 How will FDA handle classified information in an informal hearing?

Where the credible evidence or information supporting the detention order is classified under the applicable Executive order as requiring protection from unauthorized disclosure in the interest of national security ("classified information"), FDA will not provide you with this information. The presiding officer will give you notice of the general nature of the information and an opportunity to offer opposing evidence or information, if he or she may do so consistently with safeguarding the information and its source. If classified information was used to support the detention, then any confirmation of such detention will state whether it is based in whole or in part on that classified information.

Authority: 15 U.S.C. 1333, 1453, 1454, 1455, 4402; 19 U.S.C. 1490, 1491; 21 U.S.C. 321, 331, 332, 333, 334, 335a, 342, 343, 350c, 350d, 350e, 350j, 350k, 352, 355, 360b, 360ccc, 360ccc-1, 360ccc-2, 362, 371, 373, 374, 379j-31, 381, 382, 384a, 384b, 384d, 387, 387a, 387c, 393; 42 U.S.C. 216, 241, 243, 262, 264, 271; Pub. L. 107-188, 116 Stat. 594, 668-69; Pub. L. 111-353, 124 Stat. 3885, 3889.

Source: 42 FR 15553, Mar. 22, 1977, unless otherwise noted.

Subpart L—Foreign Supplier Verification Programs for Food Importers

Sec. 1.500 What definitions apply to this subpart?

The following definitions apply to words and phrases as they are used in this subpart. Other definitions of these terms may apply when they are used in other subparts of this part.

Adequate means that which is needed to accomplish the intended purpose in keeping with good public health practice.

Audit means the systematic, independent, and documented examination (through observation, investigation, discussions with employees of the audited entity, records review, and, as appropriate, sampling and laboratory analysis) to assess an audited entity's food safety processes and procedures.

Dietary supplement has the meaning given in section 201(ff) of the Federal Food, Drug, and Cosmetic Act.

Dietary supplement component means any substance intended for use in the manufacture of a dietary supplement, including those that may not appear in the finished batch of the dietary supplement. Dietary supplement components include dietary ingredients (as described in section 201(ff) of the Federal Food, Drug, and Cosmetic Act) and other ingredients.

Environmental pathogen means a pathogen capable of surviving and persisting within the manufacturing, processing, packing, or holding environment such that food may be contaminated and may result in foodborne illness if that food is consumed without treatment to significantly minimize the environmental pathogen. Examples of environmental pathogens for the purposes of this part include *Listeria monocytogenes* and *Salmonella spp.* but do not include the spores of pathogenic sporeforming bacteria.

Facility means a domestic facility or a foreign facility that is required to register under section 415 of the Federal Food, Drug, and Cosmetic Act, in accordance with the requirements of subpart H of this part.

Farm means farm as defined in 1.227.

Farm mixed-type facility means an establishment that is a farm but that also conducts activities outside the farm definition that require the establishment to be registered under section 415 of the Federal Food, Drug, and Cosmetic Act.

Food has the meaning given in section 201(f) of the Federal Food, Drug, and Cosmetic Act, except that food does not include pesticides (as defined in 7 U.S.C. 136(u)).

Food allergen means a major food allergen as defined in section 201(qq) of the Federal Food, Drug, and Cosmetic Act.

Foreign supplier means, for an article of food, the establishment that manufactures/ processes the food, raises the animal, or grows the food that is exported to the United States without further manufacturing/processing by another establishment, except for further manufacturing/processing that consists solely of the addition of labeling or any similar activity of a de minimis nature.

Good compliance standing with a foreign food safety authority means that the foreign supplier—

(1) Appears on the current version of a list, issued by the food safety authority of the country in which the foreign supplier is located and which has regulatory oversight of the supplier, of food producers that are in good compliance standing with the food safety authority; or

(2) Has otherwise been designated by such food safety authority as being in good compliance standing.

Harvesting applies to applies to farms and farm mixed-type facilities and means activities that are traditionally performed on farms for the purpose of removing raw agricultural commodities from the place they were grown or raised and preparing them for use as food. Harvesting is limited to activities performed on raw agricultural commodities, or on processed foods created by drying/dehydrating a raw agricultural commodity without additional manufacturing/processing, on a farm. Harvesting does not include activities that transform a raw agricultural commodity into a processed food as defined in section 201(gg) of the Federal Food, Drug, and Cosmetic Act. Examples of harvesting include cutting (or otherwise separating) the edible portion of the raw agricultural commodity from the crop plant and removing or trimming part of the raw agricultural commodity (e.g., foliage, husks, roots, or stems). Examples of harvesting also include cooling, field coring, filtering, gathering, hulling, shelling, sifting, threshing, trimming of outer leaves of, and washing raw agricultural commodities grown on a farm.

Hazard means any biological, chemical (including radiological), or physical agent that is reasonably likely to cause illness or injury.

Hazard requiring a control means a known or reasonably foreseeable hazard for which a person knowledgeable about the safe manufacturing, processing, packing, or holding of food would, based on the outcome of a hazard analysis (which includes an assessment of the probability that the hazard will occur in the absence of controls or measures and the severity of the illness or injury if the hazard were to occur), establish one or more controls or measures to significantly minimize or prevent the hazard in a food and components to manage those controls or measures (such as monitoring, corrections or corrective actions, verification, and records) as appropriate to the food, the facility, and the nature of the control or measure and its role in the facility's food safety system.

Holding means storage of food and also includes activities performed incidental to storage of a food (e.g., activities performed for the safe or effective storage of that food, such as fumigating food during storage, and drying/dehydrating raw agricultural commodities when the drying/dehydrating does not create a distinct commodity (such as drying/dehydrating hay or alfalfa)). Holding also includes activities performed as a practical necessity for the distribution of that food (such as blending of the same raw agricultural commodity and breaking down pallets), but does not include activities that transform a raw agricultural commodity into a processed food as defined in section 201(gg) of the Federal Food, Drug, and Cosmetic Act. Holding facilities could include warehouses, cold storage facilities, storage silos, grain elevators, and liquid storage tanks.

Importer means the U.S. owner or consignee of an article of food that is being offered for import into the United States. If there is no U.S. owner or consignee of an article of food at the time of U.S. entry, the importer is the U.S. agent or representative of the foreign owner or consignee at the time of entry, as confirmed in a signed statement of consent to serve as the importer under this subpart.

Known or reasonably foreseeable hazard means a biological, chemical (including radiological), or physical hazard that is known to be, or has the potential to be, associated with a food or the facility in which it is manufactured/processed.

Lot means the food produced during a period of time and identified by an establishment's specific code.

Manufacturing/processing means making food from one or more ingredients, or synthesizing, preparing, treating, modifying, or manipulating food, including food crops or ingredients. Examples of manufacturing/processing activities include: Baking, boiling, bottling, canning, cooking, cooling, cutting, distilling, drying/dehydrating raw agricultural commodities to create a distinct commodity (such as drying/dehydrating grapes to produce raisins), evaporating, eviscerating, extracting juice, extruding (of animal food), formulating, freezing, grinding, homogenizing, irradiating, labeling, milling, mixing, packaging (including modified atmosphere packaging), pasteurizing, peeling, pelleting (of animal food), rendering, treating to manipulate ripening, trimming, washing, or waxing. For farms and farm mixed-type facilities, manufacturing/processing does not include activities that are part of harvesting, packing, or holding.

Microorganisms means yeasts, molds, bacteria, viruses, protozoa, and microscopic parasites and includes species that are pathogens.

Packing means placing food into a container other than packaging the food and also includes re-packing and activities performed incidental to packing or re-packing a food (e.g., activities performed for the safe or effective packing or re-packing of that food (such as sorting, culling, grading, and weighing or conveying incidental to packing or re-packing)), but does not include activities that transform a raw agricultural commodity into a processed food as defined in section 201(gg) of the Federal Food, Drug, and Cosmetic Act.

Pathogen means a microorganism of public health significance.

Qualified auditor means a person who is a qualified individual as defined in this section and has technical expertise obtained through education, training, or experience (or a combination thereof) necessary to perform the auditing function as required by 1.506(e)(1)(i) or 1.511(c)(5)(i)(A). Examples of potential qualified auditors include:

(1) A government employee, including a foreign government employee; and

(2) An audit agent of a certification body that is accredited in accordance with subpart M of this part.

Qualified individual means a person who has the education, training, or experience (or a combination thereof) necessary to perform an activity required under this subpart, and can read and understand the language of any records that the person must review in performing this activity. A qualified individual may be, but is not required to be, an employee of the importer. A government employee, including a foreign government employee, may be a qualified individual.

Raw agricultural commodity has the meaning given in section 201(r) of the Federal Food, Drug, and Cosmetic Act.

Ready-to-eat food (RTE food) means any food that is normally eaten in its raw state or any food, including a processed food, for which it is reasonably foreseeable that the food will be eaten without further processing that would significantly minimize biological hazards.

Receiving facility means a facility that is subject to subparts C and G of part 117 of this chapter, or subparts C and E of part 507 of this chapter, and that manufactures/processes a raw material or other ingredient that it receives from a supplier.

U.S. owner or consignee means the person in the United States who, at the time of U.S. entry, either owns the food, has purchased the food, or has agreed in writing to purchase the food.

Very small importer means:

(1) With respect to the importation of human food, an importer (including any subsidiaries and affiliates) averaging less than $1 million per year, adjusted for inflation, during the

3-year period preceding the applicable calendar year, in sales of human food combined with the U.S. market value of human food imported, manufactured, processed, packed, or held without sale (e.g., imported for a fee); and

(2) With respect to the importation of animal food, an importer (including any subsidiaries and affiliates) averaging less than $2.5 million per year, adjusted for inflation, during the 3-year period preceding the applicable calendar year, in sales of animal food combined with the U.S. market value of animal food imported, manufactured, processed, packed, or held without sale (e.g., imported for a fee).

You means a person who is subject to some or all of the requirements in this subpart.

[80 FR 74340, Nov. 27, 2015, as amended at 81 FR 25327, Apr. 28, 2016]

Sec. 1.501 To what foods do the requirements in this subpart apply?

(a) General. Except as specified otherwise in this section, the requirements in this subpart apply to all food imported or offered for import into the United States and to the importers of such food.

(b) Exemptions for juice and seafood –

(1) Importers of certain juice and seafood products. This subpart does not apply with respect to juice, fish, and fishery products that are imported from a foreign supplier that is required to comply with, and is in compliance with, the requirements in part 120 or part 123 of this chapter. If you import juice or fish and fishery products that are subject to part 120 or part 123, respectively, you must comply with the requirements applicable to importers of those products under 120.14 or 123.12 of this chapter, respectively.

(2) Certain importers of juice or seafood raw materials or other ingredients subject to part 120 or part 123 of this chapter. This subpart does not apply with respect to any raw materials or other ingredients that you import and use in manufacturing or processing juice subject to part 120 or fish and fishery products subject to part 123, provided that you are in compliance with the requirements in part 120 or part 123 with respect to the juice or fish or fishery product that you manufacture or process from the imported raw materials or other ingredients.

(c) Exemption for food imported for research or evaluation. This subpart does not apply to food that is imported for research or evaluation use, provided that such food:

(1) Is not intended for retail sale and is not sold or distributed to the public;

(2) Is labeled with the statement "Food for research or evaluation use";

(3) Is imported in a small quantity that is consistent with a research, analysis, or quality assurance purpose, the food is used only for this purpose, and any unused quantity is properly disposed of; and

(4) Is accompanied, when filing entry with U.S. Customs and Border Protection, by an electronic declaration that the food will be used for research or evaluation purposes and will not be sold or distributed to the public.

(d) Exemption for food imported for personal consumption. This subpart does not apply to food that is imported for personal consumption, provided that such food is not intended for retail sale and is not sold or distributed to the public. Food is imported for personal consumption only if it is purchased or otherwise acquired by a person in a small quantity that is consistent with a non-commercial purpose and is not sold or distributed to the public.

(e) Exemption for alcoholic beverages.

(1) This subpart does not apply with respect to alcoholic beverages that are imported from a foreign supplier that is a facility that meets the following two conditions:

(i) Under the Federal Alcohol Administration Act (27 U.S.C. 201 et seq.) or chapter 51 of subtitle E of the Internal Revenue Code of 1986 (26 U.S.C. 5001 et seq.), the facility is a foreign facility of a type that, if it were a domestic facility, would require obtaining a permit from, registering with, or obtaining approval of a notice or application from the Secretary of the Treasury as a condition of doing business in the United States; and

(ii) Under section 415 of the Federal Food, Drug, and Cosmetic Act, the facility is required to register as a facility because it is engaged in manufacturing/processing one or more alcoholic beverages.

(2) This subpart does not apply with respect to food that is not an alcoholic beverage that is imported from a foreign supplier described in paragraph (e)(1) of this section, provided such food:

(i) Is in prepackaged form that prevents any direct human contact with such food; and

(ii) Constitutes not more than 5 percent of the overall sales of the facility, as determined by the Secretary of the Treasury.

(3) This subpart does not apply with respect to raw materials and other ingredients that are imported for use in alcoholic beverages provided that:

(i) The imported raw materials and other ingredients are used in the manufacturing/processing, packing, or holding of alcoholic beverages;

(ii) Such manufacturing/processing, packing, or holding is performed by the importer;

(iii) The importer is required to register under section 415 of the Federal Food, Drug, and Cosmetic Act; and

(iv) The importer is exempt from the regulations in part 117 of this chapter in accordance with 117.5(i) of this chapter.

(f) Inapplicability to food that is transshipped or imported for processing and export. This subpart does not apply to food:

(1) That is transshipped through the United States to another country and is not sold or distributed to the public in the United States; or

(2) That is imported for processing and future export and that is not sold or distributed to the public in the United States.

(g) Inapplicability to U.S. food returned. This subpart does not apply to food that is manufactured/processed, raised, or grown in the United States, exported, and returned to the United States without further manufacturing/processing in a foreign country.

(h) Inapplicability to certain meat, poultry, and egg products. This subpart does not apply with respect to:

(1) Meat food products that at the time of importation are subject to the requirements of the U.S. Department of Agriculture (USDA) under the Federal Meat Inspection Act (21 U.S.C. 601 et seq.);

(2) Poultry products that at the time of importation are subject to the requirements of the USDA under the Poultry Products Inspection Act (21 U.S.C. 451 et seq.); and

(3) Egg products that at the time of importation are subject to the requirements of the USDA under the Egg Products Inspection Act (21 U.S.C. 1031 et seq.).

[80 FR 74340, Nov. 27, 2015, as amended at 81 FR 25327, Apr. 28, 2016]

Sec. 1.502 What foreign supplier verification program (FSVP) must I have?

(a) General. Except as specified in paragraph (b) of this section, for each food you import, you must develop, maintain, and follow an FSVP that provides adequate assurances that your foreign supplier is producing the food in compliance with processes and procedures that provide at least the same level of public health protection as those required under section 418 (regarding hazard analysis and risk-based preventive controls for certain foods) or 419 (regarding standards for produce safety), if either is applicable, and the implementing regulations, and is producing the food in compliance with sections 402 (regarding adulteration) and 403(w) (if applicable) (regarding misbranding with respect to labeling for the presence of major food allergens) of the Federal Food, Drug, and Cosmetic Act.

(b) Low-acid canned foods –

(1) Importers of low-acid canned foods not subject to further manufacturing or processing. With respect to those microbiological hazards that are controlled by part 113 of this chapter, if you import a thermally processed low-acid food packaged in a hermetically sealed container (low-acid canned food), you must verify and document that the food was produced in accordance with part 113. With respect to all matters that are not controlled by part 113, you must have an FSVP as specified in paragraph (a) of this section.

(2) Certain importers of raw materials or other ingredients subject to part 113 of this chapter. With respect to microbiological hazards that are controlled by part 113, you are not required to comply with the requirements of this subpart for raw materials or other ingredients that you import and use in the manufacturing or processing of low-acid canned food provided that you are in compliance with part 113 with respect to the low-acid canned food that you manufacture or process from the imported raw

materials or other ingredients. With respect to all hazards other than microbiological hazards that are controlled by part 113, you must have an FSVP as specified in paragraph (a) of this section for the imported raw materials and other ingredients that you use in the manufacture or processing of low-acid canned foods.

(c) Importers subject to section 418 of the Federal Food, Drug, and Cosmetic Act. You are deemed to be in compliance with the requirements of this subpart for a food you import, except for the requirements in 1.509, if you are a receiving facility as defined in 117.3 or 507.3 of this chapter and you are in compliance with the following requirements of part 117 or part 507 of this chapter, as applicable:

   (1) You implement preventive controls for the hazards in the food in accordance with 117.135 or 507.34 of this chapter;

   (2) You are not required to implement a preventive control under 117.136 or 507.36 of this chapter with respect to the food; or

   (3) You have established and implemented a risk-based supply-chain program in compliance with subpart G of part 117 or subpart E of part 507 of this chapter with respect to the food.

Sec. 1.503 Who must develop my FSVP and perform FSVP activities?

(a) Qualified individual. A qualified individual must develop your FSVP and perform each of the activities required under this subpart. A qualified individual must have the education, training, or experience (or a combination thereof) necessary to perform their assigned activities and must be able to read and understand the language of any records that must be reviewed in performing an activity.

(b) Qualified auditor. A qualified auditor must conduct any audit conducted in accordance with 1.506(e)(1)(i) or 1.511(c)(5)(i)(A). A qualified auditor must have technical expertise obtained through education, training, or experience (or a combination thereof) necessary to perform the auditing function.

Sec. 1.504 What hazard analysis must I conduct?

(a) Requirement for a hazard analysis. Except as specified in paragraph (d) of this section, you must conduct a hazard analysis to identify and evaluate, based on experience, illness data, scientific reports, and other information, known or reasonably foreseeable hazards for each type of food you import to determine whether there are any hazards requiring a control. Your hazard analysis must be written regardless of its outcome.

(b) Hazard identification.

   (1) Your analysis of the known or reasonably foreseeable hazards in each food must include the following types of hazards:

      (i) Biological hazards, including microbiological hazards such as parasites, environmental pathogens, and other pathogens;

    (ii) Chemical hazards, including radiological hazards, pesticide and drug residues, natural toxins, decomposition, unapproved food or color additives, food allergens, and (in animal food) nutrient deficiencies or toxicities; and

    (iii) Physical hazards (such as stones, glass, and metal fragments).

  (2) Your analysis must include known or reasonably foreseeable hazards that may be present in a food for any of the following reasons:

    (i) The hazard occurs naturally;

    (ii) The hazard may be unintentionally introduced; or

    (iii) The hazard may be intentionally introduced for purposes of economic gain.

(c) Hazard evaluation.

  (1) Your hazard analysis must include an evaluation of the hazards identified in paragraph (b) of this section to assess the probability that the hazard will occur in the absence of controls and the severity of the illness or injury if the hazard were to occur.

  (2) The hazard evaluation required by paragraph (c)(1) of this section must include an evaluation of environmental pathogens whenever a ready-to-eat food is exposed to the environment before packaging and the packaged food does not receive a treatment or otherwise include a control or measure (such as a formulation lethal to the pathogen) that would significantly minimize the pathogen.

  (3) Your hazard evaluation must consider the effect of the following on the safety of the finished food for the intended consumer:

    (i) The formulation of the food;

    (ii) The condition, function, and design of the establishment and equipment of a typical entity that manufactures/processes, grows, harvests, or raises this type of food;

    (iii) Raw materials and other ingredients;

    (iv) Transportation practices;

    (v) Harvesting, raising, manufacturing, processing, and packing procedures;

    (vi) Packaging and labeling activities;

    (vii) Storage and distribution;

    (viii) Intended or reasonably foreseeable use;

    (ix) Sanitation, including employee hygiene; and

    (x) Any other relevant factors, such as the temporal (e.g., weather-related) nature of some hazards (e.g., levels of natural toxins).

(d) Review of another entity's hazard analysis. If another entity (including your foreign supplier) has, using a qualified individual, analyzed the known or reasonably foreseeable hazards for the food to determine whether there are any hazards requiring a control, you may meet your requirement to determine whether there are any hazards requiring a control in a food by reviewing and assessing the hazard analysis conducted by that entity. You must document your review and assessment of that hazard analysis, including documenting that the hazard analysis was conducted by a qualified individual.

(e) Hazards in raw agricultural commodities that are fruits or vegetables. If you are importing a raw agricultural commodity that is a fruit or vegetable that is "covered produce" as defined in 112.3 of this chapter, you are not required to determine whether there are any biological hazards requiring a control in such food because the biological hazards in such fruits or vegetables require a control and compliance with the requirements in part 112 of this chapter significantly minimizes or prevents the biological hazards. However, you must determine whether there are any other types of hazards requiring a control in such food.

(f) No hazards requiring a control. If you evaluate the known and reasonably foreseeable hazards in a food and determine that there are no hazards requiring a control, you are not required to conduct an evaluation for foreign supplier approval and verification under 1.505 and you are not required to conduct foreign supplier verification activities under 1.506. This paragraph (f) does not apply if the food is a raw agricultural commodity that is a fruit or vegetable that is "covered produce" as defined in 112.3 of this chapter.

Sec. 1.505 What evaluation for foreign supplier approval and verification must I conduct?

(a) Evaluation of a foreign supplier's performance and the risk posed by a food.

(1) Except as specified in paragraphs (d) and (e) of this section, in approving your foreign suppliers and determining the appropriate supplier verification activities that must be conducted for a foreign supplier of a type of food you import, you must consider the following:

(i) The hazard analysis of the food conducted in accordance with 1.504, including the nature of the hazard requiring a control.

(ii) The entity or entities that will be significantly minimizing or preventing the hazards requiring a control or verifying that such hazards have been significantly minimized or prevented, such as the foreign supplier, the foreign supplier's raw material or other ingredient supplier, or another entity in your supply chain.

(iii) Foreign supplier performance, including:

(A) The foreign supplier's procedures, processes, and practices related to the safety of the food;

(B) Applicable FDA food safety regulations and information relevant to the foreign supplier's compliance with those regulations, including whether the foreign supplier is the subject of an FDA warning letter, import alert, or other FDA compliance action related to food safety (or, when applicable, the relevant laws and regulations of a country whose food safety system

FDA has officially recognized as comparable or determined to be equivalent to that of the United States, and information relevant to the supplier's compliance with those laws and regulations); and

(C) The foreign supplier's food safety history, including available information about results from testing foods for hazards, audit results relating to the safety of the food, and responsiveness of the foreign supplier in correcting problems.

(iv) Any other factors as appropriate and necessary, such as storage and transportation practices.

(2) You must document the evaluation you conduct under paragraph (a)(1) of this section.

(b) Approval of foreign suppliers. You must approve your foreign suppliers on the basis of the evaluation that you conducted under paragraph (a) of this section or that you review and assess under paragraph (d) of this section, and document your approval.

(c) Reevaluation of a foreign supplier's performance and the risk posed by a food.

(1) Except as specified in paragraph (d) of this section, you must promptly reevaluate the concerns associated with the factors in paragraph (a)(1) of this section when you become aware of new information about these factors, and the reevaluation must be documented. If you determine that the concerns associated with importing a food from a foreign supplier have changed, you must promptly determine (and document) whether it is appropriate to continue to import the food from the foreign supplier and whether the supplier verification activities conducted under 1.506 or 1.511(c) need to be changed.

(2) If at the end of any 3-year period you have not reevaluated the concerns associated with the factors in paragraph (a)(1) of this section in accordance with paragraph (c)(1) of this section, you must reevaluate those concerns and take other appropriate actions, if necessary, in accordance with paragraph (c)(1). You must document your reevaluation and any subsequent actions you take in accordance with paragraph (c)(1).

(d) Review of another entity's evaluation or reevaluation of a foreign supplier's performance and the risk posed by a food. If an entity other than the foreign supplier has, using a qualified individual, performed the evaluation described in paragraph (a) of this section or the reevaluation described in paragraph (c) of this section, you may meet the requirements of the applicable paragraph by reviewing and assessing the evaluation or reevaluation conducted by that entity. You must document your review and assessment, including documenting that the evaluation or reevaluation was conducted by a qualified individual.

(e) Inapplicability to certain circumstances. You are not required to conduct an evaluation under this section or to conduct foreign supplier verification activities under 1.506 if one of the circumstances described in 1.507 applies to your importation of a food and you are in compliance with that section.

Sec. 1.506 What foreign supplier verification and related activities must I conduct?

(a) Use of approved foreign suppliers.

(1) You must establish and follow written procedures to ensure that you import foods only from foreign suppliers you have approved based on the evaluation conducted under 1.505 (or, when necessary and appropriate, on a temporary basis from unapproved foreign suppliers whose foods you subject to adequate verification activities before importing the food). You must document your use of these procedures.

(2) You may rely on an entity other than your foreign supplier to establish the procedures and perform and document the activities required under paragraph (a)(1) of this section provided that you review and assess that entity's documentation of the procedures and activities, and you document your review and assessment.

(b) Foreign supplier verification procedures. You must establish and follow adequate written procedures for ensuring that appropriate foreign supplier verification activities are conducted with respect to the foods you import.

(c) Requirement of supplier verification. The foreign supplier verification activities must provide assurance that the hazards requiring a control in the food you import have been significantly minimized or prevented.

(d) Determination of appropriate foreign supplier verification activities –

(1) (i) General. Except as provided in paragraphs (d)(2) and (3) of this section, before importing a food from a foreign supplier, you must determine and document which verification activity or activities listed in paragraphs (d)(1)(ii)(A) through (D) of this section, as well as the frequency with which the activity or activities must be conducted, are needed to provide adequate assurances that the food you obtain from the foreign supplier is produced in accordance with paragraph (c) of this section. Verification activities must address the entity or entities that are significantly minimizing or preventing the hazards or verifying that the hazards have been significantly minimized or prevented (e.g., when an entity other than the grower of produce subject to part 112 of this chapter harvests or packs the produce and significantly minimizes or prevents the hazard or verifies that the hazard has been significantly minimized or prevented, or when the foreign supplier's raw material supplier significantly minimizes or prevents a hazard). The determination of appropriate supplier verification activities must be based on the evaluation of the food and foreign supplier conducted under 1.505.

(ii) Appropriate verification activities. The following are appropriate supplier verification activities:

(A) Onsite audits as specified in paragraph (e)(1)(i) of this section;

(B) Sampling and testing of a food as specified in paragraph (e)(1)(ii) of this section;

      (C) Review of the foreign supplier's relevant food safety records as specified in paragraph (e)(1)(iii) of this section; and

      (D) Other appropriate supplier verification activities as specified in paragraph (e)(1)(iv) of this section.

  (2) Verification activities for certain serious hazards. When a hazard in a food will be controlled by the foreign supplier and is one for which there is a reasonable probability that exposure to the hazard will result in serious adverse health consequences or death to humans or animals, you must conduct or obtain documentation of an onsite audit of the foreign supplier before initially importing the food and at least annually thereafter, unless you make an adequate written determination that, instead of such initial and annual onsite auditing, other supplier verification activities listed in paragraph (d)(1)(ii) of this section and/or less frequent onsite auditing are appropriate to provide adequate assurances that the foreign supplier is producing the food in accordance with paragraph (c) of this section, based on the determination made under 1.505.

  (3) Reliance on a determination by another entity. You may rely on a determination of appropriate foreign supplier verification activities in accordance with paragraph (d)(1) or (2) of this section made by an entity other than the foreign supplier if you review and assess whether the entity's determination regarding appropriate activities (including the frequency with which such activities must be conducted) is appropriate. You must document your review and assessment, including documenting that the determination of appropriate verification activities was made by a qualified individual.

(e) Performance of foreign supplier verification activities –

  (1) Verification activities. Except as provided in paragraph (e)(2) of this section, based on the determination made in accordance with paragraph (d) of this section, you must conduct (and document) or obtain documentation of one or more of the supplier verification activities listed in paragraphs (e)(1)(i) through (iv) of this section for each foreign supplier before importing the food and periodically thereafter.

    (i) Onsite audit of the foreign supplier.

      (A) An onsite audit of a foreign supplier must be performed by a qualified auditor.

      (B) If the food is subject to one or more FDA food safety regulations, an onsite audit of the foreign supplier must consider such regulations and include a review of the supplier's written food safety plan, if any, and its implementation, for the hazard being controlled (or, when applicable, an onsite audit may consider relevant laws and regulations of a country whose food safety system FDA has officially recognized as comparable or determined to be equivalent to that of the United States).

(C) If the onsite audit is conducted solely to meet the requirements of paragraph (e) of this section by an audit agent of a certification body that is accredited in accordance with subpart M of this part, the audit is not subject to the requirements in that subpart.

(D) You must retain documentation of each onsite audit, including the audit procedures, the dates the audit was conducted, the conclusions of the audit, any corrective actions taken in response to significant deficiencies identified during the audit, and documentation that the audit was conducted by a qualified auditor.

(E) The following inspection results may be substituted for an onsite audit, provided that the inspection was conducted within 1 year of the date by which the onsite audit would have been required to be conducted:

(1) The written results of an appropriate inspection of the foreign supplier for compliance with applicable FDA food safety regulations conducted by FDA, representatives of other Federal Agencies (such as the USDA), or representatives of State, local, tribal, or territorial agencies; or

(2) The written results of an inspection of the foreign supplier by the food safety authority of a country whose food safety system FDA has officially recognized as comparable or determined to be equivalent to that of the United States, provided that the food that is the subject of the onsite audit is within the scope of the official recognition or equivalence determination, and the foreign supplier is in, and under the regulatory oversight of, such country.

(ii) Sampling and testing of the food. You must retain documentation of each sampling and testing of a food, including identification of the food tested (including lot number, as appropriate), the number of samples tested, the test(s) conducted (including the analytical method(s) used), the date(s) on which the test(s) were conducted and the date of the report of the testing, the results of the testing, any corrective actions taken in response to detection of hazards, information identifying the laboratory conducting the testing, and documentation that the testing was conducted by a qualified individual.

(iii) Review of the foreign supplier's relevant food safety records. You must retain documentation of each record review, including the date(s) of review, the general nature of the records reviewed, the conclusions of the review, any corrective actions taken in response to significant deficiencies identified during the review, and documentation that the review was conducted by a qualified individual.

(iv) Other appropriate activity.

(A) You may conduct (and document) or obtain documentation of other supplier verification activities that are appropriate based on foreign supplier performance and the risk associated with the food.

(B) You must retain documentation of each activity conducted in accordance with paragraph (e)(1)(iv) of this section, including a description of the activity, the date on which it was conducted, the findings or results of the activity, any corrective actions taken in response to significant deficiencies identified, and documentation that the activity was conducted by a qualified individual.

(2) Reliance upon performance of activities by other entities.

(i) Except as specified in paragraph (e)(2)(ii) of this section, you may rely on supplier verification activities conducted in accordance with paragraph (e)(1) of this section by another entity provided that you review and assess the results of these activities in accordance with paragraph (e)(3) of this section.

(ii) You may not rely on the foreign supplier itself or employees of the foreign supplier to perform supplier verification activities, except with respect to sampling and testing of food in accordance with paragraph (e)(1)(ii) of this section.

(3) Review of results of verification activities. You must promptly review and assess the results of the verification activities that you conduct or obtain documentation of under paragraph (e)(1) of this section, or that are conducted by other entities in accordance with paragraph (e)(2) of this section. You must document your review and assessment of the results of verification activities. If the results do not provide adequate assurances that the hazards requiring a control in the food you obtain from the foreign supplier have been significantly minimized or prevented, you must take appropriate action in accordance with 1.508(a). You are not required to retain documentation of supplier verification activities conducted by other entities, provided that you can obtain the documentation and make it available to FDA in accordance with 1.510(b).

(4) Independence of qualified individuals conducting verification activities. There must not be any financial conflicts of interests that influence the results of the verification activities set forth in paragraph (e)(1) of this section, and payment must not be related to the results of the activity.

Sec. 1.507 What requirements apply when I import a food that cannot be consumed without the hazards being controlled or for which the hazards are controlled after importation?

(a) Circumstances. You are not required to conduct an evaluation of a food and foreign supplier under 1.505 or supplier verification activities under 1.506 when you identify a hazard requiring a control (identified hazard) in a food and any of the following circumstances apply:

(1) You determine and document that the type of food (e.g., raw agricultural commodities such as cocoa beans and coffee beans) could not be consumed without application of an appropriate control;

(2) You rely on your customer who is subject to the requirements for hazard analysis and risk-based preventive controls in subpart C of part 117 or subpart C of part 507 of this chapter to ensure that the identified hazard will be significantly minimized or prevented and you:

(i) Disclose in documents accompanying the food, in accordance with the practice of the trade, that the food is "not processed to control [identified hazard]"; and

(ii) Annually obtain from your customer written assurance, subject to the requirements of paragraph (c) of this section, that the customer has established and is following procedures (identified in the written assurance) that will significantly minimize or prevent the identified hazard;

(3) You rely on your customer who is not subject to the requirements for hazard analysis and risk-based preventive controls in subpart C of part 117 or subpart C of part 507 of this chapter to provide assurance it is manufacturing, processing, or preparing the food in accordance with the applicable food safety requirements and you:

(i) Disclose in documents accompanying the food, in accordance with the practice of the trade, that the food is "not processed to control [identified hazard]"; and

(ii) Annually obtain from your customer written assurance that it is manufacturing, processing, or preparing the food in accordance with applicable food safety requirements;

(4) You rely on your customer to provide assurance that the food will be processed to control the identified hazard by an entity in the distribution chain subsequent to the customer and you:

(i) Disclose in documents accompanying the food, in accordance with the practice of the trade, that the food is "not processed to control [identified hazard]"; and

(ii) Annually obtain from your customer written assurance, subject to the requirements of paragraph (c) of this section, that your er:

(A) Will disclose in documents accompanying the food, in accordance with the practice of the trade, that the food is "not processed to control [identified hazard]"; and

(B) Will only sell the food to another entity that agrees, in writing, it will:

(1) Follow procedures (identified in a written assurance) that will significantly minimize or prevent the identified hazard (if the entity is subject to the requirements for hazard analysis and risk-based preventive controls in subpart C of part 117 or subpart C of part 507 of this chapter) or manufacture, process, or prepare the food in accordance with applicable food safety requirements (if the entity is not subject to the requirements for hazard analysis and risk-based preventive controls in subpart C of part 117 or subpart C of part 507); or

(2) Obtain a similar written assurance from the entity's customer, subject to the requirements of paragraph (c) of this section, as in paragraphs (a)(4)(ii)(A) and (B) of this section, as appropriate; or

(5) You have established, documented, and implemented a system that ensures control, at a subsequent distribution step, of the hazards in the food you distribute and you document your implementation of that system.

(b) Written assurances. Any written assurances required under this section must contain the following:

(1) Effective date;

(2) Printed names and signatures of authorized officials; and

(3) The assurance specified in the applicable paragraph.

(c) Provision of assurances. The customer or other subsequent entity in the distribution chain for a food that provides a written assurance under paragraph (a)(2), (3), or (4) of this section must act consistently with the assurance and document its actions taken to satisfy the written assurance.

Sec. 1.508 What corrective actions must I take under my FSVP?

(a) You must promptly take appropriate corrective actions if you determine that a foreign supplier of food you import does not produce the food in compliance with processes and procedures that provide at least the same level of public health protection as those required under section 418 or 419 of the Federal Food, Drug, and Cosmetic Act, if either is applicable, and the implementing regulations, or produces food that is adulterated under section 402 or misbranded under section 403(w) (if applicable) of the Federal Food, Drug, and Cosmetic Act. This determination could be based on a review of consumer, customer, or other complaints related to food safety, the verification activities conducted under 1.506 or 1.511(c), a reevaluation of the risks posed by the food and the foreign supplier's performance conducted under 1.505(c) or (d), or any other relevant information you obtain. The appropriate corrective actions will depend on the circumstances but could include discontinuing use of the foreign supplier until the cause or causes of noncompliance, adulteration, or misbranding have been adequately addressed. You must document any corrective actions you take in accordance with this paragraph.

(b) If you determine, by means other than the verification activities conducted under 1.506 or 1.511(c) or a reevaluation conducted under 1.505(c) or (d), that a foreign supplier of food that you import does not produce food in compliance with processes and procedures that provide at least the same level of public health protection as those required under section 418 or 419 of the Federal Food, Drug, and Cosmetic Act, if either is applicable, and the implementing regulations, or produces food that is adulterated under section 402 or misbranded under section 403(w) (if applicable) of the Federal Food, Drug, and Cosmetic Act, you must promptly investigate to determine whether your FSVP is adequate and, when appropriate, modify your FSVP. You must document any investigations, corrective actions, and changes to your FSVP that you undertake in accordance with this paragraph.

(c) This section does not limit your obligations with respect to other laws enforced by FDA, such as those relating to product recalls.

Sec. 1.509 How must the importer be identified at entry?

(a) You must ensure that, for each line entry of food product offered for importation into the United States, your name, electronic mail address, and unique facility identifier recognized as acceptable by FDA, identifying you as the importer of the food, are provided electronically when filing entry with U.S. Customs and Border Protection.

(b) Before an article of food is imported or offered for import into the United States, the foreign owner or consignee of the food (if there is no U.S. owner or consignee) must designate a U.S. agent or representative as the importer of the food for the purposes of the definition of "importer" in 1.500.

Sec. 1.510 How must I maintain records of my FSVP?

(a) General requirements for records.

(1) You must keep records as original records, true copies (such as photocopies, pictures, scanned copies, microfilm, microfiche, or other accurate reproductions of the original records), or electronic records.

(2) You must sign and date records concerning your FSVP upon initial completion and upon any modification of the FSVP.

(3) All records must be legible and stored to prevent deterioration or loss.

(b) Record availability.

(1) You must make all records required under this subpart available promptly to an authorized FDA representative, upon request, for inspection and copying. Upon FDA request, you must provide within a reasonable time an English translation of records maintained in a language other than English.

(2) Offsite storage of records, including records maintained by other entities in accordance with 1.504, 1.505, or 1.506, is permitted if such records can be retrieved and provided onsite within 24 hours of request for official review. Electronic records are considered to be onsite if they are accessible from an onsite location.

(3) If requested in writing by FDA, you must send records to the Agency electronically, or through another means that delivers the records promptly, rather than making the records available for review at your place of business.

(c) Record retention.

(1) Except as specified in paragraph (c)(2) of this section, you must retain records referenced in this subpart until at least 2 years after you created or obtained the records.

(2) You must retain records that relate to your processes and procedures, including the results of evaluations and determinations you conduct, for at least 2 years after their use is discontinued (e.g., because you no longer import a particular food, you no longer use a particular foreign supplier, you have reevaluated the risks associated with a food and the foreign supplier, or you have changed your supplier verification activities for a particular food and foreign supplier).

(d) Electronic records. Records that are established or maintained to satisfy the requirements of this subpart and that meet the definition of electronic records in 11.3(b)(6) of this chapter are exempt from the requirements of part 11 of this chapter. Records that satisfy the requirements of this subpart, but that also are required under other applicable statutory provisions or regulations, remain subject to part 11.

(e) Use of existing records.

(1) You do not need to duplicate existing records you have (e.g., records that you maintain to comply with other Federal, State, or local regulations) if they contain all of the information required by this subpart. You may supplement any such existing records as necessary to include all of the information required by this subpart.

(2) You do not need to maintain the information required by this subpart in one set of records. If existing records you have contain some of the required information, you may maintain any new information required by this subpart either separately or combined with the existing records.

(f) Public disclosure. Records obtained by FDA in accordance with this subpart are subject to the disclosure requirements under part 20 of this chapter.

Sec. 1.511 What FSVP must I have if I am importing a food subject to certain requirements in the dietary supplement current good manufacturing practice regulation?

(a) Importers subject to certain requirements in the dietary supplement current good manufacturing practice regulation. If you are required to establish specifications under 111.70(b) or (d) of this chapter with respect to a food that is a dietary supplement or dietary supplement component you import for further manufacturing, processing, or packaging as a dietary supplement, and you are in compliance with the requirements in 111.73 and 111.75 of this chapter applicable to determining whether the specifications you established are met for such food, then for that food you must comply with the requirements in 1.503 and 1.509, but you are not required to comply with the requirements in 1.502, 1.504 through 1.508, or 1.510. This requirement does not limit your obligations with respect to part 111 of this chapter or any other laws enforced by FDA.

(b) Importers whose customer is subject to certain requirements in the dietary supplement current good manufacturing practice regulation. If your customer is required to establish specifications under 111.70(b) or (d) of this chapter with respect to a food that is a dietary supplement or dietary supplement component you import for further manufacturing, processing, or packaging as a dietary supplement, your customer is in compliance with the requirements of 111.73 and 111.75 of this chapter applicable to determining whether the specifications it established are met for such food, and you annually obtain from your customer written assurance that it is in compliance with those requirements, then for that food you must comply with the requirements in 1.503, 1.509, and 1.510, but you are not required to comply with the requirements in 1.502 or 1.504 through 1.508.

(c) Other importers of dietary supplements —

(1) General. If the food you import is a dietary supplement and neither paragraph (a) or (b) of this section is applicable, you must comply with paragraph (c) of this section and the requirements in 1.503, 1.505(a)(1)(ii) through (iv), (a)(2), and (b) through (d), and 1.508 through 1.510, but you are not required to comply with the requirements in 1.504, 1.505(a)(1)(i), 1.506, and 1.507. This requirement does not limit your obligations with respect to part 111 of this chapter or any other laws enforced by FDA.

(2) Use of approved foreign suppliers.

(i) You must establish and follow written procedures to ensure that you import foods only from foreign suppliers that you have approved based on the evaluation conducted under 1.505 (or, when necessary and appropriate, on a temporary basis from unapproved foreign suppliers whose foods you subject to adequate verification activities before importing the food). You must document your use of these procedures.

(ii) You may rely on an entity other than the foreign supplier to establish the procedures and perform and document the activities required under paragraph (c)(2)(i) of this section provided that you review and assess that entity's documentation of the procedures and activities, and you document your review and assessment.

(3) Foreign supplier verification procedures. You must establish and follow adequate written procedures for ensuring that appropriate foreign supplier verification activities are conducted with respect to the foods you import.

(4) Determination of appropriate foreign supplier verification activities –

(i) General. Except as provided in paragraph (c)(4)(iii) of this section, before importing a dietary supplement from a foreign supplier, you must determine and document which verification activity or activities listed in paragraphs (c)(4)(ii) (A) through (D) of this section, as well as the frequency with which the activity or activities must be conducted, are needed to provide adequate assurances that the foreign supplier is producing the dietary supplement in accordance with processes and procedures that provide the same level of public health protection as those required under part 111 of this chapter. This determination must be based on the evaluation conducted under 1.505.

(ii) *Appropriate verification activities.* The following are appropriate supplier verification activities:

   (A) Onsite audits as specified in paragraph (c)(5)(i)(A) of this section;

   (B) Sampling and testing of a food as specified in paragraph (c)(5)(i)(B) of this section;

   (C) Review of the foreign supplier's relevant food safety records as specified in paragraph (c)(5)(i)(C) of this section; and

   (D) Other appropriate supplier verification activities as specified in paragraph (c)(5)(i)(D) of this section.

(iii) *Reliance upon determination by other entity.* You may rely on a determination of appropriate foreign supplier verification activities in accordance with paragraph (c)(4)(i) of this section made by an entity other than the foreign supplier if you review and assess whether the entity's determination regarding appropriate activities (including the frequency with which such activities must be conducted) is appropriate based on the evaluation conducted in accordance with 1.505. You must document your review and assessment, including documenting that the determination of appropriate verification activities was made by a qualified individual.

(5) *Performance of foreign supplier verification activities.*

   (i) Except as provided in paragraph (c)(5)(ii) of this section, for each dietary supplement you import under paragraph (c) of this section, you must conduct (and document) or obtain documentation of one or more of the verification activities listed in paragraphs (c)(5)(i)(A) through (D) of this section before importing the dietary supplement and periodically thereafter.

   (A) *Onsite auditing.* You conduct (and document) or obtain documentation of a periodic onsite audit of your foreign supplier.

      (1) An onsite audit of a foreign supplier must be performed by a qualified auditor.

      (2) The onsite audit must consider the applicable requirements of part 111 of this chapter and include a review of the foreign supplier's written food safety plan, if any, and its implementation (or, when applicable, an onsite audit may consider relevant laws and regulations of a country whose food safety system FDA has officially recognized as comparable or determined to be equivalent to that of the United States).

      (3) If the onsite audit is conducted solely to meet the requirements of paragraph (c)(5) of this section by an audit agent of a certification body that is accredited in accordance with subpart M of this part, the audit is not subject to the requirements in that subpart.

(4) You must retain documentation of each onsite audit, including the audit procedures, the dates the audit was conducted, the conclusions of the audit, any corrective actions taken in response to significant deficiencies identified during the audit, and documentation that the audit was conducted by a qualified auditor.

(5) The following inspection results may be substituted for an onsite audit, provided that the inspection was conducted within 1 year of the date by which the onsite audit would have been required to be conducted:

(i) The written results of appropriate inspection of the foreign supplier for compliance with the applicable requirements in part 111 of this chapter conducted by FDA, representatives of other Federal Agencies (such as the USDA), or representatives of State, local, tribal, or territorial agencies; or

(ii) The written results of an inspection by the food safety authority of a country whose food safety system FDA has officially recognized as comparable or determined to be equivalent to that of the United States, provided that the food that is the subject of the onsite audit is within the scope of the official recognition or equivalence determination, and the foreign supplier is in, and under the regulatory oversight of, such country.

(B) Sampling and testing of the food. You must retain documentation of each sampling and testing of a dietary supplement, including identification of the food tested (including lot number, as appropriate), the number of samples tested, the test(s) conducted (including the analytical method(s) used), the date(s) on which the test(s) were conducted and the date of the report of the testing, the results of the testing, any corrective actions taken in response to detection of hazards, information identifying the laboratory conducting the testing, and documentation that the testing was conducted by a qualified individual.

(C) Review of the foreign supplier's food safety records. You must retain documentation of each record review, including the date(s) of review, the general nature of the records reviewed, the conclusions of the review, any corrective actions taken in response to significant deficiencies identified during the review, and documentation that the review was conducted by a qualified individual.

(D) Other appropriate activity.

(1) You may conduct (and document) or obtain documentation of other supplier verification activities that are appropriate based on foreign supplier performance and the risk associated with the food.

(2) You must retain documentation of each activity conducted in accordance with paragraph (c)(5)(i)(D)(1) of this section, including a description of the activity, the date on which it was conducted, the findings or results of the activity, any corrective actions taken in response to significant deficiencies identified, and documentation that the activity was conducted by a qualified individual.

(ii) Reliance upon performance of activities by other entities.

(A) Except as specified in paragraph (c)(5)(ii)(B) of this section, you may rely on supplier verification activities conducted in accordance with paragraph (c)(5)(i) by another entity provided that you review and assess the results of these activities in accordance with paragraph (c)(5)(iii) of this section.

(B) You may not rely on the foreign supplier or employees of the foreign supplier to perform supplier verification activities, except with respect to sampling and testing of food in accordance with paragraph (c)(5)(i)(B) of this section.

(iii) Review of results of verification activities. You must promptly review and assess the results of the verification activities that you conduct or obtain documentation of under paragraph (c)(5)(i) of this section, or that are conducted by other entities in accordance with paragraph (c)(5)(ii) of this section. You must document your review and assessment of the results of verification activities. If the results show that the foreign supplier is not producing the dietary supplement in accordance with processes and procedures that provide the same level of public health protection as those required under part 111 of this chapter, you must take appropriate action in accordance with 1.508(a). You are not required to retain documentation of supplier verification activities conducted by other entities, provided that you can obtain the documentation and make it available to FDA in accordance with 1.510(b).

(iv) Independence of qualified individuals conducting verification activities. There must not be any financial conflicts of interest that influence the results of the verification activities set forth in paragraph (c)(5)(i) of this section, and payment must not be related to the results of the activity.

[80 FR 74340, Nov. 27, 2015, as amended at 81 FR 25327, Apr. 28, 2016]

Sec. 1.512 What FSVP may I have if I am a very small importer or I am importing certain food from certain small foreign suppliers?

(a) Eligibility. This section applies only if:

(1) You are a very small importer; or

(2) You are importing certain food from certain small foreign suppliers as follows:

(i) The foreign supplier is a qualified facility as defined by 117.3 or 507.3 of this chapter;

(ii) You are importing produce from a foreign supplier that is a farm that grows produce and is not a covered farm under part 112 of this chapter in accordance with 112.4(a) of this chapter, or in accordance with 112.4(b) and 112.5 of this chapter; or

(iii) You are importing shell eggs from a foreign supplier that is not subject to the requirements of part 118 of this chapter because it has fewer than 3,000 laying hens.

(b) Applicable requirements –

(1) Documentation of eligibility –

(i) Very small importer status.

(A) If you are a very small importer and you choose to comply with the requirements in this section, you must document that you meet the definition of very small importer in 1.500 with respect to human food and/or animal food before initially importing food as a very small importer and thereafter on an annual basis by December 31 of each calendar year.

(B) For the purpose of determining whether you satisfy the definition of very small importer with respect to human food and/or animal food for a given calendar year, the relevant 3-year period of sales (and U.S. market value of human or animal food, as appropriate) is the period ending 1 year before the calendar year for which you intend to import food as a very small importer. The baseline year for calculating the adjustment for inflation is 2011. If you conduct any food sales in currency other than U.S. dollars, you must use the relevant currency exchange rate in effect on December 31 of the year in which sales occurred to calculate the value of these sales.

(ii) Small foreign supplier status. If you are a importing food from a small foreign supplier as specified in paragraph (a)(2) of this section and you choose to comply with the requirements in this section, you must obtain written assurance that your foreign supplier meets the criteria in paragraph (a)(2)(i), (ii), or (iii) of this section before first approving the supplier for an applicable calendar year and thereafter on an annual basis by December 31 of each calendar year, for the following calendar year.

(2) Additional requirements. If this section applies and you choose to comply with the requirements in paragraph (b) of this section, you also are required to comply with the requirements in 1.502, 1.503, and 1.509, but you are not required to comply with the requirements in 1.504 through 1.508 or 1.510.

(3) Foreign supplier verification activities.

(i) If you are a very small importer, for each food you import, you must obtain written assurance, before importing the food and at least every 2 years thereafter, that your foreign supplier is producing the food in compliance with processes and procedures that provide at least the same level of public health protection as those required under section 418 or 419 of the Federal Food, Drug, and Cosmetic Act, if either is applicable, and the implementing regulations, and is producing the food in compliance with sections 402 and 403(w) (if applicable) of the Federal Food, Drug, and Cosmetic Act.

(ii) If your foreign supplier is a qualified facility as defined by 117.3 or 507.3 of this chapter and you choose to comply with the requirements in this section, you must obtain written assurance, before importing the food and at least every 2 years thereafter, that the foreign supplier is producing the food in compliance with applicable FDA food safety regulations (or, when applicable, relevant laws and regulations of a country whose food safety system FDA has officially recognized as comparable or determined to be equivalent to that of the United States). The written assurance must include either:

(A) A brief description of the preventive controls that the supplier is implementing to control the applicable hazard in the food; or

(B) A statement that the supplier is in compliance with State, local, county, tribal, or other applicable non-Federal food safety law, including relevant laws and regulations of foreign countries.

(iii) If your foreign supplier is a farm that grows produce and is not a covered farm under part 112 of this chapter in accordance with 112.4(a) of this chapter, or in accordance with 112.4(b) and 112.5 of this chapter, and you choose to comply with the requirements in this section, you must obtain written assurance, before importing the produce and at least every 2 years thereafter, that the farm acknowledges that its food is subject to section 402 of the Federal Food, Drug, and Cosmetic Act (or, when applicable, that its food is subject to relevant laws and regulations of a country whose food safety system FDA has officially recognized as comparable or determined to be equivalent to that of the United States).

(iv) If your foreign supplier is a shell egg producer that is not subject to the requirements of part 118 of this chapter because it has fewer than 3,000 laying hens and you choose to comply with the requirements in this section, you must obtain written assurance, before importing the shell eggs and at least every 2 years thereafter, that the shell egg producer acknowledges that its food is subject to section 402 of the Federal Food, Drug, and Cosmetic Act (or, when applicable, that its food is subject to relevant laws and regulations of a country whose food safety system FDA has officially recognized as comparable or determined to be equivalent to that of the United States).

(4) Corrective actions. You must promptly take appropriate corrective actions if you determine that a foreign supplier of food you import does not produce the food consistent with the assurance provided in accordance with 1.512(b)(3)(i) through (iv). The appropriate corrective actions will depend on the circumstances but could include discontinuing use of the foreign supplier until the cause or causes of

noncompliance, adulteration, or misbranding have been adequately addressed. You must document any corrective actions you take in accordance with this paragraph (b)(4). This paragraph (b)(4) does not limit your obligations with respect to other laws enforced by FDA, such as those relating to product recalls.

(5) Records —

(i) General requirements for records.

(A) You must keep records as original records, true copies (such as photocopies, pictures, scanned copies, microfilm, microfiche, or other accurate reproductions of the original records), or electronic records.

(B) You must sign and date records concerning your FSVP upon initial completion and upon any modification of the FSVP.

(C) All records must be legible and stored to prevent deterioration or loss.

(ii) Availability.

(A) You must make all records required under this subpart available promptly to an authorized FDA representative, upon request, for inspection and copying. Upon FDA request, you must provide within a reasonable time an English translation of records maintained in a language other than English.

(B) Offsite storage of records, including records retained by other entities in accordance with paragraph (c) of this section, is permitted if such records can be retrieved and provided onsite within 24 hours of request for official review. Electronic records are considered to be onsite if they are accessible from an onsite location.

(C) If requested in writing by FDA, you must send records to the Agency electronically or through another means that delivers the records promptly, rather than making the records available for review at your place of business.

(iii) Record retention.

(A) Except as specified in paragraph (b)(5)(iii)(B) or (C) of this section, you must retain records required under this subpart for a period of at least 2 years after you created or obtained the records.

(B) If you are subject to paragraph (c) of this section, you must retain records that relate to your processes and procedures, including the results of evaluations of foreign suppliers and procedures to ensure the use of approved suppliers, for at least 2 years after their use is discontinued (e.g., because you have reevaluated a foreign supplier's compliance history or changed your procedures to ensure the use of approved suppliers).

(C) You must retain for at least 3 years records that you rely on during the 3-year period preceding the applicable calendar year to support your status as a very small importer.

(iv) Electronic records. Records that are established or maintained to satisfy the requirements of this subpart and that meet the definition of electronic records in 11.3(b)(6) of this chapter are exempt from the requirements of part 11 of this chapter. Records that satisfy the requirements of this part, but that also are required under other applicable statutory provisions or regulations, remain subject to part 11.

(v) Use of existing records.

(A) You do not need to duplicate existing records you have (e.g., records that you maintain to comply with other Federal, State, or local regulations) if they contain all of the information required by this subpart. You may supplement any such existing records as necessary to include all of the information required by this subpart.

(B) You do not need to maintain the information required by this subpart in one set of records. If existing records you have contain some of the required information, you may maintain any new information required by this subpart either separately or combined with the existing records.

(vi) Public disclosure. Records obtained by FDA in accordance with this subpart are subject to the disclosure requirements under part 20 of this chapter.

(c) Requirements for importers of food from certain small foreign suppliers. The following additional requirements apply if you are importing food from certain small foreign suppliers as specified in paragraph (a)(2) of this section and you are not a very small importer:

(1) Evaluation of foreign supplier compliance history –

(i) Initial evaluation. Except as specified in paragraph (c)(1)(iii) of this section, in approving your foreign suppliers, you must evaluate the applicable FDA food safety regulations and information relevant to the foreign supplier's compliance with those regulations, including whether the foreign supplier is the subject of an FDA warning letter, import alert, or other FDA compliance action related to food safety, and document the evaluation. You may also consider other factors relevant to a foreign supplier's performance, including those specified in 1.505(a)(1)(iii)(A) and (C).

(ii) Reevaluation of foreign supplier compliance history.

(A) Except as specified in paragraph (c)(1)(iii) of this section, you must promptly reevaluate the concerns associated with the foreign supplier's compliance history when you become aware of new information about the matters in paragraph (c)(1)(i) of this section, and the reevaluation must be documented. If you determine that the concerns associated with importing a food from a foreign supplier have changed, you must promptly determine (and document) whether it is appropriate to continue to import the food from the foreign supplier.

(B) If at the end of any 3-year period you have not reevaluated the concerns associated with the foreign supplier's compliance history in accordance with paragraph (c)(1)(ii)(A) of this section, you must reevaluate those concerns and take other appropriate actions, if necessary, in accordance with paragraph (c)(1)(ii)(A). You must document your reevaluation and any subsequent actions you take in accordance with paragraph (c)(1)(ii)(A).

(iii) Review of another entity's evaluation or reevaluation of foreign supplier compliance history. If an entity other than the foreign supplier has, using a qualified individual, performed the evaluation described in paragraph (c)(1)(i) of this section or the reevaluation described in paragraph (c)(1)(ii), you may meet the requirements of the applicable paragraph by reviewing and assessing the evaluation or reevaluation conducted by that entity. You must document your review and assessment, including documenting that the evaluation or reevaluation was conducted by a qualified individual.

(2) Approval of foreign supplier. You must approve your foreign suppliers on the basis of the evaluation you conducted under paragraph (c)(1)(i) of this section or that you review and assess under paragraph (c)(1)(iii) of this section, and document your approval.

(3) Use of approved foreign suppliers.

(i) You must establish and follow written procedures to ensure that you import foods only from foreign suppliers you have approved based on the evaluation conducted under paragraph (c)(1)(i) of this section (or, when necessary and appropriate, on a temporary basis from unapproved foreign suppliers whose foods you subject to adequate verification activities before importing the food). You must document your use of these procedures.

(ii) You may rely on an entity other than the foreign supplier to establish the procedures and perform and document the activities required under paragraph (c)(3)(i) of this section provided that you review and assess that entity's documentation of the procedures and activities, and you document your review and assessment.

[80 FR 74340, Nov. 27, 2015, as amended at 81 FR 25327, Apr. 28, 2016]

Sec. 1.513 What FSVP may I have if I am importing certain food from a country with an officially recognized or equivalent food safety system?

(a) General.

(1) If you meet the conditions and requirements of paragraph (b) of this section for a food of the type specified in paragraph (a)(2) of this section that you are importing, then you are not required to comply with the requirements in 1.504 through 1.508. You would still be required to comply with the requirements in 1.503, 1.509, and 1.510.

(2) This section applies to food that is not intended for further manufacturing/processing, including packaged food products and raw agricultural commodities that will not be commercially processed further before consumption.

(b) Conditions and requirements.

(1) Before importing a food from the foreign supplier and annually thereafter, you must document that the foreign supplier is in, and under the regulatory oversight of, a country whose food safety system FDA has officially recognized as comparable or determined to be equivalent to that of the United States, and that the food is within the scope of that official recognition or equivalency determination.

(2) Before importing a food from the foreign supplier, you must determine and document whether the foreign supplier of the food is in good compliance standing with the food safety authority of the country in which the foreign supplier is located. You must continue to monitor whether the foreign supplier is in good compliance standing and promptly review any information obtained. If the information indicates that food safety hazards associated with the food are not being significantly minimized or prevented, you must take prompt corrective action. The appropriate corrective action will depend on the circumstances but could include discontinuing use of the foreign supplier. You must document any corrective actions that you undertake in accordance with this paragraph (b)(2).

Sec. 1.514 What are some consequences of failing to comply with the requirements of this subpart?

(a) Refusal of admission. An article of food is subject to refusal of admission under section 801(a)(3) of the Federal Food, Drug, and Cosmetic Act if it appears that the importer of that food fails to comply with this subpart with respect to that food. If there is no U.S. owner or consignee of an article of food at the time the food is offered for entry into the United States, the article of food may not be imported into the United States unless the foreign owner or consignee has appropriately designated a U.S. agent or representative as the importer in accordance with 1.500.

(b) Prohibited act. The importation or offering for importation into the United States of an article of food without the importer having an FSVP that meets the requirements of section 805 of the Federal Food, Drug, and Cosmetic Act, including the requirements of this subpart, is prohibited under section 301(zz) of the Federal Food, Drug, and Cosmetic Act.

Authority: 15 U.S.C. 1333, 1453, 1454, 1455, 4402; 19 U.S.C. 1490, 1491; 21 U.S.C. 321, 331, 332, 333, 334, 335a, 342, 343, 350c, 350d, 350e, 350j, 350k, 352, 355, 360b, 360ccc, 360ccc-1, 360ccc-2, 362, 371, 373, 374, 379j-31, 381, 382, 384a, 384b, 384d, 387, 387a, 387c, 393; 42 U.S.C. 216, 241, 243, 262, 264, 271; Pub. L. 107-188, 116 Stat. 594, 668-69; Pub. L. 111-353, 124 Stat. 3885, 3889.

Source: 42 FR 15553, Mar. 22, 1977, unless otherwise noted.

21CFR

Chapter 4

Part 101
Food Labeling

[Code of Federal Regulations]
[Title 21, Volume 2]
[Revised as of April 1, 2017]
[CITE: 21CFR101.36]

Title 21–Food and Drugs
Chapter I–Food and Drug Administration
Department of Health and Human Services
Subchapter B–Food for Human Consumption
Part 101–Food Labeling[1]

Subpart A–General Provisions

Sec. 101.3 Identity labeling of food in packaged form.

(a) The principal display panel of a food in package form shall bear as one of its principal features a statement of the identity of the commodity.

(b) Such statement of identity shall be in terms of:

    (1) The name now or hereafter specified in or required by any applicable Federal law or regulation; or, in the absence thereof,

    (2) The common or usual name of the food; or, in the absence thereof,

    (3) An appropriately descriptive term, or when the nature of the food is obvious, a fanciful name commonly used by the public for such food.

(c) Where a food is marketed in various optional forms (whole, slices, diced, etc.), the particular form shall be considered to be a necessary part of the statement of identity and shall be declared in letters of a type size bearing a reasonable relation to the size of the letters forming the other components of the statement of identity; except that if the optional form is visible through the container or is depicted by an appropriate vignette, the particular form need not be included in the statement. This specification does not affect the required declarations of identity under definitions and standards for foods promulgated pursuant to section 401 of the act.

---

[1] 21CFR§101 is available on the FDA website at https://www.accessdata.fda.gov/scripts/cdrh/cfdocs/cfcfr/CFRSearch.cfm

(d) This statement of identity shall be presented in bold type on the principal display panel, shall be in a size reasonably related to the most prominent printed matter on such panel, and shall be in lines generally parallel to the base on which the package rests as it is designed to be displayed.

(e) Under the provisions of section 403(c) of the Federal Food, Drug, and Cosmetic Act, a food shall be deemed to be misbranded if it is an imitation of another food unless its label bears, in type of uniform size and prominence, the word "imitation" and, immediately thereafter, the name of the food imitated.

   (1) A food shall be deemed to be an imitation and thus subject to the requirements of section 403(c) of the act if it is a substitute for and resembles another food but is nutritionally inferior to that food.

   (2) A food that is a substitute for and resembles another food shall not be deemed to be an imitation provided it meets each of the following requirements:

      (i) It is not nutritionally inferior to the food for which it substitutes and which it resembles.

      (ii) Its label bears a common or usual name that complies with the provisions of 102.5 of this chapter and that is not false or misleading, or in the absence of an existing common or usual name, an appropriately descriptive term that is not false or misleading. The label may, in addition, bear a fanciful name which is not false or misleading.

   (3) A food for which a common or usual name is established by regulation (e.g., in a standard of identity pursuant to section 401 of the act, in a common or usual name regulation pursuant to part 102 of this chapter, or in a regulation establishing a nutritional quality guideline pursuant to part 104 of this chapter), and which complies with all of the applicable requirements of such regulation(s), shall not be deemed to be an imitation.

   (4) Nutritional inferiority includes:

      (i) Any reduction in the content of an essential nutrient that is present in a measurable amount, but does not include a reduction in the caloric or fat content provided the food is labeled pursuant to the provisions of 101.9, and provided the labeling with respect to any reduction in caloric content complies with the provisions applicable to caloric content in part 105 of this chapter.

      (ii) For the purpose of this section, a measurable amount of an essential nutrient in a food shall be considered to be 2 percent or more of the Daily Reference Value (DRV) of protein listed under 101.9(c)(7)(iii) and of potassium listed under 101.9(c)(9) per reference amount customarily consumed and 2 percent or more of the Reference Daily Intake (RDI) of any vitamin or mineral listed under 101.9(c)(8)(iv) per reference amount customarily consumed, except that selenium, molybdenum, chromium, and chloride need not be considered.

    (iii) If the Commissioner concludes that a food is a substitute for and resembles another food but is inferior to the food imitated for reasons other than those set forth in this paragraph, he may propose appropriate revisions to this regulation or he may propose a separate regulation governing the particular food.

(f) A label may be required to bear the percentage(s) of a characterizing ingredient(s) or information concerning the presence or absence of an ingredient(s) or the need to add an ingredient(s) as part of the common or usual name of the food pursuant to subpart B of part 102 of this chapter.

(g) Dietary supplements shall be identified by the term "dietary supplement" as a part of the statement of identity, except that the word "dietary" may be deleted and replaced by the name of the dietary ingredients in the product (e.g., calcium supplement) or an appropriately descriptive term indicating the type of dietary ingredients that are in the product (e.g., herbal supplement with vitamins).

[42 FR 14308, Mar. 15, 1977, as amended at 48 FR 10811, Mar. 15, 1983; 58 FR 2227, Jan. 6, 1993; 60 FR 67174, Dec. 28, 1995; 62 FR 49847, Sept. 23, 1997]

Sec. 101.4 Food; designation of ingredients.

(a) (1) Ingredients required to be declared on the label or labeling of a food, including foods that comply with standards of identity, except those ingredients exempted by 101.100, shall be listed by common or usual name in descending order of predominance by weight on either the principal display panel or the information panel in accordance with the provisions of 101.2, except that ingredients in dietary supplements that are listed in the nutrition label in accordance with 101.36 need not be repeated in the ingredient list. Paragraph (g) of this section describes the ingredient list on dietary supplement products.

    (2) The descending order of predominance requirements of paragraph (a)(1) of this section do not apply to ingredients present in amounts of 2 percent or less by weight when a listing of these ingredients is placed at the end of the ingredient statement following an appropriate quantifying statement, e.g., "Contains _ percent or less of ___" or "Less than _ percent of ___." The blank percentage within the quantifying statement shall be filled in with a threshold level of 2 percent, or, if desired, 1.5 percent, 1.0 percent, or 0.5 percent, as appropriate. No ingredient to which the quantifying phrase applies may be present in an amount greater than the stated threshold.

(b) The name of an ingredient shall be a specific name and not a collective (generic) name, except that:

    (1) Spices, flavorings, colorings and chemical preservatives shall be declared according to the provisions of 101.22.

    (2) An ingredient which itself contains two or more ingredients and which has an established common or usual name, conforms to a standard established pursuant to

the Meat Inspection or Poultry Products Inspection Acts by the U.S. Department of Agriculture, or conforms to a definition and standard of identity established pursuant to section 401 of the Federal Food, Drug, and Cosmetic Act, shall be designated in the statement of ingredients on the label of such food by either of the following alternatives:

(i) By declaring the established common or usual name of the ingredient followed by a parenthetical listing of all ingredients contained therein in descending order of predominance except that, if the ingredient is a food subject to a definition and standard of identity established in subchapter B of this chapter that has specific labeling provisions for optional ingredients, optional ingredients may be declared within the parenthetical listing in accordance with those provisions.

(ii) By incorporating into the statement of ingredients in descending order of predominance in the finished food, the common or usual name of every component of the ingredient without listing the ingredient itself.

(3) Skim milk, concentrated skim milk, reconstituted skim milk, and nonfat dry milk may be declared as "skim milk" or "nonfat milk".

(4) Milk, concentrated milk, reconstituted milk, and dry whole milk may be declared as "milk".

(5) Bacterial cultures may be declared by the word "cultured" followed by the name of the substrate, e.g., "made from cultured skim milk or cultured buttermilk".

(6) Sweetcream buttermilk, concentrated sweetcream buttermilk, reconstituted sweetcream buttermilk, and dried sweetcream buttermilk may be declared as "buttermilk".

(7) Whey, concentrated whey, reconstituted whey, and dried whey may be declared as "whey".

(8) Cream, reconstituted cream, dried cream, and plastic cream (sometimes known as concentrated milk fat) may be declared as "cream".

(9) Butteroil and anhydrous butterfat may be declared as "butterfat".

(10) Dried whole eggs, frozen whole eggs, and liquid whole eggs may be declared as "eggs".

(11) Dried egg whites, frozen egg whites, and liquid egg whites may be declared as "egg whites".

(12) Dried egg yolks, frozen egg yolks, and liquid egg yolks may be declared as "egg yolks".

(13) [Reserved]

(14) Each individual fat and/or oil ingredient of a food intended for human consumption shall be declared by its specific common or usual name (e.g., "beef fat", "cottonseed oil") in its order of predominance in the food except that blends of fats and/

or oils may be designated in their order of predominance in the foods as "___ shortening" or "blend of ___ oils", the blank to be filled in with the word "vegetable", "animal", "marine", with or without the terms "fat" or "oils", or combination of these, whichever is applicable if, immediately following the term, the common or usual name of each individual vegetable, animal, or marine fat or oil is given in parentheses, e.g., "vegetable oil shortening (soybean and cottonseed oil)". For products that are blends of fats and/or oils and for foods in which fats and/or oils constitute the predominant ingredient, i.e., in which the combined weight of all fat and/or oil ingredients equals or exceeds the weight of the most predominant ingredient that is not a fat or oil, the listing of the common or usual names of such fats and/or oils in parentheses shall be in descending order of predominance. In all other foods in which a blend of fats and/or oils is used as an ingredient, the listing of the common or usual names in parentheses need not be in descending order of predominance if the manufacturer, because of the use of varying mixtures, is unable to adhere to a constant pattern of fats and/or oils in the product. If the fat or oil is completely hydrogenated, the name shall include the term *hydrogenated*, or if partially hydrogenated, the name shall include the term *partially hydrogenated*. If each fat and/or oil in a blend or the blend is completely hydrogenated, the term "hydrogenated" may precede the term(s) describing the blend, e.g., "hydrogenated vegetable oil (soybean, cottonseed, and palm oils)", rather than preceding the name of each individual fat and/or oil; if the blend of fats and/or oils is partially hydrogenated, the term "partially hydrogenated" may be used in the same manner. Fat and/or oil ingredients not present in the product may be listed if they may sometimes be used in the product. Such ingredients shall be identified by words indicating that they may not be present, such as "or", "and/or", "contains one or more of the following:", e.g., "vegetable oil shortening (contains one or more of the following: cottonseed oil, palm oil, soybean oil)". No fat or oil ingredient shall be listed unless actually present if the fats and/or oils constitute the predominant ingredient of the product, as defined in this paragraph (b)(14).

(15) When all the ingredients of a wheat flour are declared in an ingredient statement, the principal ingredient of the flour shall be declared by the name(s) specified in 137.105, 137.200, 137.220 and 137.225 of this chapter, i.e., the first ingredient designated in the ingredient list of flour, or bromated flour, or enriched flour, or self-rising flour is "flour", "white flour", "wheat flour", or "plain flour"; the first ingredient designated in the ingredient list of durum flour is "durum flour"; the first ingredient designated in the ingredient list of whole wheat flour, or bromated whole wheat flour is "whole wheat flour", "graham flour", or "entire wheat flour"; and the first ingredient designated in the ingredient list of whole durum wheat flour is "whole durum wheat flour".

(16) Ingredients that act as leavening agents in food may be declared in the ingredient statement by stating the specific common or usual name of each individual leavening agent in parentheses following the collective name "leavening", e.g., "leavening (baking soda, monocalcium phosphate, and calcium carbonate)". The listing of the

common or usual name of each individual leavening agent in parentheses shall be in descending order of predominance: *Except*, That if the manufacturer is unable to adhere to a constant pattern of leavening agents in the product, the listing of individual leavening agents need not be in descending order of predominance. Leavening agents not present in the product may be listed if they are sometimes used in the product. Such ingredients shall be identified by words indicating that they may not be present, such as "or", "and/or", "contains one or more of the following:".

(17) Ingredients that act as yeast nutrients in foods may be declared in the ingredient statement by stating the specific common or usual name of each individual yeast nutrient in parentheses following the collective name "yeast nutrients", e.g., "yeast nutrients (calcium sulfate and ammonium phosphate)". The listing of the common or usual name of each individual yeast nutrient in parentheses shall be in descending order of predominance: *Except*, That if the manufacturer is unable to adhere to a constant pattern of yeast nutrients in the product, the listing of the common or usual names of individual yeast nutrients need not be in descending order of predominance. Yeast nutrients not present in the product may be listed if they are sometimes used in the product. Such ingredients shall be identified by words indicating that they may not be present, such as "or", "and/or", or "contains one or more of the following:".

(18) Ingredients that act as dough conditioners may be declared in the ingredient statement by stating the specific common or usual name of each individual dough conditioner in parentheses following the collective name "dough conditioner", e.g., "dough conditioners (L-cysteine, ammonium sulfate)". The listing of the common or usual name of each dough conditioner in parentheses shall be in descending order of predominance: Except, That if the manufacturer is unable to adhere to a constant pattern of dough conditioners in the product, the listing of the common or usual names of individual dough conditioners need not be in descending order of predominance. Dough conditioners not present in the product may be listed if they are sometimes used in the product. Such ingredients shall be identified by words indicating that they may not be present, such as "or", "and/or", or "contains one or more of the following:".

(19) Ingredients that act as firming agents in food (e.g., salts of calcium and other safe and suitable salts in canned vegetables) may be declared in the ingredient statement, in order of predominance appropriate for the total of all firming agents in the food, by stating the specific common or usual name of each individual firming agent in descending order of predominance in parentheses following the collective name "firming agents". If the manufacturer is unable to adhere to a constant pattern of firming agents in the food, the listing of the individual firming agents need not be in descending order of predominance. Firming agents not present in the product may be listed if they are sometimes used in the product. Such ingredients shall be identified by words indicating that they may not be present, such as "or", "and/or", "contains one or more of the following:".

(20) For purposes of ingredient labeling, the term *sugar* shall refer to sucrose, which is obtained from sugar cane or sugar beets in accordance with the provisions of 184.1854 of this chapter.

(21) [Reserved]

(22) Wax and resin ingredients on fresh produce when such produce is held for retail sale, or when held for other than retail sale by packers or repackers shall be declared collectively by the phrase "coated with food-grade animal-based wax, to maintain freshness" or the phrase "coated with food-grade vegetable-, petroleum-, beeswax-, and/or shellac-based wax or resin, to maintain freshness" as appropriate. The terms "food-grade" and "to maintain freshness" are optional. The term *lac-resin* may be substituted for the term *shellac*.

(23) When processed seafood products contain fish protein ingredients consisting primarily of the myofibrillar protein fraction from one or more fish species and the manufacturer is unable to adhere to a constant pattern of fish species in the fish protein ingredient, because of seasonal or other limitations of species availability, the common or usual name of each individual fish species need not be listed in descending order of predominance. Fish species not present in the fish protein ingredient may be listed if they are sometimes used in the product. Such ingredients must be identified by words indicating that they may not be present, such as "or", "and/or", or "contains one or more of the following:" Fish protein ingredients may be declared in the ingredient statement by stating the specific common or usual name of each fish species that may be present in parentheses following the collective name "fish protein", e.g., "fish protein (contains one or more of the following: Pollock, cod, and/or pacific whiting)".

(c) When water is added to reconstitute, completely or partially, an ingredient permitted by paragraph (b) of this section to be declared by a class name, the position of the ingredient class name in the ingredient statement shall be determined by the weight of the unreconstituted ingredient plus the weight of the quantity of water added to reconstitute that ingredient, up to the amount of water needed to reconstitute the ingredient to single strength. Any water added in excess of the amount of water needed to reconstitute the ingredient to single strength shall be declared as "water" in the ingredient statement.

(d) When foods characterized on the label as "nondairy" contain a caseinate ingredient, the caseinate ingredient shall be followed by a parenthetical statement identifying its source. For example, if the manufacturer uses the term "nondairy" on a creamer that contains sodium caseinate, it shall include a parenthetical term such as "a milk derivative" after the listing of sodium caseinate in the ingredient list.

(e) If the percentage of an ingredient is included in the statement of ingredients, it shall be shown in parentheses following the name of the ingredient and expressed in terms of percent by weight. Percentage declarations shall be expressed to the nearest 1 percent, except that where ingredients are present at levels of 2 percent or less, they may be grouped together and expressed in accordance with the quantifying guidance set forth in paragraph (a)(2) of this section.

(f) Except as provided in 101.100, ingredients that must be declared on labeling because there is no label for the food, including foods that comply with standards of identity, shall be listed prominently and conspicuously by common or usual name in the manner prescribed by paragraph (b) of this section.

(g) When present, the ingredient list on dietary supplement products shall be located immediately below the nutrition label, or, if there is insufficient space below the nutrition label, immediately contiguous and to the right of the nutrition label and shall be preceded by the word "Ingredients," unless some ingredients (i.e., sources) are identified within the nutrition label in accordance with 101.36(d), in which case the ingredients listed outside the nutrition label shall be in a list preceded by the words "Other ingredients." Ingredients in dietary supplements that are not dietary ingredients or that do not contain dietary ingredients, such as excipients, fillers, artificial colors, artificial sweeteners, flavors, or binders, shall be included in the ingredient list.

(h) The common or usual name of ingredients of dietary supplements that are botanicals (including fungi and algae) shall be consistent with the names standardized in *Herbs of Commerce*, 1992 edition, which is incorporated by reference in accordance with 5 U.S.C. 552(a) and 1 CFR part 51. Copies may be obtained from the American Herbal Products Association, 8484 Georgia Ave., suite 370, Silver Spring, MD 20910, 301-588-1171, FAX 301-588-1174, e-mail: ahpa@ahpa.org, or may be examined at the Food and Drug Administration's Main Library, 10903 New Hampshire Ave., Bldg. 2, Third Floor, Silver Spring, MD 20993, 301-796-2039, or at the National Archives and Records Administration (NARA). For information on the availability of this material at NARA, call 202-741-6030, or go to: *http://www.archives.gov/federal_register/code_of_federal_regulations/ibr_locations.html*. The listing of these names on the label shall be followed by statements of:

(1) The part of the plant (e.g., root, leaves) from which the dietary ingredient is derived (e.g., "Garlic bulb" or "Garlic (bulb)"), except that this designation is not required for algae. The name of the part of the plant shall be expressed in English (e.g., "flower" rather than "flos");

(2) The Latin binomial name of the plant, in parentheses, except that this name is not required when it is available in the reference entitled: *Herbs of Commerce* for the common or usual name listed on the label, and, when required, the Latin binomial name may be listed before the part of the plant. Any name in Latin form shall be in accordance with internationally accepted rules on nomenclature, such as those found in the *International Code of Botanical Nomenclature* and shall include the designation of the author or authors who published the Latin name, when a positive identification cannot be made in its absence. The *International Code of Botanical Nomenclature* (Tokyo Code), 1994 edition, a publication of the International Association for Plant Taxonomy, is incorporated by reference in accordance with 5 U.S.C. 552(a) and 1 CFR part 51. Copies of the *International Code of Botanical Nomenclature* may be obtained from Koeltz Scientific Books, D-61453 Konigstein, Germany, and University Bookstore, Southern Illinois University, Carbondale, IL 62901-4422, 618-536-3321, FAX 618-453-5207, or may be examined at the Food and

Drug Administration's Main Library, 10903 New Hampshire Ave., Bldg. 2, Third Floor, Silver Spring, MD 20993, 301-796-2039, or at the National Archives and Records Administration (NARA). For information on the availability of this material at NARA, call 202-741-6030, or go to: *http://www.archives.gov/federal_register/code_of_ federal_regulations/ibr_locations.html.*

(3) On labels of single-ingredient dietary supplements that do not include an ingredient list, the identification of the Latin binomial name, when needed, and the part of the plant may be prominently placed on the principal display panel or information panel, or included in the nutrition label.

> [42 FR 14308, Mar. 15, 1977, as amended at 43 FR 12858, Mar. 28, 1978; 43 FR 24519, June 6, 1978; 48 FR 8054, Feb. 25, 1983; 55 FR 17433, Apr. 25, 1990; 58 FR 2875, Jan. 6, 1993; 62 FR 49847, Sept. 23, 1997; 62 FR 64634, Dec. 8, 1997; 64 FR 50448, Sept. 17, 1999; 66 FR 17358, Mar. 30, 2001; 66 FR 66742, Dec. 27, 2001; 68 FR 15355, Mar. 31, 2003; 81 FR 5590, Feb. 3, 2016]

Sec. 101.9 Nutrition labeling of food.

(a) Nutrition information relating to food shall be provided for all products intended for human consumption and offered for sale unless an exemption is provided for the product in paragraph (j) of this section.

(1) When food is in package form, the required nutrition labeling information shall appear on the label in the format specified in this section.

(2) When food is not in package form, the required nutrition labeling information shall be displayed clearly at the point of purchase (e.g., on a counter card, sign, tag affixed to the product, or some other appropriate device). Alternatively, the required information may be placed in a booklet, looseleaf binder, or other appropriate format that is available at the point of purchase.

(3) Solicitation of requests for nutrition information by a statement "For nutrition information write to _____ " on the label or in the labeling or advertising for a food, or providing such information in a direct written reply to a solicited or unsolicited request, does not subject the label or the labeling of a food exempted under paragraph (j) of this section to the requirements of this section if the reply to the request conforms to the requirements of this section.

(4) If any vitamin or mineral is added to a food so that a single serving provides 50 percent or more of the Reference Daily Intake (RDI) for the age group for which the product is intended, as specified in paragraph (c)(8)(iv) of this section, of any one of the added vitamins or minerals, unless such addition is permitted or required in other regulations, e.g., a standard of identity or nutritional quality guideline, or is otherwise exempted by the Commissioner, the food shall be considered a food for special dietary use within the meaning of 105.3(a)(1)(iii) of this chapter.

(b) Except as provided in 101.9(h)(3), all nutrient and food component quantities shall be declared in relation to a serving as defined in this section.

(1) The term serving or serving size means an amount of food customarily consumed per eating occasion by persons 4 years of age or older which is expressed in a common household measure that is appropriate to the food. When the food is specially formulated or processed for use by infants or by toddlers, a serving or serving size means an amount of food customarily consumed per eating occasion by infants up to 12 months of age or by children 1 through 3 years of age, respectively.

(2) Except as provided in paragraphs (b)(3), (b)(4), and (b)(6) of this section and for products that are intended for weight control and are available only through a weight-control or weight-maintenance program, serving size declared on a product label shall be determined from the "Reference Amounts Customarily Consumed Per Eating Occasion * * * *" (reference amounts) that appear in 101.12(b) using the procedures described below. For products that are both intended for weight control and available only through a weight-control program, a manufacturer may determine the serving size that is consistent with the meal plan of the program. Such products must bear a statement, "for sale only through the ___ program" (fill in the blank with the name of the appropriate weight-control program, e.g., Smith's Weight Control), on the principal display panel. However, the reference amounts in 101.12(b) shall be used for purposes of evaluating whether weight-control products that are available only through a weight-control program qualify for nutrient content claims or health claims.

   (i) For products in discrete units (e.g., muffins, sliced products, such as sliced bread, or individually packaged products within a multiserving package) and for products which consist of two or more foods packaged and presented to be consumed together where the ingredient represented as the main ingredient is in discrete units (e.g., pancakes and syrup), the serving size shall be declared as follows:

      (A) If a unit weighs 50 percent or less of the reference amount, the serving size shall be the number of whole units that most closely approximates the reference amount for the product category;

      (B) If a unit weighs more than 50 percent, but less than 67 percent of the reference amount, the manufacturer may declare one unit or two units as the serving size;

      (C) If a unit weighs 67 percent or more, but less than 200 percent of the reference amount, the serving size shall be one unit;

      (D) If a unit weighs at least 200 percent and up to and including 300 percent of the applicable reference amount, the serving size shall be the amount that approximates the reference amount. In addition to providing a column within the Nutrition Facts label that lists the quantitative amounts and percent Daily Values per serving size, the manufacturer shall provide a column within the Nutrition Facts label that lists the quantitative amounts and percent Daily Values per individual unit. The first column would be based on the serving size for the product and the second column would be based on the individual unit. The exemptions in paragraphs (b)(12)(i)(A), (B), and (C) of this section apply to this provision.

(E) The serving size for maraschino cherries shall be expressed as 1 cherry with the parenthetical metric measure equal to the average weight of a medium size cherry.

(F) The serving size for products that naturally vary in size (e.g., pickles, shellfish, whole fish, and fillet of fish) may be the amount in ounces that most closely approximates the reference amount for the product category. Manufacturers shall adhere to the requirements in paragraph (b)(5)(vi) of this section for expressing the serving size in ounces.

(G) For products which consist of two or more foods packaged and presented to be consumed together where the ingredient represented as the main ingredient is in discrete units (e.g., pancakes and syrup), the serving size may be the number of discrete units represented as the main ingredient plus proportioned minor ingredients used to make the reference amount for the combined product determined in 101.12(f).

(H) For packages containing several individual single-serving containers, each of which is labeled with all required information including nutrition labeling as specified in 101.9 (that is, are labeled appropriately for individual sale as single-serving containers), the serving size shall be 1 unit.

(ii) For products in large discrete units that are usually divided for consumption (e.g., cake, pie, pizza, melon, cabbage), for unprepared products where the entire contents of the package is used to prepare large discrete units that are usually divided for consumption (e.g., cake mix, pizza kit), and for products which consist of two or more foods packaged and presented to be consumed together where the ingredient represented as the main ingredient is a large discrete unit usually divided for consumption (e.g., prepared cake packaged with a can of frosting), the serving size shall be the fractional slice of the ready-to-eat product (e.g., 1/12 cake, 1/8 pie, 1/4 pizza, 1/4 melon, 1/6 cabbage) that most closely approximates the reference amount for the product category, and may be the fraction of the package used to make the reference amount for the unprepared product determined in 101.12(c) or the fraction of the large discrete unit represented as the main ingredient plus proportioned minor ingredients used to make the reference amount for the combined product determined in 101.12(f). In expressing the fractional slice, manufacturers shall use 1/2, 1/3, 1/4, 1/5, 1/6, or smaller fractions that can be generated by further division by 2 or 3.

(iii) For nondiscrete bulk products (e.g., breakfast cereal, flour, sugar, dry mixes, concentrates, pancake mixes, macaroni and cheese kits), and for products which consist of two or more foods packaged and presented to be consumed together where the ingredient represented as the main ingredient is a bulk product (e.g., peanut butter and jelly), the serving size shall be the amount in household measure that most closely approximates the reference amount for the product category and may be the amount of the bulk product represented as the main ingredient plus proportioned minor ingredients used to make the reference amount for the combined product determined in 101.12(f).

(3) The serving size for meal products and main dish products as defined in 101.13 (l) and (m) that comes in single-serving containers as defined in paragraph (b)(6) of this section shall be the entire content (edible portion only) of the package. Serving size for meal products and main dish products in multiserving containers shall be based on the reference amount applicable to the product in 101.12(b) if the product is listed in 101.12(b). Serving size for meal products and main dish products in multiserving containers that are not listed in 101.12(b) shall be based on the reference amount according to 101.12(f).

(4) A variety pack, such as a package containing several varieties of single-serving units as defined in paragraph (b)(2)(i) of this section, and a product having two or more compartments with each compartment containing a different food, shall provide nutrition information for each variety or food per serving size that is derived from the reference amount in 101.12(b) applicable for each variety or food and the procedures to convert the reference amount to serving size in paragraph (b)(2) of this section.

(5) For labeling purposes, the term common household measure or common household unit means cup, tablespoon, teaspoon, piece, slice, fraction (e.g., 1/4 pizza), ounce (oz), fluid ounce (fl oz), or other common household equipment used to package food products (e.g., jar, tray). In expressing serving size in household measures, except as specified in paragraphs (b)(5)(iv), (b)(5)(v), (b)(5)(vi), and (b)(5)(vii) of this section, the following rules shall be used:

(i) Cups, tablespoons, or teaspoons shall be used wherever possible and appropriate except for beverages. For beverages, a manufacturer may use fluid ounces. Cups shall be expressed in 1/4- or 1/3-cup increments. Tablespoons shall be expressed as 1, 1 1/3, 1 1/2, 1 2/3, 2, or 3 tablespoons. Teaspoons shall be expressed as 1/8, 1/4, 1/2, 3/4, 1, or 2 teaspoons.

(ii) If cups, tablespoons or teaspoons are not applicable, units such as piece, slice, tray, jar, and fraction shall be used.

(iii) If paragraphs (b)(5)(i) and (b)(5)(ii) of this section are not applicable, ounces may be used with an appropriate visual unit of measure such as a dimension of a piece, e.g., 1 oz (28 g/about 1/2 pickle). Ounce measurements shall be expressed in 0.5 oz increments most closely approximating the reference amount.

(iv) A description of the individual container or package shall be used for single serving containers and for individually packaged products within multiserving containers (e.g., can, box, package). A description of the individual unit shall be used for other products in discrete units (e.g., piece, slice, cracker, bar).

(v) For unprepared products where the entire contents of the package is used to prepare large discrete units that are usually divided for consumption (e.g., cake mix, pizza kit), the fraction or portion of the package may be used.

(vi) Ounces with an appropriate visual unit of measure, as described in paragraph (b)(5)(iii) of this section, may be used for products that naturally vary in size as provided for in paragraph (b)(2)(i)(G) of this section.

(vii) As provided for in 101.9(h)(1), for products that consist of two or more distinct ingredients or components packaged and presented to be consumed together (e.g. dry macaroni and cheese mix, cake and muffin mixes with separate ingredient packages, pancakes and syrup), nutrition information may be declared for each component or as a composite. The serving size may be provided in accordance with the provisions of paragraphs (b)(2)(i), (b)(2)(ii), and (b)(2)(iii) of this section, or alternatively in ounces with an appropriate visual unit of measure, as described in paragraph (b)(5)(iii) of this section (e.g., declared as separate components: "3 oz dry macaroni (84 g/about 2/3 cup)" and "1 oz dry cheese mix (28 g/about 2 tbsp);" declared as a composite value: "4 oz (112 g/about 2/3 cup macaroni and 2 tbsp dry cheese mix)").

(viii) For nutrition labeling purposes, a teaspoon means 5 milliliters (mL), a tablespoon means 15 mL, a cup means 240 mL, 1 fl oz means 30 mL, and 1 oz in weight means 28 g.

(ix) When a serving size, determined from the reference amount in 101.12(b) and the procedures described in this section, falls exactly half way between two serving sizes, e.g., 2.5 tbsp, manufacturers shall round the serving size up to the next incremental size.

(6) A product that is packaged and sold individually that contains less than 200 percent of the applicable reference amount must be considered to be a single-serving container, and the entire content of the product must be labeled as one serving. In addition to providing a column within the Nutrition Facts label that lists the quantitative amounts and percent Daily Values per serving, for a product that is packaged and sold individually that contains more than 150 percent and less than 200 percent of the applicable reference amount, the Nutrition Facts label may voluntarily provide, to the left of the column that provides nutrition information per container (i.e., per serving), an additional column that lists the quantitative amounts and percent Daily Values per common household measure that most closely approximates the reference amount.

(7) A label statement regarding a serving shall be the serving size expressed in common household measures as set forth in paragraphs (b)(2) through (b)(6) of this section and shall be followed by the equivalent metric quantity in parenthesis (fluids in milliliters and all other foods in grams) except for single-serving containers.

(i) For a single-serving container, the parenthetical metric quantity, which will be presented as part of the net weight statement on the principal display panel, is not required except where nutrition information is required on a drained weight basis according to 101.9(b)(9). However, if a manufacturer voluntarily provides the metric quantity on products that can be sold as single servings, then the numerical value provided as part of the serving size declaration must be identical to the metric quantity declaration provided as part of the net quantity of contents statement.

(ii) The gram or milliliter quantity equivalent to the household measure should be rounded to the nearest whole number except for quantities that are less than 5 g (mL). The gram (mL) quantity between 2 and 5 g (mL) should be rounded to the nearest 0.5 g (mL) and the g (mL) quantity less than 2 g (mL) should be expressed in 0.1-g (mL) increments.

(iii) In addition, serving size may be declared in ounce and fluid ounce, in parenthesis, following the metric measure separated by a slash where other common household measures are used as the primary unit for serving size, e.g., 1 slice (28 g/1 oz) for sliced bread. The ounce quantity equivalent to the metric quantity should be expressed in 0.1 oz increments.

(iv) If a manufacturer elects to use abbreviations for units, the following abbreviations shall be used: tbsp for tablespoon, tsp for teaspoon, g for gram, mL for milliliter, oz for ounce, and fl oz for fluid ounce.

(v) For products that only require the addition of water or another ingredient that contains insignificant amounts of nutrients in the amount added and that are prepared in such a way that there are no significant changes to the nutrient profile, the amount of the finished product may be declared in parentheses at the end of the serving size declaration (e.g., 1/2 cup (120 mL) concentrated soup (makes 1 cup prepared)).

(vi) To promote uniformity in label serving sizes in household measures declared by different manufacturers, FDA has provided a guidance document entitled, "Guidelines for Determining the Gram Weight of the Household Measure." The guidance document can be obtained from the Office of Nutritional Products, Labeling and Dietary Supplements (HFS-800), Center for Food Safety and Applied Nutrition, Food and Drug Administration, 5001 Campus Dr., College Park, MD 20740.

(8) Determination of the number of servings per container shall be based on the serving size of the product determined by following the procedures described in this section.

(i) The number of servings shall be rounded to the nearest whole number except for the number of servings between 2 and 5 servings and random weight products. The number of servings between 2 and 5 servings shall be rounded to the nearest 0.5 serving. Rounding should be indicated by the use of the term about (e.g., about 2 servings, about 3.5 servings).

(ii) When the serving size is required to be expressed on a drained solids basis and the number of servings varies because of a natural variation in unit size (e.g., maraschino cherries, pickles), the manufacturer may state the typical number of servings per container (e.g., usually 5 servings).

(iii) For random weight products, manufacturers may declare "varied" for the number of servings per container provided the nutrition information is based on the reference amount expressed in the appropriate household measure based on the hierarchy described in paragraph (b)(5) of this section. Random weight products are foods such as cheeses that are sold as random weights that vary in size, such that the net contents for different containers would vary. The manufacturer may provide the typical number of servings in parentheses following the "varied" statement.

(iv) For packages containing several individual single-serving containers, each of which is labeled with all required information including nutrition labeling as specified in 101.9 (that is, are labeled appropriately for individual sale as single-serving containers), the number of servings shall be the number of individual packages within the total package.

(v) For packages containing several individually packaged multiserving units, the number of servings shall be determined by multiplying the number of individual multiserving units in the total package by the number of servings in each individual unit.

(9) The declaration of nutrient and food component content shall be on the basis of food as packaged or purchased with the exception of raw fish covered under 101.42 (see 101.44), packaged single-ingredient products that consist of fish or game meat as provided for in paragraph (j)(11) of this section, and of foods that are packed or canned in water, brine, or oil but whose liquid packing medium is not customarily consumed (e.g., canned fish, maraschino cherries, pickled fruits, and pickled vegetables). Declaration of nutrient and food component content of raw fish shall follow the provisions in 101.45. Declaration of the nutrient and food component content of foods that are packed in liquid which is not customarily consumed shall be based on the drained solids.

(10) Another column of figures may be used to declare the nutrient and food component information:

(i) Per 100 g or 100 mL, or per 1 oz or 1 fl oz of the food as packaged or purchased;

(ii) Per one unit if the serving size of a product in discrete units is more than 1 unit.

(iii) Per cup popped for popcorn in a multiserving container.

(11) If a product is promoted on the label, labeling, or advertising for a use that differs in quantity by twofold or greater from the use upon which the reference amount in 101.12(b) was based (e.g., liquid cream substitutes promoted for use with breakfast cereals), the manufacturer shall provide a second column of nutrition information based on the amount customarily consumed in the promoted use, in addition to the nutrition information per serving derived from the reference amount in 101.12(b), except that nondiscrete bulk products that are used primarily as ingredients (e.g., flour, sweeteners, shortenings, oils), or traditionally used for multipurposes (e.g., eggs, butter, margarine), and multipurpose baking mixes are exempt from this requirement.

(12) (i) Products that are packaged and sold individually and that contain at least 200 percent and up to and including 300 percent of the applicable reference amount must provide an additional column within the Nutrition Facts label that lists the quantitative amounts and percent Daily Values for the entire package, as well as a column listing the quantitative amounts and percent Daily Values for a serving that is less than the entire package (i.e., the serving size derived from the reference amount). The first column would be based on the serving size for the product and the second column would be based on the entire contents of the package.

(A) This provision does not apply to products that meet the requirements to use the tabular format in paragraph (j)(13)(ii)(A)(1) of this section or to products that meet the requirements to use the linear format in paragraph (J)(13)(ii)(A)(2) of this section.

(B) This provision does not apply to raw fruits, vegetables, and seafood for which voluntary nutrition labeling is provided in the product labeling or advertising or when claims are made about the product.

(C) This provision does not apply to products that require further preparation and provide an additional column of nutrition information under paragraph (e) of this section, to products that are commonly consumed in combination with another food and provide an additional column of nutrition information under paragraph (e) of this section, to products that provide an additional column of nutrition information for two or more groups for which RDIs are established (e.g., both infants and children less than 4 years of age), to popcorn products that provide an additional column of nutrition information per 1 cup popped popcorn, or to varied-weight products covered under paragraph (b)(8)(iii) of this section.

(ii) When a nutrient content claim or health claim is made on the label of a product that uses a dual column as required in paragraph (b)(2)(i)(D) or (b)(12)(i) of this section, the claim must be followed by a statement that sets forth the basis on which the claim is made, except that the statement is not required for products when the nutrient that is the subject of the claim meets the criteria for the claim based on the reference amount for the product and the entire container or the unit amount. When a nutrient content claim is made, the statement must express that the claim refers to the amount of the nutrient per serving (e.g., "good source of calcium per serving" or "per X [insert unit]_serving") or per reference amount (e.g., "good source of calcium per [insert reference amount (e.g., per 8 ounces)]), as required based on 101.12(g). When a health claim is made, the statement shall be "A serving of _ounces of this product conforms to such a diet."

(c) The declaration of nutrition information on the label and in labeling of a food shall contain information about the level of the following nutrients, except for those nutrients whose inclusion, and the declaration of amounts, is voluntary as set forth in this paragraph.

No nutrients or food components other than those listed in this paragraph as either mandatory or voluntary may be included within the nutrition label. Except as provided for in paragraphs (f) or (j) of this section, nutrient information shall be presented using the nutrient names specified and in the following order in the formats specified in paragraphs (d) or (e) of this section.

(1) "Calories, total," "Total calories," or "Calories": A statement of the caloric content per serving, expressed to the nearest 5-calorie increment up to and including 50 calories, and 10-calorie increment above 50 calories, except that amounts less than 5 calories may be expressed as zero. Energy content per serving may also be expressed in kilojoule units, added in parentheses immediately following the statement of the caloric content.

(i) Caloric content may be calculated by the following methods. Where either specific or general food factors are used, the factors shall be applied to the actual amount (i.e., before rounding) of food components (e.g., fat, carbohydrate, protein, or ingredients with specific food factors) present per serving.

(A) Using specific Atwater factors (i.e., the Atwater method) given in table 13, USDA Handbook No. 74 (slightly revised, 1973),

(B) Using the general factors of 4, 4, and 9 calories per gram for protein, total carbohydrate, and total fat, respectively, as described in USDA Handbook No. 74 (slightly revised, 1973) pp. 9-11;

(C) Using the general factors of 4, 4, and 9 calories per gram for protein, total carbohydrate (less the amount of non-digestible carbohydrates and sugar alcohols), and total fat, respectively, as described in USDA Handbook No. 74 (slightly revised, 1973) pp. 9-11. A general factor of 2 calories per gram for soluble non-digestible carbohydrates shall be used. The general factors for caloric value of sugar alcohols provided in paragraph (c)(1)(i)(F) of this section shall be used;

(D) Using data for specific food factors for particular foods or ingredients approved by the Food and Drug Administration (FDA) and provided in parts 172 or 184 of this chapter, or by other means, as appropriate;

(E) Using bomb calorimetry data subtracting 1.25 calories per gram protein to correct for incomplete digestibility, as described in USDA Handbook No. 74 (slightly revised, 1973) p. 10; or

(F) Using the following general factors for caloric value of sugar alcohols: Isomalt—2.0 calories per gram, lactitol—2.0 calories per gram, xylitol—2.4 calories per gram, maltitol—2.1 calories per gram, sorbitol—2.6 calories per gram, hydrogenated starch hydrolysates—3.0 calories per gram, mannitol—1.6 calories per gram, and erythritol—0 calories per gram.

(ii) "Calories from saturated fat" or "Calories from saturated" (VOLUNTARY): A statement of the caloric content derived from saturated fat as defined in paragraph (c)(2)(i) of this section in a serving may be declared voluntarily, expressed to the nearest 5-calorie increment, up to and including 50 calories, and the nearest 10-calorie increment above 50 calories, except that amounts less than 5 calories may be expressed as zero. This statement shall be indented under the statement of calories as provided in paragraph (d)(5) of this section.

(2) "Fat, total" or "Total fat": A statement of the number of grams of total fat in a serving defined as total lipid fatty acids and expressed as triglycerides where fatty acids are aliphatic carboxylic acids consisting of a chain of alkyl groups and characterized by a terminal carboxyl group. Amounts shall be expressed to the nearest 0.5 (1/2) gram increment below 5 grams and to the nearest gram increment above 5 grams. If the serving contains less than 0.5 gram, the content shall be expressed as zero.

(3) "Cholesterol": A statement of the cholesterol content in a serving expressed in milligrams to the nearest 5-milligram increment, except that label declaration of cholesterol information is not required for products that contain less than 2 milligrams cholesterol in a serving and make no claim about fat, fatty acids, or cholesterol content, or such products may state the cholesterol content as zero. Except as provided for in paragraph (f) of this section, if cholesterol content is not required and, as a result, not declared, the statement "Not a significant source of cholesterol" shall be placed at the bottom of the table of nutrient values in the same type size. If the food contains 2 to 5 milligrams of cholesterol per serving, the content may be stated as "less than 5 milligrams."

(4) "Sodium": A statement of the number of milligrams of sodium in a specified serving of food expressed as zero when the serving contains less than 5 milligrams of sodium, to the nearest 5-milligram increment when the serving contains 5 to 140 milligrams of sodium, and to the nearest 10-milligram increment when the serving contains greater than 140 milligrams.

(5) "Fluoride" (VOLUNTARY): A statement of the number of milligrams of fluoride in a specified serving of food may be declared voluntarily, except that when a claim is made about fluoride content, label declaration shall be required. Fluoride content shall be expressed as zero when the serving contains less than 0.1 milligrams of fluoride, to the nearest 0.1-milligram increment when the serving contains less than or equal to 0.8 milligrams of fluoride, and the nearest 0.2 milligram-increment when a serving contains more than 0.8 milligrams of fluoride. Bottled water that bears a statement about added fluoride, as permitted by 101.13(q)(8), must bear nutrition labeling that complies with requirements for the simplified format in paragraph (f) of this section.

(6) "Carbohydrate, total" or "Total carbohydrate": A statement of the number of grams of total carbohydrate in a serving expressed to the nearest gram, except that if a serving contains less than 1 gram, the statement "Contains less than 1 gram" or "less than 1 gram" may be used as an alternative, or if the serving contains less than 0.5 gram, the content may be expressed as zero. Total carbohydrate content shall be calculated by subtraction of the sum of the crude protein, total fat, moisture, and ash from the total weight of the food. This calculation method is described in A. L. Merrill

and B. K. Watt, "Energy Value of Foods—Basis and Derivation," USDA Handbook 74 (slightly revised 1973) pp. 2 and 3, which is incorporated by reference in accordance with 5 U.S.C. 552(a) and 1 CFR part 51 (the availability of this incorporation by reference is given in paragraph (c)(1)(i)(A) of this section).

(i) "Dietary fiber": A statement of the number of grams of total dietary fiber in a serving, indented and expressed to the nearest gram, except that if a serving contains less than 1 gram, declaration of dietary fiber is not required or, alternatively, the statement "Contains less than 1 gram" or "less than 1 gram" may be used, and if the serving contains less than 0.5 gram, the content may be expressed as zero. Dietary fiber is defined as non-digestible soluble and insoluble carbohydrates (with 3 or more monomeric units), and lignin that are intrinsic and intact in plants; isolated or synthetic non-digestible carbohydrates (with 3 or more monomeric units) determined by FDA to have physiological effects that are beneficial to human health. Except as provided for in paragraph (f) of this section, if dietary fiber content is not required, and as a result not declared, the statement "Not a significant source of dietary fiber" shall be placed at the bottom of the table of nutrient values in the same type size. The following isolated or synthetic non-digestible carbohydrate(s) have been determined by FDA to have physiological effects that are beneficial to human health and, therefore, shall be included in the calculation of the amount of dietary fiber: [beta]-glucan soluble fiber (as described in 101.81(c)(2)(ii)(A)), psyllium husk (as described in 101.81(c)(2)(ii)(A)(6)), cellulose, guar gum, pectin, locust bean gum, and hydroxypropylmethylcellulose. The manufacturer must make and keep records in accordance with paragraphs (g)(10) and (11) of this section to verify the declared amount of dietary fiber in the label and labeling of food when a mixture of dietary fiber, and added non-digestible carbohydrate(s) that does not meet the definition of dietary fiber, is present in the food.

(A) "Soluble fiber" (VOLUNTARY): A statement of the number of grams of soluble dietary fiber in a serving may be declared voluntarily except that when a claim is made on the label or in labeling about soluble fiber, label declaration shall be required. Soluble fiber must meet the definition of dietary fiber in this paragraph (c)(6)(i). The manufacturer must make and keep records in accordance with paragraphs (g)(10) and (11) of this section to verify the declared amount of soluble fiber in the label and labeling of food when a mixture of soluble fiber and added non-digestible carbohydrate(s) that does not meet the definition of dietary fiber is present in the food. Soluble fiber content shall be indented under dietary fiber and expressed to the nearest gram, except that if a serving contains less than 1 gram, the statement "Contains less than 1 gram" or "less than 1 gram" may be used as an alternative, and if the serving contains less than 0.5 gram, the content may be expressed as zero."

(B) "Insoluble fiber" (VOLUNTARY): A statement of the number of grams of insoluble dietary fiber in a serving may be declared voluntarily except that when a claim is made on the label or in labeling about insoluble fiber, label declaration shall be required. Insoluble fiber must meet the definition of dietary fiber in this paragraph (c)(6)(i). The manufacturer must make and keep records in accordance with paragraphs (g)(10) and (11) of this section to verify the declared amount of insoluble fiber in the label and labeling of food when a mixture of insoluble and added non-digestible carbohydrate(s) that does not meet the definition of dietary fiber is present in the food. Insoluble fiber content shall be indented under dietary fiber and expressed to the nearest gram, except that if a serving contains less than 1 gram, the statement "Contains less than 1 gram" or "less than 1 gram" may be used as an alternative, and if the serving contains less than 0.5 gram, the content may be expressed as zero.

(ii) "Total Sugars": A statement of the number of grams of sugars in a serving, except that the label declaration of sugars content is not required for products that contain less than 1 gram of sugars in a serving if no claims are made about sweeteners, sugars, or sugar alcohol content. Except as provided for in paragraph (f) of this section, if a statement of the total sugars content is not required and, as a result, not declared, the statement "Not a significant source of total sugars" shall be placed at the bottom of the table of nutrient values in the same type size. Total sugars shall be defined as the sum of all free mono- and disaccharides (such as glucose, fructose, lactose, and sucrose). Total sugars content shall be indented and expressed to the nearest gram, except that if a serving contains less than 1 gram, the statement "Contains less than 1 gram" or "less than 1 gram" may be used as an alternative, and if the serving contains less than 0.5 gram, the content may be expressed as zero.

(iii) "Added Sugars": A statement of the number of grams of added sugars in a serving, except that label declaration of added sugars content is not required for products that contain less than 1 gram of added sugars in a serving if no claims are made about sweeteners, sugars, added sugars, or sugar alcohol content. If a statement of the added sugars content is not required and, as a result, not declared, the statement "Not a significant source of added sugars" shall be placed at the bottom of the table of nutrient values in the same type size. Added sugars are either added during the processing of foods, or are packaged as such, and include sugars (free, mono- and disaccharides), sugars from syrups and honey, and sugars from concentrated fruit or vegetable juices that are in excess of what would be expected from the same volume of 100 percent fruit or vegetable juice of the same type, except that fruit or vegetable juice concentrated from 100 percent juices sold to consumers, fruit or vegetable juice concentrates used towards the total juice percentage label declaration under 101.30 or for Brix standardization under 102.33(g)(2) of this chapter, fruit juice concentrates which are used to formulate the fruit component of jellies, jams, or preserves in accordance with the standard of identities set forth in 150.140 and 150.160 of this chapter, or the fruit component of fruit spreads shall not be labeled as added sugars. Added sugars content shall be indented under Total Sugars and shall be prefaced with the word "Includes" followed by the amount (in grams) "Added Sugars" ("Includes `X' g Added Sugars"). It shall be expressed to the nearest gram, except that if a serving contains less than 1 gram, the statement "Contains less than 1 gram" or "less than 1 gram" may be used as an alternative, and if the serving contains less than 0.5 gram, the content may be expressed as zero. When a mixture of naturally occurring and added sugars is present in the food, and for specific foods containing added sugars, alone or in combination with naturally occurring sugars, where the added sugars are subject to fermentation and/or non-enzymatic browning, the manufacturer must make and keep records in accordance with paragraphs (g)(10) and (11) of this section to verify the declared amount of added sugars in the label and labeling of food.

(iv) "Sugar alcohol" (VOLUNTARY): A statement of the number of grams of sugar alcohols in a serving may be declared voluntarily on the label, except that when a claim is made on the label or in labeling about sugar alcohol or total sugars, or added sugars when sugar alcohols are present in the food, sugar alcohol content shall be declared. For nutrition labeling purposes, sugar alcohols are defined as the sum of saccharide derivatives in which a hydroxyl group replaces a ketone or aldehyde group and whose use in the food is listed by FDA (e.g., mannitol or xylitol) or is generally recognized as safe (e.g., sorbitol). In lieu of the term "sugar alcohol," the name of the specific sugar alcohol (e.g., "xylitol") present in the food may be used in the nutrition label provided that only one sugar alcohol is present in the food. Sugar alcohol content shall be indented and expressed to the nearest gram, except that if a serving contains less than 1 gram, the statement "Contains less than 1 gram" or "less than 1 gram" may be used as an alternative, and if the serving contains less than 0.5 gram, the content may be expressed as zero.

(7) "Protein": A statement of the number of grams of protein in a serving, expressed to the nearest gram, except that if a serving contains less than 1 gram, the statement "Contains less than 1 gram" or "less than 1 gram" may be used as an alternative, and if the serving contains less than 0.5 gram, the content may be expressed as zero. When the protein in foods represented or purported to be for adults and children 4 or more years of age has a protein quality value that is a protein digestibility-corrected amino acid score of less than 20 expressed as a percent, or when the protein in a food represented or purported to be for children greater than 1 but less than 4 years of age has a protein quality value that is a protein digestibility-corrected amino acid score of less than 40 expressed as a percent, either of the following shall be placed adjacent to the declaration of protein content by weight: The statement "not a significant source of protein," or a listing aligned under the column headed "Percent Daily Value" of the corrected amount of protein per serving, as determined in paragraph (c)(7)(ii) of this section, calculated as a percentage of the Daily Reference Value (DRV) or Reference Daily Intake (RDI), as appropriate, for protein and expressed as a Percent of Daily Value. When the protein quality in a

food as measured by the Protein Efficiency Ratio (PER) is less than 40 percent of the reference standard (casein) for a food represented or purported to be specifically for infants through 12 months, the statement "not a significant source of protein" shall be placed adjacent to the declaration of protein content. Protein content may be calculated on the basis of the factor 6.25 times the nitrogen content of the food as determined by the appropriate method of analysis as given in the "Official Methods of Analysis of the AOAC International," except when official AOAC procedures described in this paragraph (c)(7) require a specific factor other than 6.25, that specific factor shall be used.

(i) A statement of the corrected amount of protein per serving, as determined in paragraph (c)(7)(ii) of this section, calculated as a percentage of the RDI or DRV for protein, as appropriate, and expressed as Percent of Daily Value, may be placed on the label, except that such a statement shall be given if a protein claim is made for the product, or if the product is represented or purported to be specifically for infants through 12 months or children 1 through 3 years of age. When such a declaration is provided, it should be placed on the label adjacent to the statement of grams of protein and aligned under the column headed "Percent Daily Value," and expressed to the nearest whole percent. However, the percentage of the RDI for protein shall not be declared if the food is represented or purported to be specifically for infants through 12 months and the protein quality value is less than 40 percent of the reference standard.

(ii) The "corrected amount of protein (gram) per serving" for foods represented or purported for adults and children 1 or more years of age is equal to the actual amount of protein (gram) per serving multiplied by the amino acid score corrected for protein digestibility. If the corrected score is above 1.00, then it shall be set at 1.00. The protein digestibility-corrected amino acid score shall be determined by methods given in sections 5.4.1, 7.2.1, and 8.00 in "Report of the Joint FAO/WHO Expert Consultation on Protein Quality Evaluation," except that when official AOAC procedures described in paragraph (c)(7) of this section require a specific factor other than 6.25, that specific factor shall be used. For foods represented or purported to be specifically for infants through 12 months, the corrected amount of protein (grams) per serving is equal to the actual amount of protein (grams) per serving multiplied by the relative protein quality value. The relative protein quality value shall be determined by dividing the subject food protein PER value by the PER value for casein. If the relative protein value is above 1.00, it shall be set at 1.00.

(iii) For the purpose of labeling with a percent of the DRV or RDI, a value of 50 grams of protein shall be the DRV for adults and children 4 or more years of age, a value of 11 grams of protein shall be the RDI for infants through 12 months, a value of 13 grams shall be the DRV for children 1 through 3 years of age, and a value of 71 grams of protein shall be the RDI for pregnant women and lactating women.

(8) "Vitamins and minerals": The requirements related to including a statement of the amount per serving of vitamins and minerals are described in this paragraph (c)(8).

(i) For purposes of declaration of percent of Daily Value as provided for in paragraphs (d), (e), and (f) of this section, foods represented or purported to be specifically for infants through 12 months, children 1 through 3 years, pregnant women, and lactating women shall use the RDIs that are specified for the intended group. For foods represented or purported to be specifically for both infants through 12 months of age and children 1 through 3 years of age, the percent of Daily Value shall be presented by separate declarations according to paragraph (e) of this section based on the RDI values for infants through 12 months of age and children 1 through 3 years of age. When such dual declaration is used on any label, it shall be included in all labeling, and equal prominence shall be given to both values in all such labeling. The percent Daily Value based on the RDI values for pregnant women and lactating women shall be declared on food represented or purported to be specifically for pregnant women and lactating women. All other foods shall use the RDI for adults and children 4 or more years of age.

(ii) The declaration of vitamins and minerals as a quantitative amount by weight and percent of the RDI shall include vitamin D, calcium, iron, and potassium in that order, for infants through 12 months, children 1 through 3 years of age, pregnant women, lactating women, and adults and children 4 or more years of age. The declaration of folic acid shall be included as a quantitative amount by weight when added as a nutrient supplement or a claim is made about the nutrient. The declaration of vitamins and minerals in a food, as a quantitative amount by weight and percent of the RDI, may include any of the other vitamins and minerals listed in paragraph (c)(8)(iv) of this section. The declaration of vitamins and minerals shall include any of the other vitamins and minerals listed in paragraph (c)(8)(iv) of this section as a statement of the amount per serving of the vitamins and minerals as described in this paragraph, calculated as a percent of the RDI and expressed as a percent of the Daily Value, when they are added as a nutrient supplement, or when a claim is made about them, unless otherwise stated as quantitative amount by weight and percent of the Daily Value. Other vitamins and minerals need not be declared if neither the nutrient nor the component is otherwise referred to on the label or the labeling or advertising and the vitamins and minerals are:

(A) Required or permitted in a standardized food (e.g., thiamin, riboflavin, and niacin in enriched flour) and that standardized food is included as an ingredient (i.e., component) in another food; or

(B) Included in a food solely for technological purposes and declared only in the ingredient statement. The declaration may also include any of the other vitamins and minerals listed in paragraph (c)(8)(iv) of this section when they are naturally occurring in the food. The additional vitamins and minerals shall be listed in the order established in paragraph (c)(8)(iv) of this section.

(iii) The percentages for vitamins and minerals shall be expressed to the nearest 2-percent increment up to and including the 10-percent level, the nearest 5-percent increment above 10 percent and up to and including the 50-percent level, and the nearest 10-percent increment above the 50-percent level. Quantitative amounts and percentages of vitamins and minerals present at less than 2 percent of the RDI are not required to be declared in nutrition labeling but may be declared by a zero or by the use of an asterisk (or other symbol) that refers to another asterisk (or symbol) that is placed at the bottom of the table and that is followed by the statement "Contains less than 2 percent of the Daily Value of this (these) nutrient (nutrients)" or "Contains <2 percent of the Daily Value of this (these) nutrient (nutrients)." Alternatively, except as provided for in paragraph (f) of this section, if vitamin D, calcium, iron, or potassium is present in amounts less than 2 percent of the RDI, label declaration of the nutrient(s) is not required if the statement "Not a significant source of—(listing the vitamins or minerals omitted)" is placed at the bottom of the table of nutrient values. Either statement shall be in the same type size as nutrients that are indented. The quantitative amounts of vitamins and minerals, excluding sodium, shall be the amount of the vitamin or mineral included in one serving of the product, using the units of measurement and the levels of significance given in paragraph (c)(8)(iv) of this section, except that zeros following decimal points may be dropped, and additional levels of significance may be used when the number of decimal places indicated is not sufficient to express lower amounts (e.g., the RDI for zinc is given in whole milligrams, but the quantitative amount may be declared in tenths of a milligram).

(iv) The following RDIs, nomenclature, and units of measure are established for the following vitamins and minerals which are essential in human nutrition:

Nutrient	Unit of measure	RDI			
		Adults and children ≥4 years	Infants [1] through 12 months	Children 1 through 3 years	Pregnant/ lactating women
Vitamin A	Micrograms RAE [2] (mcg)	900	500	300	1,300
Vitamin C	Milligrams (mg)	90	50	15	120
Calcium	Milligrams (mg)	1,300	260	700	1,300
Iron	Milligrams (mg)	18	11	7	27
Vitamin D	Micrograms (mcg) [3]	20	10	15	15
Vitamin E	Milligrams (mg) [4]	15	5	6	19
Vitamin K	Micrograms (mcg)	120	2.5	30	90
Thiamin	Milligrams (mg)	1.2	0.3	0.5	1.4
Riboflavin	Milligrams (mg)	1.3	0.4	0.5	1.6
Niacin	Milligrams NE [5] (mg)	16	4	6	18

Nutrient	Unit of measure	RDI			
		Adults and children ≥4 years	Infants [1] through 12 months	Children 1 through 3 years	Pregnant/ lactating women
Vitamin B6	Milligrams (mg)	1.7	0.3	0.5	2.0
Folate [6]	Micrograms DFE [7] (mcg)	400	80	150	600
Vitamin B12	Micrograms (mcg)	2.4	0.5	0.9	2.8
Biotin	Micrograms (mcg)	30	6	8	35
Pantothenic acid	Milligrams (mg)	5	1.8	2	7
Phosphorus	Milligrams (mg)	1,250	275	460	1,250
Iodine	Micrograms (mcg)	150	130	90	290
Magnesium	Milligrams (mg)	420	75	80	400
Zinc	Milligrams (mg)	11	3	3	13
Selenium	Micrograms (mcg)	55	20	20	70
Copper	Milligrams (mg)	0.9	0.2	0.3	1.3
Manganese	Milligrams (mg)	2.3	0.6	1.2	2.6
Chromium	Micrograms (mcg)	35	5.5	11	45
Molybdenum	Micrograms (mcg)	45	3	17	50
Chloride	Milligrams (mg)	2,300	570	1,500	2,300
Potassium	Milligrams (mg)	4,700	700	3,000	5,100
Choline	Milligrams (mg)	550	150	200	550
Protein	Grams (g)	N/A	11	N/A	[8]71

[1] RDIs are based on dietary reference intake recommendations for infants through 12 months of age.

[2] RAE = Retinol activity equivalents; 1 microgram RAE = 1 microgram retinol, 2 microgram supplemental [beta]-carotene, 12 micrograms [beta]-carotene, or 24 micrograms [alpha]-carotene, or 24 micrograms [beta]-cryptoxanthin.

[3] The amount of vitamin D may, but is not required to, be expressed in international units (IU), in addition to the mandatory declaration in mcg. Any declaration of the amount of vitamin D in IU must appear in parentheses after the declaration of the amount of vitamin D in mcg.

[4] 1 mg [alpha]-tocopherol (label claim) = 1 mg [alpha]-tocopherol = 1 mg RRR- [alpha]-tocopherol = 2 mg all rac-[alpha]-tocopherol .

[5] NE = Niacin equivalents, 1 mg NE = 1 mg niacin = 60 milligrams tryptophan.

[6] "Folate" and "Folic Acid" must be used for purposes of declaration in the labeling of conventional foods and dietary supplements. The declaration for folate must be in mcg DFE (when expressed as a quantitative amount by weight in a conventional food or a dietary supplement), and percent DV based on folate in mcg DFE. Folate may be expressed as a percent DV in conventional foods. When folic acid is added or when a claim is made about the nutrient, folic acid must be declared in parentheses, as mcg of folic acid.

[7] DFE = Dietary Folate Equivalents; 1 DFE = 1 mcg naturally-occurring folate = 0.6 mcg folic acid.

[8] Based on the reference caloric intake of 2,000 calories for adults and children aged 4 years and older, and for pregnant women and lactating women.

(v) The following synonyms may be added in parentheses immediately following the name of the nutrient or dietary component:

Calories—Energy

Vitamin C—Ascorbic acid

Thiamin—Vitamin B1

Riboflavin—Vitamin B2

(vi) A statement of the percent of vitamin A that is present as beta -carotene may be declared voluntarily. When the vitamins and minerals are listed in a single column, the statement shall be indented under the information on vitamin A. When vitamins and minerals are arrayed horizontally, the statement of percent shall be presented in parenthesis following the declaration of vitamin A and the percent DV of vitamin A in the food (e.g., "Percent Daily Value: Vitamin A 50 (90 percent as beta -carotene)"). When declared, the percentages shall be expressed in the same increments as are provided for vitamins and minerals in paragraph (c)(8)(iii) of this section.

(vii) When the amount of folate is declared in the labeling of a conventional food or a dietary supplement, the nutrient name "folate" shall be listed for products containing folate (natural folate, and/or synthetic folate as a component of dietary supplement, such as calcium salt of L-5-MTHF), folic acid, or a mixture of folate and folic acid. The name of the synthetic form of the nutrient "folic acid", when added or a claim is made about the nutrient, shall be included in parentheses after this declaration with the amount of folic acid. The declaration must be folate in mcg DFE (when expressed as a quantitative amount by weight in a conventional food or a dietary supplement) and the percent DV based on folate in mcg DFE, or for conventional food, may be expressed as folate and the percent DV based on folate in mcg DFE. When declared, folic acid must be in parentheses, mcg of folic acid as shown in paragraph (d)(12) of this section in the display that illustrates voluntary declaration of nutrition information.

(9) The following DRVs, nomenclature, and units of measure are established for the following food components:

Food component	Unit of measure	Adults and children ≥4 years	Infants through 12 months	Children 1 through 3 years	Pregnant/ lactating women
Fat	Grams (g)	[1]78	30	[2]39	[1]78
Saturated fat	Grams (g)	[1]20	N/A	[2]10	[1]20
Cholesterol	Milligrams (mg)	300	N/A	300	300
Total carbohydrate	Grams (g)	[1]275	95	[2]150	[1]275
Sodium	Milligrams (mg)	2,300	N/A	1,500	2,300
Dietary Fiber	Grams (g)	[1]28	N/A	[2]14	[1]28
Protein	Grams (g)	[1]50	N/A	[2]13	N/A

Food component	Unit of measure	Adults and children ≥4 years	Infants through 12 months	Children 1 through 3 years	Pregnant/ lactating women
Added Sugars	Grams (g)	[1]50	N/A	[2]25	[1]50

[1]Based on the reference caloric intake of 2,000 calories for adults and children aged 4 years and older, and for pregnant women and lactating women

[2]Based on the reference caloric intake of 1,000 calories for children 1 through 3 years of age.

(d) (1) Nutrient information specified in paragraph (c) of this section shall be presented on foods in the following format, as shown in paragraph (d)(12) of this section, except on foods where the tabular display is permitted as provided for in paragraph (d)(11) of this section, on which dual columns of nutrition information are declared as provided for in paragraph (e) of this section, on those food products on which the simplified format is required to be used as provided for in paragraph (f) of this section, on foods for infants through 12 months of age and children 1 through 3 years of age as provided for in paragraph (j)(5) of this section, and on foods in small or intermediate-sized packages as provided for in paragraph (j)(13) of this section. In the interest of uniformity of presentation, FDA strongly recommends that the nutrition information be presented using the graphic specifications set forth in appendix B to part 101.

(i) The nutrition information shall be set off in a box by use of hairlines and shall be all black or one color type, printed on a white or other neutral contrasting background whenever practical.

(ii) All information within the nutrition label shall utilize:

(A) Except as provided for in paragraph (c)(2)(ii) of this section, a single easy-to-read type style,

(B) Upper and lower case letters,

(C) At least one point leading (i.e., space between two lines of text) except that at least four points leading shall be utilized for the information required by paragraphs (d)(7) and (d)(8) of this section as shown in paragraph (d)(12), and

(D) Letters should never touch.

(iii) Information required in paragraphs (d)(7) and (8) of this section shall be in type size no smaller than 8 point. Information required in paragraph (d)(5) of this section for the "Calories" declaration shall be highlighted in bold or extra bold and shall be in a type size no smaller than 16 point except the type size for this information required in the tabular displays as shown in paragraphs (d)(11), (e)(6)(ii), and (j)(13)(ii)(A)(1) of this section and the linear display for small packages as shown in paragraph (j)(13)(ii)(A)(2) of this section shall be in a type size no smaller than 10 point. The numeric amount for the information required in paragraph (d)(5) of this section shall also be highlighted in bold or extra bold type and shall be in a type size no smaller than 22 point, except the type size for this information required for the tabular display for small packages as shown in paragraph (j)(13)(ii)(A)(1) of this section, and for the linear display for small packages as shown in paragraph (j)(13)(ii)(A)(2) of this section no smaller than 14 point. The information required in paragraph (d)(9) of this section shall be in a type size no smaller than 6 point. When provided, the information described in paragraph (d)(10) of this section shall be in a type size no smaller than 6 point.

(iv) The headings required by paragraphs (d)(2), (d)(3)(ii), (d)(4), and (d)(6) of this section (i.e., "Nutrition Facts," "Serving size," "Amount per serving," and "% Daily Value*"), the names of all nutrients that are not indented according to requirements of paragraph (c) of this section (i.e., "Calorles," "Total Fat," "Cholesterol," "Sodium," "Total Carbohydrate" and "Protein"), and the percentage amounts required by paragraph (d)(7)(ii) of this section shall be highlighted in bold or extra bold type or other highlighting (reverse printing is not permitted as a form of highlighting) that prominently distinguishes it from other information. No other information shall be highlighted.

(v) A hairline rule that is centered between the lines of text shall separate "Nutrition Facts" from the servings per container statement required in paragraph (d)(3) (i) of this section and shall separate each nutrient and its corresponding percent Daily Value required in paragraphs (d)(7)(i) and (ii) of this section from the nutrient and percent Daily Value above and below it, as shown in paragraph (d) (12) of this section and in Appendix B to Part 101.

(2) The information shall be presented under the identifying heading of "Nutrition Facts" which shall be set in a type size no smaller than all other print size in the nutrition label except for the numerical information for "Calories" required in paragraph (d) (5) of this section, and except for labels presented according to the format provided for in paragraphs (d)(11), (d)(13)(ii), (e)(6)(ii), (j)(13)(ii)(A)(1), and (j)(13)(ii)(A)(2) of this section, unless impractical, shall be set the full width of the information provided under paragraph (d)(7) of this section, as shown in paragraph (d)(12) of this section.

(3) Information on servings per container and serving size shall immediately follow the heading as shown in paragraph (d)(12) of this section. Such information shall include:

(i) "__ servings per container": The number of servings per container, except that this statement is not required on single serving containers as defined in paragraph (b)(6) of this section or on other food containers when this information is stated in the net quantity of contents declaration. The information required in this paragraph shall be located immediately after the "Nutrition Facts" heading and shall be in a type size no smaller than 10 point, except the type size for this information shall be no smaller than 9 point in the tabular display for small packages as shown in paragraph (j)(13)(ii)(A)(1) of this section and the linear display for small packages as shown in paragraph (j)(13)(ii)(A)(2) of this section. For the linear display for small packages as shown in paragraph (j)(13)(ii)(A)(2) of this section, the actual number of servings may be listed after the servings per container declaration.

(ii) "Serving size": A statement of the serving size as specified in paragraph (b)(7) of this section which shall immediately follow the "__servings per container" declaration. The information required in this paragraph shall be highlighted in bold or extra bold and be in a type size no smaller than 10 point, except the type size shall be no smaller than 9 point for this information in the tabular displays as shown in paragraphs (d)(11) and (e)(6)(ii) of this section, the tabular display for small packages as shown in paragraph (j)(13)(ii)(A)(1) of this section, and the linear display for small packages as shown in paragraph (j)(13)(ii)(A)(2) of this section. The serving size amount must be right justified if adequate space is available. If the "Serving size" declaration does not fit in the allocated space a type size of no smaller than 8 point may be used on packages of any size.

(4) A subheading "Amount per serving" shall be separated from the serving size information by a bar as shown in paragraph (d)(12) of this section, except this information is not required for the dual column formats shown in paragraphs (e)(5), (e)(6)(i), and (e)(6)(ii) of this section.

(5) Information on calories shall immediately follow the subheading "Amount per serving" and shall be declared in one line. If "Calories from saturated fat" is declared, it shall be indented under "Calories" and shall be in a type size no smaller than 8 point.

(6) The column heading "% Daily Value," followed by an asterisk (e.g., "% Daily Value*"), shall be separated from information on calories by a bar as shown in paragraph (d)(12) of this section. The position of this column heading shall allow for a list of nutrient names and amounts as described in paragraph (d)(7) of this section to be to the left of, and below, this column heading. The column headings "Percent Daily Value," "Percent DV," or "% DV" may be substituted for "% Daily Value."

(7) Except as provided for in paragraph (j)(13)(ii)(A)(2) of this section, nutrient information for both mandatory and any voluntary nutrients listed in paragraph (c) of this section that are to be declared in the nutrition label, except for folic acid in conventional food and voluntarily declared vitamins and minerals expressed as a statement of the amount per serving calculated as a percent of the RDI and expressed as a percent Daily Value, shall be declared as follows:

(i) The name of each nutrient, as specified in paragraph (c) of this section, shall be given in a column and followed immediately by the quantitative amount by weight for that nutrient appended with a "g" for grams, "mg" for milligrams, or "mcg" for micrograms as shown in paragraph (d)(12) of this section. The symbol "<" may be used in place of "less than."

(ii) A listing of the percent of the DRV as established in paragraphs (c)(7)(iii) and (c)(9) of this section shall be given in a column aligned under the heading "% Daily Value" established in paragraph (d)(6) of this section with the percent expressed to the nearest whole percent for each nutrient declared in the column described in paragraph (d)(7)(i) of this section for which a DRV has been established, except that the percent for protein may be omitted as provided in paragraph (c)(7) of this section. The percent shall be calculated by dividing either the amount declared on the label for each nutrient or the actual amount of each nutrient (i.e., before rounding) by the DRV for the nutrient, except that the percent for protein shall be calculated as specified in paragraph (c)(7)(ii) of this section. The numerical value shall be followed by the symbol for percent (i.e., %).

(8) Nutrient information for vitamins and minerals (except sodium) shall be separated from information on other nutrients by a bar and may be arrayed vertically as shown in paragraph (d)(12) of this section (e.g., Vitamin D 2 mcg 10%, Calcium 260 mg 20%, Iron 8 mg 45%, Potassium 235 mg 6%) or may be listed horizontally. When listed horizontally in two columns, vitamin D and calcium should be listed on the first line and iron and potassium should be listed on the second line, as shown in paragraph (d)(12) of this section in the side-by-side display. When more than four vitamins and minerals are declared voluntarily as shown in paragraph (d)(12) of this section in the label which illustrates the mandatory plus voluntary provisions of paragraph (d) of this section, they may be declared vertically with percentages listed under the column headed "% Daily Value."

(9) A footnote, preceded by an asterisk, shall be placed beneath the list of vitamins and minerals and shall be separated from the list by a bar, except that the footnote may be omitted from foods that can use the terms "calorie free," "free of calories," "without calories," "trivial source of calories," "negligible source of calories," or "dietary insignificant source of calories" on the label or in the labeling of foods as defined in 101.60(b). The first sentence of the footnote: "The % Daily Value tells you how much a nutrient in a serving of food contributes to a daily diet" may be used on foods that can use the terms "calorie free," "free of calories," "without calories," "trivial source of calories," "negligible source of calories," or "dietary insignificant source of calories" on the label or in the labeling of foods as defined in 101.60(b). The footnote shall state: "*The % Daily Value tells you how much a nutrient in a serving of food contributes to a daily diet. 2,000 calories a day is used for general nutrition advice." If the food product is represented or purported to be for children 1 through 3 years of age, the second sentence of the footnote shall substitute "1,000 calories" for "2,000 calories."

(10) Caloric conversion information on a per gram basis for fat, carbohydrate, and protein may be presented beneath the information required in paragraph (d)(9) of this section, separated from that information by a hairline. This information may be presented horizontally as shown in paragraph (d)(12) of this section (i.e., "Calories per gram: fat 9, carbohydrate 4, protein 4") or vertically in columns.

(11) (i) If the space beneath the information on vitamins and minerals is not adequate to accommodate the information required in paragraph (d)(9) of this section, the information required in paragraph (d)(9) may be moved to the right of the

column required in paragraph (d)(7)(ii) of this section and set off by a line that distinguishes it and sets it apart from the percent Daily Value information. The caloric conversion information provided for in paragraph (d)(10) of this section may be presented beneath either side or along the full length of the nutrition label.

(ii) If the space beneath the mandatory declaration of potassium is not adequate to accommodate any remaining vitamins and minerals to be declared or the information required in paragraph (d)(9) of this section, the remaining information may be moved to the right and set off by a line that distinguishes it and sets it apart from the nutrients and the percent DV information given to the left. The caloric conversion information provided for in paragraph (d)(10) of this section may be presented beneath either side or along the full length of the nutrition label.

(iii) If there is not sufficient continuous vertical space (i.e., approximately 3 in) to accommodate the required components of the nutrition label up to and including the mandatory declaration of potassium, the nutrition label may be presented in a tabular display as shown in the following sample label.

Tabular Format

(12) The following sample labels illustrate the mandatory provisions and mandatory plus voluntary provisions of paragraph (d) of this section and the side-by-side display.

Standard Vertical

Standard Vertical
(w/ Voluntary)

Standard Vertical
(Side-by-side Display)

(13)(i) Nutrition labels on the outer label of packages of products that contain two or more separately packaged foods that are intended to be eaten individually (e.g., variety packs of cereals or snack foods) or of packages that are used interchangeably for the same type of food (e.g., round ice cream containers) may use an aggregate display.

(ii) Aggregate displays shall comply with the format requirements of paragraph (d) of this section to the maximum extent possible, except that the identity of each food shall be specified immediately to the right of the "Nutrition Facts" heading, and both the quantitative amount by weight (i.e., g/mg/mcg amounts) and the percent Daily Value for each nutrient shall be listed in separate columns under the name of each food. The following sample label illustrates an aggregate display.

Aggregate Display

Nutrition Facts	Wheat Squares Sweetened	Corn Flakes Not Sweetened	Mixed Grain Flakes Sweetened
1 serving per container			
Serving size 1 box	(35g)	(19g)	(27g)
Amount per serving			
Calories	**130**	**70**	**100**
	% Daily Value*	% Daily Value*	% Daily Value*
Total Fat	0g 0%	0g 0%	0g 0%
Saturated Fat	0g 0%	0g 0%	0g 0%
Trans Fat	0g	0g	0g
Cholesterol	0mg 0%	0mg 0%	0mg 0%
Sodium	0mg 0%	200mg 9%	120mg 5%
Total Carbohydrate	29g 11%	17g 6%	24g 9%
Dietary Fiber	3g 11%	1g 4%	1g 4%
Total Sugars	8g	6g	13g
Includes Added Sugars	8g 16%	5g 10%	13g 26%
Protein	4g	1g	1g
Vitamin D	2mcg 10%	2mcg 10%	0mcg 0%
Calcium	0mg 0%	0mg 0%	0mg 0%
Iron	2mg 10%	1mg 6%	4mg 20%
Potassium	125mg 4%	25mg 1%	30mg 1%
Vitamin A	0%	10%	10%
Vitamin C	0%	15%	90%
Thiamin	35%	15%	25%
Riboflavin	30%	10%	25%
Niacin	30%	10%	20%
Vitamin B₆	30%	20%	20%

* The % Daily Value (DV) tells you how much a nutrient in a serving of food contributes to a daily diet. 2,000 calories a day is used for general nutrition advice.

(14) In accordance with 101.15(c)(2), when nutrition labeling must appear in a second language, the nutrition information may be presented in a separate nutrition label for each language or in one nutrition label with the information in the second language following that in English. Numeric characters that are identical in both languages need not be repeated (e.g., "Protein/Proteinas 2 g"). All required information must be included in both languages.

(e) Nutrition information may be presented for two or more forms of the same food (e.g., both "as purchased" and "as prepared") or for common combinations of food as provided for in paragraph (h)(4) of this section, for different units (e.g., slices of bread or per 100 grams) as provided for in paragraph (b) of this section, or for two or more groups for which RDIs are established (e.g., both infants through 12 months of age and children 1 through 3 years of age) as shown in paragraph (e)(5) of this section. When such dual labeling is provided, equal prominence shall be given to both sets of values. Information shall be presented in a format consistent with paragraph (d) of this section, except that:

(1) Following the serving size information there shall be two or more column headings accurately describing the amount per serving size of the form of the same food (e.g., "Per 1/4 cup mix" and "Per prepared portion"), the combinations of food, the units, or the RDI groups that are being declared as shown in paragraph (e)(5) of this section.

(2) The quantitative information by weight as required in paragraph (d)(7)(i) and the information required in paragraph (d)(7)(ii) of this section shall be presented for the form of the product as packaged and for any other form of the product (e.g., "as prepared" or combined with another ingredient as shown in paragraph (e)(5) of this section).

(3) When the dual labeling is presented for two or more forms of the same food, for combinations of food, for different units, or for two or more groups for which RDIs are established, the quantitative information by weight and the percent Daily Value shall be presented in two columns and the columns shall be separated by vertical lines as shown in paragraph (e)(5) of this section.

(4) Nutrient information for vitamins and minerals (except sodium) shall be separated from information on other nutrients by a bar and shall be arrayed vertically in the following order: Vitamin D, calcium, iron, potassium as shown in paragraph (e)(5) of this section.

(5) The following sample label illustrates the provisions of paragraph (e) of this section:

(6) When dual labeling is presented for a food on a per serving basis and per container basis as required in paragraph (b)(12)(i) of this section or on a per serving basis and per unit basis as required in paragraph (b)(2)(i)(D) of this section, the quantitative information by weight as required in paragraph (d)(7)(i) and the percent Daily Value as required in paragraph (d)(7)(ii) shall be presented in two columns, and the columns shall be separated by vertical lines as shown in the displays in paragraph (e) (6)(i) of this section.

(i) Nutrient information for vitamins and minerals shall be separated from information on other nutrients by a bar and shall be arrayed vertically in the following order: Vitamin D, calcium, iron, and potassium as shown in the following sample labels.

Dual Column Display

Nutrition Facts

2 servings per container
Serving size 1 cup (255g)

Calories	Per serving	Per container
	220	440

		% DV*		% DV*
Total Fat	5g	6%	10g	13%
Saturated Fat	2g	10%	4g	20%
Trans Fat	0g		0g	
Cholesterol	15mg	5%	30mg	10%
Sodium	240mg	10%	480mg	21%
Total Carb.	35g	13%	70g	25%
Dietary Fiber	6g	21%	12g	43%
Total Sugars	7g		14g	
Incl. Added Sugars	4g	8%	8g	16%
Protein	9g		18g	
Vitamin D	5mcg	25%	10mcg	50%
Calcium	200mg	15%	400mg	30%
Iron	1mg	6%	2mg	10%
Potassium	470mg	10%	940mg	20%

* The % Daily Value (DV) tells you how much a nutrient in a serving of food contributes to a daily diet. 2,000 calories a day is used for general nutrition advice.

Dual Column, Per Serving and Per Unit

Nutrition Facts

Calories	Per 1/2 muffin	Per 1 muffin
	380	760

		% DV*		% DV*
Total Fat	16g	21%	32g	41%
Saturated Fat	3g	15%	6g	30%
Trans Fat	0g		0g	
Cholesterol	50mg	17%	100mg	33%
Sodium	480mg	21%	960mg	42%
Total Carb.	56g	20%	112g	41%
Dietary Fiber	2g	7%	4g	14%
Total Sugars	32g		64g	
Incl. Added Sugars	30g	60%	60g	120%
Protein	3g		6g	
Vitamin D	0.1mcg	0%	0.2mcg	2%
Calcium	40mg	4%	80mg	6%
Iron	2mg	10%	4mg	20%
Potassium	190mg	4%	380mg	8%

* The % Daily Value (DV) tells you how much a nutrient in a serving of food contributes to a daily diet. 2,000 calories a day is used for general nutrition advice.

(ii) The following sample label illustrates the provisions of paragraphs (b)(2)(i)(D) and (b)(12)(i) of this section for labels that use the tabular display.

Tabular Dual Column Display

Nutrition Facts

2 servings per container
Serving size
1 cup (255g)

Calories
220 | 440
per serving | per container

		Per serving % DV*		Per container % DV*			Per serving % DV*		Per container % DV*
Total Fat	5g	6%	10g	13%	Total Carb.	35g	13%	70g	25%
Saturated Fat	2g	10%	4g	20%	Dietary Fiber	6g	21%	12g	43%
Trans Fat	0g		0g		Total Sugars	7g		14g	
Cholesterol	15mg	5%	30mg	10%	Incl. Added Sugars	4g	8%	8g	16%
Sodium	240mg	10%	480mg	21%	Protein	9g		18g	
Vitamin D	5mcg	25%	10mcg	50%	Iron	1mg	6%	2mg	10%
Calcium	200mg	15%	400mg	30%	Potassium	470mg	10%	940mg	20%

*The % Daily Value (DV) tells you how much a nutrient in a serving of food contributes to a daily diet. 2,000 calories a day is used for general nutrition advice.

(f) The declaration of nutrition information may be presented in the simplified format set forth herein when a food product contains insignificant amounts of eight or more of the following: Calories, total fat, saturated fat, trans fat, cholesterol, sodium, total carbohydrate, dietary fiber, total sugars, added sugars, protein, vitamin D, calcium, iron, and potassium; except that for foods intended for infants through 12 months of age and children 1 through 3 years of age to which paragraph (j)(5)(i) of this section applies, nutrition information may be presented in the simplified format when a food product contains insignificant amounts of six or more of the following: Calories, total fat, sodium, total carbohydrate, dietary fiber, total sugars, added sugars, protein, vitamin D, calcium, iron, and potassium.

(1) An "insignificant amount" shall be defined as that amount that allows a declaration of zero in nutrition labeling, except that for total carbohydrate, dietary fiber, and protein, it shall be an amount that allows a declaration of "less than 1 gram."

(2) The simplified format shall include information on the following nutrients:

(i) Total calories, total fat, total carbohydrate, protein, and sodium;

(ii) Any other nutrients identified in paragraph (f) of this section that are present in the food in more than insignificant amounts; and

(iii) Any vitamins and minerals listed in paragraph (c)(8)(iv) of this section when they are required to be added as a nutrient supplement to foods for which a standard of identity exists.

(iv) Any vitamins or minerals listed in paragraph (c)(8)(iv) of this section voluntarily added to the food as nutrient supplements.

(3) Other nutrients that are naturally present in the food in more than insignificant amounts may be voluntarily declared as part of the simplified format.

(4) If any nutrients are declared as provided in paragraphs (f)(2)(iii), (f)(2)(iv), or (f)(3) of this section as part of the simplified format or if any nutrition claims are made on the label or in labeling, the statement "Not a significant source of _____" (with the blank filled in with the name(s) of any nutrient(s) identified in paragraph (f) of this section that are present in insignificant amounts) shall be included at the bottom of the nutrition label.

Simplified Display

(5) Except as provided for in paragraphs (j)(5) and (j)(13) of this section, nutrient information declared in the simplified format shall be presented in the same manner as specified in paragraphs (d) or (e) of this section, except that the footnote required in paragraph (d)(9) of this section is not required, and an asterisk shall be placed at the bottom of the label followed by the statement "% DV = % Daily Value" when "Daily Value" is not spelled out in the heading, as shown in paragraph (f)(4).

(g) Compliance with this section shall be determined as follows:

(1) A collection of primary containers or units of the same size, type, and style produced under conditions as nearly uniform as possible, designated by a common container code or marking, or in the absence of any common container code or marking, a day's production, constitutes a "lot."

(2) The sample for nutrient analysis shall consist of a composite of 12 subsamples (consumer units), taken 1 from each of 12 different randomly chosen shipping cases, to be representative of a lot. Unless a particular method of analysis is specified in paragraph (c) of this section, composites shall be analyzed by appropriate methods as given in the "Official Methods of Analysis of the AOAC International," or, if no AOAC method is available or appropriate, by other reliable and appropriate analytical procedures.

(3) Two classes of nutrients are defined for purposes of compliance:

(i) Class I. Added nutrients in fortified or fabricated foods; and

(ii) Class II. Naturally occurring (indigenous) nutrients. When a nutrient is naturally occurring (indigenous) in a food or an ingredient that is added to a food, the total amount of such nutrient in the final food product is subject to class II requirements, except that when an exogenous source of the nutrient is also added to the final food product, the total amount of the nutrient in the final food product (indigenous and exogenous) is subject to class I requirements.

(4) A food with a label declaration of a vitamin, mineral, protein, total carbohydrate, dietary fiber, soluble fiber, insoluble fiber, polyunsaturated or monounsaturated fat shall be deemed to be misbranded under section 403(a) of the Federal Food, Drug, and Cosmetic Act (the act) unless it meets the following requirements:

(i) When a vitamin, mineral, protein, or dietary fiber meets the definition of a Class I nutrient, the nutrient content of the composite must be formulated to be at least equal to the value for that nutrient declared on the label.

(ii) When a vitamin, mineral, protein, total carbohydrate, polyunsaturated or monounsaturated fat, or dietary fiber meets the definition of a Class II nutrient, the nutrient content of the composite must be at least equal to 80 percent of the value for that nutrient declared on the label. Provided, That no regulatory action will be based on a determination of a nutrient value that falls below this level by a factor less than the variability generally recognized for the analytical method used in that food at the level involved.

(5) A food with a label declaration of calories, total sugars, added sugars (when the only source of sugars in the food is added sugars), total fat, saturated fat, trans fat, cholesterol, or sodium shall be deemed to be misbranded under section 403(a) of the act if the nutrient content of the composite is greater than 20 percent in excess of the value for that nutrient declared on the label. Provided, That no regulatory action will be based on a determination of a nutrient value that falls above this level by a

factor less than the variability generally recognized for the analytical method used in that food at the level involved.

(6) Reasonable excesses of vitamins, minerals, protein, total carbohydrate, dietary fiber, soluble fiber, insoluble fiber, sugar alcohols, polyunsaturated or monounsaturated fat over labeled amounts are acceptable within current good manufacturing practice. Reasonable deficiencies of calories, total sugars, added sugars, total fat, saturated fat, trans fat, cholesterol, or sodium under labeled amounts are acceptable within current good manufacturing practice.

(7) Compliance will be based on the metric measure specified in the label statement of serving size.

(8) Alternatively, compliance with the provisions set forth in paragraphs (g)(1) through (6) of this section may be provided by use of an FDA approved database that has been computed following FDA guideline procedures and where food samples have been handled in accordance with current good manufacturing practice to prevent nutrition loss. FDA approval of a database shall not be considered granted until the Center for Food Safety and Applied Nutrition has agreed to all aspects of the database in writing. The approval will be granted where a clear need is presented (e.g., raw produce and seafood). Approvals will be in effect for a limited time, e.g., 10 years, and will be eligible for renewal in the absence of significant changes in agricultural or industry practices. Approval requests shall be submitted in accordance with the provisions of 10.30 of this chapter. Guidance in the use of databases may be found in the "FDA Nutrition Labeling Manual—A Guide for Developing and Using Data Bases," available from the Office of Nutrition and Food Labeling (HFS-800), Center for Food Safety and Applied Nutrition, Food and Drug Administration, 5001 Campus Dr., College Park, MD 20740 or by going to http://www.fda.gov .

(9) When it is not technologically feasible, or some other circumstance makes it impracticable, for firms to comply with the requirements of this section (e.g., to develop adequate nutrient profiles to comply with the requirements of paragraph (c) of this section), FDA may permit alternative means of compliance or additional exemptions to deal with the situation. Firms in need of such special allowances shall make their request in writing to the Center for Food Safety and Applied Nutrition (HFS-800), Food and Drug Administration, 5001 Campus Dr., College Park, MD 20740.

(10) The manufacturer must make and keep written records (e.g., analyses of databases, recipes, formulations, information from recipes or formulations, or batch records) to verify the declared amount of that nutrient on the Nutrition Facts label as follows:

(i) When a mixture of dietary fiber, and added non-digestible carbohydrate(s) that does not meet the definition of dietary fiber, is present in the food, a manufacturer must make and keep written records of the amount of non-digestible carbohydrate(s) added to the food that does not meet the definition of dietary fiber.

(ii) When a mixture of soluble fiber and added non-digestible carbohydrate(s) that does not meet the definition of dietary fiber is present in the food, a manufacturer must make and keep written records necessary to verify the amount of the non-digestible carbohydrate(s) added to the food that does not meet the definition of dietary fiber.

(iii) When a mixture of insoluble fiber and added non-digestible carbohydrate(s) that does not meet the definition of dietary fiber is present in the food, a manufacturer must make and keep written records necessary to verify the amount of the non-digestible carbohydrate(s) added to the food that does not meet the definition of dietary fiber.

(iv) When a mixture of naturally occurring and added sugars is present in the food, a manufacturer must make and keep written records of the amount of added sugars added to the food during the processing of the food, and if packaged as a separate ingredient, as packaged (whether as part of a package containing one or more ingredients or packaged as a single ingredient).

(v) When the amount of sugars added to food products is reduced through non-enzymatic browning and/or fermentation, manufacturers must:

(A) Make and keep records of all relevant scientific data and information relied upon by the manufacturer that demonstrates the amount of added sugars in the food after non-enzymatic browning and/or fermentation and a narrative explaining why the data and information are sufficient to demonstrate the amount of added sugars declared in the finished food, provided the data and information used is specific to the type of food that is subject to non-enzymatic browning and/or fermentation; or

(B) Make and keep records of the amount of added sugars added to the food before and during the processing of the food, and if packaged as a separate ingredient, as packaged (whether as part of a package containing one or more ingredients or packaged as a single ingredient) and in no event shall the amount of added sugars declared exceed the amount of total sugars on the label; or

(C) Submit a petition, under 21 CFR 10.30, to request an alternative means of compliance. The petition must provide scientific data or other information for why the amount of added sugars in a serving of the product is likely to have a significant reduction in added sugars compared to the amount added prior to non-enzymatic browning and/or fermentation. A significant reduction would be where reduction in added sugars after non-enzymatic browning and/or fermentation may be significant enough to impact the label declaration for added sugars by an amount that exceeds the reasonable deficiency acceptable within good manufacturing practice under paragraph (g)(6) of this section. In addition, the scientific data or other information must include the reason that the manufacturer is unable to determine a reasonable approximation of the amount of added sugars in a serving of their finished product and a description of the process that they used to come to that conclusion.

(vi) When a mixture of all rac -[alpha]-tocopherol and RRR-[alpha]-tocopherol is present in a food, manufacturers must make and keep written records of the amount of all rac -[alpha]-tocopherol added to the food and RRR-[alpha]-tocopherol in the finished food.

(vii) When a mixture of folate and folic acid is present in a food, manufacturers must make and keep written records of the amount of synthetic folate and/or folic acid added to the food and the amount of naturally-occurring folate in the finished food.

(11) Records necessary to verify certain nutrient declarations that are specified in paragraph (g)(10) of this section must be kept for a period of at least 2 years after introduction or delivery for introduction of the food into interstate commerce. Such records must be provided to FDA upon request, during an inspection, for official review and photocopying or other means of reproduction. Records required to verify information on the label may be kept either as original records, true copies (such as photocopies, pictures, scanned copies, microfilm, microfiche, or other accurate reproductions of the original records), or electronic records which must be kept in accordance with part 11 of this chapter. These records must be accurate, indelible, and legible.

Failure to make and keep the records or provide the records to appropriate regulatory authorities, as required by this paragraph (g)(11), would result in the food being misbranded under section 403(a)(1) of the act.

(h) Products with separately packaged ingredients or foods, with assortments of food, or to which other ingredients are added by the user may be labeled as follows:

(1) If a product consists of two or more separately packaged ingredients enclosed in an outer container or of assortments of the same type of food (e.g., assorted nuts or candy mixtures) in the same retail package, nutrition labeling shall be located on the outer container or retail package (as the case may be) to provide information for the consumer at the point of purchase. However, when two or more food products are simply combined together in such a manner that no outer container is used, or no outer label is available, each product shall have its own nutrition information, e.g., two boxes taped together or two cans combined in a clear plastic overwrap. When separately packaged ingredients or assortments of the same type of food are intended to be eaten at the same time, the nutrition information may be specified per serving for each component or as a composite value.

(2) If a product consists of two or more separately packaged foods that are intended to be eaten individually and that are enclosed in an outer container (e.g., variety packs of cereals or snack foods), the nutrition information shall:

(i) Be specified per serving for each food in a location that is clearly visible to the consumer at the point of purchase; and

(ii) Be presented in separate nutrition labels or in one aggregate nutrition label with separate columns for the quantitative amount by weight and the percent Daily Value for each food.

(3) If a package contains a variety of foods, or an assortment of foods, and is in a form intended to be used as a gift, the nutrition labeling shall be in the form required by paragraphs (a) through (f) of this section, but it may be modified as follows:

(i) Nutrition information may be presented on the label of the outer package or in labeling within or attached to the outer package.

(ii) In the absence of a reference amount customarily consumed in 101.12(b) that is appropriate for the variety or assortment of foods in a gift package, the following may be used as the standard serving size for purposes of nutrition labeling of foods subject to this paragraph: 1 ounce for solid foods; 2 fluid ounces for nonbeverage liquids (e.g., syrups); 8 ounces for beverages that consist of milk and fruit juices, nectars and fruit drinks; and 12 fluid ounces for other beverages. However, the reference amounts customarily consumed in 101.12(b) shall be used for purposes of evaluating whether individual foods in a gift package qualify for nutrient content claims or health claims.

(iii) The number of servings per container may be stated as "varied."

(iv) Nutrition information may be provided per serving for individual foods in the package, or, alternatively, as a composite per serving for reasonable categories of foods in the package having similar dietary uses and similar significant nutritional characteristics. Reasonable categories of foods may be used only if accepted by FDA. In determining whether a proposed category is reasonable, FDA will consider whether the values of the characterizing nutrients in the foods proposed to be in the category meet the compliance criteria set forth in paragraphs (g)(3) through (6) of this section. Proposals for such categories may be submitted in writing to the Office of Nutrition and Food Labeling (HFS-800), Center for Food Safety and Applied Nutrition, Food and Drug Administration, 5001 Campus Dr., College Park, MD 20740.

(v) If a food subject to paragraph (j)(13) of this section because of its small size is contained in a gift package, the food need not be included in the determination of nutrition information under paragraph (h) of this section if it is not specifically listed in a promotional catalogue as being present in the gift package, and:

(A) It is used in small quantities primarily to enhance the appearance of the gift package; or

(B) It is included in the gift package as a free gift or promotional item.

(4) If a food is commonly combined with other ingredients or is cooked or otherwise prepared before eating, and directions for such combination or preparations are provided, another column of figures may be used to declare nutrition information on the basis of the food as consumed in the format required in paragraph (e) of this

section; e.g., a dry ready-to-eat cereal may be described with the percent Daily Value and the quantitative amounts for the cereal as sold (e.g., per ounce), and the percent Daily Value and the quantitative amounts for the cereal and milk as suggested in the label (e.g., per ounce of cereal and 1/2cup of vitamin D fortified skim milk); and a cake mix may be labeled with the percent Daily Value and the quantitative amounts for the dry mix (per serving) and the percent Daily Value and the quantitative amounts for the serving of the final cake when prepared, as shown in paragraph (e)(5) of this section: Provided, that, the type and quantity of the other ingredients to be added to the product by the user and the specific method of cooking and other preparation shall be specified prominently on the label.

(i) Except as provided in paragraphs (j)(13) and (j)(17) of this section, the location of nutrition information on a label shall be in compliance with 101.2.

(j) The following foods are exempt from this section or are subject to special labeling requirements:

(1) (i) Food offered for sale by a person who makes direct sales to consumers (e.g., a retailer) who has annual gross sales made or business done in sales to consumers that is not more than $500,000 or has annual gross sales made or business done in sales of food to consumers of not more than $50,000, Provided, That the food bears no nutrition claims or other nutrition information in any context on the label or in labeling or advertising. Claims or other nutrition information subject the food to the provisions of this section, 101.10, or 101.11, as applicable.

(ii) For purposes of this paragraph, calculation of the amount of sales shall be based on the most recent 2-year average of business activity. Where firms have been in business less than 2 years, reasonable estimates must indicate that annual sales will not exceed the amounts specified. For foreign firms that ship foods into the United States, the business activities to be included shall be the total amount of food sales, as well as other sales to consumers, by the firm in the United States.

(2) Except as provided in 101.11, food products that are:

(i) Served in restaurants, Provided, That the food bears no nutrition claims or other nutrition information in any context on the label or in labeling or advertising. Claims or other nutrition information subject the food to the provisions of this section;

(ii) Served in other establishments in which food is served for immediate human consumption (e.g., institutional food service establishments, such as schools, hospitals, and cafeterias; transportation carriers, such as trains and airplanes; bakeries, delicatessens, and retail confectionery stores where there are facilities for immediate consumption on the premises; food service vendors, such as lunch wagons, ice cream shops, mall cookie counters, vending machines, and sidewalk carts where foods are generally consumed immediately where purchased or while the consumer is walking away, including similar foods sold from convenience stores; and food delivery systems or establishments where ready-to-eat foods are delivered to homes or offices), *Provided*, That the food bears no nutrition claims or other nutrition information in any context on the label or in labeling or advertising, except as provided in 101.8(c). Claims or other nutrition information, except as provided in 101.8(c), subject the food to the provisions of this section;

(iii) Sold only in such facilities, *Provided*, That the food bears no nutrition claims or other nutrition information in any context on the label or in labeling or advertising. Claims or other nutrition information subject the food to the provisions of this section;

(iv) Used only in such facilities and not served to the consumer in the package in which they are received (e.g., foods that are not packaged in individual serving containers); or

(v) Sold by a distributor who principally sells food to such facilities: *Provided*, That:

(A) This exemption shall not be available for those foods that are manufactured, processed, or repackaged by that distributor for sale to any persons other than restaurants or other establishments that serve food for immediate human consumption, and

(B) The manufacturer of such products is responsible for providing the nutrition information on the products if there is a reasonable possibility that the product will be purchased directly by consumers.

(3) Except as provided in 101.11, food products that are:

(i) Of the type of food described in paragraphs (j)(2)(i) and (j)(2)(ii) of this section,

(ii) Ready for human consumption,

(iii) Offered for sale to consumers but not for immediate human consumption,

(iv) Processed and prepared primarily in a retail establishment, and

(v) Not offered for sale outside of that establishment (e.g., ready-to-eat foods that are processed and prepared on-site and sold by independent delicatessens, bakeries, or retail confectionery stores where there are no facilities for immediate human consumption; by in-store delicatessen, bakery, or candy departments; or at self-service food bars such as salad bars), *Provided*, That the food bears no nutrition claims or other nutrition information in any context on the label or in labeling or advertising. Claims or other nutrition information subject the food to the provisions of this section.

(4) Except as provided in 101.11, foods that contain insignificant amounts of all of the nutrients and food components required to be included in the declaration of nutrition information under paragraph (c) of this section, *Provided*, That the food bears no nutrition claims or other nutrition information in any context on the label or in labeling or advertising. Claims or other nutrition information, except as provided in

101.8(c), subject the food to the provisions of this section. An insignificant amount of a nutrient or food component shall be that amount that allows a declaration of zero in nutrition labeling, except that for total carbohydrate, dietary fiber, and protein, it shall be an amount that allows a declaration of "less than 1 gram." Examples of foods that are exempt under this paragraph include coffee beans (whole or ground), tea leaves, plain unsweetened instant coffee and tea, condiment-type dehydrated vegetables, flavor extracts, and food colors.

(5)(i) Foods, other than infant formula, represented or purported to be specifically for infants through 12 months of age and children 1 through 3 years of age shall bear nutrition labeling. The nutrients declared for infants through 12 months of age and children 1 through 3 years of age shall include calories, total fat, saturated fat, trans fat, cholesterol, sodium, total carbohydrates, dietary fiber, total sugars, added sugars, protein, and the following vitamins and minerals: Vitamin D, calcium, iron, and potassium.

(ii) Foods, other than infant formula, represented or purported to be specifically for infants through 12 months of age shall bear nutrition labeling, except that:

(A) Such labeling shall not declare a percent Daily Value for saturated fat, trans fat, cholesterol, sodium, dietary fiber, total sugars, or added sugars and shall not include a footnote.

(B) The following sample label illustrates the provisions of paragraph (j)(5)(ii) of this section.

Infants through 12 Months of Age

(C)-(E) [Reserved]

(iii) Foods, other than infant formula, represented or purported to be specifically for children 1 through 3 years of age shall include a footnote that states: "*The % Daily Value tells you how much a nutrient in a serving of food contributes to a daily diet. 1,000 calories a day is used for general nutrition advice."

    (A) The following sample label illustrates the provisions of paragraph (j)(5)(iii) of this section.

Children 1-3 Years

    (B) [Reserved]

(6) Dietary supplements, except that such foods shall be labeled in compliance with 101.36.

(7) Infant formula subject to section 412 of the act, as amended, except that such foods shall be labeled in compliance with part 107 of this chapter.

(8) Medical foods as defined in section 5(b) of the Orphan Drug Act (21 U.S.C. 360ee(b)(3)). A medical food is a food which is formulated to be consumed or administered enterally under the supervision of a physician and which is intended for the specific dietary management of a disease or condition for which distinctive nutritional requirements, based on recognized scientific principles, are established by medical evaluation. A food is subject to this exemption only if:

    (i) It is a specially formulated and processed product (as opposed to a naturally occurring foodstuff used in its natural state) for the partial or exclusive feeding of a patient by means of oral intake or enteral feeding by tube;

    (ii) It is intended for the dietary management of a patient who, because of therapeutic or chronic medical needs, has limited or impaired capacity to ingest, digest, absorb, or metabolize ordinary foodstuffs or certain nutrients, or who has other special medically determined nutrient requirements, the dietary management of which cannot be achieved by the modification of the normal diet alone;

(iii) It provides nutritional support specifically modified for the management of the unique nutrient needs that result from the specific disease or condition, as determined by medical evaluation;

(iv) It is intended to be used under medical supervision; and

(v) It is intended only for a patient receiving active and ongoing medical supervision wherein the patient requires medical care on a recurring basis for, among other things, instructions on the use of the medical food.

(9) Food products shipped in bulk form that are not for distribution to consumers in such form and that are for use solely in the manufacture of other foods or that are to be processed, labeled, or repacked at a site other than where originally processed or packed.

(10) Raw fruits, vegetables, and fish subject to section 403(q)(4) of the act, except that the labeling of such foods should adhere to guidelines in 101.45. This exemption is contingent on the food bearing no nutrition claims or other nutrition information in any context on the label or in labeling or advertising. Claims or other nutrition information subject the food to nutrition labeling in accordance with 101.45. The term fish includes freshwater or marine fin fish, crustaceans, and mollusks, including shellfish, amphibians, and other forms of aquatic animal life.

(11) Packaged single-ingredient products that consist of fish or game meat (i.e., animal products not covered under the Federal Meat Inspection Act or the Poultry Products Inspection Act, such as flesh products from deer, bison, rabbit, quail, wild turkey, or ostrich) subject to this section may provide required nutrition information for a 3-ounce cooked edible portion (i.e., on an "as prepared" basis), except that:

(i) Such products that make claims that are based on values as packaged must provide nutrition information on an as packaged basis, and

(ii) Nutrition information is not required for custom processed fish or game meats.

(12) Game meats (i.e., animal products not covered under the Federal Meat Inspection Act or the Poultry Products Inspection Act, such as flesh products from deer, bison, rabbit, quail, wild turkey, or ostrich) may provide required nutrition information on labeling in accordance with the provisions of paragraph (a)(2) of this section.

(13) (i) Foods in small packages that have a total surface area available to bear labeling of less than 12 square inches, Provided, That the labels for these foods bear no nutrition claims or other nutrition information in any context on the label or in labeling or advertising, except as provided in 101.8(c). Claims or other nutrition information, except as provided in 101.8(c), subject the food to the provisions of this section.

(ii) Foods in packages that have a total surface area available to bear labeling of 40 or less square inches may modify the requirements of paragraphs (c) through (f) and (i) of this section by one or more of the following means:

(A) Presenting the required nutrition information in a tabular or, as provided below, linear (i.e., string) fashion rather than in vertical columns if the product has a total surface area available to bear labeling of less than 12 square inches, or if the product has a total surface area available to bear labeling of 40 or less square inches and the package shape or size cannot accommodate a standard vertical column or tabular display on any label panel. Nutrition information may be given in a linear fashion only if the label will not accommodate a tabular display.

(1) The following sample label illustrates the tabular display for small packages.

Tabular Display for Small Packages

Nutrition Facts	Amount/serving	% DV*	Amount/serving	% DV*
5 servings per container	Total Fat 2g	3%	Total Carb. 15g	5%
	Sat. Fat 1g	5%	Fiber 0g	0%
	Trans Fat 0.5g		Total Sugars 14g	
Serving size 1/6 cup (28g)	Cholesterol 10mg	3%	Incl. 13g Added Sugars 26%	
	Sodium 200mg	9%	Protein 3g	
Calories per serving 90	Vitamin D 0% • Calcium 6% • Iron 6% • Potassium 10%			

(2) The following sample label illustrates the linear display.

Linear Display for Small Packages

Nutrition Facts Servings: 12, **Serv. size: 1 mint (2g),**
Amount per serving: **Calories 5, Total Fat** 0g (0% DV), Sat. Fat 0g (0% DV), Trans Fat 0g. **Cholest.** 0mg (0% DV), **Sodium** 0mg (0% DV), **Total Carb.** 2g (1% DV), Fiber 0g (0% DV), Total Sugars 2g (Incl. 2g Added Sugars, 4% DV), **Protein** 0g. Vit. D (0% DV), Calcium (0% DV), Iron (0% DV), Potas. (5% DV).

(B) Using any of the following abbreviations:

Serving size–Serv size

Servings per container–Servings

Calories from saturated fat–Sat fat cal

Saturated fat–Sat fat

Monounsaturated fat–Monounsat fat

Polyunsaturated fat–Polyunsat fat

Cholesterol–Cholest

Total carbohydrate–Total carb. This abbreviation can also be used on dual-column displays as shown in paragraphs (e)(5), (e)(6)(i), and (e)(6)(ii).

Dietary fiber–Fiber

Soluble fiber–Sol fiber

Insoluble fiber–Insol fiber

Sugar alcohol–Sugar alc

Vitamin–Vit

Potassium–Potas

Includes–Incl. This abbreviation can also be used on dual-column displays as shown in paragraphs (e)(5), (e)(6)(i), and (e)(6)(ii) of this section.

(C) Presenting the required nutrition information on any label panel.

(14) Shell eggs packaged in a carton that has a top lid designed to conform to the shape of the eggs are exempt from outer carton label requirements where the required nutrition information is clearly presented immediately beneath the carton lid or in an insert that can be clearly seen when the carton is opened.

(15) The unit containers in a multiunit retail food package where:

(i) The multiunit retail food package labeling contains all nutrition information in accordance with the requirements of this section;

(ii) The unit containers are securely enclosed within and not intended to be separated from the retail package under conditions of retail sale; and

(iii) Each unit container is labeled with the statement "This Unit Not Labeled For Retail Sale" in type size not less than 1/16-inch in height, except that this statement shall not be required when the inner unit containers bear no labeling at all. The word "individual" may be used in lieu of or immediately preceding the word "Retail" in the statement.

(16) Food products sold from bulk containers: *Provided*, That nutrition information required by this section be displayed to consumers either on the labeling of the bulk container plainly in view or in accordance with the provisions of paragraph (a)(2) of this section.

(17) Foods in packages that have a total surface area available to bear labeling greater than 40 square inches but whose principal display panel and information panel do not provide sufficient space to accommodate all required information may use any alternate panel that can be readily seen by consumers for the nutrition label. The space needed for vignettes, designs, and other nonmandatory label information on the principal display panel may be considered in determining the sufficiency of available space on the principal display panel for the placement of the nutrition label. Nonmandatory label information on the information panel shall not be considered in determining the sufficiency of available space for the placement of the nutrition label.

(18) Food products that are low-volume (that is, they meet the requirements for units sold in paragraphs (j)(18)(i) or (j)(18)(ii) of this section); that, except as provided in

paragraph (j)(18)(iv) of this section, are the subject of a claim for an exemption that provides the information required under paragraph (j)(18)(iv) of this section, that is filed before the beginning of the time period for which the exemption is claimed, and that is filed by a person, whether it is the manufacturer, packer, or distributor, that qualifies to claim the exemption under the requirements for average full-time equivalent employees in paragraphs (j)(18)(i) or (j)(18)(ii) of this section; and whose labels, labeling, and advertising do not provide nutrition information or make a nutrient content or health claim.

(i) For food products first introduced into interstate commerce before May 8, 1994, the product shall be exempt for the period:

(A) Between May 8, 1995, and May 7, 1996, if, for the period between May 8, 1994, and May 7, 1995, the person claiming the exemption employed fewer than an average of 300 full-time equivalent employees and fewer than 400,000 units of that product were sold in the United States; and

(B) Between May 8, 1996, and May 7, 1997, if for the period between May 8, 1995, and May 7, 1996, the person claiming the exemption employed fewer than an average of 200 full-time equivalent employees and fewer than 200,000 units of that product were sold in the United States.

(ii) For all other food products, the product shall be eligible for an exemption for any 12-month period if, for the preceding 12 months, the person claiming the exemption employed fewer than an average of 100 full-time equivalent employees and fewer than 100,000 units of that product were sold in the United States, or in the case of a food product that was not sold in the 12-month period preceding the period for which exemption is claimed, fewer than 100,000 units of such product are reasonably anticipated to be sold in the United States during the period for which exemption is claimed.

(iii) If a person claims an exemption under paragraphs (j)(18)(i) or (j)(18)(ii) of this section for a food product and then, during the period of such exemption, the number of full-time equivalent employees of such person exceeds the appropriate number, or the number of food products sold in the United States exceeds the appropriate number, or, if at the end of the period of such exemption, the food product no longer qualifies for an exemption under the provisions of paragraphs (j)(18)(i) or (j)(18)(ii) of this section, such person shall have 18 months from the date that the product was no longer qualified as a low-volume product of a small business to comply with this section.

(iv) A notice shall be filed with the Office of Nutrition and Food Labeling (HFS-800), Center for Food Safety and Applied Nutrition, Food and Drug Administration, 5001 Campus Dr., College Park, MD 20740 and contain the following information, except that if the person is not an importer and has fewer than 10 full-time equivalent employees, that person does not have to file a notice for any food product with annual sales of fewer than 10,000 total units:

(A) Name and address of person requesting exemption. This should include a telephone number or FAX number that can be used to contact the person along with the name of a specific contact;

(B) Names of the food products (including the various brand names) for which exemption is claimed;

(C) Name and address of the manufacturer, distributor, or importer of the food product for which an exemption is claimed, if different than the person that is claiming the exemption;

(D) The number of full-time equivalent employees. Provide the average number of full-time equivalent individuals employed by the person and its affiliates for the 12 months preceding the period for which a small business exemption is claimed for a product. The average number of full-time equivalent employees is to be determined by dividing the total number of hours of salary or wages paid to employees of the person and its affiliates by the number of hours of work in a year, 2,080 hours (i.e., 40 hours * 52 weeks);

(E) Approximate total number of units of the food product sold by the person in the United States in the 12-month period preceding that for which a small business exemption is claimed. Provide the approximate total number of units sold, or expected to be sold, in a 12-month period for each product for which an exemption is claimed. For products that have been in production for 1 year or more prior to the period for which exemption is claimed, the 12-month period is the period immediately preceding the period for which an exemption is claimed. For other products, the 12-month period is the period for which an exemption is claimed; and

(F) The notice shall be signed by a responsible individual for the person who can certify the accuracy of the information presented in the notice. The individual shall certify that the information contained in the notice is a complete and accurate statement of the average number of full-time equivalent employees of this person and its affiliates and of the number of units of the product for which an exemption is claimed sold by the person. The individual shall also state that should the average number of full-time equivalent employees or the number of units of food products sold in the United States by the person exceed the applicable numbers for the time period for which exemption is claimed, the person will notify FDA of that fact and the date on which the number of employees or the number of products sold exceeded the standard.

(v) FDA may by regulation lower the employee or units of food products requirements of paragraph (j)(18)(ii) of this section for any food product first introduced into interstate commerce after May 8, 2002, if the agency determines that the cost of compliance with such lower requirement will not place an undue burden on persons subject to it.

(vi) For the purposes of this paragraph, the following definitions apply:

(A) *Unit* means the packaging or, if there is no packaging, the form in which a food product is offered for sale to consumers.

(B) *Food product* means food in any sized package which is manufactured by a single manufacturer or which bears the same brand name, which bears the same statement of identity, and which has similar preparation methods.

(C) *Person* means all domestic and foreign affiliates, as defined in 13 CFR 121.401, of the corporation, in the case of a corporation, and all affiliates, as defined in 13 CFR 121.401, of a firm or other entity, when referring to a firm or other entity that is not a corporation.

(D) *Full-time equivalent employee* means all individuals employed by the person claiming the exemption. This number shall be determined by dividing the total number of hours of salary or wages paid directly to employees of the person and of all of its affiliates by the number of hours of work in a year, 2,080 hours (i.e., 40 hours * 52 weeks).

(k) A food labeled under the provisions of this section shall be deemed to be misbranded under sections 201(n) and 403(a) of the act if its label or labeling represents, suggests, or implies:

(1) That the food, because of the presence or absence of certain dietary properties, is adequate or effective in the prevention, cure, mitigation, or treatment of any disease or symptom. Information about the relationship of a dietary property to a disease or health-related condition may only be provided in conformance with the requirements of 101.14 and part 101, subpart E.

(2) That the lack of optimum nutritive quality of a food, by reason of the soil on which that food was grown, is or may be responsible for an inadequacy or deficiency in the quality of the daily diet.

(3) That the storage, transportation, processing, or cooking of a food is or may be responsible for an inadequacy or deficiency in the quality of the daily diet.

(4) That a natural vitamin in a food is superior to an added or synthetic vitamin.

(l) The standards required in this section are incorporated by reference into this section with the approval of the Director of the Federal Register under 5 U.S.C. 552(a) and 1 CFR part 51. All approved material is available for inspection at the Office of Nutrition and Food Labeling (HFS-800), Center for Food Safety and Applied Nutrition, Food and Drug Administration, 5001 Campus Dr., College Park, MD 20740, 240-402-2404 and is available from the sources indicated below. It is also available for inspection at the National Archives and Records Administration (NARA). For information on the availability of this material at NARA, call 202-741-6030, or go to: *http://www.archives.gov/federal_register/ code_of_federal_regulations/ibr_locations.html* .

(1) AOAC Reseller. Techstreet, 6300 Interfirst Dr., Ann Arbor, MI 48108, Toll free in United States: 1-800-699-9277, Outside United States: 1-734-780-8000, Fax: 1-734-780-2046, *www.techstreet.com,techstreet.service@thomsonreuters.com* . FDA does not endorse any particular reseller and notes that other resellers also may have the reference for sale. Consult FDA at 240-402-2404 for more information on additional resellers.

    (i) "Official Methods of Analysis of the AOAC INTERNATIONAL," 19th Edition, Volumes 1 and 2, 2012.

    (ii) [Reserved]

(2) Food and Agriculture Organization of the United Nations/World Health Organization (FAO/WHO), Publications Division, Viale delle Terme di Caracalla, 00100 Rome, Italy

    (i) FAO Food and Nutrition Paper 51,"Report of the Joint FAO/WHO Expert Consultation on Protein Quality Evaluation," Rome, 1991. *http://apps.who.int/iris/bitstream/10665/38133/1/9251030979_eng.pdf* .

    (ii) [Reserved]

(3) United States Department of Agriculture (USDA), Agricultural Research Service, Washington, DC, Nutrient Data Laboratory, Bldg. 005 Room 105 BARC-West, Beltsville, MD 20705, 301-504-0630. *http://www.ars.usda.gov/News/docs.htm?docid=9447* .

    (i) USDA Handbook No. 74, Energy Value of Foods—basis and derivation, by A. L. Merrill and B. K. Watt, (slightly revised, 1973) *http://www.ars.usda.gov/SP2UserFiles/Place/80400525/Data/Classics/ah74.pdf* .

    (ii) [Reserved]

[58 FR 2175, Jan. 6, 1993]

Editorial Note: For Federal Register citations affecting 101.9, see the List of CFR Sections Affected, which appears in the Finding Aids section of the printed volume and at www.fdsys.gov.

Sec. 101.13 Nutrient content claims—general principles.

(a) This section and the regulations in subpart D of this part apply to foods that are intended for human consumption and that are offered for sale, including conventional foods and dietary supplements.

(b) A claim that expressly or implicitly characterizes the level of a nutrient of the type required to be in nutrition labeling under 101.9 or under 101.36 (that is, a nutrient content claim) may not be made on the label or in labeling of foods unless the claim is made in accordance with this regulation and with the applicable regulations in subpart D of this part or in part 105 or part 107 of this chapter.

(1) An expressed nutrient content claim is any direct statement about the level (or range) of a nutrient in the food, e.g., "low sodium" or "contains 100 calories."

(2) An implied nutrient content claim is any claim that:

(i) Describes the food or an ingredient therein in a manner that suggests that a nutrient is absent or present in a certain amount (e.g., "high in oat bran"); or

(ii) Suggests that the food, because of its nutrient content, may be useful in maintaining healthy dietary practices and is made in association with an explicit claim or statement about a nutrient (e.g., "healthy, contains 3 grams (g) of fat").

(3) Except for claims regarding vitamins and minerals described in paragraph (q)(3) of this section, no nutrient content claims may be made on food intended specifically for use by infants and children less than 2 years of age unless the claim is specifically provided for in parts 101, 105, or 107 of this chapter.

(4) Reasonable variations in the spelling of the terms defined in part 101 and their synonyms are permitted provided these variations are not misleading (e.g., "hi" or "lo").

(5) For dietary supplements, claims for calories, fat, saturated fat, and cholesterol may not be made on products that meet the criteria in 101.60(b)(1) or (b)(2) for "calorie free" or "low calorie" claims, except, in the case of calorie claims, when an equivalent amount of a similar dietary supplement (e.g., another protein supplement) that the labeled food resembles and for which it substitutes, normally exceeds the definition for "low calorie" in 101.60(b)(2).

(c) Information that is required or permitted by 101.9 or 101.36, as applicable, to be declared in nutrition labeling, and that appears as part of the nutrition label, is not a nutrient content claim and is not subject to the requirements of this section. If such information is declared elsewhere on the label or in labeling, it is a nutrient content claim and is subject to the requirements for nutrient content claims.

(d) A "substitute" food is one that may be used interchangeably with another food that it resembles, i.e., that it is organoleptically, physically, and functionally (including shelf life) similar to, and that it is not nutritionally inferior to unless it is labeled as an "imitation."

(1) If there is a difference in performance characteristics that materially limits the use of the food, the food may still be considered a substitute if the label includes a disclaimer adjacent to the most prominent claim as defined in paragraph (j)(2)(iii) of this section, informing the consumer of such difference (e.g., "not recommended for frying").

(2) This disclaimer shall be in easily legible print or type and in a size no less than that required by 101.7(i) for the net quantity of contents statement, except where the size of the claim is less than two times the required size of the net quantity of contents statement, in which case the disclaimer shall be no less than one-half the size of the claim but no smaller than one-sixteenth of an inch, unless the package complies with 101.2(c)(5), in which case the disclaimer may be in type of not less than one thirty-second of an inch.

(e) (1) Because the use of a "free" or "low" claim before the name of a food implies that the food differs from other foods of the same type by virtue of its having a lower amount of the nutrient, only foods that have been specially processed, altered, formulated, or reformulated so as to lower the amount of the nutrient in the food, remove the nutrient from the food, or not include the nutrient in the food, may bear such a claim (e.g., "low sodium potato chips").

(2) Any claim for the absence of a nutrient in a food, or that a food is low in a nutrient when the food has not been specially processed, altered, formulated, or reformulated to qualify for that claim shall indicate that the food inherently meets the criteria and shall clearly refer to all foods of that type and not merely to the particular brand to which the labeling attaches (e.g., "corn oil, a sodium-free food").

(f) A nutrient content claim shall be in type size no larger than two times the statement of identity and shall not be unduly prominent in type style compared to the statement of identity.

(g) [Reserved]

(h) (1) If a food, except a meal product as defined in 101.13(l), a main dish product as defined in 101.13(m), or food intended specifically for use by infants and children less than 2 years of age, contains more than 13.0 g of fat, 4.0 g of saturated fat, 60 milligrams (mg) of cholesterol, or 480 mg of sodium per reference amount customarily consumed, per labeled serving, or, for a food with a reference amount customarily consumed of 30 g or less or 2 tablespoons or less, per 50 g (for dehydrated foods that must be reconstituted before typical consumption with water or a diluent containing an insignificant amount, as defined in 101.9(f)(1), of all nutrients per reference amount customarily consumed, the per 50 g criterion refers to the "as prepared" form), then that food must bear a statement disclosing that the nutrient exceeding the specified level is present in the food as follows: "See nutrition information for __ content" with the blank filled in with the identity of the nutrient exceeding the specified level, e.g., "See nutrition information for fat content."

(2) If a food is a meal product as defined in 101.13(l), and contains more than 26 g of fat, 8.0 g of saturated fat, 120 mg of cholesterol, or 960 mg of sodium per labeled serving, then that food must disclose, in accordance with the requirements as provided in paragraph (h)(1) of this section, that the nutrient exceeding the specified level is present in the food.

(3) If a food is a main dish product as defined in 101.13(m), and contains more than 19.5 g of fat, 6.0 g of saturated fat, 90 mg of cholesterol, or 720 mg of sodium per labeled serving, then that food must disclose, in accordance with the requirements as provided in paragraph (h)(1) of this section, that the nutrient exceeding the specified level is present in the food.

(4) (i) The disclosure statement "See nutrition information for __ content" shall be in easily legible boldface print or type, in distinct contrast to other printed or graphic matter, and in a size no less than that required by 101.7(i) for the net quantity of contents statement, except where the size of the claim is less than

two times the required size of the net quantity of contents statement, in which case the disclosure statement shall be no less than one-half the size of the claim but no smaller than one-sixteenth of an inch, unless the package complies with 101.2(c)(2), in which case the disclosure statement may be in type of not less than one thirty-second of an inch.

(ii) The disclosure statement shall be immediately adjacent to the nutrient content claim and may have no intervening material other than, if applicable, other information in the statement of identity or any other information that is required to be presented with the claim under this section (e.g., see paragraph (j)(2) of this section) or under a regulation in subpart D of this part (e.g., see 101.54 and 101.62). If the nutrient content claim appears on more than one panel of the label, the disclosure statement shall be adjacent to the claim on each panel except for the panel that bears the nutrition information where it may be omitted.

(iii) If a single panel of a food label or labeling contains multiple nutrient content claims or a single claim repeated several times, a single disclosure statement may be made. The statement shall be adjacent to the claim that is printed in the largest type on that panel.

(i) Except as provided in 101.9 or 101.36, as applicable, or in paragraph (q)(3) of this section, the label or labeling of a product may contain a statement about the amount or percentage of a nutrient if:

(1) The use of the statement on the food implicitly characterizes the level of the nutrient in the food and is consistent with a definition for a claim, as provided in subpart D of this part, for the nutrient that the label addresses. Such a claim might be, "less than 3 g of fat per serving;"

(2) The use of the statement on the food implicitly characterizes the level of the nutrient in the food and is not consistent with such a definition, but the label carries a disclaimer adjacent to the statement that the food is not "low" in or a "good source" of the nutrient, such as "only 200 mg sodium per serving, not a low sodium food." The disclaimer must be in easily legible print or type and in a size no less than that required by 101.7(i) for the net quantity of contents statement except where the size of the claim is less than two times the required size of the net quantity of contents statement, in which case the disclaimer shall be no less than one-half the size of the claim but no smaller than one-sixteenth of an inch unless the package complies with 101.2(c)(5), in which case the disclaimer may be in type of not less less than one thirty-second of an inch, or

(3) The statement does not in any way implicitly characterize the level of the nutrient in the food and it is not false or misleading in any respect (e.g., "100 calories" or "5 grams of fat"), in which case no disclaimer is required.

(4) "Percent fat free" claims are not authorized by this paragraph. Such claims shall comply with 101.62(b)(6).

(j) A food may bear a statement that compares the level of a nutrient in the food with the level of a nutrient in a reference food. These statements shall be known as "relative claims" and include "light," "reduced," "less" (or "fewer"), and "more" claims.

(1) To bear a relative claim about the level of a nutrient, the amount of that nutrient in the food must be compared to an amount of nutrient in an appropriate reference food as specified below.

(i) (A) For "less" (or "fewer") and "more" claims, the reference food may be a dissimilar food within a product category that can generally be substituted for one another in the diet (e.g., potato chips as reference for pretzels, orange juice as a reference for vitamin C tablets) or a similar food (e.g., potato chips as reference for potato chips, one brand of multivitamin as reference for another brand of multivitamin).

(B) For "light," "reduced," "added," "extra," "plus," "fortified," and "enriched" claims, the reference food shall be a similar food (e.g., potato chips as a reference for potato chips, one brand of multivitamin for another brand of multivitamin), and

(ii) (A) For "light" claims, the reference food shall be representative of the type of food that includes the product that bears the claim. The nutrient value for the reference food shall be representative of a broad base of foods of that type; e.g., a value in a representative, valid data base; an average value determined from the top three national (or regional) brands, a market basket norm; or, where its nutrient value is representative of the food type, a market leader. Firms using such a reference nutrient value as a basis for a claim, are required to provide specific information upon which the nutrient value was derived, on request, to consumers and appropriate regulatory officials.

(B) For relative claims other than "light," including "less" and "more" claims, the reference food may be the same as that provided for "light" in paragraph (j)(1)(ii)(A) of this section, or it may be the manufacturer's regular product, or that of another manufacturer, that has been offered for sale to the public on a regular basis for a substantial period of time in the same geographic area by the same business entity or by one entitled to use its trade name. The nutrient values used to determine the claim when comparing a single manufacturer's product to the labeled product shall be either the values declared in nutrition labeling or the actual nutrient values, provided that the resulting label is internally consistent to (i.e., that the values stated in the nutrition information, the nutrient values in the accompanying information and the declaration of the percentage of nutrient by which the food has been modified are consistent and will not cause consumer confusion when compared), and that the actual modification is at least equal to the percentage specified in the definition of the claim.

(2) For foods bearing relative claims:

(i) The label or labeling must state the identity of the reference food and the percentage (or fraction) of the amount of the nutrient in the reference food by which the nutrient in the labeled food differs (e.g., "50 percent less fat than (reference food)" or "1/3 fewer calories than (reference food)"),

(ii) This information shall be immediately adjacent to the most prominent claim. The type size shall be in accordance with paragraph (h)(4)(i) of this section.

(iii) The determination of which use of the claim is in the most prominent location on the label or labeling will be made based on the following factors, considered in order:

(A) A claim on the principal display panel adjacent to the statement of identity;

(B) A claim elsewhere on the principal display panel;

(C) A claim on the information panel; or

(D) A claim elsewhere on the label or labeling.

(iv) The label or labeling must also bear:

(A) Clear and concise quantitative information comparing the amount of the subject nutrient in the product per labeled serving with that in the reference food; and

(B) This statement shall appear adjacent to the most prominent claim or to the nutrition label, except that if the nutrition label is on the information panel, the quantitative information may be located elsewhere on the information panel in accordance with 101.2.

(3) A relative claim for decreased levels of a nutrient may not be made on the label or in labeling of a food if the nutrient content of the reference food meets the requirement for a "low" claim for that nutrient (e.g., 3 g fat or less).

(k) The term "modified" may be used in the statement of identity of a food that bears a relative claim that complies with the requirements of this part, followed immediately by the name of the nutrient whose content has been altered (e.g., "Modified fat cheesecake"). This statement of identity must be immediately followed by the comparative statement such as "Contains 35 percent less fat than ___." The label or labeling must also bear the information required by paragraph (j)(2) of this section in the manner prescribed.

(l) For purposes of making a claim, a "meal product shall be defined as a food that:

(1) Makes a major contribution to the total diet by:

(i) Weighing at least 10 ounces (oz) per labeled serving; and

(ii) Containing not less than three 40-g portions of food, or combinations of foods, from two or more of the following four food groups, except as noted in paragraph (l)(1)(ii)(E) of this section.

(A) Bread, cereal, rice, and pasta group;

(B) Fruits and vegetables group;

(C) Milk, yogurt, and cheese group;

(D) Meat, poultry, fish, dry beans, eggs, and nuts group; except that;

(E) These foods shall not be sauces (except for foods in the above four food groups that are in the sauces), gravies, condiments, relishes, pickles, olives, jams, jellies, syrups, breadings or garnishes; and

(2) Is represented as, or is in a form commonly understood to be, a breakfast, lunch, dinner, or meal. Such representations may be made either by statements, photographs, or vignettes.

(m) For purposes of making a claim, a "main dish product" shall be defined as a food that:

(1) Makes a major contribution to a meal by

(i) Weighing at least 6 oz per labeled serving; and

(ii) Containing not less than 40 g of food, or combinations of foods, from each of at least two of the following four food groups, except as noted in paragraph (m)(1)(ii)(E) of this section.

(A) Bread, cereal, rice, and pasta group;

(B) Fruits and vegetables group;

(C) Milk, yogurt, and cheese group;

(D) Meat, poultry, fish, dry beans, eggs, and nuts groups; except that:

(E) These foods shall not be sauces (except for foods in the above four food groups that are in the sauces) gravies, condiments, relishes, pickles, olives, jams, jellies, syrups, breadings, or garnishes; and

(2) Is represented as, or is in a form commonly understood to be, a main dish (e.g, not a beverage or a dessert). Such representations may be made either by statements, photographs, or vignettes.

(n) Nutrition labeling in accordance with 101.9, 101.10, or 101.36, as applicable, shall be provided for any food for which a nutrient content claim is made.

(o) Except as provided in 101.10, compliance with requirements for nutrient content claims in this section and in the regulations in subpart D of this part, will be determined using the analytical methodology prescribed for determining compliance with nutrition labeling in 101.9.

(p) (1) Unless otherwise specified, the reference amount customarily consumed set forth in 101.12(b) through (f) shall be used in determining whether a product meets the criteria for a nutrient content claim. If the serving size declared on the product label differs from the reference amount customarily consumed, and the amount of the nutrient contained in the labeled serving does not meet the maximum or minimum amount criterion in the definition for the descriptor for that nutrient, the claim shall be followed by the criteria for the claim as required by 101.12(g) (e.g., "very low sodium, 35 mg or less per 240 milliliters (8 fl oz.)").

(2) The criteria for the claim shall be immediately adjacent to the most prominent claim in easily legible print or type and in a size in accordance with paragraph (h)(4)(i) of this section.

(q) The following exemptions apply:

(1) Nutrient content claims that have not been defined by regulation and that are contained in the brand name of a specific food product that was the brand name in use on such food before October 25, 1989, may continue to be used as part of that brand name for such product, provided that they are not false or misleading under section 403(a) of the Federal Food, Drug, and Cosmetic Act (the act). However, foods bearing such claims must comply with section 403(f), (g), and (h) of the act;

(2) A soft drink that used the term *diet* as part of its brand name before October 25, 1989, and whose use of that term was in compliance with 105.66 of this chapter as that regulation appeared in the Code of Federal Regulations on that date, may continue to use that term as part of its brand name, provided that its use of the term is not false or misleading under section 403(a) of the act. Such claims are exempt from the requirements of section 403(r)(2) of the act (e.g., the disclosure statement also required by 101.13(h)). Soft drinks marketed after October 25, 1989, may use the term "diet" provided they are in compliance with the current 105.66 of this chapter and the requirements of 101.13.

(3) (i) A statement that describes the percentage of a vitamin or mineral in the food, including foods intended specifically for use by infants and children less than 2 years of age, in relation to a Reference Daily Intake (RDI) as defined in 101.9 may be made on the label or in labeling of a food without a regulation authorizing such a claim for a specific vitamin or mineral unless such claim is expressly prohibited by regulation under section 403(r)(2)(A)(vi) of the act.

(ii) Percentage claims for dietary supplements. Under section 403(r)(2)(F) of the act, a statement that characterizes the percentage level of a dietary ingredient for which a reference daily intake (RDI) or daily reference value (DRV) has not been established may be made on the label or in labeling of dietary supplements without a regulation that specifically defines such a statement. All such claims shall be accompanied by any disclosure statement required under paragraph (h) of this section.

(A) *Simple percentage claims.* Whenever a statement is made that characterizes the percentage level of a dietary ingredient for which there is no RDI or DRV, the statement of the actual amount of the dietary ingredient per serving shall be declared next to the percentage statement (e.g., "40 percent omega-3 fatty acids, 10 mg per capsule").

(B) *Comparative percentage claims.* Whenever a statement is made that characterizes the percentage level of a dietary ingredient for which there is no RDI or DRV and the statement draws a comparison to the amount of the dietary ingredient in a reference food, the reference food shall be clearly identified, the amount of that food shall be identified, and the information on the actual amount of the dietary ingredient in both foods shall be declared in accordance with paragraph (j)(2)(iv) of this section (e.g., "twice the omega-3 fatty acids per capsule (80 mg) as in 100 mg of menhaden oil (40 mg)").

(4) The requirements of this section do not apply to:

   (i) Infant formulas subject to section 412(h) of the act; and

   (ii) Medical foods defined by section 5(b) of the Orphan Drug Act.

(5) A nutrient content claim used on food that is served in restaurants or other establishments in which food is served for immediate human consumption or which is sold for sale or use in such establishments shall comply with the requirements of this section and the appropriate definition in subpart D of this part, except that:

   (i) Such claim is exempt from the requirements for disclosure statements in paragraph (h) of this section and 101.54(d), 101.62(c), (d)(1)(ii)(D), (d)(2)(iii)(C), (d)(3), (d)(4)(ii)(C), and (d)(5)(ii)(C); and

   (ii) In lieu of analytical testing, compliance may be determined using a reasonable basis for concluding that the food that bears the claim meets the definition for the claim. This reasonable basis may derive from recognized data bases for raw and processed foods, recipes, and other means to compute nutrient levels in the foods or meals and may be used provided reasonable steps are taken to ensure that the method of preparation adheres to the factors on which the reasonable basis was determined (e.g., types and amounts of ingredients, cooking temperatures, etc.). Firms making claims on foods based on this reasonable basis criterion are required to provide to appropriate regulatory officials on request the specific information on which their determination is based and reasonable assurance of operational adherence to the preparation methods or other basis for the claim; and

   (iii) A term or symbol that may in some contexts constitute a claim under this section may be used, provided that the use of the term or symbol does not characterize the level of a nutrient, and a statement that clearly explains the basis for the use of the term or symbol is prominently displayed and does not characterize the level of a nutrient. For example, a term such as "lite fare" followed by an asterisk referring to a note that makes clear that in this restaurant "lite fare" means smaller portion sizes than normal; or an item bearing a symbol referring to a note that makes clear that this item meets the criteria for the dietary guidance established by a recognized dietary authority would not be considered a nutrient content claim under 101.13.

(6) Nutrient content claims that were part of the common or usual names of foods that were subject to a standard of identity on November 8, 1990, are not subject to the requirements of paragraphs (b) and (h) of this section or to definitions in subpart D of this part.

(7) Implied nutrient content claims may be used as part of a brand name, provided that the use of the claim has been authorized by the Food and Drug Administration. Petitions requesting approval of such a claim may be submitted under 101.69(o).

(8) The term *fluoridated, fluoride added* or with added *fluoride* may be used on the label or in labeling of bottled water that contains added fluoride.

> [58 FR 2410, Jan. 6, 1993; 58 FR 17341, 17342, Apr. 2, 1993, as amended at 58 FR 44030, Aug. 18, 1993; 59 FR 393, Jan. 4, 1994; 59 FR 15051, Mar. 31, 1994; 60 FR 17205, Apr. 5, 1995; 61 FR 11731, Mar. 22, 1996; 61 FR 40332, Aug. 2, 1996; 61 FR 67452, Dec. 23, 1996; 62 FR 31339, June 9, 1997; 62 FR 49867, Sept. 23, 1997; 63 FR 14818, Mar. 27, 1998; 63 FR 26980, May 15, 1998; 81 FR 59131, Aug. 29, 2016]

Sec. 101.14 Health claims: general requirements.

(a) *Definitions*. For purposes of this section, the following definitions apply:

(1) *Health claim* means any claim made on the label or in labeling of a food, including a dietary supplement, that expressly or by implication, including "third party" references, written statements (e.g., a brand name including a term such as "heart"), symbols (e.g., a heart symbol), or vignettes, characterizes the relationship of any substance to a disease or health-related condition. Implied health claims include those statements, symbols, vignettes, or other forms of communication that suggest, within the context in which they are presented, that a relationship exists between the presence or level of a substance in the food and a disease or health-related condition.

(2) *Substance* means a specific food or component of food, regardless of whether the food is in conventional food form or a dietary supplement that includes vitamins, minerals, herbs, or other similar nutritional substances.

(3) *Nutritive value* means a value in sustaining human existence by such processes as promoting growth, replacing loss of essential nutrients, or providing energy.

(4) *Disqualifying nutrient levels* means the levels of total fat, saturated fat, cholesterol, or sodium in a food above which the food will be disqualified from making a health claim. These levels are 13.0 grams (g) of fat, 4.0 g of saturated fat, 60 milligrams (mg) of cholesterol, or 480 mg of sodium, per reference amount customarily consumed, per label serving size, and, only for foods with reference amounts customarily consumed of 30 g or less or 2 tablespoons or less, per 50 g. For dehydrated foods that must have water added to them prior to typical consumption, the per 50-g criterion refers to the as prepared form. Any one of the levels, on a per reference amount customarily consumed, a per label serving size or, when applicable, a per

50 g basis, will disqualify a food from making a health claim unless an exception is provided in subpart E of this part, except that:

(i) The levels for a meal product as defined in 101.13(l) are 26.0 g of fat, 8.0 g of saturated fat, 120 mg of cholesterol, or 960 mg of sodium per label serving size, and

(ii) The levels for a main dish product as defined in 101.13(m) are 19.5 g of fat, 6.0 g of saturated fat, 90 mg of cholesterol, or 720 mg of sodium per label serving size.

(5) *Disease* or *health-related condition* means damage to an organ, part, structure, or system of the body such that it does not function properly (e.g., cardiovascular disease), or a state of health leading to such dysfunctioning (e.g., hypertension); except that diseases resulting from essential nutrient deficiencies (e.g., scurvy, pellagra) are not included in this definition (claims pertaining to such diseases are thereby not subject to 101.14 or 101.70).

(b) *Eligibility*. For a substance to be eligible for a health claim:

(1) The substance must be associated with a disease or health-related condition for which the general U.S. population, or an identified U.S. population subgroup (e.g., the elderly) is at risk, or, alternatively, the petition submitted by the proponent of the claim otherwise explains the prevalence of the disease or health-related condition in the U.S. population and the relevance of the claim in the context of the total daily diet and satisfies the other requirements of this section.

(2) If the substance is to be consumed as a component of a conventional food at decreased dietary levels, the substance must be a nutrient listed in 21 U.S.C. 343(q)(1)(C) or (q)(1)(D), or one that the Food and Drug Administration (FDA) has required to be included in the label or labeling under 21 U.S.C. 343(q)(2)(A); or

(3) If the substance is to be consumed at other than decreased dietary levels:

(i) The substance must, regardless of whether the food is a conventional food or a dietary supplement, contribute taste, aroma, or nutritive value, or any other technical effect listed in 170.3(o) of this chapter, to the food and must retain that attribute when consumed at levels that are necessary to justify a claim; and

(ii) The substance must be a food or a food ingredient or a component of a food ingredient whose use at the levels necessary to justify a claim has been demonstrated by the proponent of the claim, to FDA's satisfaction, to be safe and lawful under the applicable food safety provisions of the Federal Food, Drug, and Cosmetic Act.

(c) *Validity requirement*. FDA will promulgate regulations authorizing a health claim only when it determines, based on the totality of publicly available scientific evidence (including evidence from well-designed studies conducted in a manner which is consistent with generally recognized scientific procedures and principles), that there is significant scientific agreement, among experts qualified by scientific training and experience to evaluate such claims, that the claim is supported by such evidence.

(d) *General health claim labeling requirements.* (1) When FDA determines that a health claim meets the validity requirements of paragraph (c) of this section, FDA will propose a regulation in subpart E of this part to authorize the use of that claim. If the claim pertains to a substance not provided for in 101.9 or 101.36, FDA will propose amending that regulation to include declaration of the substance.

(2) When FDA has adopted a regulation in subpart E of this part providing for a health claim, firms may make claims based on the regulation in subpart E of this part, provided that:

(i) All label or labeling statements about the substance-disease relationship that is the subject of the claim are based on, and consistent with, the conclusions set forth in the regulations in subpart E of this part;

(ii) The claim is limited to describing the value that ingestion (or reduced ingestion) of the substance, as part of a total dietary pattern, may have on a particular disease or health-related condition;

(iii) The claim is complete, truthful, and not misleading. Where factors other than dietary intake of the substance affect the relationship between the substance and the disease or health-related condition, such factors may be required to be addressed in the claim by a specific regulation in subpart E of this part;

(iv) All information required to be included in the claim appears in one place without other intervening material, except that the principal display panel of the label or labeling may bear the reference statement, "See ___ for information about the relationship between ___ and ___," with the blanks filled in with the location of the labeling containing the health claim, the name of the substance, and the disease or health-related condition (e.g., "See attached pamphlet for information about calcium and osteoporosis"), with the entire claim appearing elsewhere on the other labeling, Provided that, where any graphic material (e.g., a heart symbol) constituting an explicit or implied health claim appears on the label or labeling, the reference statement or the complete claim shall appear in immediate proximity to such graphic material;

(v) The claim enables the public to comprehend the information provided and to understand the relative significance of such information in the context of a total daily diet; and

(vi) If the claim is about the effects of consuming the substance at decreased dietary levels, the level of the substance in the food is sufficiently low to justify the claim. To meet this requirement, if a definition for use of the term *low* has been established for that substance under this part, the substance must be present at a level that meets the requirements for use of that term, unless a specific alternative level has been established for the substance in subpart E of this part. If no definition for "low" has been established, the level of the substance must meet the level established in the regulation authorizing the claim; or

(vii) If the claim is about the effects of consuming the substance at other than decreased dietary levels, the level of the substance is sufficiently high and in an appropriate form to justify the claim. To meet this requirement, if a definition for use of the term *high* for that substance has been established under this part, the substance must be present at a level that meets the requirements for use of that term, unless a specific alternative level has been established for the substance in subpart E of this part. If no definition for "high" has been established (e.g., where the claim pertains to a food either as a whole food or as an ingredient in another food), the claim must specify the daily dietary intake necessary to achieve the claimed effect, as established in the regulation authorizing the claim; *Provided* That:

(A) Where the food that bears the claim meets the requirements of paragraphs (d)(2)(vi) or (d)(2)(vii) of this section based on its reference amount customarily consumed, and the labeled serving size differs from that amount, the claim shall be followed by a statement explaining that the claim is based on the reference amount rather than the labeled serving size (e.g., "Diets low in sodium may reduce the risk of high blood pressure, a disease associated with many factors. A serving of _ ounces of this product conforms to such a diet.").

(B) Where the food that bears the claim is sold in a restaurant or in other establishments in which food that is ready for immediate human consumption is sold, the food can meet the requirements of paragraphs (d)(2)(vi) or (d)(2)(vii) of this section if the firm that sells the food has a reasonable basis on which to believe that the food that bears the claim meets the requirements of paragraphs (d)(2)(vi) or (d)(2)(vii) of this section and provides that basis upon request.

(3) Nutrition labeling shall be provided in the label or labeling of any food for which a health claim is made in accordance with 101.9; for restaurant foods, in accordance with 101.10; or for dietary supplements, in accordance with 101.36.

(e) *Prohibited health claims.* No expressed or implied health claim may be made on the label or in labeling for a food, regardless of whether the food is in conventional food form or dietary supplement form, unless:

(1) The claim is specifically provided for in subpart E of this part; and

(2) The claim conforms to all general provisions of this section as well as to all specific provisions in the appropriate section of subpart E of this part;

(3) None of the disqualifying levels identified in paragraph (a)(4) of this section is exceeded in the food, unless specific alternative levels have been established for the substance in subpart E of this part; or unless FDA has permitted a claim despite the fact that a disqualifying level of a nutrient is present in the food based on a finding that such a claim will assist consumers in maintaining healthy dietary practices, and, in accordance with the regulation in subpart E of this part that makes such a finding,

the label bears a disclosure statement that complies with 101.13(h), highlighting the nutrient that exceeds the disqualifying level;

(4) Except as provided in paragraph (e)(3) of this section, no substance is present at an inappropriate level as determined in the specific provision authorizing the claim in subpart E of this part;

(5) The label does not represent or purport that the food is for infants and toddlers less than 2 years of age except if the claim is specifically provided for in subpart E of this part; and

(6) Except for dietary supplements or where provided for in other regulations in part 101, subpart E, the food contains 10 percent or more of the Reference Daily Intake or the Daily Reference Value for vitamin A, vitamin C, iron, calcium, protein, or fiber per reference amount customarily consumed prior to any nutrient addition.

(f) The requirements of this section do not apply to:

(1) Infant formulas subject to section 412(h) of the Federal Food, Drug, and Cosmetic Act, and

(2) Medical foods defined by section 5(b) of the Orphan Drug Act.

(g) Applicability. The requirements of this section apply to foods intended for human consumption that are offered for sale, regardless of whether the foods are in conventional food form or dietary supplement form.

[58 FR 2533, Jan. 6, 1993; 58 FR 17097, Apr. 1, 1993, as amended at 58 FR 44038, Aug. 18, 1993; 59 FR 425, Jan. 4, 1994; 59 FR 15050, Mar. 31, 1994; 61 FR 40332, Aug. 2, 1996; 62 FR 49867, Sept. 23, 1997; 63 FR 26980, May 15, 1998; 66 FR 17358, Mar. 30, 2001]

Sec. 101.17 Food labeling warning, notice, and safe handling statements.

(a) *Self-pressurized containers*.

(1) The label of a food packaged in a self-pressurized container and intended to be expelled from the package under pressure shall bear the following warning:

WARNING—Avoid spraying in eyes. Contents under pressure. Do not puncture or incinerate. Do not store at temperature above 120 deg. F. Keep out of reach of children.

(2) In the case of products intended for use by children, the phrase "except under adult supervision" may be added at the end of the last sentence in the warning required by paragraph (a)(1) of this section.

(3) In the case of products packaged in glass containers, the word "break" may be substituted for the word "puncture" in the warning required by paragraph (a)(1) of this section.

PART **101**

(4) The words "Avoid spraying in eyes" may be deleted from the warning required by paragraph (a)(1) of this section in the case of a product not expelled as a spray.

(b) *Self-pressurized containers with halocarbon or hydrocarbon propellants.*

(1) In addition to the warning required by paragraph (a) of this section, the label of a food packaged in a self-pressurized container in which the propellant consists in whole or in part of a halocarbon or a hydrocarbon shall bear the following warning:

WARNING—Use only as directed. Intentional misuse by deliberately concentrating and inhaling the contents can be harmful or fatal.

(2) The warning required by paragraph (b)(1) of this section is not required for the following products:

(i) Products expelled in the form of a foam or cream, which contain less than 10 percent propellant in the container.

(ii) Products in a container with a physical barrier that prevents escape of the propellant at the time of use.

(iii) Products of a net quantity of contents of less than 2 ounces that are designed to release a measured amount of product with each valve actuation.

(iv) Products of a net quantity of contents of less than one-half ounce.

(c) *Food containing or manufactured with a chlorofluorocarbon or other ozone-depleting substance.* Labeling requirements for foods that contain or are manufactured with a chlorofluorocarbon or other ozone-depleting substance designated by the Environmental Protection Agency (EPA) are set forth in 40 CFR part 82.

(d) *Protein products.*

(1) The label and labeling of any food product in liquid, powdered, tablet, capsule, or similar forms that derives more than 50 percent of its total caloric value from either whole protein, protein hydrolysates, amino acid mixtures, or a combination of these, and that is represented for use in reducing weight shall bear the following warning:

WARNING: Very low calorie protein diets (below 400 Calories per day) may cause serious illness or death. Do Not Use for Weight Reduction in Such Diets Without Medical Supervision. Not for use by infants, children, or pregnant or nursing women.

(2) Products described in paragraph (d)(1) of this section are exempt from the labeling requirements of that paragraph if the protein products are represented as part of a nutritionally balanced diet plan providing 400 or more Calories (kilocalories) per day and the label or labeling of the product specifies the diet plan in detail or provides a brief description of that diet plan and adequate information describing where the detailed diet plan may be obtained and the label and labeling bear the following statement:

Notice: For weight reduction, use only as directed in the accompanying diet

plan (the name and specific location in labeling of the diet plan may be included in this statement in place of "accompanying diet plan"). **Do not use in diets supplying less than 400 Calories per day without medical supervision**.

(3) The label and labeling of food products represented or intended for dietery (food) supplementation that derive more than 50 percent of their total caloric value from either whole protein, protein hydrolysates, amino acid mixtures, or a combination of these, that are represented specifically for purposes other than weight reduction; and that are not covered by the requirements of paragraph (d) (1) and (2) of this section; shall bear the following statement:

Notice: Use this product as a food supplement only. Do not use for weight reduction.

(4) The provisions of this paragraph are separate from and in addition to any labeling requirements promulgated by the Federal Trade Commission for protein supplements.

(5) Protein products shipped in bulk form for use solely in the manufacture of other foods and not for distribution to consumers in such container are exempt from the labeling requirements of this paragraph.

(6) The warning and notice statements required by paragraphs (d) (1), (2), and (3) of this section shall appear prominently and conspicuously on the principal display panel of the package label and any other labeling.

(e) *Dietary supplements containing iron or iron salts*.

(1) The labeling of any dietary supplement in solid oral dosage form (e.g., tablets or capsules) that contains iron or iron salts for use as an iron source shall bear the following statement:

WARNING: Accidental overdose of iron-containing products is a leading cause of fatal poisoning in children under 6. Keep this product out of reach of children. In case of accidental overdose, call a doctor or poison control center immediately.

(2)　(i) The warning statement required by paragraph (e)(1) of this section shall appear prominently and conspicuously on the information panel of the immediate container label.

(ii) If a product is packaged in unit-dose packaging, and if the immediate container bears labeling but not a label, the warning statement required by paragraph (e)(1) of this section shall appear prominently and conspicuously on the immediate container labeling in a way that maximizes the likelihood that the warning is intact until all of the dosage units to which it applies are used.

(3) Where the immediate container is not the retail package, the warning statement required by paragraph (e)(1) of this section shall also appear prominently and conspicuously on the information panel of the retail package label.

(4) The warning statement shall appear on any labeling that contains warnings.

(5) The warning statement required by paragraph (e)(1) of this section shall be set off in a box by use of hairlines.

(f) *Foods containing psyllium husk.*

(1) Foods containing dry or incompletely hydrated psyllium husk, also known as psyllium seed husk, and bearing a health claim on the association between soluble fiber from psyllium husk and reduced risk of coronary heart disease, shall bear a label statement informing consumers that the appropriate use of such foods requires consumption with adequate amounts of fluids, alerting them of potential consequences of failing to follow usage recommendations, and informing persons with swallowing difficulties to avoid consumption of the product (e.g., "NOTICE: This food should be eaten with at least a full glass of liquid. Eating this product without enough liquid may cause choking. Do not eat this product if you have difficulty in swallowing."). However, a product in conventional food form may be exempt from this requirement if a viscous adhesive mass is not formed when the food is exposed to fluids.

(2) The statement shall appear prominently and conspicuously on the information panel or principal display panel of the package label and any other labeling to render it likely to be read and understood by the ordinary individual under customary conditions of purchase and use. The statement shall be preceded by the word "NOTICE" in capital letters.

(g) *Juices that have not been specifically processed to prevent, reduce, or eliminate the presence of pathogens.*

(1) For purposes of this paragraph (g), "juice" means the aqueous liquid expressed or extracted from one or more fruits or vegetables, purees of the edible portions of one or more fruits or vegetables, or any concentrate of such liquid or puree.

(2) The label of:

(i) Any juice that has not been processed in the manner described in paragraph (g)(7) of this section; or

(ii) Any beverage containing juice where neither the juice ingredient nor the beverage has been processed in the manner described in paragraph (g)(7) of this section, shall bear the following warning statement:

> **WARNING: This product has not been pasteurized and, therefore, may contain harmful bacteria that can cause serious illness in children, the elderly, and persons with weakened immune systems.**

(3) The warning statement required by this paragraph (g) shall not apply to juice that is not for distribution to retail consumers in the form shipped and that is for use solely in the manufacture of other foods or that is to be processed, labeled, or repacked at a site other than originally processed, provided that for juice that has not been processed in the manner described in paragraph (g)(7) of this section, the lack of such processing is disclosed in documents accompanying the juice, in accordance with the practice of the trade.

(4) The warning statement required by paragraph (g)(2) of this section shall appear prominently and conspicuously on the information panel or on the principal display panel of the label of the container.

(5) The word "**WARNING**" shall be capitalized and shall appear in bold type.

(6) The warning statement required by paragraph (g)(2) of this section, when on a label, shall be set off in a box by use of hairlines.

(7)   (i) The requirements in this paragraph (g) shall not apply to a juice that has been processed in a manner that will produce, at a minimum, a reduction in the pertinent microorganism for a period at least as long as the shelf life of the product when stored under normal and moderate abuse conditions, of the following magnitude:

    (A) A 5-log (i.e., 100,000-fold) reduction; or

    (B) A reduction that is equal to, or greater than, the criterion established for process controls by any final regulation requiring the application of Hazard Analysis and Critical Control Point (HACCP) principles to the processing of juice.

  (ii) For the purposes of this paragraph (g), the "pertinent microorganism" is the most resistant microorganism of public health significance that is likely to occur in the juice.

(h) *Shell eggs.*

(1) The label of all shell eggs, whether in intrastate or interstate commerce, shall bear the following statement:

SAFE HANDLING INSTRUCTIONS: To prevent illness from bacteria: keep eggs refrigerated, cook eggs until yolks are firm, and cook foods containing eggs thoroughly.

(2) The label statement required by paragraph (h)(1) of this section shall appear prominently and conspicuously, with the words "SAFE HANDLING INSTRUCTIONS" in bold type, on the principal display panel, the information panel, or on the inside of the lid of egg cartons. If this statement appears on the inside of the lid, the words "Keep Refrigerated" must appear on the principal display panel or information panel.

(3) The label statement required by paragraph (h)(1) of this section shall be set off in a box by use of hairlines.

(4) Shell eggs that have been, before distribution to consumers, specifically processed to destroy all viable *Salmonella* shall be exempt from the requirements of paragraph (h) of this section.

(5) The safe handling statement for shell eggs that are not for direct sale to consumers, e.g., those that are to be repacked or labeled at a site other than where originally processed, or are sold for use in food service establishments, may be provided on cartons or in labeling, e.g., invoices or bills of lading in accordance with the practice of the trade.

PART

101

(6) Under sections 311 and 361 of the Public Health Service Act (PHS Act), any State or locality that is willing and able to assist the agency in the enforcement of paragraphs (h)(1) through (h)(5) of this section, and is authorized to inspect or regulate establishments handling packed shell eggs, may in its own jurisdiction, enforce paragraphs (h)(1) through (h)(5) of this section through inspections under paragraph (h)(8) of this section and through administrative enforcement remedies identified in paragraph (h)(7) of this section until FDA notifies the State or locality in writing that such assistance is no longer needed. When providing such assistance, a State or locality may follow the hearing procedures set out in paragraphs (h)(7)(ii)(C) through (h)(7)(ii)(D) of this section, substituting, where necessary, appropriate State or local officials for designated FDA officials or may utilize State or local hearing procedures if such procedures satisfy due process.

(7) This paragraph (h) is established under authority of both the Federal Food, Drug, and Cosmetic Act (the act) and the PHS Act. Under the act, the agency can enforce the food misbranding provisions under 21 U.S.C. 331, 332, 333, and 334. However, 42 U.S.C. 264 provides for the issuance of implementing enforcement regulations; therefore, FDA has established the following administrative enforcement procedures for the relabeling, diversion, or destruction of shell eggs and informal hearings under the PHS Act:

(i) Upon finding that any shell eggs are in violation of this section an authorized FDA representative or State or local representative in accordance with paragraph (h)(6) of this section may order such eggs to be relabeled under the supervision of said representative, diverted, under the supervision of said representative for processing in accordance with the Egg Products Inspection Act (EPIA) (21 U.S.C. 1031 et seq.), or destroyed by or under the supervision of an officer or employee of the FDA, or, if applicable, of the State or locality, in accordance with the following procedures:

(A) *Order for relabeling, diversion, or destruction under the PHS Act.* Any district office of the FDA or any State or locality acting under paragraph (h)(6) of this section, upon finding shell eggs held in violation of this regulation, may serve upon the person in whose possession such eggs are found a written order that such eggs be relabeled with the required statement in paragraph (h)(1) of this section before further distribution. If the person chooses not to relabel, the district office of the FDA or, if applicable, the appropriate State or local agency may serve upon the person a written order that such eggs be diverted (from direct consumer sale, e.g., to food service) under the supervision of an officer or employee of the issuing entity, for processing in accordance with the EPIA (21 U.S.C. 1031 et seq.) or destroyed by or under the supervision of the issuing entity, within 10-working days from the date of receipt of the order.

(B) *Issuance of order.* The order shall include the following information:

(1) A statement that the shell eggs identified in the order are subject to relabeling, diversion for processing in accordance with the EPIA, or destruction;

(2) A detailed description of the facts that justify the issuance of the order;

(3) The location of the eggs;

(4) A statement that these eggs shall not be sold, distributed, or otherwise disposed of or moved except as provided in paragraph (h)(7)(i)(E) of this section;

(5) Identification or description of the eggs;

(6) The order number;

(7) The date of the order;

(8) The text of this entire section;

(9) A statement that the order may be appealed by written appeal or by requesting an informal hearing;

(10) The name and phone number of the person issuing the order; and

(11) The location and telephone number of the responsible office or agency and the name of its director.

(C) *Approval of director.* An order, before issuance, shall be approved by the director of the office or agency issuing the order. If prior written approval is not feasible, prior oral approval shall be obtained and confirmed by written memorandum as soon as possible.

(D) *Labeling or marking of shell eggs under order.* An FDA, State, or local representative issuing an order under paragraph (h)(7)(i)(A) of this section shall label or mark the shell eggs with official tags that include the following information:

(1) A statement that the shell eggs are detained in accordance with regulations issued under section 361(a) of the PHS Act (42 U.S.C. 264(a)).

(2) A statement that the shell eggs shall not be sold, distributed or otherwise disposed of or moved except, after notifying the issuing entity in writing, to:

(i) Relabel, divert them for processing in accordance with the EPIA, or destroy them, or

(ii) Move them to another location for holding pending appeal.

(3) A statement that the violation of the order or the removal or alteration of the tag is punishable by fine or imprisonment or both (section 368 of the PHS Act, 42 U.S.C. 271).

PART
101

    (4) The order number and the date of the order, and the name of the government representative who issued the order.

(E) *Sale or other disposition of shell eggs under order*. After service of the order, the person in possession of the shell eggs that are the subject of the order shall not sell, distribute, or otherwise dispose of or move any eggs subject to the order unless and until the notice is withdrawn after an appeal except, after notifying FDA's district office or, if applicable, the State or local agency in writing, to:

    (1) Relabel, divert, or destroy them as specified in paragraph (h)(7)(i) of this section, or

    (2) Move them to another location for holding pending appeal.

(ii) The person on whom the order for relabeling, diversion, or destruction is served may either comply with the order or appeal the order to an Office of Regulatory Affairs Program Director.

    (A) *Appeal of a detention order*. Any appeal shall be submitted in writing to the FDA District Director in whose district the shell eggs are located within 5-working days of the issuance of the order. If the appeal includes a request for an informal hearing, the hearing shall be held within 5-working days after the appeal is filed or, if requested by the appellant, at a later date, which shall not be later than 20-calendar days after the issuance of the order. The order may also be appealed within the same period of 5-working days by any other person having an ownership or proprietary interest in such shell eggs. The appellant of an order shall state the ownership or proprietary interest the appellant has in the shell eggs.

    (B) *Summary decision.* A request for a hearing may be denied, in whole or in part and at any time after a request for a hearing has been submitted, if the Office of Regulatory Affairs Program Director or another FDA official senior to an FDA District Director determines that no genuine and substantial issue of fact has been raised by the material submitted in connection with the hearing or from matters officially noticed. If the presiding FDA official determines that a hearing is not justified, written notice of the determination will be given to the parties explaining the reason for denial.

    (C) *Informal hearing.* Appearance by any appellant at the hearing may be by mail or in person, with or without counsel. The informal hearing shall be conducted by an Office of Regulatory Affairs Program Director or another FDA official senior to an FDA District Director, and a written summary of the proceedings shall be prepared by the presiding FDA official.

        (1) The presiding FDA official may direct that the hearing be conducted in any suitable manner permitted by law and this section. The presiding FDA official has the power to take such actions and make such rulings

as are necessary or appropriate to maintain order and to conduct an informal, fair, expeditious, and impartial hearing, and to enforce the requirements concerning the conduct of hearings.

(2) Employees of FDA will first give a full and complete statement of the action which is the subject of the hearing, together with the information and reasons supporting it, and may present oral or written information relevant to the hearing. The party requesting the hearing may then present oral or written information relevant to the hearing. All parties may conduct reasonable examination of any person (except for the presiding officer and counsel for the parties) who makes any statement on the matter at the hearing.

(3) The hearing shall be informal in nature, and the rules of evidence do not apply. No motions or objections relating to the admissibility of information and views will be made or considered, but any party may comment upon or rebut any information and views presented by another party.

(4) The party requesting the hearing may have the hearing transcribed, at the party's expense, in which case a copy of the transcript is to be furnished to FDA. Any transcript of the hearing will be included with the presiding FDA official's report of the hearing.

(5) The presiding FDA official shall prepare a written report of the hearing. All written material presented at the hearing will be attached to the report. Whenever time permits, the presiding FDA official may give the parties the opportunity to review and comment on the report of the hearing.

(6) The presiding FDA official shall include as part of the report of the hearing a finding on the credibility of witnesses (other than expert witnesses) whenever credibility is a material issue, and shall include a recommended decision, with a statement of reasons.

(D) *Written appeal.* If the appellant appeals the detention order but does not request a hearing, the presiding FDA official shall render a decision on the appeal affirming or revoking the detention within 5-working days after the receipt of the appeal.

(E) *Presiding FDA official's decision.* If, based on the evidence presented at the hearing or by the appellant in a written appeal, the presiding FDA official finds that the shell eggs were held in violation of this section, he shall affirm the order that they be relabeled, diverted under the supervision of an officer or employee of FDA for processing under the EPIA, or destroyed by or under the supervision of an officer or employee of FDA; otherwise, the presiding FDA official shall issue a written notice that the prior order is withdrawn. If the presiding FDA official affirms the order, he shall order that the relabeling, diversion, or destruction be accomplished within 10-working days from the date of the issuance of his decision. The presiding FDA official's decision shall be accompanied by a statement of the reasons for the decision. The decision of the presiding FDA official shall constitute final agency action, reviewable in the courts.

(F) *No appeal.* If there is no appeal of the order and the person in possession of the shell eggs that are subject to the order fails to relabel, divert, or destroy them within 10-working days, or if the demand is affirmed by the presiding FDA official after an appeal and the person in possession of such eggs fails to relabel, divert, or destroy them within 10-working days, the FDA district office, or, if applicable, the State or local agency may designate an officer or employee to divert or destroy such eggs. It shall be unlawful to prevent or to attempt to prevent such diversion or destruction of the shell eggs by the designated officer or employee.

(8) Persons engaged in handling or storing packed shell eggs for retail distribution shall permit authorized representatives of FDA to make at any reasonable time such inspection of the establishment in which shell eggs are being held, including inspection and sampling of the labeling of such eggs as may be necessary in the judgment of such representatives to determine compliance with the provisions of this section. Inspections may be made with or without notice and will ordinarily be made during regular business hours.

(9) No State or local governing entity shall establish or continue in effect any law, rule, regulation, or other requirement requiring safe handling instructions on unpasteurized shell eggs that are less stringent than those required in paragraphs (h)(1) through (h)(5) of this section.

[42 FR 14308, Mar. 15, 1977]

EDITORIAL NOTE: FOR FEDERAL REGISTER citations affecting 101.17, see the List of CFR Sections Affected, which appears in the Finding Aids section of the printed volume and at *www.fdsys.gov*.

Subpart C–Specific Nutrition Labeling Requirements and Guidelines

Sec. 101.36 Nutrition labeling of dietary supplements.

(a) The label of a dietary supplement that is offered for sale shall bear nutrition labeling in accordance with this regulation unless an exemption is provided for the product in paragraph (h) of this section.

(b) The declaration of nutrition information on the label and in labeling shall contain the following information, using the subheadings and the format specified in paragraph (e) of this section.

    (1) *Serving size.*

        (i) The subheading "Serving Size" shall be placed under the heading "Supplement Facts" and aligned on the left side of the nutrition label. The serving size shall be determined in accordance with 101.9(b) and 101.12(b), Table 2. Serving size for dietary supplements shall be expressed using a term that is appropriate for the form of the supplement, such as "tablets," "capsules," "packets," or "teaspoonfuls."

        (ii) The subheading "Servings Per Container" shall be placed under the subheading "Serving Size" and aligned on the left side of the nutrition label, except that this information need not be provided when it is stated in the net quantity of contents declaration.

    (2) *Information on dietary ingredients that have a Reference Daily Intake (RDI) or a Daily Reference Value (DRV) as established in 101.9(c) and their subcomponents (hereinafter referred to as "(b)(2)-dietary ingredients").*

        (i) The (b)(2)-dietary ingredients to be declared, that is, total calories, total fat, saturated fat, trans fat, cholesterol, sodium, total carbohydrate, dietary fiber, total sugars, added sugars, protein, vitamin D, calcium, iron, and potassium, shall be declared when they are present in a dietary supplement in quantitative amounts by weight that exceed the amount that can be declared as zero in nutrition labeling of foods in accordance with 101.9(c). Calories from saturated fat, polyunsaturated fat, monounsaturated fat, soluble fiber, insoluble fiber, and sugar alcohol may be declared, but they shall be declared when a claim is made about them. Any (b)(2)-dietary ingredients that are not present, or that are present in amounts that can be declared as zero in 101.9(c), shall not be declared (e.g., amounts corresponding to less than 2 percent of the RDI for vitamins and minerals). Protein shall not be declared on labels of products that, other than ingredients added solely for technological reasons, contain only individual amino acids.

           (A) The names and the quantitative amounts by weight of each (b)(2)-dietary ingredient shall be presented under the heading "Amount Per Serving." When the quantitative amounts by weight are presented in a separate column, the heading may be centered over a column of quantitative amounts, described by paragraph (b)(2)(ii) of this section, if space permits. A heading consistent with the declaration of the serving size, such as "Each Tablet Contains," or "Amount Per 2 Tablets" may be used in place of the heading "Amount Per Serving." Other appropriate terms, such as capsule, packet, or teaspoonful, also may be used in place of the term "Serving."

(B) The names of dietary ingredients that are declared under paragraph (b)(2)(i) of this section shall be presented in a column aligned on the left side of the nutritional label in the order and manner of indentation specified in 101.9(c), except that calcium and iron shall follow choline, and sodium and potassium shall follow chloride. This results in the following order for vitamins and minerals: Vitamin A, vitamin C, vitamin D, vitamin E, vitamin K, thiamin, riboflavin, niacin, vitamin B6, folate and folic acid, vitamin B12, biotin, pantothenic acid, choline, calcium, iron, phosphorous, iodine, magnesium, zinc, selenium, copper, manganese, chromium, molybdenum, chloride, sodium, potassium, and fluoride. The (b)(2)-dietary ingredients shall be listed according to the nomenclature specified in 101.9 or in paragraph (b)(2)(i)(B)(2) of this section.

(1) When "Calories" are declared, they shall be listed first in the column of names, beneath a light bar separating the heading "Amount Per Serving" from the list of names. When "Calories from saturated fat" are declared, they shall be indented under "Calories."

(2) The following synonyms may be added in parentheses immediately following the name of these (b)(2)-dietary ingredients: Vitamin C (ascorbic acid), thiamin (vitamin B1), riboflavin (vitamin B2), and calories (energy). Energy content per serving may be expressed in kilojoule units, added in parentheses immediately following the statement of caloric content.

(3) Beta-carotene may be declared as the percent of vitamin A that is present as beta-carotene, except that the declaration is required when a claim is made about beta-carotene. When declared, the percent shall be declared to the nearest whole percent, immediately adjacent to or beneath the name vitamin A (e.g., "Vitamin A (90% as beta-carotene)"). The amount of beta-carotene in terms of micrograms (mcg) may be included in the parentheses following the percent statement (e.g., "Vitamin A (90% (810 mcg) as beta-carotene)").

(ii) The number of calories, if declared, and the quantitative amount by weight per serving of each dietary ingredient required to be listed under paragraph (b)(2)(i) of this section shall be presented either in a separate column aligned to the right of the column of names or immediately following the listing of names within the same column. The quantitative amounts by weight shall represent the weight of the dietary ingredient rather than the weight of the source of the dietary ingredient (e.g., the weight of calcium rather than that of calcium carbonate).

(A) The amounts shall be expressed in the increments specified in 101.9(c)(1) through (7), which includes increments for sodium.

(B) The amounts of vitamins and minerals, excluding sodium and potassium, shall be the amount of the vitamin or mineral included in one serving of the product, using the units of measurement and the levels of significance given in 101.9(c)(8)(iv), except that zeros following decimal points may be dropped, and additional levels of significance may be used when the number of decimal places indicated is not sufficient to express lower amounts (e.g., the RDI for zinc is given in whole milligrams (mg), but the quantitative amount may be declared in tenths of a mg). The amount of vitamin D may, but is not required to, be expressed in IUs, in addition to the mandatory declaration in mcg. Any declaration of the amount of vitamin D in IUs must appear in parentheses after the declaration of the amount of vitamin D in mcg.

(iii) The percent of the Daily Value of all dietary ingredients declared under paragraph (b)(2)(i) of this section shall be listed, except that the percent Daily Value for protein, when present, shall be calculated using the corrected amount of protein as specified in 101.9(c)(7)(ii); no percent of the Daily Value shall be given for subcomponents for which DRVs or RDIs have not been established (e.g., total sugars). Additionally, the percentage of the RDI for protein shall be omitted when a food is purported to be for infants through 12 months of age.

(A) When information on the percent of Daily Values is listed, this information shall be presented in one column aligned under the heading of "% Daily Value" and to the right of the column of amounts. The headings "% Daily Value (DV)," "% DV," "Percent Daily Value," or "Percent DV" may be substituted for "% Daily Value." The heading "% Daily Value" shall be placed on the same line as the heading "Amount Per Serving." When the acronym "DV" is unexplained in the heading and a footnote is required under (b)(2)(iii)(D), (b)(2)(iii)(F), or (b)(3)(iv) of this section, the footnote shall explain the acronym (e.g. "Daily Value (DV) not established").

(B) The percent of Daily Value shall be calculated by dividing the quantitative amount by weight of each (b)(2)-dietary ingredient by the RDI as established in 101.9(c)(8)(iv) or the DRV as established in 101.9(c)(9) for the specified dietary ingredient and multiplying by 100, except that the percent of Daily Value for protein, when present, shall be calculated as specified in 101.9(c)(7)(ii). The quantitative amount by weight of each dietary ingredient in this calculation shall be the unrounded amount, except that for total fat, saturated fat, cholesterol, sodium, potassium, total carbohydrate, and dietary fiber, the quantitative amount by weight declared on the label (i.e, rounded amount) may be used. The numerical value shall be followed by the symbol for percent (i.e., %).

(C) The percentages based on RDI's and on DRV's shall be expressed to the nearest whole percent, except that for dietary ingredients for which DRV's have been established, "Less than 1%" or "<1%" shall be used to declare the "% Daily Value" when the quantitative amount of the dietary ingredient by weight is great enough to require that the dietary ingredient be listed, but the amount is so small that the "% Daily Value" when rounded to the nearest percent is zero (e.g., a product that contains 1 gram of total carbohydrate would list the percent Daily Value as "Less than 1%" or "<1%").

(D) If the percent of Daily Value is declared for total fat, saturated fat, total carbohydrate, dietary fiber, or protein, or added sugars, a symbol shall follow the value listed for those nutrients that refers to the same symbol that is placed at the bottom of the nutrition label, below the bar required under paragraph (e)(6) of this section and inside the box, that is followed by the statement "Percent Daily Values are based on a 2,000 calorie diet." If the product is represented or purported to be for use by children 1 through 3 years of age, and if the percent of Daily Value is declared for total fat, total carbohydrate, dietary fiber, or protein, or added sugars, a symbol shall follow the value listed for those nutrients that refers to the same symbol that is placed at the bottom of the nutrition label, below the bar required under paragraph (e)(6) of this section and inside the box, that is followed by the statement "Percent Daily Values are based on a 1,000 calorie diet."

(E) The percent of Daily Value shall be based on RDI or DRV values for adults and children 4 or more years of age, unless the product is represented or purported to be specifically for infants through 12 months of age, children 1 through 3 years of age, pregnant women, or lactating women, in which case the column heading shall clearly state the intended group. If the product is for persons within more than one group, the percent of Daily Value for each group shall be presented in separate columns as shown in paragraph (e)(11)(ii) of this section.

(F) For declared subcomponents that have no DRVs or RDIs, a symbol (e.g., an asterisk) shall be placed in the "Percent Daily Value" column that shall refer to the same symbol that is placed at the bottom of the nutrition label, below the last heavy bar and inside the box, and followed by a statement "Daily Value not established."

(G) When calories or calories from saturated fat are declared, the space under the "% DV" column shall be left blank for these items. When there are no other (b)(2)-dietary ingredients listed for which a value must be declared in the "% DV" column, the column may be omitted as shown in paragraph (e)(11)(vii) of this section. When the "% DV" column is not required, but the dietary ingredients listed are subject to paragraph (b)(2)(iii)(F) of this section, the symbol required in that paragraph shall immediately follow the quantitative amount by weight for each dietary ingredient listed under "Amount Per Serving."

(3) *Information on dietary ingredients for which RDI's and DRV's have not been established.*

(i) Dietary ingredients for which FDA has not established RDI's or DRV's and that are not subject to regulation under paragraph (b)(2) of this section (hereinafter referred to as "other dietary ingredients") shall be declared by their common or usual name when they are present in a dietary supplement, in a column that is under the column of names described in paragraph (b)(2)(i)(B) of this section or, as long as the constituents of an other dietary ingredient are not listed, in a linear display, under the heavy bar described in paragraph (e)(6) of this section, except that if no (b)(2)-dietary ingredients are declared, other dietary ingredients shall be declared directly beneath the heading "Amount Per Serving" described in paragraph (b)(2)(i)(A) of this section.

(ii) The quantitative amount by weight per serving of other dietary ingredients shall be presented in the same manner as the corresponding information required in paragraph (b)(2)(ii) of this section or, when a linear display is used, shall be presented immediately following the name of the other dietary ingredient. The quantitative amount by weight shall be the weight of the other dietary ingredient listed and not the weight of any component, or the source, of that dietary ingredient.

(A) These amounts shall be expressed using metric measures in appropriate units.

(B) For any dietary ingredient that is a liquid extract from which the solvent has not been removed, the quantity listed shall be the volume or weight of the total extract. Information on the condition of the starting material shall be indicated when it is fresh and may be indicated when it is dried. Information may be included on the concentration of the dietary ingredient and the solvent used, e.g., "fresh dandelion root extract, x (y:z) in 70% ethanol," where x is the number of milliliters (mL) or mg of the entire extract, y is the weight of the starting material and z is the volume (mL) of solvent. Where the solvent has been partially removed (not to dryness), the final concentration, when indicated, shall be stated (e.g., if the original extract was 1:5 and 50 percent of the solvent was removed, then the final concentration shall be stated as 1:2.5). Where the name of the solvent used is not included in the nutrition label, it is required to be listed in the ingredient statement in accordance with 101.4(g).

(C) For a dietary ingredient that is an extract from which the solvent has been removed, the weight of the ingredient shall be the weight of the dried extract.

(iii) The constituents of a dietary ingredient described in paragraph (b)(3)(i) of this section may be listed indented under the dietary ingredient and followed by their quantitative amounts by weight per serving, except that dietary ingredients described in paragraph (b)(2) of this section shall be listed in accordance with that section. When the constituents of a dietary ingredient described in paragraph (b)(3)(i) of this section are listed, all other dietary ingredients shall be declared in a column; however, the constituents themselves may be declared in a column or in a linear display.

(iv) Other dietary ingredients shall bear a symbol (e.g., an asterisk) in the column under the heading of "% Daily Value" that refers to the same symbol placed at the bottom of the nutrition label and followed by the statement "Daily Value not established," except that when the heading "% Daily Value" is not used, the symbol shall follow the quantitative amount by weight for each dietary ingredient listed.

(c) A proprietary blend of dietary ingredients shall be included in the list of dietary ingredients described in paragraph (b)(3)(i) of this section and identified by the term "Proprietary Blend" or other appropriately descriptive term or fanciful name and may be highlighted by bold type. Except as specified in this paragraph, all other requirements for the listing of dietary ingredients in dietary supplements are applicable.

(1) Dietary ingredients contained in the proprietary blend that are listed under paragraph (b)(2) of this section shall be declared in accordance with paragraph (b)(2) of this section.

(2) Dietary ingredients contained in the proprietary blend that are listed under paragraph (b)(3) of this section (i.e., "other dietary ingredients") shall be declared in descending order of predominance by weight, in a column or linear fashion, and indented under the term "Proprietary Blend" or other appropriately descriptive term or fanciful name.

(3) The quantitative amount by weight specified for the proprietary blend shall be the total weight of all other dietary ingredients contained in the proprietary blend and shall be placed on the same line to the right of the term "Proprietary Blend" or other appropriately descriptive term or fanciful name underneath the column of amounts described in paragraph (b)(2)(ii) of this section. A symbol (e.g., asterisk), which refers to the same symbol placed at the bottom of the nutrition label that is followed by the statement "Daily Value not established," shall be placed under the heading "% Daily Value," if present, or immediately following the quantitative amount by weight for the proprietary blend.

(4) The sample label shown in paragraph (e)(11)(v) of this section illustrates one method of nutrition labeling a proprietary blend of dietary ingredients.

(d) The source ingredient that supplies a dietary ingredient may be identified within the nutrition label in parentheses immediately following or indented beneath the name of a dietary ingredient and preceded by the words "as" or "from", e.g., "Calcium (as calcium carbonate)," except that manner of presentation is unnecessary when the name of the dietary ingredient (e.g., Oriental ginseng) or its synonym (e.g., ascorbic acid) is itself the source ingredient. When a source ingredient is identified in parentheses within the nutrition label, or when the name of the dietary ingredient or its synonym is the source ingredient, it shall not be required to be listed again in the ingredient statement that appears outside of the nutrition label. When a source ingredient is not identified within the nutrition label, it shall be listed in an ingredient statement in accordance with 101.4(g), which shall appear outside and immediately below the nutrition label or, if there is insufficient space below the nutrition label, immediately contiguous and to the right of the nutrition label.

(1) Source ingredients shall be identified in accordance with 101.4 (i.e., shall be listed by common or usual name, and the listing of botanicals shall specify the part of the plant from which the ingredient is derived) regardless of whether they are listed in an ingredient statement or in the nutrition label.

(2) When source ingredients are listed within the nutrition label, and two or more are used to provide a single dietary ingredient, all of the sources shall be listed within the parentheses in descending order by weight.

(3) Representations that the source ingredient conforms to an official compendium may be included either in the nutrition label or in the ingredient list (e.g., "Calcium (as calcium carbonate USP)").

(e) Except as provided for small and intermediate sized packages under paragraph (i)(2) of this section, information other than the title, headings, and footnotes shall be in uniform type size no smaller than 8 point. A font size at least two points greater shall be used for "Calories" and the heading "Calories" and the actual number of calories per serving shall be highlighted in bold or extra bold type. Type size no smaller than 6 point may be used for column headings (e.g., "Amount Per Serving" and "% Daily Value") and for footnotes (e.g., "Percent Daily Values are based on a 2,000 calorie diet).

(1) The title, "Supplement Facts," shall be set in a type size larger than all other print size in the nutrition label and, unless impractical, shall be set full width of the nutrition label. The title and all headings shall be bolded to distinguish them from other information.

(2) The nutrition information shall be enclosed in a box by using hairlines.

(3) All information within the nutrition label shall utilize:

(i) A single easy-to-read type style,

(ii) All black or one color type, printed on a white or other neutral contrasting background whenever practical,

(iii) Upper- and lowercase letters, except that all uppercase lettering may be utilized for packages that have a total surface area available to bear labeling of less than 12 square inches,

(iv) At least one point leading (i.e., space between lines of text), and

(v) Letters that do not touch.

(4) Except as provided for small and intermediate-sized packages under paragraph (i)(2) of this section, information other than the title, headings, and footnotes shall be in uniform type size no smaller than 8 point. Type size no smaller than 6 point may be used for column headings (e.g., "Amount Per Serving" and "% Daily Value") and for footnotes (e.g., "Percent Daily Values are based on a 2,000 calorie diet").

(5) A hairline rule that is centered between the lines of text shall separate each dietary ingredient required in paragraph (b)(2) and (b)(3) of this section from the dietary ingredient above and beneath it, as shown in paragraph (e)(10) of this section.

(6) A heavy bar shall be placed:

(i) Beneath the subheading "Servings Per Container" except that if "Servings Per Container" is not required and, as a result, not declared, the bar shall be placed beneath the subheading "Serving Size,"

(ii) Beneath the last dietary ingredient to be listed under paragraph (b)(2)(i) of this section, if any, and

(iii) Beneath the last other dietary ingredient to be listed under paragraph (b)(3) of this section, if any.

(7) A light bar shall be placed beneath the headings "Amount Per Serving" and "% Daily Value."

(8) If the product contains two or more separately packaged dietary supplements that differ from each other (e.g., the product has a packet of supplements to be taken in the morning and a different packet to be taken in the afternoon), the quantitative amounts and percent of Daily Value may be presented as specified in this paragraph in individual nutrition labels or in one aggregate nutrition label as illustrated in paragraph (e)(11)(iii) of this section.

(9) (i) The quantitative amount by weight (or volume, if permitted) and the percent of Daily Value of each dietary ingredient may be presented on a "per unit" basis in addition to the "per serving" basis required by paragraphs (b)(2)(ii) and (b)(2)(iii) of this section for (b)(2)-dietary ingredients and (b)(3)(ii) and (b)(3)(iv) of this section for other dietary ingredients. If "per unit" information is provided, it must be presented in additional columns to the right of the "per serving" information and be clearly identified by appropriate headings.

(ii) Alternatively, if a recommendation is made in other parts of the label that a dietary supplement be consumed more than once per day, the total quantitative amount by weight (or volume, if permitted) and the percent of Daily Value of each dietary ingredient may be presented on a "per day" basis in addition to the "per serving" basis required by paragraphs (b)(2)(ii) and (b)(2)(iii) of this section for (b)(2)-dietary ingredients and (b)(3)(ii) and (b)(3)(iv) of this section for other dietary ingredients. If "per day" information is provided, it must be presented in additional columns to the right of the "per serving" information and be clearly identified by appropriate headings and/or be presented in a parenthetical statement as part of the "Serving Size" declaration. A sample illustration for "per day" information in a column format is provided in paragraph (e)(11)(viii) of this section. As illustrated, the additional "Per Day" column heading is followed parenthetically by the number of servings recommended per day in other parts of the label (e.g., "Per Day (3 Caplets)"). When the parenthetical statement format following the "Serving Size" declaration is used as an alternative to the column format, the statement must provide no more than simple instructions regarding how to calculate the "per day" amount for the number of servings per day recommended in other parts of the label (e.g., "Serving Size: 1 Caplet (Multiply amounts by 3 for total daily amount)"). When the parenthetical statement format following the "Serving Size" declaration is used in addition to the column format, the statement must provide no more than a simple declaration of the number of servings recommended in other parts of the label (e.g., "Serving Size: 1 Caplet (Total daily amount: 3 caplets per day)").

(10) In the interest of uniformity of presentation, FDA urges that the information be presented using the graphic specifications set forth in appendix B to part 101, as applicable.

(11) The following sample labels are presented for the purpose of illustration:

    (i) Multiple vitamins (Includes voluntary listing of vitamin D in IUs)

Supplement Facts

Serving Size 1 Gelcap
Servings Per Container 100

	Amount Per Serving	% Daily Value
Vitamin A (as retinyl acetate and 50% as beta-carotene)	900 mcg	100%
Vitamin C (as ascorbic acid)	90 mg	100%
Vitamin D (as cholecalciferol)	20 mcg (800 IU)	100%
Vitamin E (as d-alpha tocopheryl acetate)	15 mg	100%
Thiamin (as thiamin mononitrate)	1.2 mg	100%
Riboflavin	1.3 mg	100%
Niacin (as niacinamide)	16 mg	100%
Vitamin B₆ (as pyridoxine hydrochloride)	1.7 mg	100%
Folate	400 mcg DFE	100%
	(240 mcg folic acid)	
Vitamin B₁₂ (as cyanocobalamin)	2.4 mcg	100%
Biotin	3 mcg	10%
Pantothenic Acid (as calcium pantothenate)	5 mg	100%

Other ingredients: Gelatin, lactose, magnesium stearate, microcrystalline cellulose, FD&C Yellow No. 6, propylene glycol, preservatives (propylparaben and sodium benzoate).

(ii) Multiple vitamins for children and adults (excludes Servings Per Container which is stated in the net quantity of contents declaration)

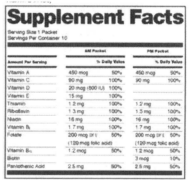

(iii) Multiple vitamins in packets (includes voluntary listing of vitamin D in IUs)

(iv) Dietary supplement containing dietary ingredient with and without RDIs and DRVs

(v) A proprietary blend of dietary ingredients

Supplement Facts

Serving Size 1 tsp (3g) (makes 8 fl oz prepared)
Servings Per Container 24

	Amount Per Teaspoon	% Daily Value
Calories	10	
Total Carbohydrate	2 g	<1%*
Total Sugars	2 g	†
Includes 2g Added Sugars		4%*
Proprietary Blend	0.7 g	
German Chamomile (flower)		†
Hyssop (leaf)		†

* Percent Daily Values are based on a 2,000 calorie diet
† Daily Value not established

Other ingredients: Fructose, lactose, starch, and stearic acid.

(vi) Dietary supplement of an herb

Supplement Facts

Serving Size 1 Capsule
Servings Per Container 100

Amount Per Capsule

Oriental Ginseng, powdered (root)	250 mcg*

* Daily Value not established

Other ingredients: Gelatin, water, and glycerin.

(vii) Dietary supplemet of amino acids

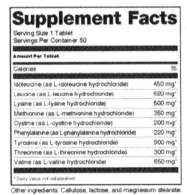

Supplement Facts

Serving Size 1 Tablet
Servings Per Container 50

Amount Per Tablet

Calories	15
Isoleucine (as L-isoleucine hydrochloride)	450 mg*
Leucine (as L-leucine hydrochloride)	620 mg*
Lysine (as L-lysine hydrochloride)	500 mg*
Methionine (as L-methionine hydrochloride)	350 mg*
Cystine (as L-cystine hydrochloride)	200 mg*
Phenylalanine (as L-phenylalanine hydrochloride)	220 mg*
Tyrosine (as L-tyrosine hydrochloride)	900 mg*
Threonine (as L-threonine hydrochloride)	300 mg*
Valine (as L-valine hydrochloride)	650 mg*

* Daily Value not established

Other ingredients: Cellulose, lactose, and magnesium stearate.

(viii) Dietary supplement illustrating "per serving" and "per day" information (Includes voluntary listing of vitamin D in IUs)

Supplement Facts

Serving Size 1 Caplet
Servings Per Container 100

	Per Caplet		Per Day (3 Caplets)	
	Amount	% Daily Value	Amount	% Daily Value
Vitamin D (as cholecalciferol)	7 mcg (280 IU)	35%	21 mcg (840 IU)	105%
Calcium (as calcium citrate)	650 mg	50%	1950 mg	150%

Other ingredients: Hydroxypropylmethylcellulose (HPMC), microcrystalline cellulose, maltodextrin, and magnesium stearate

(12) If space is not adequate to list the required information as shown in the sample labels in paragraph (e)(11) of this section, the list may be split and continued to the right as long as the headings are repeated. The list to the right must be set off by a line that distinguishes it and sets it apart from the dietary ingredients and percent of Daily Value information given to the left. The following sample label illustrates this display:

Supplement Facts

Serving Size 1 Packet
Servings Per Container 10

Amount Per Packet		% Daily Value	Amount Per Packet		% Daily Value
Vitamin A (from cod liver oil)	900 mcg	100%	Zinc (as zinc oxide)	11 mg	100%
Vitamin C (as ascorbic acid)	250 mg	278%	Selenium (as sodium selenate)	25 mcg	45%
Vitamin D (as ergocalciferol)	20 mcg	100%	Copper (as cupric oxide)	0.5 mg	56%
Vitamin E (as d-alpha tocopherol)	75 mg	500%	Manganese (as manganese sulfate)	5 mg	217%
Thiamin (as thiamin mononitrate)	60 mg	5000%	Chromium (as chromium chloride)	50 mcg	143%
Riboflavin	60 mg	4615%	Molybdenum (as sodium molybdate)	50 mcg	111%
Niacin (as niacinamide)	60 mg	375%	Potassium (as potassium chloride)	10 mg	<1%
Vitamin B₆ (as pyridoxine hydrochloride)	60 mg	3529%	Choline (as choline chloride)	100 mg	18%
Folate	400 mcg DFE	100%	Betaine (as betaine hydrochloride)	25 mg	*
	(240 mcg folic acid)		Glutamic Acid (as L-glutamic acid)	25 mg	*
Vitamin B₁₂ (as cyanocobalamin)	100 mcg	4167%	Inositol (as inositol monophosphate)	75 mg	*
Biotin	100 mcg	333%	para-Aminobenzoic acid	30 mg	*
Pantothenic Acid (as calcium pantothenate)	60 mg	1200%	Deoxyribonucleic acid	50 mg	*
Calcium (from oyster shell)	130 mg	10%	Boron	500 mcg	*
Iron (as ferrous fumarate)	10 mg	56%	*Daily Value not established		
Iodine (from kelp)	150 mcg	100%			
Magnesium (as magnesium oxide)	63 mg	15%			

Other ingredients: Cellulose, stearic acid, and silica.

(f) (1) Compliance with this section will be determined in accordance with 101.9(g)(1) through (g)(8), (g)(10), and (g)(11), except that the sample for analysis shall consist of a composite of 12 subsamples (consumer packages) or 10 percent of the number of packages in the same inspection lot, whichever is smaller, randomly selected to be representative of the lot. The criteria on class I and class II nutrients given in 101.9(g)(3) and (g)(4) also are applicable to other dietary ingredients described in paragraph (b)(3)(i) of this section. Reasonable excesses over labeled amounts are acceptable within current good manufacturing practice.

(2) When it is not technologically feasible, or some other circumstance makes it impracticable, for firms to comply with the requirements of this section, FDA may permit alternative means of compliance or additional exemptions to deal with the situation in accordance with 101.9(g)(9). Firms in need of such special allowances shall make their request in writing to the Office of Nutrition and Food Labeling (HFS-800), Food and Drug Administration, 5001 Campus Dr., College Park, MD 20740.

(g) Except as provided in paragraphs (i)(2) and (i)(5) of this section, the location of nutrition information on a label shall be in compliance with 101.2.

(h) Dietary supplements are subject to the exemptions specified as follows in:

(1) Section 101.9(j)(1) for foods that are offered for sale by a person who makes direct sales to consumers (i.e., a retailer) who has annual gross sales or business done in sales to consumers that is not more than $500,000 or has annual gross sales made or business done in sales of food to consumers of not more than $50,000, and whose labels, labeling, and advertising do not provide nutrition information or make a nutrient content or health claim;

(2) Section 101.9(j)(18) for foods that are low-volume products (that is, they meet the requirements for units sold in 101.9(j)(18)(i) or (j)(18)(ii)); that, except as provided in 101.9(j)(18)(iv), are the subject of a claim for an exemption that provides the information required under 101.9(j)(18)(iv), that is filed before the beginning of the time period for which the exemption is claimed, and that is filed by a person, whether it is the manufacturer, packer, or distributor, that qualifies to claim the exemption under the requirements for average full-time equivalent employees in 101.9(j)(18)(i) or (j)(18)(ii), and whose labels, labeling, and advertising do not provide nutrition information or make a nutrient content or health claim;

(3) Section 101.9(j)(9) for foods shipped in bulk form that are not for distribution to consumers in such form and that are for use solely in the manufacture of other dietary supplements or that are to be processed, labeled, or repacked at a site other than where originally processed or packed.

(i) (1) Dietary supplements are subject to the special labeling provisions specified in 101.9(j)(5)(i) for foods other than infant formula, represented or purported to be specifically for infants through 12 months of age and children 1 through 3 years of age.

(2) Section 101.9(j)(13) for foods in small or intermediate-sized packages, except that:

(i) All information within the nutrition label on small-sized packages, which have a total surface area available to labeling of less than 12 square inches, shall be in type size no smaller than 4.5 point;

(ii) All information within the nutrition label on intermediate-sized packages, which have from 12 to 40 square inches of surface area available to bear labeling, shall be in type size no smaller than 6 point, except that type size no smaller than 4.5 point may be used on packages that have less than 20 square inches available for labeling and more than 8 dietary ingredients to be listed and on packages that have 20 to 40 square inches available for labeling and more than 16 dietary ingredients to be listed.

(iii) When the nutrition information is presented on any panel under 101.9(j)(13)(ii)(D), the ingredient list shall continue to be located immediately below the nutrition label, or, if there is insufficient space below the nutrition label, immediately contiguous and to the right of the nutrition label as specified in 101.4(g).

(iv) When it is not possible for a small or intermediate-sized package that is enclosed in an outer package to comply with these type size requirements, the type size of the nutrition label on the primary (inner) container may be as small as needed to accommodate all of the required label information provided that the primary container is securely enclosed in outer packaging, the nutrition labeling on the outer packaging meets the applicable type size requirements, and such outer packaging is not intended to be separated from the primary container under conditions of retail sale.

(v) Where there is not sufficient space on a small or intermediate-sized package for a nutrition label that meets minimum type size requirements of 4.5 points if hairlines are used in accordance with paragraph (e)(5) of this section, the hairlines may be omitted and replaced by a row of dots connecting the columns containing the name of each dietary ingredient and the quantitative amounts (by weight and as a percent of Daily Value).

(3) Section 101.9(j)(15) for foods in multiunit food containers;

(4) Section 101.9(j)(16) for foods sold in bulk containers; and

(5) Section 101.9(j)(17) for foods in packages that have a total surface area available to bear labeling greater than 40 square inches but whose principal display panel and information panel do not provide sufficient space to accommodate all required label information, except that the ingredient list shall continue to be located immediately below the nutrition label, or, if there is insufficient space below the nutrition label, immediately contiguous and to the right of the nutrition label as specified in 101.4(g).

(j) Dietary supplements shall be subject to the misbranding provisions of 101.9(k).

[62 FR 49849, Sept. 23, 1997, as amended at 63 FR 30620, June 5, 1998; 66 FR 56035, Nov. 6, 2001; 71 FR 51726, Aug. 31, 2006; 71 FR 74791, Dec. 13, 2006; 81 FR 33994, May 27, 2016]

Subpart D—Specific Requirements for Nutrient Content Claims

Sec. 101.54 Nutrient content claims for "good source," "high," "more," and "high potency."

(a) *General requirements.* Except as provided in paragraph (e) of this section, a claim about the level of a nutrient in a food in relation to the Reference Daily Intake (RDI) established for that nutrient in 101.9(c)(8)(iv) or Daily Reference Value (DRV) established for that nutrient in 101.9(c)(9), (excluding total carbohydrates) may only be made on the label or in labeling of the food if:

   (1) The claim uses one of the terms defined in this section in accordance with the definition for that term;

   (2) The claim is made in accordance with the general requirements for nutrient content claims in 101.13; and

   (3) The food for which the claim is made is labeled in accordance with 101.9, 101.10, or 101.36, as applicable.

(b) *"High" claims.* (1) The terms "high," "rich in," or "excellent source of" may be used on the label and in the labeling of foods, except meal products as defined in 101.13(l) and main dish products as defined in 101.13(m), provided that the food contains 20 percent or more of the RDI or the DRV per reference amount customarily consumed.

   (2) The terms defined in paragraph (b)(1) of this section may be used on the label and in the labeling of meal products as defined in 101.13(l) and main dish products as defined in 101.13(m), provided that:

      (i) The product contains a food that meets the definition of "high" in paragraph (b)(1) of this section; and

      (ii) The label or labeling clearly identifies the food that is the subject of the claim (e.g., the serving of broccoli in this product is high in vitamin C).

(c) *"Good Source" claims.*

   (1) The terms "good source," "contains," or "provides" may be used on the label and in the labeling of foods, except meal products as defined in 101.13(l) and main dish products as defined in 101.13(m), provided that the food contains 10 to 19 percent of the RDI or the DRV per reference amount customarily consumed.

   (2) The terms defined in paragraph (c)(1) of this section may be used on the label and in the labeling of meal products as defined in 101.13(l) and main dish products as defined in 101.13(m), provided that:

      (i) The product contains a food that meets the definition of "good source" in paragraph (c)(1) of this section; and

      (ii) The label or labeling clearly identifies the food that is the subject of the claim (e.g., the serving of sweet potatoes in this product is a "good source" of fiber).

(d) *"Fiber" claims.* (1) If a nutrient content claim is made with respect to the level of dietary fiber, that is, that the product is high in fiber, a good source of fiber, or that the food contains "more" fiber, and the food is not "low" in total fat as defined in 101.62(b)(2) or, in the case of a meal product, as defined in 101.13(l), or main dish product, as defined in 101.13(m), is not "low" in total fat as defined in 101.62(b)(3), then the label shall disclose the level of total fat per labeled serving.

(2) The disclosure shall appear in immediate proximity to such claim, be in a type size no less than one-half the size of the claim and precede any disclosure statement required under 101.13(h) (e.g., "contains [x amount] of total fat per serving. See nutrition information for fat content").

(e) *"More" claims.*

(1) A relative claim using the terms "more," "fortified," "enriched," "added," "extra," and "plus" may be used on the label or in labeling of foods to describe the level of protein, vitamins, minerals, dietary fiber, or potassium, except as limited by 101.13(j)(1)(i) and except meal products as defined in 101.13(l) and main dish products as defined in 101.13(m), provided that:

(i) The food contains at least 10 percent more of the RDI for vitamins or minerals or of the DRV for protein, dietary fiber, or potassium (expressed as a percent of the Daily Value) per reference amount customarily consumed than an appropriate reference food; and

(ii) Where the claim is based on a nutrient that has been added to the food, that fortification is in accordance with the policy on fortification of foods in 104.20 of this chapter; and

(iii) As required in 101.13(j)(2) for relative claims:

(A) The identity of the reference food and the percentage (or fraction) that the nutrient is greater relative to the RDI or DRV are declared in immediate proximity to the most prominent such claim (e.g., "contains 10 percent more of the Daily Value for fiber than white bread"); and

(B) Quantitative information comparing the level of the nutrient in the product per labeled serving with that of the reference food that it replaces (e.g., "Fiber content of white bread is 1 gram (g) per serving; (this product) 3.5 g per serving") is declared adjacent to the most prominent claim or to the nutrition label, except that if the nutrition label is on the information panel, the quantitative information may be located elsewhere on the information panel in accordance with 101.2.

(2) A relative claim using the terms "more," "fortified," "enriched," "added," "extra," and "plus" may be used on the label or in labeling to describe the level of protein, vitamins, minerals, dietary fiber or potassium, except as limited in 101.13(j)(1)(i), in meal products as defined in 101.13(l) or main dish products as defined in 101.13(m), provided that:

(i) The food contains at least 10 percent more of the RDI for vitamins or minerals or of the DRV for protein, dietary fiber, or potassium (expressed as a percent of the Daily Value) per 100 g of food than an appropriate reference food.

(ii) Where the claim is based on a nutrient that has been added to the food, that fortification is in accordance with the policy on fortification of foods in 104.20 of this chapter; and

(iii) As required in 101.13(j)(2) for relative claims:

(A) The identity of the reference food and the percentage (or fraction) that the nutrient was increased relative to the RDI or DRV are declared in immediate proximity to the most prominent such claim (e.g., "contains 10 percent more of the Daily Value for fiber per 3 oz than does `X brand of product'"), and

(B) Quantitative information comparing the level of the nutrient in the product per specified weight with that of the reference food that it replaces (e.g., "The fiber content of `X brand of product' is 2 g per 3 oz. This product contains 4.5 g per 3 oz.") is declared adjacent to the most prominent claim or to the nutrition label, except that if the nutrition label is on the information panel, the quantitative information may be located elsewhere on the information panel in accordance with 101.2.

(f) *"High potency" claims.*

(1) (i) The term "high potency" may be used on the label or in the labeling of foods to describe individual vitamins or minerals that are present at 100 percent or more of the RDI per reference amount customarily consumed.

(ii) When the term "high potency" is used to describe individual vitamins or minerals in a product that contains other nutrients or dietary ingredients, the label or labeling shall clearly identify which vitamin or mineral is described by the term "high potency" (e.g., "Botanical `X' with high potency vitamin E").

(2) The term "high potency" may be used on the label or in the labeling of a multiingredient food product to describe the product if the product contains 100 percent or more of the RDI for at least two-thirds of the vitamins and minerals that are listed in 101.9(c)(8)(iv) and that are present in the product at 2 percent or more of the RDI (e.g., "High potency multivitamin, multimineral dietary supplement tablets").

(3) Where compliance with paragraphs (f)(1)(i), (f)(1)(ii), or (f)(2) of this section is based on a nutrient that has been added to a food (other than a dietary supplement), that fortification shall be in accordance with the policy on fortification of foods in 104.20 of this chapter.

(g) *Nutrient content claims using the term "antioxidant."* A nutrient content claim that characterizes the level of antioxidant nutrients present in a food may be used on the label or in the labeling of that food when:

(1) An RDI has been established for each of the nutrients;

(2) The nutrients that are the subject of the claim have recognized antioxidant activity; that is, when there exists scientific evidence that, following absorption from the gastrointestinal tract, the substance participates in physiological, biochemical, or cellular processes that inactivate free radicals or prevent free radical-initiated chemical reactions;

(3) The level of each nutrient that is the subject of the claim is sufficient to qualify for the 101.54 (b), (c), or (e) claim (e.g., to bear the claim "high in antioxidant vitamin C," the product must contain 20 percent or more of the RDI for vitamin C). Beta-carotene may be a subject of the claim when the level of vitamin A present as beta-carotene in the food that bears the claim is sufficient to qualify for the claim. For example, for the claim "good source of antioxidant beta-carotene," 10 percent or more of the RDI for vitamin A must be present as beta-carotene per reference amount customarily consumed; and

(4) The names of the nutrients that are the subject of the claim are included as part of the claim (e.g., "high in antioxidant vitamins C and E"). Alternatively, when used as part of a nutrient content claim, the term "antioxidant" or "antioxidants" (as in "high in antioxidants") may be linked by a symbol (e.g., an asterisk) that refers to the same symbol that appears elsewhere on the same panel of a product label followed by the name or names of the nutrients with recognized antioxidant activity. The list of nutrients shall appear in letters of a type size height no smaller than the larger of one-half of the type size of the largest nutrient content claim or 1/16 inch.

[58 FR 2413, Jan. 6, 1993; 58 FR 17342, Apr. 2, 1993, as amended at 59 FR 394, Jan. 4, 1994; 59 FR 15051, Mar. 31, 1994; 60 FR 17206, Apr. 5, 1995; 61 FR 11731, Mar. 22, 1996; 62 FR 31339, June 9, 1997; 62 FR 49867, 49880, Sept. 23, 1997; 63 FR 26980, May 15, 1998; 66 FR 17358, Mar. 30, 2001]

Sec. 101.60 Nutrient content claims for the calorie content of foods.

(a) *General requirements.* A claim about the calorie or sugar content of a food may only be made on the label or in the labeling of a food if:

(1) The claim uses one of the terms defined in this section in accordance with the definition for that term;

(2) The claim is made in accordance with the general requirements for nutrient content claims in 101.13;

(3) The food for which the claim is made is labeled in accordance with 101.9, 101.10, or 101.36, as applicable; and

(4) For dietary supplements, claims regarding calories may not be made on products that meet the criteria in 101.60(b)(1) or (b)(2) for "calorie free" or "low calorie" claims except when an equivalent amount of a similar dietary supplement (e.g., another

protein supplement) that the labeled food resembles and for which it substitutes, normally exceeds the definition for "low calorie" in 101.60(b)(2).

(b) *Calorie content claims.*

(1) The terms "calorie free," "free of calories," "no calories," "zero calories," "without calories," "trivial source of calories," "negligible source of calories," or "dietarily insignificant source of calories" may be used on the label or in the labeling of foods, provided that:

(i) The food contains less than 5 calories per reference amount customarily consumed and per labeled serving.

(ii) As required in 101.13(e)(2), if the food meets this condition without the benefit of special processing, alteration, formulation, or reformulation to lower the caloric content, it is labeled to disclose that calories are not usually present in the food (e.g., "cider vinegar, a calorie free food").

(2) The terms "low calorie," "few calories," "contains a small amount of calories," "low source of calories," or "low in calories" may be used on the label or in labeling of foods, except meal products as defined in 101.13(l) and main dish products as defined in 101.13(m), provided that:

(i)(A) The food has a reference amount customarily consumed greater than 30 grams (g) or greater than 2 tablespoons and does not provide more than 40 calories per reference amount customarily consumed; or

(B) The food has a reference amount customarily consumed of 30 g or less or 2 tablespoons or less and does not provide more than 40 calories per reference amount customarily consumed and, except for sugar substitutes, per 50 g (for dehydrated foods that must be reconstituted before typical consumption with water or a diluent containing an insignificant amount, as defined in 101.9(f)(1), of all nutrients per reference amount customarily consumed, the per 50 g criterion refers to the "as prepared" form).

(ii) If a food meets these conditions without the benefit of special processing, alteration, formulation, or reformulation to vary the caloric content, it is labeled to clearly refer to all foods of its type and not merely to the particular brand to which the label attaches (e.g., "celery, a low calorie food").

(3) The terms defined in paragraph (b)(2) of this section may be used on the label or in labeling of meal products as defined in 101.13(l) or main dish products as defined in 101.13(m), provided that:

(i) The product contains 120 calories or less per 100 g; and

(ii) If the product meets this condition without the benefit of special processing, alteration, formulation, or reformulation to lower the calorie content, it is labeled to clearly refer to all foods of its type and not merely to the particular brand to which it attaches.

(4) The terms "reduced calorie," "reduced in calories," "calorie reduced," "fewer calories," "lower calorie," or "lower in calories" may be used on the label or in the labeling of foods, except as limited by 101.13(j)(1)(i) and except meal products as defined in 101.13(l) and main dish products as defined in 101.13(m), provided that:

  (i) The food contains at least 25 percent fewer calories per reference amount customarily consumed than an appropriate reference food as described in 101.13(j)(1); and

  (ii) As required in 101.13(j)(2) for relative claims:

    (A) The identity of the reference food and the percent (or fraction) that the calories differ between the two foods are declared in immediate proximity to the most prominent such claim (e.g., reduced calorie cupcakes "33 1/3 percent fewer calories than regular cupcakes"); and

    (B) Quantitative information comparing the level of the nutrient per labeled serving size with that of the reference food that it replaces (e.g., "Calorie content has been reduced from 150 to 100 calories per serving.") is declared adjacent to the most prominent claim or to the nutrition label, except that if the nutrition label is on the information panel, the quantitative information may be located elsewhere on the information panel in accordance with 101.2.

  (iii) Claims described in paragraph (b)(4) of this section may not be made on the label or labeling of foods if the reference food meets the definition for "low calorie."

(5) The terms defined in paragraph (b)(4) of this section may be used on the label or in the labeling of meal products as defined in 101.13(l) and main dish products as defined in 101.13(m), provided that:

  (i) The food contains at least 25 percent fewer calories per 100 g of food than an appropriate reference food as described in 101.13(j)(1); and

  (ii) As required in 101.13(j)(2) for relative claims:

    (A) The identity of the reference food and the percent (or fraction) that the calories differ between the two foods are declared in immediate proximity to the most prominent such claim (e.g., Larry's Reduced Calorie Lasagna, "25 percent fewer calories per oz (or 3 oz) than our regular Lasagna"); and

    (B) Quantitative information comparing the level of the nutrient in the product per specified weight with that of the reference food that it replaces (e.g., "Calorie content has been reduced from 108 calories per 3 oz to 83 calories per 3 oz.") is declared adjacent to the most prominent claim or to the nutrition label, except that if the nutrition label is on the information panel, the quantitative information may be located elsewhere on the information panel in accordance with 101.2.

(iii) Claims described in paragraph (b)(5) of this section may not be made on the label or labeling of food if the reference food meets the definition for "low calorie."

(c) *Sugar content claims* —

(1) Use of terms such as "sugar free," "free of sugar," "no sugar," "zero sugar," "without sugar," "sugarless," "trivial source of sugar," "negligible source of sugar," or "dietarily insignificant source of sugar." Consumers may reasonably be expected to regard terms that represent that the food contains no sugars or sweeteners e.g., "sugar free," or "no sugar," as indicating a product which is low in calories or significantly reduced in calories. Consequently, except as provided in paragraph (c)(2) of this section, a food may not be labeled with such terms unless:

(i) The food contains less than 0.5 g of sugars, as defined in 101.9(c)(6)(ii), per reference amount customarily consumed and per labeled serving or, in the case of a meal product or main dish product, less than 0.5 g of sugars per labeled serving; and

(ii) The food contains no ingredient that is a sugar or that is generally understood by consumers to contain sugars unless the listing of the ingredient in the ingredient statement is followed by an asterisk that refers to the statement below the list of ingredients, which states "adds a trivial amount of sugar," "adds a negligible amount of sugar," or "adds a dietarily insignificant amount of sugar;" and

(iii) (A) It is labeled "low calorie" or "reduced calorie" or bears a relative claim of special dietary usefulness labeled in compliance with paragraphs (b)(2), (b)(3), (b)(4), or (b)(5) of this section, or, if a dietary supplement, it meets the definition in paragraph (b)(2) of this section for "low calorie" but is prohibited by 101.13(b)(5) and 101.60(a)(4) from bearing the claim; or

(B) Such term is immediately accompanied, each time it is used, by either the statement "not a reduced calorie food," "not a low calorie food," or "not for weight control."

(2) The terms "no added sugar," "without added sugar," or "no sugar added" may be used only if:

(i) No amount of sugars, as defined in 101.9(c)(6)(ii), or any other ingredient that contains sugars that functionally substitute for added sugars is added during processing or packaging; and

(ii) The product does not contain an ingredient containing added sugars such as jam, jelly, or concentrated fruit juice; and

(iii) The sugars content has not been increased above the amount present in the ingredients by some means such as the use of enzymes, except where the intended functional effect of the process is not to increase the sugars content of a food, and a functionally insignificant increase in sugars results; and

(iv) The food that it resembles and for which it substitutes normally contains added sugars; and

(v) The product bears a statement that the food is not "low calorie" or "calorie reduced" (unless the food meets the requirements for a "low" or "reduced calorie" food) and that directs consumers' attention to the nutrition panel for further information on sugar and calorie content.

(3) Paragraph (c)(1) of this section shall not apply to a factual statement that a food, including foods intended specifically for infants and children less than 2 years of age, is unsweetened or contains no added sweeteners in the case of a food that contains apparent substantial inherent sugar content, e.g., juices.

(4) The claims provided for in paragraph (c)(1) and (c)(2) of this section may be used on labels or in labeling of dietary supplements of vitamins or minerals that are intended specifically for use by infants and children less than 2 years of age.

(5) The terms "reduced sugar," "reduced in sugar," "sugar reduced," "less sugar," "lower sugar" or "lower in sugar" may be used on the label or in labeling of foods, except meal products as defined in 101.13(l), main dish products as defined in 101.13(m), and dietary supplements of vitamins or minerals, provided that:

(i) The food contains at least 25 percent less sugar per reference amount customarily consumed than an appropriate reference food as described in 101.13(j)(1); and

(ii) As required in 101.13(j)(2) for relative claims:

(A) The identity of the reference food and the percent (or fraction) that the sugar differs between the two foods are declared in immediate proximity to the most prominent such claim (e.g., "these corn flakes contain 25 percent less sugar than our sugar coated corn flakes"); and

(B) Quantitative information comparing the level of the sugar in the product per labeled serving with that of the reference food that it replaces (e.g., "Sugar content has been lowered from 8 g to 6 g per serving.") is declared adjacent to the most prominent claim or to the nutrition label, except that if the nutrition label is on the information panel, the quantitative information may be located elsewhere on the information panel in accordance with 101.2.

(6) The terms defined in paragraph (c)(5) of this section may be used on the label or in the labeling of a meal product as defined in 101.13(l) and a main dish product as defined in 101.13(m), provided that:

(i) The food contains at least 25 percent less sugars per 100 g of food than an appropriate reference food as described in 101.13(j)(1), and

(ii) As required in 101.13(j)(2) for relative claims:

(A) The identity of the reference food and the percent (or fraction) that the sugars differ between the two foods are declared in immediate proximity to the most prominent such claim (e.g., reduced sweet and sour shrimp dinner, "25 percent less sugar per 3 oz than our regular sweet and sour shrimp dinner"); and

(B) Quantitative information comparing the level of the nutrient in the product per specified weight with that of the reference food that it replaces (e.g., "Sugar content has been reduced from 17 g per 3 oz to 13 g per 3 oz.") is declared adjacent to the most prominent claim or to the nutrition label, except that if the nutrition label is on the information panel, the quantitative information may be located elsewhere on the information panel in accordance with 101.2.

> [58 FR 2413, Jan. 6, 1993; 58 FR 17342, Apr. 2, 1993, as amended at 58 FR 44031, Aug. 18, 1993; 59 FR 394, Jan. 4, 1994; 60 FR 17206, Apr. 5, 1995; 62 FR 15342, Mar. 31, 1997; 62 FR 49881, Sept. 23, 1997]

Sec. 101.62 Nutrient content claims for fat, fatty acid, and cholesterol content of foods.

(a) *General requirements.* A claim about the level of fat, fatty acid, and cholesterol in a food may only be made on the label or in the labeling of foods if:

(1) The claim uses one of the terms defined in this section in accordance with the definition for that term;

(2) The claim is made in accordance with the general requirements for nutrient content claims in 101.13;

(3) The food for which the claim is made is labeled in accordance with 101.9, 101.10, or 101.36, as applicable; and

(4) For dietary supplements, claims for fat, saturated fat, and cholesterol may not be made on products that meet the criteria in 101.60(b)(1) or (b)(2) for "calorie free" or "low calorie" claims.

(b) *Fat content claims.*

(1) The terms "fat free," "free of fat," "no fat," "zero fat," "without fat," "negligible source of fat," or "dietarily insignificant source of fat" or, in the case of milk products, "skim" may be used on the label or in labeling of foods, provided that:

(i) The food contains less than 0.5 gram (g) of fat per reference amount customarily consumed and per labeled serving or, in the case of a meal product or main dish product, less than 0.5 g of fat per labeled serving; and

(ii) The food contains no added ingredient that is a fat or is generally understood by consumers to contain fat unless the listing of the ingredient in the ingredient statement is followed by an asterisk that refers to the statement below the list of ingredients, which states "adds a trivial amount of fat," "adds a negligible amount of fat," or "adds a dietarily insignificant amount of fat;" and

(iii) As required in 101.13(e)(2), if the food meets these conditions without the benefit of special processing, alteration, formulation, or reformulation to lower fat content, it is labeled to disclose that fat is not usually present in the food (e.g., "broccoli, a fat free food").

(2) The terms "low fat," "low in fat," "contains a small amount of fat," "low source of fat," or "little fat" may be used on the label or in labeling of foods, except meal products as defined in 101.13(l) and main dish products as defined in 101.13(m), provided that:

(i) (A) The food has a reference amount customarily consumed greater than 30 g or greater than 2 tablespoons and contains 3 g or less of fat per reference amount customarily consumed; or

(B) The food has a reference amount customarily consumed of 30 g or less or 2 tablespoons or less and contains 3 g or less of fat per reference amount customarily consumed and per 50 g of food (for dehydrated foods that must be reconstituted before typical consumption with water or a diluent containing an insignificant amount, as defined in 101.9(f)(1), of all nutrients per reference amount customarily consumed, the per 50-g criterion refers to the "as prepared" form); and

(ii) If the food meets these conditions without the benefit of special processing, alteration, formulation, or reformulation to lower fat content, it is labeled to clearly refer to all foods of its type and not merely to the particular brand to which the label attaches (e.g., "frozen perch, a low fat food").

(3) The terms defined in paragraph (b)(2) of this section may be used on the label or in labeling of meal products as defined in 101.13(l) or main dish products as defined in 101.13(m), provided that:

(i) The product contains 3 g or less of total fat per 100 g and not more than 30 percent of calories from fat; and

(ii) If the product meets these conditions without the benefit of special processing, alteration, formulation, or reformulation to lower fat content, it is labeled to clearly refer to all foods of its type and not merely to the particular brand to which the label attaches.

(4) The terms "reduced fat," "reduced in fat," "fat reduced," "less fat," "lower fat," or "lower in fat" may be used on the label or in the labeling of foods, except meal products as defined in 101.13(l) and main dish products as defined in 101.13(m), provided that:

(i) The food contains at least 25 percent less fat per reference amount customarily consumed than an appropriate reference food as described in 101.13(j)(1); and

(ii) As required in 101.13(j)(2) for relative claims:

(A) The identity of the reference food and the percent (or fraction) that the fat differs between the two foods and are declared in immediate proximity to the most prominent such claim (e.g., "reduced fat—50 percent less fat than our regular brownies"); and

(B) Quantitative information comparing the level of fat in the product per labeled serving with that of the reference food that it replaces (e.g., "Fat content has been reduced from 8 g to 4 g per serving.") is declared adjacent to the most prominent claim or to the nutrition label, except that if the nutrition label is on the information panel, the quantitative information may be located elsewhere on the information panel in accordance with 101.2.

(iii) Claims described in paragraph (b)(4) of this section may not be made on the label or in the labeling of a food if the nutrient content of the reference food meets the definition for "low fat."

(5) The terms defined in paragraph (b)(4) of this section may be used on the label or in the labeling of meal products as defined in 101.13(l) and main dish products as defined in 101.13(m), provided that:

(i) The food contains at least 25 percent less fat per 100 g of food than an appropriate reference food as described in 101.13(j)(1); and

(ii) As required in 101.13(j)(2) for relative claims:

(A) The identity of the reference food and the percent (or fraction) that the fat differs between the two foods are declared in immediate proximity to the most prominent such claim (e.g., reduced fat spinach souffle, "33 percent less fat per 3 oz than our regular spinach souffle"); and

(B) Quantitative information comparing the level of fat in the product per specified weight with that of the reference food that it replaces (e.g., "Fat content has been reduced from 7.5 g per 3 oz to 5 g per 3 oz.") is declared adjacent to the most prominent claim, to the nutrition label, or, if the nutrition label is located on the information panel, it may appear elsewhere on the information panel in accordance with 101.2.

(iii) Claims described in paragraph (b)(5) of this section may not be made on the label or in the labeling of a food if the nutrient content of the reference food meets the definition for "low fat."

(6) The term "_ percent fat free" may be used on the label or in the labeling of foods, provided that:

(i) The food meets the criteria for "low fat" in paragraph (b)(2) or (b)(3) of this section;

(ii) The percent declared and the words "fat free" are in uniform type size; and

(iii) A "100 percent fat free" claim may be made only on foods that meet the criteria for "fat free" in paragraph (b)(1) of this section, that contain less than 0.5 g of fat per 100 g, and that contain no added fat.

(c) *Fatty acid content claims.* The label or labeling of foods that bear claims with respect to the level of saturated fat shall disclose the level of total fat and cholesterol in the food in immediate proximity to such claim each time the claim is made and in type that shall be no less than one-half the size of the type used for the claim with respect to the level of saturated fat. Declaration of cholesterol content may be omitted when the food contains less than 2 milligrams (mg) of cholesterol per reference amount customarily consumed or in the case of a meal or main dish product less than 2 mg of cholesterol per labeled serving. Declaration of total fat may be omitted with the term defined in paragraph (c)(1) of this section when the food contains less than 0.5 g of total fat per reference amount customarily consumed or, in the case of a meal product or a main dish product, when the product contains less than 0.5 g of total fat per labeled serving. The declaration of total fat may be omitted with the terms defined in paragraphs (c)(2) through (c)(5) of this section when the food contains 3 g or less of total fat per reference amount customarily consumed or in the case of a meal product or a main dish product, when the product contains 3 g or less of total fat per 100 g and not more than 30 percent calories from fat.

(1) The terms "saturated fat free," "free of saturated fat," "no saturated fat," "zero saturated fat," "without saturated fat," "trivial source of saturated fat," "negligible source of saturated fat," or "dietarily insignificant source of saturated fat" may be used on the label or in the labeling of foods, provided that:

    (i) The food contains less than 0.5 g of saturated fat and less than 0.5 g trans fatty acid per reference amount customarily consumed and per labeled serving, or in the case of a meal product or main dish product, less than 0.5 g of saturated fat and less than 0.5 g trans fatty acid per labeled serving; and

    (ii) The food contains no ingredient that is generally understood by consumers to contain saturated fat unless the listing of the ingredient in the ingredient statement is followed by an asterisk that refers to the statement below the list of ingredients which states, "adds a trivial amount of saturated fat," "adds a negligible amount of saturated fat," or "adds a dietarily insignificant amount of saturated fat;" and

    (iii) As required in 101.13(e)(2), if the food meets these conditions without the benefit of special processing, alteration, formulation, or reformulation to lower saturated fat content, it is labeled to disclose that saturated fat is not usually present in the food.

(2) The terms "low in saturated fat," "low saturated fat," "contains a small amount of saturated fat," "low source of saturated fat," or "a little saturated fat" may be used on the label or in the labeling of foods, except meal products as defined in 101.13(l) and main dish products as defined in 101.13(m), provided that:

    (i) The food contains 1 g or less of saturated fatty acids per reference amount customarily consumed and not more than 15 percent of calories from saturated fatty acids; and

(ii) If a food meets these conditions without benefit of special processing, alteration, formulation, or reformulation to lower saturated fat content, it is labeled to clearly refer to all foods of its type and not merely to the particular brand to which the label attaches (e.g., "raspberries, a low saturated fat food").

(3) The terms defined in paragraph (c)(2) of this section may be used on the label or in the labeling of meal products as defined in 101.13(l) and main dish products as defined in 101.13(m), provided that:

(i) The product contains 1 g or less of saturated fatty acids per 100 g and less than 10 percent calories from saturated fat; and

(ii) If the product meets these conditions without the benefit of special processing, alteration, formulation, or reformulation to lower saturated fat content, it is labeled to clearly refer to all foods of its type and not merely to the particular brand to which the label attaches.

(4) The terms "reduced saturated fat," "reduced in saturated fat," "saturated fat reduced," "less saturated fat," "lower saturated fat," or "lower in saturated fat" may be used on the label or in the labeling of foods, except as limited by 101.13(j)(1)(i) and except meal products as defined in 101.13(l) and main dish products as defined in 101.13(m), provided that:

(i) The food contains at least 25 percent less saturated fat per reference amount customarily consumed than an appropriate reference food as described in 101.13(j)(1); and

(ii) As required in 101.13(j)(2) for relative claims:

(A) The identity of the reference food and the percent (or fraction) that the saturated fat differs between the two foods are declared in immediate proximity to the most prominent such claim (e.g., "reduced saturated fat. Contains 50 percent less saturated fat than the national average for nondairy creamers"); and

(B) Quantitative information comparing the level of saturated fat in the product per labeled serving with that of the reference food that it replaces (e.g., "Saturated fat reduced from 3 g to 1.5 g per serving") is declared adjacent to the most prominent claim or to the nutrition label, except that if the nutrition label is on the information panel, the quantitative information may be located elsewhere on the information panel in accordance with 101.2.

(iii) Claims described in paragraph (c)(4) of this section may not be made on the label or in the labeling of a food if the nutrient content of the reference food meets the definition for "low saturated fat."

(5) The terms defined in paragraph (c)(4) of this section may be used on the label or in the labeling of meal products as defined in 101.13(l) and main dish products as defined in 101.13(m), provided that:

(i) The food contains at least 25 percent less saturated fat per 100 g of food than an appropriate reference food as described in 101.13(j)(1), and

(ii) As required in 101.13(j)(2) for relative claims:

(A) The identity of the reference food, and the percent (or fraction) that the fat differs between the two foods are declared in immediate proximity to the most prominent such claim (e.g., reduced saturated fat Macaroni and Cheese, "33 percent less saturated fat per 3 oz than our regular Macaroni and Cheese").

(B) Quantitative information comparing the level of saturated fat in the product per specified weight with that of the reference food that it replaces (e.g., "Saturated fat content has been reduced from 2.5 g per 3 oz to 1.7 g per 3 oz.") is declared adjacent to the most prominent claim or to the nutrition label, except that if the nutrition label in on the information panel, the quantitative information may be located elsewhere on the information panel in accordance with 101.2.

(iii) Claims described in paragraph (c)(5) of this section may not be made on the label or in the labeling of a food if the nutrient content of the reference food meets the definition for "low saturated fat."

(d) *Cholesterol content claims.*

(1) The terms "cholesterol free," "free of cholesterol," "zero cholesterol," "without cholesterol," "no cholesterol," "trivial source of cholesterol," "negligible source of cholesterol," or "dietarily insignificant source of cholesterol" may be used on the label or in the labeling of foods, provided that:

(i) For foods that contain 13 g or less of total fat per reference amount customarily consumed, per labeled serving, and per 50 g if the reference amount customarily consumed is 30 g or less or 2 tablespoons or less (for dehydrated foods that must be reconstituted before typical consumption with water or a diluent containing an insignificant amount, as defined in 101.9(f)(1), of all nutrients per reference amount customarily consumed, the per 50-g criterion refers to the "as prepared" form), or, in the case of meal products, 26.0 g or less total fat per labeled serving, or, in the case of main dish products, 19.5 g or less total fat per labeled serving:

(A) The food contains less than 2 mg of cholesterol per reference amount customarily consumed and per labeling serving or, in the case of a meal product or main dish product, less than 2 mg of cholesterol per labeled serving; and

(B) The food contains no ingredient that is generally understood by consumers to contain cholesterol, unless the listing of the ingredient in the ingredient statement is followed by an asterisk that refers to the statement below the list of ingredients, which states "adds a trivial amount of cholesterol," "adds a negligible amount of cholesterol," or "adds a dietarily insignificant amount of cholesterol;" and

(C) The food contains 2 g or less of saturated fatty acids per reference amount customarily consumed or, in the case of a meal product or main dish product, 2 g or less of saturated fatty acids per labeled serving; and

(D) As required in 101.13(e)(2), if the food contains less than 2 mg of cholesterol per reference amount customarily consumed or in the case of a meal product or main dish product, less than 2 mg of cholesterol per labeled serving without the benefit of special processing, alteration, formulation, or reformulation to lower cholesterol content, it is labeled to disclose that cholesterol is not usually present in the food (e.g., "applesauce, a cholesterol-free food").

(ii) For food that contain more than 13 g of total fat per reference amount customarily consumed, per labeling serving, or per 50 g if the reference amount customarily consumed is 30 g or less or 2 tablespoons or less (for dehydrated foods that must be reconstituted before typical consumption with water or a diluent containing an insignificant amount, as defined in 101.9(f)(1), of all nutrients per reference amount customarily consumed, the per 50-g criterion refers to the "as prepared" form), or in the case of a meal product, more than 26 g of total fat per labeled serving, or, in the case of a main dish product more than 19.5 g of total fat per labeled serving:

(A) The food contains less than 2 mg of cholesterol per reference amount customarily consumed and per labeling serving or, in the case of a meal product or main dish product, less than 2 mg of cholesterol per labeled serving; and

(B) The food contains no ingredient that is generally understood by consumers to contain cholesterol, unless the listing of the ingredient in the ingredient statement is followed by an asterisk that refers to the statement below the list of ingredients, which states "adds a trivial amount of cholesterol," "adds a negligible amount of cholesterol," or "adds a dietarily insignificant amount of cholesterol;" and

(C) The food contains 2 g or less of saturated fatty acids per reference amount cutomarily consumed or, in the case of a meal product or main dish product less than 2 g of saturated fatty acids per labeled serving; and

(D) The label or labeling discloses the level of total fat in a serving (as declared on the label) of the food. Such disclosure shall appear in immediate proximity to such claim preceding any disclosure statement required under 101.13(h) in type that shall be no less than one-half the size of the type used for such claim. If the claim appears on more than one panel, the disclosure shall be made on each panel except for the panel that bears nutrition labeling. If the claim appears more than once on a panel, the disclosure shall be made in immediate proximity to the claim that is printed in the largest type; and

(E) As required in 101.13(e)(2), if the food contains less than 2 mg of cholesterol per reference amount customarily consumed or in the case of a meal product or main dish product less than 2 mg of cholesterol per labeled serving without the benefit of special processing, alteration, formulation, or reformulation to lower cholesterol content, it is labeled to disclose that cholesterol is not usually present in the food (e.g., "canola oil, a cholesterol-free food, contains 14 g of fat per serving"); or

(F) If the food contains less than 2 mg of cholesterol per reference amount customarily consumed or in the case of a meal product or main dish product less than 2 mg of cholesterol per labeled serving only as a result of special processing, alteration, formulation, or reformulation, the amount of cholesterol is substantially less (i.e., meets requirements of paragraph (d)(4)(ii)(A) of this section) than the food for which it substitutes as specified in 101.13(d) that has a significant (e.g., 5 percent or more of a national or regional market) market share. As required in 101.13(j)(2) for relative claims:

(1) The identity of the reference food and the percent (or fraction) that the cholesterol was reduced are declared in immediate proximity to the most prominent such claim (e.g., "cholesterol-free margarine, contains 100 percent less cholesterol than butter"); and

(2) Quantitative information comparing the level of cholesterol in the product per labeled serving with that of the reference food that it replaces (e.g., "Contains no cholesterol compared with 30 mg cholesterol in one serving of butter. Contains 13 g of fat per serving.") is declared adjacent to the most prominent claim or to the nutrition label, except that if the nutrition label is on the information panel, the quantitative information may be located elsewhere on the information panel in accordance with 101.2.

(2) The terms "low in cholesterol," "low cholesterol," "contains a small amount of cholesterol," "low source of cholesterol," or "little cholesterol" may be used on the label or in the labeling of foods, except meal products as defined in 101.13(l) and main dish products as defined in 101.13(m), provided that:

(i) For foods that have a reference amount customarily consumed greater than 30 g or greater than 2 tablespoons and contain 13 g or less of total fat per reference amount customarily consumed and per labeled serving:

(A) The food contains 20 mg or less of cholesterol per reference amount customarily consumed;

(B) The food contains 2 g or less of saturated fatty acids per reference amount customarily consumed; and

(C) As required in 101.13(e)(2), if the food meets these conditions without the benefit of special processing, alteration, formulation, or reformulation to lower cholesterol content, it is labeled to clearly refer to all foods of that type and not merely to the particular brand to which the label attaches (e.g., "low fat cottage cheese, a low cholesterol food.").

(ii) For foods that have a reference amount customarily consumed of 30 g or less or 2 tablespoons or less and contain 13 g or less of total fat per reference amount customarily consumed, per labeled serving, and per 50 g (for dehydrated foods that must be reconstituted before typical consumption with water or a diluent containing an insignificant amount, as defined in 101.9(f)(1), of all nutrients per reference amount customarily consumed, the per 50-g criterion refers to the "as prepared" form);

   (A) The food contains 20 mg or less of cholesterol per reference amount customarily consumed and per 50 g (for dehydrated foods that must be reconstituted before typical consumption with water or a diluent containing an insignificant amount, as defined in 101.9(f)(1), of all nutrients per reference amount customarily consumed, the per 50-g criterion refers to the "as prepared" form);

   (B) The food contains 2 g or less of saturated fatty acids per reference amount customarily consumed; and

   (C) As required in 101.13(e)(2), if the food meets these conditions without the benefit of special processing, alteration, formulation, or reformulation to lower cholesterol content, it is labeled to clearly refer to all foods of that type and not merely to the particular brand to which the label attaches (e.g., "low fat cottage cheese, a low cholesterol food").

(iii) For foods that have a reference amount customarily consumed greater than 30 g or greater than 2 tablespoons and contain more than 13 g of total fat per reference amount customarily consumed or per labeled serving,

   (A) The food contains 20 mg or less of cholesterol per reference amount customarily consumed;

   (B) The food contains 2 g or less of saturated fatty acids per reference amount customarily consumed;

   (C) The label or labeling discloses the level of total fat in a serving (as declared on the label) of the food. Such disclosure shall appear in immediate proximity to such claim preceding any disclosure statement required under 101.13(h) in type that shall be no less than one-half the size of the type used for such claim. If the claim appears on more than one panel, the disclosure shall be made on each panel except for the panel that bears nutrition labeling. If the claim is made more than once on a panel, the disclosure shall be made in immediate proximity to the claim that is printed in the largest type; and

(D) As required in 101.13(e)(2), if the food meets these conditions without the benefit of special processing, alteration, formulation, or reformulation to lower cholesterol content, it is labeled to clearly refer to all foods of that type and not merely to the particular brand to which the label attaches; or

(E) If the food contains 20 mg or less of cholesterol only as a result of special processing, alteration, formulation, or reformulation, the amount of cholesterol is substantially less (i.e., meets requirements of paragraph (d)(4)(ii)(A) of this section) than the food for which it substitutes as specified in 101.13(d) that has a significant (e.g., 5 percent or more of a national or regional market) market share. As required in 101.13(j)(2) for relative claims:

(1) The identity of the reference food and the percent (or fraction) that the cholesterol has been reduced are declared in immediate proximity to the most prominent such claim (e.g., "low-cholesterol peanut butter sandwich crackers, contains 83 percent less cholesterol than our regular peanut butter sandwich crackers"); and

(2) Quantitative information comparing the level of cholesterol in the product per labeled serving with that of the reference food that it replaces (e.g., "Cholesterol lowered from 30 mg to 5 mg per serving; contains 13 g of fat per serving.") is declared adjacent to the most prominent claim or to the nutrition label, except that if the nutrition label is on the information panel, the quantitative information may be located elsewhere on the information panel in accordance with 101.2.

(iv) For foods that have a reference amount customarily consumed of 30 g or less or 2 tablespoons or less and contain more than 13 g of total fat per reference amount customarily consumed, per labeled serving, or per 50 g (for dehydrated foods that must be reconstituted before typical consumption with water or a diluent containing an insignificant amount, as defined in 101.9(f)(1), of all nutrients per reference amount customarily consumed, the per 50-g criterion refers to the "as prepared" form),

(A) The food contains 20 mg or less of cholesterol per reference amount customarily consumed and per 50 g (for dehydrated foods that must be reconstituted before typical consumption with water or a diluent containing an insignificant amount, as defined in 101.9(f)(1), of all nutrients per reference amount customarily consumed, the per 50-g criterion refers to the "as prepared" form),

(B) The food contains 2 g or less of saturated fatty acids per reference amount customarily consumed;

(C) The label or labeling discloses the level of total fat in a serving (as declared on the label) of the food. Such disclosure shall appear in immediate proximity to such claim preceding any disclosure statement required under 101.13(h) in type that shall be no less than one-half the size of the type used for such claim. If the claim appears on more than one panel, the disclosure shall be made on each panel except for the panel that bears nutrition labeling. If the claim is made more than once on a panel, the disclosure shall be made in immediate proximity to the claim that is printed in the largest type; and

(D) As required in 101.13(e)(2), if the food meets these conditions without the benefit of special processing, alteration, formulation, or reformulation to lower cholesterol content, it is labeled to clearly refer to all foods of that type and not merely to the particular brand to which the label attaches; or

(E) If the food contains 20 mg or less of cholesterol only as a result of special processing, alteration, formulation, or reformulation, the amount of cholesterol is substantially less (i.e., meets requirements of paragraph (d)(4)(ii)(A) of this section) than the food for which it substitutes as specified in 101.13(d) that has a significant (i.e., 5 percent or more of a national or regional market) market share. As required in 101.13(j)(2) for relative claims:

   (1) The identity of the reference food and the percent (or fraction) that the cholesterol has been reduced are declared in immediate proximity to the most prominent such claim (e.g., "low-cholesterol peanut butter sandwich crackers, contains 83 percent less cholesterol than our regular peanut butter sandwich crackers"); and

   (2) Quantitative information comparing the level of cholesterol in the product per labeled serving with that of the reference food that it replaces (e.g., "Cholesterol lowered from 30 mg to 5 mg per serving; contains 13 g of fat per serving.") is declared adjacent to the most prominent claim or to the nutrition label, except that if the nutrition label is on the information panel, the quantitative information may be located elsewhere on the information panel in accordance with 101.2.

(3) The terms defined in paragraph (d)(2) of this section may be used on the label and in labeling of meal products as defined in 101.13(l) or a main dish product as defined in 101.13(m) provided that the product meets the requirements of paragraph (d)(2) of this section except that the determination as to whether paragraph (d)(2)(i) or (d)(2)(iii) of this section applies to the product will be made only on the basis of whether the meal product contains 26 g or less of total fat per labeled serving or the main dish product contain 19.5 g or less of total fat per labeled serving, the requirement in paragraphs (d)(2)(i)(A) and (d)(2)(iii)(A) of this section shall be limited to 20 mg of cholesterol per 100 g, and the requirement in paragraphs (d)(2)(i)(B) and (d)(2)(iii)(B) of this section shall be modified to require that the food contain 2 g or less of saturated fat per 100 g rather than per reference amount customarily consumed.

(4) The terms "reduced cholesterol," "reduced in cholesterol," "cholesterol reduced," "less cholesterol," "lower cholesterol," or "lower in cholesterol" except as limited by 101.13(j)(1)(i) may be used on the label or in labeling of foods or foods that

substitute for those foods as specified in 101.13(d), excluding meal products as defined in 101.13(l) and main dish products as defined in 101.13(m), provided that:

(i) For foods that contain 13 g or less of total fat per reference amount customarily consumed, per labeled serving, and per 50 g if the reference amount customarily consumed is 30 g or less or 2 tablespoons or less (for dehydrated foods that must be reconstituted before typical consumption with water or a diluent containing an insignificant amount, as defined in 101.9(f)(1), of all nutrients per reference amount customarily consumed, the per 50-g criterion refers to the "as prepared" form):

  (A) The food has been specifically formulated, altered, or processed to reduce its cholesterol by 25 percent or more from the reference food it resembles as defined in 101.13(j)(1) and for which it substitutes as specified in 101.13(d) that has a significant (i.e., 5 percent or more) market share; and

  (B) The food contains 2 g or less of saturated fatty acids per reference amount customarily consumed; and

  (C) As required in 101.13(j)(2) for relative claims:

    (1) The identity of the reference food and the percent (or fraction) that the cholesterol has been reduced are declared in immediate proximity to the most prominent such claim; and

    (2) Quantitative information comparing the level of cholesterol in the product per labeled serving with that of the reference food that it replaces (e.g., "[labeled product] 50 mg cholesterol per serving; [reference product] 30 mg cholesterol per serving") is declared adjacent to the most prominent claim or to the nutrition label, except that if the nutrition label is on the information panel, the quantitative information may be located elsewhere on the information panel in accordance with 101.2.

(ii) For foods that contain more than 13 g of total fat per reference amount customarily consumed, per labeled serving, or per 50 g if the reference amount customarily consumed is 30 g or less or 2 tablespoons or less (for dehydrated foods that must be reconstituted before typical consumption with water or a diluent containing an insignificant amount, as defined in 101.9(f)(1), of all nutrients per reference amount customarily consumed, the per 50-g criterion refers to the "as prepared" form):

  (A) The food has been specifically formulated, altered, or processed to reduce its cholesterol by 25 percent or more from the reference food it resembles as defined in 101.13(j)(1) and for which it substitutes as specified in 101.13(d) that has a significant (i.e., 5 percent or more of a national or regional market) market share;

  (B) The food contains 2 g or less of saturated fatty acids per reference amount customarily consumed;

(C) The label or labeling discloses the level of total fat in a serving (as declared on the label) of the food. Such disclosure shall appear in immediate proximity to such claim preceding any disclosure statement required under 101.13(h) in type that shall be no less than one-half the size of the type used for such claim. If the claim appears on more than one panel, the disclosure shall be made on each panel except for the panel that bears nutrition labeling. If the claim is made more than once on a panel, the disclosure shall be made in immediate proximity to the claim that is printed in the largest type; and

(D) As required in 101.13(j)(2) for relative claims:

(1) The identity of the reference food and the percent (or fraction) that the cholesterol has been reduced are declared in immediate proximity to the most prominent such claim (e.g., 25 percent less cholesterol than ___); and

(2) Quantitative information comparing the level of cholesterol in the product per labeled serving with that of the reference food that it replaces (e.g., "Cholesterol lowered from 55 mg to 30 mg per serving. Contains 13 g of fat per serving.") is declared adjacent to the most prominent claim or to the nutrition label, except that if the nutrition label is on the information panel, the quantitative information may be located elsewhere on the information panel in accordance with 101.2.

(iii) Claims described in paragraph (d)(4) of this section may not be made on the label or in labeling of a food if the nutrient content of the reference food meets the definition for "low cholesterol."

(5) The terms defined in paragraph (d)(4) of this section may be used on the label or in the labeling of meal products as defined in 101.13(l) and main dish products as defined in 101.13(m), provided that:

(i) For meal products that contain 26.0 g or less of total fat per labeled serving or for main dish products that contain 19.5 g or less of total fat per labeled serving;

(A) The food has been specifically formulated, altered, or processed to reduce its cholesterol by 25 percent or more from the reference food it resembles as defined in 101.13(j)(1) and for which it substitutes as specified in 101.13(d) that has a significant (e.g., 5 percent or more of a national or regional market) market share;

(B) The food contains 2 g or less of saturated fatty acids per 100 g; and

(C) As required in 101.13(j)(2) for relative claims:

(1) The identity of the reference food, and the percent (or fraction) that the cholesterol has been reduced are declared in immediate proximity to the most prominent such claim (e.g., "25% less cholesterol per 3 oz than ___); and

(2) Quantitative information comparing the level of cholesterol in the product per specified weight with that of the reference food that it replaces (e.g., "Cholesterol content has been reduced from 35 mg per 3 oz to 25 mg per 3 oz.") is declared adjacent to the most prominent claim or to the nutrition label, except that if the nutrition label is on the information panel, the quantitative information may be located elsewhere on the information panel in accordance with 101.2.

(ii) For meal products that contain more than 26.0 g of total fat per labeled serving or for main dish products that contain more than 19.5 g of total fat per labeled serving:

(A) The food has been specifically formulated, altered, or processed to reduce its cholesterol by 25 percent or more from the reference food it resembles as defined in 101.13(j)(1) and for which it substitutes as specified in 101.13(d) that has a significant (e.g., 5 percent or more of a national or regional market) market share.

(B) The food contains 2 g or less of saturated fatty acids per 100 g;

(C) The label or labeling discloses the level of total fat in a serving (as declared on the label) of the food. Such disclosure shall appear in immediate proximity to such claim preceding any disclosure statement required under 101.13(h) in type that shall be no less than one-half the size of the type used for such claim. If the claim appears on more than one panel the disclosure shall be made on each panel except for the panel that bears nutrition labeling. If the claim is made more than once on a panel, the disclosure shall be made in immediate proximity to the claim that is printed in the largest type; and

(D) As required in 101.13(j)(2) for relative claims:

(1) The identity of the reference food and the percent (or fraction) that the cholesterol has been reduced are declared in immediate proximity to the most prominent such claim (e.g., 25 percent less cholesterol than ___); and

(2) Quantitative information comparing the level of cholesterol in the product per specified weight with that of the reference food that it replaces (e.g., "Cholesterol lowered from 30 mg to 22 mg per 3 oz of product.") is declared adjacent to the most prominent claim or to the nutrition label, except that if the nutrition label is on the information panel, the quantitative information may be located elsewhere on the information panel in accordance with 101.2.

(iii) Claims described in paragraph (d)(5) of this section may not be made on the label or in the labeling of a food if the nutrient content of the reference food meets the definition for "low cholesterol."

(e) *"Lean" and "extra lean" claims.*

(1) The term "lean" may be used on the label or in labeling of foods except meal products as defined in 101.13(l) and main dish products as defined in 101.13(m) provided that the food is a seafood or game meat product and as packaged contains less than 10 g total fat, 4.5 g or less saturated fat, and less than 95 mg cholesterol per reference amount customarily consumed and per 100 g;

(2) The term defined in paragraph (e)(1) of this section may be used on the label or in labeling of a mixed dish not measurable with a cup as defined in 101.12(b) in table 2, provided that the food contains less than 8 g total fat, 3.5 g or less saturated fat and less than 80 mg cholesterol per reference amount customarily consumed;

(3) The term defined in paragraph (e)(1) of this section may be used on the label or in the labeling of meal products as defined in 101.13(l) or main dish products as defined in 101.13(m) provided that the food contains less than 10 g total fat, 4.5 g or less saturated fat, and less than 95 mg cholesterol per 100 g and per labeled serving;

(4) The term "extra lean" may be used on the label or in the labeling of foods except meal products as defined in 101.13(l) and main dish products as defined in 101.13(m) provided that the food is a discrete seafood or game meat product and as packaged contains less than 5 g total fat, less than 2 g saturated fat, and less than 95 mg cholesterol per reference amount customarily consumed and per 100 g; and

(5) The term defined in paragraph (e)(4) of this section may be used on the label or in labeling of meal products as defined in 101.13(l) and main dish products as defined in 101.13(m) provided that the food contains less than 5 g of fat, less than 2 g of saturated fat, and less than 95 mg of cholesterol per 100 g and per labeled serving.

(f) *Misbranding.* Any label or labeling containing any statement concerning fat, fatty acids, or cholesterol that is not in conformity with this section shall be deemed to be misbranded under sections 201(n), 403(a), and 403(r) of the Federal Food, Drug, and Cosmetic Act.

[58 FR 2413, Jan. 6, 1993; 58 FR 17342, 17343, Apr. 2, 1993, as amended at 58 FR 44032, Aug. 18, 1993; 58 FR 60105, Nov. 15, 1993; 59 FR 394, Jan. 4, 1994; 60 FR 17207, Apr. 5, 1995; 61 FR 59001, Nov. 20, 1996; 63 FR 26980, May 15, 1998; 72 FR 1459, Jan. 12, 2007]

Sec. 101.65 Implied nutrient content claims and related label statements.

(a) *General requirements.* An implied nutrient content claim can only be made on the label and in labeling of the food if:

 (1) The claim uses one of the terms described in this section in accordance with the definition for that term;

 (2) The claim is made in accordance with the general requirements for nutrient content claims in 101.13; and

 (3) The food for which the claim is made is labeled in accordance with 101.9, 101.10, or 101.36, as applicable.

(b) *Label statements that are not implied claims.* Certain label statements about the nature of a product are not nutrient content claims unless such statements are made in a context that would make them an implied claim under 101.13(b)(2). The following types of label statements are generally not implied nutrient content claims and, as such, are not subject to the requirements of 101.13 and this section:

 (1) A claim that a specific ingredient or food component is absent from a product, provided that the purpose of such claim is to facilitate avoidance of the substances because of food allergies (see 105.62 of this chapter), food intolerance, religious beliefs, or dietary practices such as vegetarianism or other nonnutrition related reason, e.g., "100 percent milk free;"

 (2) A claim about a substance that is nonnutritive or that does not have a nutritive function, e.g., "contains no preservatives," "no artificial colors;"

 (3) A claim about the presence of an ingredient that is perceived to add value to the product, e.g., "made with real butter," "made with whole fruit," or "contains honey," except that claims about the presence of ingredients other than vitamins or minerals or that are represented as a source of vitamins and minerals are not allowed on labels or in labeling of dietary supplements of vitamins and minerals that are not in conventional food form.

 (4) A statement of identity for a food in which an ingredient constitutes essentially 100 percent of a food (e.g., "corn oil," "oat bran," "dietary supplement of vitamin C 60 mg tablet").

 (5) A statement of identity that names as a characterizing ingredient, an ingredient associated with a nutrient benefit (e.g., "corn oil margarine," "oat bran muffins," or "whole wheat bagels"), unless such claim is made in a context in which label or labeling statements, symbols, vignettes, or other forms of communication suggest that a nutrient is absent or present in a certain amount; and

 (6) A label statement made in compliance with a specific provision of part 105 of this chapter, solely to note that a food has special dietary usefulness relative to a physical, physiological, pathological, or other condition, where the claim identifies the special diet of which the food is intended to be a part.

(c) *Particular implied nutrient content claims.*

(1) Claims about the food or an ingredient therein that suggest that a nutrient or an ingredient is absent or present in a certain amount (e.g., "high in oat bran") are implied nutrient content claims and must comply with paragraph (a) of this section.

(2) The phrases "contains the same amount of [nutrient] as a [food]" and "as much [nutrient] as a [food]" may be used on the label or in the labeling of foods, provided that the amount of the nutrient in the reference food is enough to qualify that food as a "good source" of that nutrient, and the labeled food, on a per serving basis, is an equivalent, good source of that nutrient (e.g., "as much fiber as an apple," "Contains the same amount of Vitamin C as an 8 oz glass of orange juice.").

(3) Claims may be made that a food contains or is made with an ingredient that is known to contain a particular nutrient, or is prepared in a way that affects the content of a particular nutrient in the food, if the finished food is either "low" in or a "good source" of the nutrient that is associated with the ingredient or type of preparation. If a more specific level is claimed (e.g., "high in ___"), that level of the nutrient must be present in the food. For example, a claim that a food contains oat bran is a claim that it is a good source of dietary fiber; that a food is made only with vegetable oil is a claim that it is low in saturated fat; and that a food contains no oil is a claim that it is fat free.

(d) *General nutritional claims.*

(1) This paragraph covers labeling claims that are implied nutrient content claims because they:

(i) Suggest that a food because of its nutrient content may help consumers maintain healthy dietary practices; and

(ii) Are made in connection with an explicit or implicit claim or statement about a nutrient (e.g., "healthy, contains 3 grams of fat").

(2) You may use the term "healthy" or related terms (e.g., "health," "healthful," "healthfully," "healthfulness," "healthier," "healthiest," "healthily," and "healthiness") as an implied nutrient content claim on the label or in labeling of a food that is useful in creating a diet that is consistent with dietary recommendations if:

(i) The food meets the following conditions for fat, saturated fat, cholesterol, and other nutrients:

If the food is...	The fat level must be...	The saturated fat level must be...	The cholesterol level must be...	The food must contain...
(A) A raw fruit or vegetable	Low fat as defined in 101.62(b)(2)	Low saturated fat as defined in 101.62(c)(2)	The disclosure level for cholesterol specified in 101.13(h) or less	N/A
(B) A single-ingredient or a mixture of frozen or canned fruits and vegetables 1	Low fat as defined in 101.62(b)(2)	Low saturated fat as defined in 101.62(c)(2)	The disclosure level for cholesterol specified in 101.13(h) or less	N/A
(C) An enriched cereal-grain product that conforms to a standard of identity in part 136, 137 or 139 of this chapter	Low fat as defined in 101.62(b)(2)	Low saturated fat as defined in 101.62(c)(2)	The disclosure level for cholesterol specified in 101.13(h) or less	N/A
(D) A raw, single-ingredient seafood or game meat	Less than 5 grams (g) total fat per RA 2 and per 100 g	Less than 2 g saturated fat per RA and per 100 g	Less than 95 mg cholesterol per RA and per 100 g	At least 10 percent of the RDI 3 or the DRV 4 per RA of one or more of vitamin A, vitamin C, calcium, iron, protein, or fiber
(E) A meal product as defined in 101.13(l) or a main dish product as defined in 101.13(m)	Low fat as defined in 101.62(b)(3)	Low saturated fat as defined in 101.62(c)(3)	90 mg or less cholesterol per LS 5	At least 10 percent of the RDI or DRV per LS of two nutrients (for a main dish product) or of three nutrients (for a meal product) of: vitamin A, vitamin C, calcium, iron, protein, or fiber
(F) A food not specifically listed in this table	Low fat as defined in 101.62(b)(2)	Low saturated fat as defined in 101.62(c)(2)	The disclosure level for cholesterol specified in 101.13(h) or less	At least 10 percent of the RDI or the DRV per RA of one or more of vitamin A, vitamin C, calcium, iron, protein or fiber

[1]May include ingredients whose addition does not change the nutrient profile of the fruit or vegetable.

[2]RA means Reference Amount Customarily Consumed per Eating Occasion (101.12(b)).

[3]RDI means Reference Daily Intake (101.9(c)(8)(iv)).

[4]DRV means Daily Reference Value (101.9(c)(9)).

[5]LS means Labeled Serving, i.e., the serving size that is specified in the nutrition information on the product label (101.9(b)).

(ii) The food meets the following conditions for sodium:

If the food is...	The sodium level must be...
(A) A food with a RA that is greater than 30 g or 2 table-spoons (tbsp.)	480 mg or less sodium per RA and per LS
(B) A food with a RA that is equal to or less than 30 g or 2 tbsp.	480 mg or less sodium per 50 g [1]
(C) A meal product as defined in 101.13(l) or a main dish product as defined in 101.13(m)	600 mg or less sodium per LS

[1] For dehydrated food that is typically reconstituted with water or a liquid that contains insignificant amounts per RA of all nutrients (as defined in 101.9(f)(1)), the 50 g refers to the "prepared" form of the product.

(iii) The food complies with the definition and declaration requirements in this part 101 for any specific nutrient content claim on the label or in labeling, and

(iv) If you add a nutrient to the food specified in paragraphs (d)(2)(i)(D), (d)(2)(i)(E), or (d)(2)(i)(F) of this section to meet the 10 percent requirement, that addition must be in accordance with the fortification policy for foods in 104.20 of this chapter.

[58 FR 2413, Jan. 6, 1993; 58 FR 17343, Apr. 2, 1993, as amended at 59 FR 394, Jan. 4, 1994; 59 FR 24249, May 10, 1994; 59 FR 50828, Oct. 6, 1994; 62 FR 49858, Sept. 23, 1997; 63 FR 14355, Mar. 25, 1998; 70 FR 56848, Sept. 29, 2005]

Subpart E—Specific Requirements for Health Claims

Sec. 101.70 Petitions for health claims.

(a) Any interested person may petition the Food and Drug Administration (FDA) to issue a regulation regarding a health claim. An original and one copy of the petition shall be submitted, or the petitioner may submit an original and a computer readable disk containing the petition. Contents of the disk should be in a standard format, such as ASCII format. (Petitioners interested in submitting a disk should contact the Center for Food Safety and Applied Nutrition for details.) If any part of the material submitted is in a foreign language, it shall be accompanied by an accurate and complete English translation. The petition shall state the petitioner's post office address to which any correspondence required by section 403 of the Federal Food, Drug, and Cosmetic Act may be sent.

(b) Pertinent information may be incorporated in, and will be considered as part of, a petition on the basis of specific reference to such information submitted to and retained in the files of FDA. Such information may include any findings, along with the basis of the findings, of an outside panel with expertise in the subject area. Any reference to published information shall be accompanied by reprints, or easily readable copies of such information.

(c) If nonclinical laboratory studies are included in a petition, the petition shall include, with respect to each nonclinical study contained in the petition, either a statement that the study has been conducted in compliance with the good laboratory practice regulations as set forth in part 58 of this chapter, or, if any such study was not conducted in compliance with such regulations, a brief statement of the reason for the noncompliance.

(d) If clinical or other human investigations are included in a petition, the petition shall include a statement that they were either conducted in compliance with the requirements for institutional review set forth in part 56 of this chapter, or were not subject to such requirements in accordance with 56.104 or 56.105, and a statement that they were conducted in compliance with the requirements for informed consent set forth in part 50 of this chapter.

(e) All data and information in a health claim petition are available for public disclosure after the notice of filing of petition is issued to the petitioner, except that clinical investigation reports, adverse reaction reports, product experience reports, consumer complaints, and other similar data and information shall only be available after deletion of:

   (1) Names and any information that would identify the person using the product.

   (2) Names and any information that would identify any third party involved with the report, such as a physician or hospital or other institution.

(f) Petitions for a health claim shall include the following data and be submitted in the following form:

(Date)_____
Name of petitioner _____
Post office address _____
Subject of the petition _____

Food and Drug Administration,
Office of Nutritional Products, Labeling and Dietary Supplements (HFS-800),
5001 Campus Dr.,
College Park, MD 20740,

The undersigned, _____ submits this petition pursuant to section 403(r)(4) or 403(r)(5)(D) of the Federal Food, Drug, and Cosmetic Act with respect to (statement of the substance and its health claim).

Attached hereto, and constituting a part of this petition, are the following:

A. Preliminary requirements. A complete explanation of how the substance conforms to the requirements of 101.14(b) (21 CFR 101.14(b)). For petitions where the subject substance is a food ingredient or a component of a food ingredient, the petitioner should compile a comprehensive list of the specific ingredients that will be added to the food to supply the substance in the food bearing the health claim. For each such ingredient listed, the petitioner should state how the ingredient complies with the requirements of 101.14(b)(3)(ii), e.g., that its use is generally recognized as safe (GRAS), listed as a food additive, or authorized by a prior sanction issued by the agency, and what the basis is for the GRAS claim, the food additive status, or prior sanctioned status.

B. Summary of scientific data. The summary of scientific data provides the basis upon which authorizing a health claim can be justified as providing the health benefit. The summary must establish that, based on the totality of publicly available scientific evidence (including evidence from well-designed studies conducted in a manner which is consistent with generally recognized scientific procedures and principles), there is significant scientific agreement among experts qualified by scientific training and experience to evaluate such claims, that the claim is supported by such evidence.

The summary shall state what public health benefit will derive from use of the claim as proposed. If the claim is intended for a specific group within the population, the summary shall specifically address nutritional needs of such group and shall include scientific data showing how the claim is likely to assist in meeting such needs.

The summary shall concentrate on the findings of appropriate review articles, National Institutes of Health consensus development conferences, and other appropriate resource materials. Issues addressed in the summary shall include answers to such questions as:

1. Is there an optimum level of the particular substance to be consumed beyond which no benefit would be expected?

2. Is there any level at which an adverse effect from the substance or from foods containing the substance occurs for any segment of the population?

3. Are there certain populations that must receive special consideration?

4. What other nutritional or health factors (both positive and negative) are important to consider when consuming the substance?

In addition, the summary of scientific data shall include a detailed analysis of the potential effect of the use of the proposed claim on food consumption, specifically any change due to significant alterations in eating habits and corresponding changes in nutrient intake resulting from such changes in food consumption. The latter item shall specifically address the effect on the intake of nutrients that have beneficial and negative consequences in the total diet.

If the claim is intended for a significant subpopulation within the general U.S. population, the analysis shall specifically address the dietary practices of such group, and shall include data sufficient to demonstrate that the dietary analysis is representative of such group (e.g., adolescents or the elderly).

If appropriate, the petition shall explain the prevalence of the disease or health-related condition in the U.S. population and the relevance of the claim in the context of the total daily diet.

Also, the summary shall demonstrate that the substance that is the subject of the proposed claim conforms to the definition of the term "substance" in 101.14(a)(2).

C. Analytical data that show the amount of the substance that is present in representative foods that would be candidates to bear the claim should be obtained from representative samples using methods from the AOAC INTERNATIONAL (AOAC), where available. If no AOAC method is available, the petitioner shall submit the assay method used and data establishing the validity of the method for assaying the substance in food. The validation data should include a statistical analysis of the analytical and product variability.

D. Model health claim. One or more model health claims that represent label statements that may be used on a food label or in labeling for a food to characterize the relationship between the substance in a food to a disease or health-related condition that is justified by the summary of scientific data provided in section C of the petition. The model health claim shall include:

1. A brief capsulized statement of the relevant conclusions of the summary, and

2. A statement of how this substance helps the consumer to attain a total dietary pattern or goal associated with the health benefit that is provided.

E. The petition shall include the following attachments:

1. Copies of any computer literature searches done by the petitioner (e.g., Medline).

2. Copies of articles cited in the literature searches and other information as follows:

a. All information relied upon for the support of the health claim, including copies of publications or other information cited in review articles and used to perform meta-analyses.

b. All information concerning adverse consequences to any segment of the population (e.g., sensitivity to the substance).

c. All information pertaining to the U.S. population.

F. The petitioner is required to submit either a claim for categorical exclusion under 25.30 or 25.32 of this chapter or an environmental assessment under 25.40 of this chapter.

Yours very truly,
Petitioner _____
By _____
(Indicate authority)

(g) The data specified under the several lettered headings should be submitted on separate pages or sets of pages, suitably identified. If such data have already been submitted with an earlier application from the petitioner or any other final petition, the present petition may incorporate it by specific reference to the earlier petition.

(h) The petition shall include a statement signed by the person responsible for the petition that, to the best of his/her knowledge, it is a representative and balanced submission that includes unfavorable information as well as favorable information, known to him/her to be pertinent to the evaluation of the proposed health claim.

(i) The petition shall be signed by the petitioner or by his/her attorney or agent, or (if a corporation) by an authorized official.

(j) Agency action on the petition.

(1) Within 15 days of receipt of the petition, the petitioner will be notified by letter of the date on which the petition was received. Such notice will inform the petitioner that the petition is undergoing agency review and that the petitioner will subsequently be notified of the agency's decision to file for comprehensive review or deny the petition.

(2) Within 100 days of the date of receipt of the petition, FDA will notify the petitioner by letter that the petition has either been filed for comprehensive review or denied. The agency will deny a petition without reviewing the information contained in "B. Summary of Scientific Data" if the information in "A. Preliminary Requirements" is inadequate in explaining how the substance conforms to the requirements of 101.14(b). If the petition is denied, the notification will state the reasons therefor, including justification of the rejection of any report from an authoritative scientific body of the U.S. Government. If filed, the date of the notification letter becomes the date of filing for the purposes of this regulation. If FDA does not act within such 100 days, the petition shall be deemed to be denied unless an extension is mutually agreed upon by FDA and the petitioner. A petition that has been denied, or has been deemed to be denied, without filing will not be made available to the public. A filed petition will be available to the public to the extent provided under paragraph (e) of this section.

(3) Within 90 days of the date of filing, FDA will by letter of notification to the petitioner:

(i) Deny the petition, or

(ii) Inform the petitioner that a proposed regulation to provide for the requested use of the health claim will be published in the Federal Register. If the petition is denied, the notification will state the reasons therefor, including justification for the rejection of any report from an authoritative scientific body of the U.S. Government. FDA will publish the proposal to amend the regulations to provide for the requested use of the health claim in the Federal Register within 90 days of the date of filing. The proposal will also announce the availability of the petition for public review.

(iii) If FDA does not act within 90 days of the date of filing, the petition shall be deemed to be denied unless an extension is mutually agreed upon by FDA and the petitioner.

(4)(i) Within 270 of the date of publication of the proposal, FDA will publish a final rule that either authorizes use of the health claim or explains why the agency has decided not to authorize one.

(ii) For cause, FDA may extend, no more than twice, the period in which it will publish a final rule; each such extension will be for no more than 90 days. FDA will publish a notice of each extension in the Federal Register. The document will state the basis for the extension, the length of the extension, and the date by which the final rule will be published, which date shall be within 540 days of the date of receipt of the petition.

[58 FR 2534, Jan. 6, 1993; 58 FR 17097, Apr. 1, 1993, as amended at 59 FR 425, Jan. 4, 1994; 62 FR 28232, May 22, 1997; 62 FR 40599, July 29, 1997; 63 FR 26719, May 14, 1998; 63 FR 40024, July 27, 1998; 66 FR 56035, Nov. 6, 2001]

Sec. 101.71 Health claims: claims not authorized.

Health claims not authorized for foods in conventional food form or for dietary supplements of vitamins, minerals, herbs, or other similar substances:

(a) Dietary fiber and cardiovascular disease.

(b) Zinc and immune function in the elderly.

[58 FR 2534, Jan. 6, 1993, as amended at 58 FR 2548, 2578, 2620, 2639, 2664, 2714, Jan. 6, 1993; 58 FR 17100, Apr. 1, 1993; 59 FR 437, Jan. 4, 1994; 65 FR 58918, Oct. 3, 2000]

Sec. 101.72 Health claims: calcium, vitamin D, and osteoporosis.

(a) *Relationship between calcium, vitamin D, and osteoporosis.* An inadequate intake of calcium or calcium and vitamin D contributes to low peak bone mass, which has been identified as one of many risk factors in the development of osteoporosis. Peak bone mass is the total quantity of bone present at maturity, and experts believe that it has the greatest bearing on whether a person will be at risk of developing osteoporosis and related bone fractures later in life. Another factor that influences total bone mass and susceptibility to osteoporosis is the rate of bone loss after skeletal maturity. Vitamin D is required for normal absorption of calcium and to prevent the occurrence of high serum parathyroid hormone (PTH) concentration, which stimulates mobilization of calcium from the skeleton and can lower bone mass. Calcium, along with vitamin D and several other nutrients, is required for normal bone mineralization. While vitamin D is required for optimal bone mineralization, it is more effective when calcium intake is adequate. An adequate intake of calcium and vitamin D is thought to exert a positive effect during adolescence and early adulthood in optimizing the amount of bone that is laid down. However, the upper limit of peak bone mass is genetically determined. The mechanism through which adequate intakes of calcium and vitamin D and optimal peak bone mass reduce the risk of osteoporosis is thought to be as follows. All persons lose bone with age. Hence, those with higher bone mass at maturity take longer to reach the critically reduced mass at which bones can fracture easily. The rate of bone loss after skeletal maturity also influences the amount of bone present at old age and can influence an individual's risk of developing osteoporosis. Maintenance of adequate intakes of calcium and vitamin D later in life is thought to be important in reducing the rate of bone loss particularly in the elderly and in women during the first decade following menopause, but a significant protective effect is also seen among men and younger women.

(b) *Significance of calcium or calcium and vitamin D.* Adequate calcium intake, or adequate calcium and vitamin D intake, is not the only recognized risk factor in the development of osteoporosis, which is a multifactorial bone disease. Maintenance of adequate calcium and vitamin D intakes throughout life is necessary to achieve optimal peak bone mass and to reduce the risk of osteoporosis in later life. However, vitamin D is most effective in this regard when calcium intake is adequate. Increasing intake of calcium has been shown to have beneficial effects on bone health independent of dietary vitamin D.

(c) *Requirements.*

(1) All requirements set forth in 101.14 shall be met.

(2) Specific requirements —

(i) Nature of the claim. A health claim associating calcium or, when appropriate, calcium and vitamin D with a reduced risk of osteoporosis may be made on the label or labeling of a food described in paragraphs (c)(2)(ii) and (d)(1) of this section, provided that:

(A) The claim makes clear the importance of adequate calcium intake, or when appropriate, adequate calcium and vitamin D intake, throughout life, in a healthful diet, are essential to reduce osteoporosis risk. The claim does not imply that adequate calcium intake, or when appropriate, adequate calcium and vitamin D intake, is the only recognized risk factor for the development of osteoporosis;

(B) The claim does not attribute any degree of reduction in risk of osteoporosis to maintaining an adequate dietary calcium intake, or when appropriate, an adequate dietary calcium and vitamin D intake, throughout life.

(ii) Nature of the food.

(A) The food shall meet or exceed the requirements for a "high" level of calcium as defined in 101.54(b);

(B) The calcium content of the product shall be assimilable;

(C) Dietary supplements shall meet the United States Pharmacopeia (USP) standards for disintegration and dissolution applicable to their component calcium salts, except that dietary supplements for which no USP standards exist shall exhibit appropriate assimilability under the conditions of use stated on the product label;

(D) A food or total daily recommended supplement intake shall not contain more phosphorus than calcium on a weight per weight basis.

(d) *Optional information.*

(1) The claim may include the term "vitamin D" if the food meets or exceeds the requirements for a "high" level of vitamin D as defined in 101.54(b);

(2) The claim may include information from paragraphs (a) and (b) of this section.

(3) The claim may make reference to physical activity.

(4) The claim may include information on the number of people in the United States, including the number of people in certain subpopulations in the United States, who have osteoporosis or low bone density. The sources of this information must be identified, and it must be current information from the National Center for Health Statistics, the National Institutes of Health, or the National Osteoporosis Foundation.

(5) The claim may state that the role of adequate calcium intake, or when appropriate, the role of adequate calcium and vitamin D intake, throughout life is linked to reduced risk of osteoporosis through the mechanism of optimizing peak bone mass during adolescence and early adulthood. The phrase "build and maintain good bone health" may be used to convey the concept of optimizing peak bone mass. The claim may also state that adequate intake of calcium, or when appropriate, adequate intake of calcium and vitamin D, is linked to reduced risk of osteoporosis through the mechanism of slowing the rate of bone loss for persons with a family history of the disease, post-menopausal women, and elderly men and women.

(e) *Model health claims.* The following model health claims may be used in food labeling to describe the relationship between calcium and osteoporosis:

Adequate calcium throughout life, as part of a well-balanced diet, may reduce the risk of osteoporosis.

Adequate calcium as part of a healthful diet, along with physical activity, may reduce the risk of osteoporosis in later life.

(f) *Model additional health claims for calcium and vitamin D.* The following model health claims may be used in food labeling to describe the relationship between calcium, vitamin D, and osteoporosis:

Adequate calcium and vitamin D throughout life, as part of a well-balanced diet, may reduce the risk of osteoporosis.

Adequate calcium and vitamin D as part of a healthful diet, along with physical activity, may reduce the risk of osteoporosis in later life.

[73 FR 56486, Sept. 29, 2008]

Sec. 101.79 Health claims: Folate and neural tube defects.

(a) *Relationship between folate and neural tube defects –*

(1) *Definition.* Neural tube defects are serious birth defects of the brain or spinal cord that can result in infant mortality or serious disability. The birth defects anencephaly and spina bifida are the most common forms of neural tube defects and account for about 90 percent of these defects. These defects result from failure of closure of the covering of the brain or spinal cord during early embryonic development. Because the neural tube forms and closes during early pregnancy, the defect may occur before a woman realizes that she is pregnant.

(2) *Relationship.* The available data show that diets adequate in folate may reduce the risk of neural tube defects. The strongest evidence for this relationship comes from an intervention study by the Medical Research Council of the United Kingdom that showed that women at risk of recurrence of a neural tube defect pregnancy who consumed a supplement containing 4 milligrams (mg)(4,000 micrograms (mcg)) folic acid daily before conception and continuing into early pregnancy had a reduced risk of having a child with a neural tube defect. (Products containing this level of folic acid are drugs). In addition, based on its review of a Hungarian intervention trial that reported periconceptional use of a multivitamin and multimineral preparation containing 800 mcg (0.8 mg) of folic acid, and its review of the observational studies that reported periconceptional use of multivitamins containing 0 to 1,000 mcg of folic acid, the Food and Drug Administration concluded that most of these studies had results consistent with the conclusion that folate, at levels attainable in usual diets, may reduce the risk of neural tube defects.

(b) *Significance of folate –*

(1) *Public health concern.* Neural tube defects occur in approximately 0.6 of 1,000 live births in the United States (i.e., approximately 6 of 10,000 live births; about 2,500 cases among 4 million live births annually). Neural tube defects are believed to be caused by many factors. The single greatest risk factor for a neural tube defect-affected pregnancy is a personal or family history of a pregnancy affected with a such a defect. However, about 90 percent of infants with a neural tube defect are born to women who do not have a family history of these defects. The available evidence shows that diets adequate in folate may reduce the risk of neural tube defects but not of other birth defects.

(2) *Populations at risk.* Prevalence rates for neural tube defects have been reported to vary with a wide range of factors including genetics, geography, socioeconomic status, maternal birth cohort, month of conception, race, nutrition, and maternal health, including maternal age and reproductive history. Women with a close relative (i.e., sibling, niece, nephew) with a neural tube defect, those with insulin-dependent diabetes mellitus, and women with seizure disorders who are being treated with valproic acid or carbamazepine are at significantly increased risk compared with women without these characteristics. Rates for neural tube defects vary within the

United States, with lower rates observed on the west coast than on the east coast.

(3) *Those who may benefit*. Based on a synthesis of information from several studies, including those which used multivitamins containing folic acid at a daily dose level of =400 mcg (=0.4 mg), the Public Health Service has inferred that folate alone at levels of 400 mcg (0.4 mg) per day may reduce the risk of neural tube defects. The protective effect found in studies of lower dose folate measured by the reduction in neural tube defect incidence, ranges from none to substantial; a reasonable estimate of the expected reduction in the United States is 50 percent. It is expected that consumption of adequate folate will avert some, but not all, neural tube defects. The underlying causes of neural tube defects are not known. Thus, it is not known what proportion of neural tube defects will be averted by adequate folate consumption. From the available evidence, the Public Health Service estimates that there is the potential for averting 50 percent of cases that now occur (i.e., about 1,250 cases annually). However, until further research is done, no firm estimate of this proportion will be available.

(c) *Requirements*. The label or labeling of food may contain a folate/neural tube defect health claim provided that:

(1) *General requirements*. The health claim for a food meets all of the general requirements of 101.14 for health claims, except that a food may qualify to bear the health claim if it meets the definition of the term "good source."

(2) *Specific requirements* –

(i) *Nature of the claim* –

(A) *Relationship*. A health claim that women who are capable of becoming pregnant and who consume adequate amounts of folate daily during their childbearing years may reduce their risk of having a pregnancy affected by spina bifida or other neural tube defects may be made on the label or labeling of food provided that:

(B) *Specifying the nutrient*. In specifying the nutrient, the claim shall use the terms "folate," "folic acid," "folacin," "folate, a B vitamin," "folic acid, a B vitamin," or "folacin, a B vitamin."

(C) *Specifying the condition*. In specifying the health- related condition, the claim shall identify the birth defects as "neural tube defects," "birth defects spina bifida or anencephaly," "birth defects of the brain or spinal cord anencephaly or spina bifida," "spina bifida and anencephaly, birth defects of the brain or spinal cord," "birth defects of the brain or spinal cord;" or "brain or spinal cord birth defects."

(D) *Multifactorial nature*. The claim shall not imply that folate intake is the only recognized risk factor for neural tube defects.

(E) *Reduction in risk*. The claim shall not attribute any specific degree of reduction in risk of neural tube defects from maintaining an adequate folate intake throughout the childbearing years. The claim shall state that some women may reduce their risk of a neural tube defect pregnancy by maintaining adequate intakes of folate during their childbearing years. Optional statements about population-based estimates of risk reduction may be made in accordance with paragraph (c)(3)(vi) of this section.

(F) *Safe upper limit of daily intake*. Claims on foods that contain more than 100 percent of the Daily Value (DV) (400 mcg) when labeled for use by adults and children 4 or more years of age, or 800 mcg when labeled for use by pregnant or lactating women) shall identify the safe upper limit of daily intake with respect to the DV. The safe upper limit of daily intake value of 1,000 mcg (1 mg) may be included in parentheses.

(G) The claim shall state that folate needs to be consumed as part of a healthful diet.

(ii) *Nature of the food* –

(A) *Requirements*. The food shall meet or exceed the requirements for a "good source" of folate as defined in 101.54;

(B) *Dietary supplements*. Dietary supplements shall meet the United States Pharmacopeia (USP) standards for disintegration and dissolution, except that if there are no applicable USP standards, the folate in the dietary supplement shall be shown to be bioavailable under the conditions of use stated on the product label.

(iii) *Limitation*. The claim shall not be made on foods that contain more than 100 percent of the RDI for vitamin A as retinol or preformed vitamin A or vitamin D per serving or per unit.

(iv) *Nutrition labeling*. The nutrition label shall include information about the amount of folate in the food. This information shall be declared after the declaration for iron if only the levels of vitamin A, vitamin C, calcium, and iron are provided, or in accordance with 101.9 (c)(8) and (c)(9) if other optional vitamins or minerals are declared.

(3) *Optional information* –

(i) *Risk factors*. The claim may specifically identify risk factors for neural tube defects. Where such information is provided, it may consist of statements from 101.79(b)(1) or (b)(2) (e.g., Women at increased risk include those with a personal history of a neural tube defect-affected pregnancy, those with a close relative (i.e., sibling, niece, nephew) with a neural tube defect; those with insulin-dependent diabetes mellitus; those with seizure disorders who are being treated with valproic acid or carbamazepine) or from other parts of this paragraph (c)(3)(i).

(ii) *Relationship between folate and neural tube defects*. The claim may include statements from paragraphs (a) and (b) of this section that summarize the relationship between folate and neural tube defects and the significance of the relationship except for information specifically prohibited from the claim.

(iii) *Personal history of a neural tube defect-affected pregnancy.* The claim may state that women with a history of a neural tube defect pregnancy should consult their physicians or health care providers before becoming pregnant. If such a statement is provided, the claim shall also state that all women should consult a health care provider when planning a pregnancy.

(iv) *Daily value.* The claim may identify 100 percent of the DV (100% DV; 400 mcg) for folate as the target intake goal.

(v) *Prevalence.* The claim may provide estimates, expressed on an annual basis, of the number of neural tube defect-affected births among live births in the United States. Current estimates are provided in 101.79(b)(1), and are approximately 6 of 10,000 live births annually (i.e., about 2,500 cases among 4 million live births annually). Data provided in 101.79(b)(1) shall be used, unless more current estimates from the U.S. Public Health Service are available, in which case the latter may be cited.

(vi) *Reduction in risk.* An estimate of the reduction in the number of neural tube defect-affected births that might occur in the United States if all women consumed adequate folate throughout their childbearing years may be included in the claim. Information contained in paragraph (b)(3) of this section may be used. If such an estimate (i.e., 50 percent) is provided, the estimate shall be accompanied by additional information that states that the estimate is population-based and that it does not reflect risk reduction that may be experienced by individual women.

(vii) *Diets adequate in folate.* The claim may identify diets adequate in folate by using phrases such as "Sources of folate include fruits, vegetables, whole grain products, fortified cereals, and dietary supplements." or "Adequate amounts of folate can be obtained from diets rich in fruits, dark green leafy vegetables, legumes, whole grain products, fortified cereals, or dietary supplements." or "Adequate amounts of folate can be obtained from diets rich in fruits, including citrus fruits and juices, vegetables, including dark green leafy vegetables, legumes, whole grain products, including breads, rice, and pasta, fortified cereals, or a dietary supplement."

(d) *Model health claims.* The following are examples of model health claims that may be used in food labeling to describe the relationship between folate and neural tube defects:

(1) *Examples 1 and 2.* Model health claims appropriate for foods containing 100 percent or less of the DV for folate per serving or per unit (general population). The examples contain only the required elements:

(i) Healthful diets with adequate folate may reduce a woman's risk of having a child with a brain or spinal cord birth defect.

      (ii) Adequate folate in healthful diets may reduce a woman's risk of having a child with a brain or spinal cord birth defect.

  (2) *Example 3*. Model health claim appropriate for foods containing 100 percent or less of the DV for folate per serving or per unit. The example contains all required elements plus optional information: Women who consume healthful diets with adequate folate throughout their childbearing years may reduce their risk of having a child with a birth defect of the brain or spinal cord. Sources of folate include fruits, vegetables, whole grain products, fortified cereals, and dietary supplements.

  (3) *Example 4*. Model health claim appropriate for foods intended for use by the general population and containing more than 100 percent of the DV of folate per serving or per unit: Women who consume healthful diets with adequate folate may reduce their risk of having a child with birth defects of the brain or spinal cord. Folate intake should not exceed 250% of the DV (1,000 mcg).

[61 FR 8779, Mar. 5, 1996; 61 FR 48529, Sept. 13, 1996, as amended at 65 FR 58918, Oct. 3, 2000]

Sec. 101.83 Health claims: plant sterol/stanol esters and risk of coronary heart disease (CHD).

(a) *Relationship between diets that include plant sterol/stanol esters and the risk of CHD.*

  (1) Cardiovascular disease means diseases of the heart and circulatory system. Coronary heart disease (CHD) is one of the most common and serious forms of cardiovascular disease and refers to diseases of the heart muscle and supporting blood vessels. High blood total cholesterol and low density lipoprotein (LDL) cholesterol levels are associated with increased risk of developing coronary heart disease. High CHD rates occur among people with high total cholesterol levels of 240 milligrams per deciliter (mg/dL) (6.21 millimole per liter (mmol/l)) or above and LDL cholesterol levels of 160 mg/dL (4.13 mmol/l) or above. Borderline high risk blood cholesterol levels range from 200 to 239 mg/dL (5.17 to 6.18 mmol/l) for total cholesterol, and 130 to 159 mg/dL (3.36 to 4.11 mmol/l) of LDL cholesterol.

  (2) Populations with a low incidence of CHD tend to have relatively low blood total cholesterol and LDL cholesterol levels. These populations also tend to have dietary patterns that are not only low in total fat, especially saturated fat and cholesterol, but are also relatively high in plant foods that contain dietary fiber and other components.

  (3) Scientific evidence demonstrates that diets that include plant sterol/stanol esters may reduce the risk of CHD.

(b) *Significance of the relationship between diets that include plant sterol/stanol esters and the risk of CHD.*

(1) CHD is a major public health concern in the United States. It accounts for more deaths than any other disease or group of diseases. Early management of risk factors for CHD is a major public health goal that can assist in reducing risk of CHD. High blood total and LDL cholesterol are major modifiable risk factors in the development of CHD.

(2) The scientific evidence establishes that including plant sterol/stanol esters in the diet helps to lower blood total and LDL cholesterol levels.

(c) *Requirements* –

(1) *General.* All requirements set forth in 101.14 shall be met, except 101.14(a)(4) with respect to the disqualifying level for total fat per 50 grams (g) in dressings for salad and spreads and 101.14(e)(6) with respect to dressings for salad.

(2) *Specific requirements* —

(i) *Nature of the claim.* A health claim associating diets that include plant sterol/stanol esters with reduced risk of heart disease may be made on the label or labeling of a food described in paragraph (c)(2)(iii) of this section, provided that:

(A) The claim states that plant sterol/stanol esters should be consumed as part of a diet low in saturated fat and cholesterol;

(B) The claim states that diets that include plant sterol/stanol esters "may" or "might" reduce the risk of heart disease;

(C) In specifying the disease, the claim uses the following terms: "heart disease" or "coronary heart disease";

(D) In specifying the substance, the claim uses the term "plant sterol esters" or "plant stanol esters," except that if the sole source of the plant sterols or stanols is vegetable oil, the claim may use the term "vegetable oil sterol esters" or "vegetable oil stanol esters";

(E) The claim does not attribute any degree of risk reduction for CHD to diets that include plant sterol/stanol esters;

(F) The claim does not imply that consumption of diets that include plant sterol/stanol esters is the only recognized means of achieving a reduced risk of CHD; and

(G) The claim specifies the daily dietary intake of plant sterol or stanol esters that is necessary to reduce the risk of CHD and the contribution one serving of the product makes to the specified daily dietary intake level. Daily dietary intake levels of plant sterol and stanol esters that have been associated with reduced risk of are:

(1) 1.3 g or more per day of plant sterol esters.

(2) 3.4 g or more per day of plant stanol esters.

(H) The claim specifies that the daily dietary intake of plant sterol or stanol esters should be consumed in two servings eaten at different times of the day with other foods.

(ii) *Nature of the substance* –

(A) *Plant sterol esters.*

(1) Plant sterol esters prepared by esterifying a mixture of plant sterols from edible oils with food-grade fatty acids. The plant sterol mixture shall contain at least 80 percent beta-sitosterol, campesterol, and stigmasterol (combined weight).

(2) FDA will measure plant sterol esters by the method entitled "Determination of the Sterol Content in Margarines, Halvarines, Dressings, Fat Blends and Sterol Fatty Acid Ester Concentrates by Capillary Gas Chromatography," developed by Unilever United States, Inc., dated February 1, 2000. The method, which is incorporated by reference in accordance with 5 U.S.C. 552(a) and 1 CFR part 51, may be obtained from the Center for Food Safety and Applied Nutrition, Office of Nutrition, Labeling and Dietary Supplements, Nutrition Programs Staff, 5001 Campus Dr., College Park, MD 20740, and may be examined at the Food and Drug Administration's Main Library, 10903 New Hampshire Ave., Bldg. 2, Third Floor, Silver Spring, MD 20993, 301-796-2039, or at the National Archives and Records Administration (NARA). For information on the availability of this material at NARA, call 202-741-6030, or go to: http://www.archives.gov/federal_register/code_of_federal_regulations/ibr_locations.html.

(B) *Plant stanol esters.*

(1) Plant stanol esters prepared by esterifying a mixture of plant stanols derived from edible oils or byproducts of the kraft paper pulping process with food-grade fatty acids. The plant stanol mixture shall contain at least 80 percent sitostanol and campestanol (combined weight).

(2) FDA will measure plant stanol esters by the following methods developed by McNeil Consumer Heathcare dated February 15, 2000: "Determination of Stanols and Sterols in Benecol Tub Spread"; "Determination of Stanols and Sterols in Benecol Dressing"; "Determination of Stanols and Sterols in Benecol Snack Bars"; or "Determination of Stanols and Sterols in Benecol Softgels." These methods are incorporated by reference in accordance with 5 U.S.C. 552(a) and 1 CFR part 51. Copies may be obtained from the Center for Food Safety and Applied Nutrition, Office of Nutrition, Labeling and Dietary Supplements, Nutrition Programs Staff, 5001 Campus Dr., College Park, MD 20740, or may be examined at the Food and Drug Administration's Main Library, 10903 New Hampshire Ave., Bldg. 2,

Third Floor, Silver Spring, MD 20993, 301-796-2039, and at the National Archives and Records Administration (NARA). For information on the availability of this material at NARA, call 202-741-6030, or go to: http://www.archives.gov/federal_register/code_of_federal_regulations/ibr_locations.html.

    (iii) *Nature of the food eligible to bear the claim.*

        (A) The food product shall contain:

            (1) At least 0.65 g of plant sterol esters that comply with paragraph (c)(2)(ii)(A)(1) of this section per reference amount customarily consumed of the food products eligible to bear the health claim, specifically spreads and dressings for salad, or

            (2) At least 1.7 g of plant stanol esters that comply with paragraph (c)(2)(ii)(B)(1) of this section per reference amount customarily consumed of the food products eligible to bear the health claim, specifically spreads, dressings for salad, snack bars, and dietary supplements in softgel form.

        (B) The food shall meet the nutrient content requirements in 101.62 for a "low saturated fat" and "low cholesterol" food; and

        (C) The food must meet the limit for total fat in 101.14(a)(4), except that spreads and dressings for salad are not required to meet the limit for total fat per 50 g if the label of the food bears a disclosure statement that complies with 101.13(h); and

        (D) The food must meet the minimum nutrient contribution requirement in 101.14(e)(6) unless it is a dressing for salad.

(d) *Optional information.*

    (1) The claim may state that the development of heart disease depends on many factors and may identify one or more of the following risk factors for heart disease about which there is general scientific agreement: A family history of CHD; elevated blood total and LDL cholesterol; excess body weight; high blood pressure; cigarette smoking; diabetes; and physical inactivity. The claim may also provide additional information about the benefits of exercise and management of body weight to help lower the risk of heart disease.

    (2) The claim may state that the relationship between intake of diets that include plant sterol/stanol esters and reduced risk of heart disease is through the intermediate link of "blood cholesterol" or "blood total and LDL cholesterol."

    (3) The claim may include information from paragraphs (a) and (b) of this section, which summarize the relationship between diets that include plant sterol/stanol esters and the risk of CHD and the significance of the relationship.

    (4) The claim may include information from the following paragraph on the relationship between saturated fat and cholesterol in the diet and the risk of CHD: The scientific

evidence establishes that diets high in saturated fat and cholesterol are associated with increased levels of blood total and LDL cholesterol and, thus, with increased risk of CHD. Intakes of saturated fat exceed recommended levels in the diets of many people in the United States. One of the major public health recommendations relative to CHD risk is to consume less than 10 percent of calories from saturated fat and an average of 30 percent or less of total calories from all fat. Recommended daily cholesterol intakes are 300 mg or less per day. Scientific evidence demonstrates that diets low in saturated fat and cholesterol are associated with lower blood total and LDL cholesterol levels.

(5) The claim may state that diets that include plant sterol or stanol esters and are low in saturated fat and cholesterol are consistent with "Nutrition and Your Health: Dietary Guidelines for Americans," U.S. Department of Agriculture (USDA) and Department of Health and Human Services (DHHS), Government Printing Office (GPO).

(6) The claim may state that individuals with elevated blood total and LDL cholesterol should consult their physicians for medical advice and treatment. If the claim defines high or normal blood total and LDL cholesterol levels, then the claim shall state that individuals with high blood cholesterol should consult their physicians for medical advice and treatment.

(7) The claim may include information on the number of people in the United States who have heart disease. The sources of this information shall be identified, and it shall be current information from the National Center for Health Statistics, the National Institutes of Health, or "Nutrition and Your Health: Dietary Guidelines for Americans," U.S. Department of Agriculture (USDA) and Department of Health and Human Services (DHHS), Government Printing Office (GPO).

(e) *Model health claim*. The following model health claims may be used in food labeling to describe the relationship between diets that include plant sterol or stanol esters and reduced risk of heart disease:

(1) *For plant sterol esters*:

(i) Foods containing at least 0.65 g per serving of plant sterol esters, eaten twice a day with meals for a daily total intake of at least 1.3 g, as part of a diet low in saturated fat and cholesterol, may reduce the risk of heart disease. A serving of [name of the food] supplies ____grams of vegetable oil sterol esters.

(ii) Diets low in saturated fat and cholesterol that include two servings of foods that provide a daily total of at least 1.3 g of vegetable oil sterol esters in two meals may reduce the risk of heart disease. A serving of [name of the food] supplies ____grams of vegetable oil sterol esters.

(2) *For plant stanol esters*:

(i) Foods containing at least 1.7 g per serving of plant stanol esters, eaten twice a day with meals for a total daily intake of at least 3.4 g, as part of a diet low in saturated fat and cholesterol, may reduce the risk of heart disease. A serving of [name of the food] supplies ____grams of plant stanol esters.

(ii) Diets low in saturated fat and cholesterol that include two servings of foods that provide a daily total of at least 3.4 g of vegetable oil stanol esters in two meals may reduce the risk of heart disease. A serving of [name of the food] supplies ___grams of vegetable oil stanol esters.

[65 FR 54717, Sept. 8, 2000; 65 FR 70466, Nov. 24, 2000, as amended at 66 FR 66742, Dec. 27, 2001; 68 FR 15355, Mar. 31, 2003; 70 FR 41958, July 21,2005]

Subpart F– Specific Requirements for Descriptive Claims That Are Neither Nutrient Content Claims nor Health Claims

Sec. 101.91 Gluten-free labeling of food.

(a) *Definitions*.

(1) The term "gluten-containing grain" means any one of the following grains or their crossbred hybrids (e.g., triticale, which is a cross between wheat and rye):

(i) Wheat, including any species belonging to the genus *Triticum*;

(ii) Rye, including any species belonging to the genus *Secale*; or

(iii) Barley, including any species belonging to the genus *Hordeum*.

(2) The term "gluten" means the proteins that naturally occur in a gluten-containing grain and that may cause adverse health effects in persons with celiac disease (e.g., prolamins and glutelins).

(3) The labeling claim "gluten-free" means:

(i) That the food bearing the claim in its labeling:

(A) Does not contain any one of the following:

(1) An ingredient that is a gluten-containing grain (e.g., spelt wheat);

(2) An ingredient that is derived from a gluten-containing grain and that has not been processed to remove gluten (e.g., wheat flour); or

(3) An ingredient that is derived from a gluten-containing grain and that has been processed to remove gluten (e.g., wheat starch), if the use of that ingredient results in the presence of 20 parts per million (ppm) or more gluten in the food (i.e., 20 milligrams (mg) or more gluten per kilogram (kg) of food); or

(B) Inherently does not contain gluten; and

(ii) Any unavoidable presence of gluten in the food bearing the claim in its labeling is below 20 ppm gluten (i.e., below 20 mg gluten per kg of food).

(b) *Requirements.*

(1) A food that bears the claim "gluten-free" in its labeling and fails to meet the requirements of paragraph (a)(3) of this section will be deemed misbranded.

(2) A food that bears the claim "no gluten," "free of gluten," or "without gluten" in its labeling and fails to meet the requirements of paragraph (a)(3) of this section will be deemed misbranded.

(3) A food that bears the term "wheat" in the ingredient list or in a separate "Contains wheat" statement in its labeling, as required by 21 U.S.C. 343(w)(1)(A), and also bears the claim "gluten-free" or a claim identified in paragraph (b)(2) of this section will be deemed misbranded unless the word "wheat" in the ingredient list or in the "Contains wheat" statement is followed immediately by an asterisk (or other symbol) that refers to another asterisk (or other symbol) in close proximity to the ingredient statement that immediately precedes the following: "The wheat has been processed to allow this food to meet the Food and Drug Administration (FDA) requirements for gluten-free foods."

(c) *Compliance.* When compliance with paragraph (b) of this section is based on an analysis of the food, FDA will use a scientifically valid method that can reliably detect the presence of 20 ppm gluten in a variety of food matrices, including both raw and cooked or baked products.

(d) Preemption. A State or political subdivision of a State may not establish or continue into effect any law, rule, regulation, or other requirement that is different from the requirements in this section for the definition and use of the claim "gluten-free," as well as the claims "no gluten," "free of gluten," or "without gluten."

[78 FR 47178, Aug. 5, 2013]

Sec. 101.93 Certain types of statements for dietary supplements.

(a)(1) No later than 30 days after the first marketing of a dietary supplement that bears one of the statements listed in section 403(r)(6) or the Federal Food, Drug, and Cosmetic Act, the manufacturer, packer, or distributor of the dietary supplement shall notify the Office of Nutritional Products, Labeling and Dietary Supplements (HFS-810), Center for Food Safety and Applied Nutrition, Food and Drug Administration, 5001 Campus Dr., College Park, MD 20740, that it has included such a statement on the label or in the labeling of its product. An original and two copies of this notification shall be submitted.

(2) The notification shall include the following:

(i) The name and address of the manufacturer, packer, or distributor of the dietary supplement that bears the statement;

(ii) The text of the statement that is being made;

(iii) The name of the dietary ingredient or supplement that is the subject of the statement, if not provided in the text of the statement; and

(iv) The name of the dietary supplement (including brand name), if not provided in response to paragraph (a)(2)(iii) on whose label, or in whose labeling, the statement appears.

(3) The notice shall be signed by a responsible individual or the person who can certify the accuracy of the information presented and contained in the notice. The individual shall certify that the information contained in the notice is complete and accurate, and that the notifying firm has substantiation that the statement is truthful and not misleading.

(b) *Disclaimer.* The requirements in this section apply to the label or labeling of dietary supplements where the dietary supplement bears a statement that is provided for by section 403(r)(6) of the Federal Food, Drug, and Cosmetic Act (the act), and the manufacturer, packer, or distributor wishes to take advantage of the exemption to section 201(g)(1)(C) of the act that is provided by compliance with section 403(r)(6) of the act.

(c) *Text for disclaimer.*

(1) Where there is one statement, the disclaimer shall be placed in accordance with paragraph (d) of this section and shall state:

> **This statement has not been evaluated by the Food and Drug Administration. This product is not intended to diagnose, treat, cure, or prevent any disease.**

(2) Where there is more than one such statement on the label or in the labeling, each statement shall bear the disclaimer in accordance with paragraph (c)(1) of this section, or a plural disclaimer may be placed in accordance with paragraph (d) of this section and shall state:

> **These statements have not been evaluated by the Food and Drug Administration. This product is not intended to diagnose, treat, cure, or prevent any disease.**

(d) *Placement.* The disclaimer shall be placed adjacent to the statement with no intervening material or linked to the statement with a symbol (e.g., an asterisk) at the end of each such statement that refers to the same symbol placed adjacent to the disclaimer specified in paragraphs (c)(1) or (c)(2) of this section. On product labels and in labeling (e.g., pamphlets, catalogs), the disclaimer shall appear on each panel or page where there such is a statement. The disclaimer shall be set off in a box where it is not adjacent to the statement in question.

(e) *Typesize.* The disclaimer in paragraph (c) of this section shall appear in boldface type in letters of a typesize no smaller than one-sixteenth inch.

(f) *Permitted structure/function statements.* Dietary supplement labels or labeling may, subject to the requirements in paragraphs (a) through (e) of this section, bear statements that describe the role of a nutrient or dietary ingredient intended to affect the structure or function in humans or that characterize the documented mechanism by which a nutrient or dietary ingredient acts to maintain such structure or function, provided that such statements are not disease claims under paragraph (g) of this section. If the label or labeling of a product marketed as a dietary supplement bears a disease claim as defined in paragraph (g) of this section, the product will be subject to regulation as a drug unless the claim is an authorized health claim for which the product qualifies.

(g) *Disease claims.*

(1) For purposes of 21 U.S.C. 343(r)(6), a "disease" is damage to an organ, part, structure, or system of the body such that it does not function properly (e.g., cardiovascular disease), or a state of health leading to such dysfunctioning (e.g., hypertension); except that diseases resulting from essential nutrient deficiencies (e.g., scurvy, pellagra) are not included in this definition.

(2) FDA will find that a statement about a product claims to diagnose, mitigate, treat, cure, or prevent disease (other than a classical nutrient deficiency disease) under 21 U.S.C. 343(r)(6) if it meets one or more of the criteria listed below. These criteria are not intended to classify as disease claims statements that refer to the ability of a product to maintain healthy structure or function, unless the statement implies disease prevention or treatment. In determining whether a statement is a disease claim under these criteria, FDA will consider the context in which the claim is presented. A statement claims to diagnose, mitigate, treat, cure, or prevent disease if it claims, explicitly or implicitly, that the product:

(i) Has an effect on a specific disease or class of diseases;

(ii) Has an effect on the characteristic signs or symptoms of a specific disease or class of diseases, using scientific or lay terminology;

(iii) Has an effect on an abnormal condition associated with a natural state or process, if the abnormal condition is uncommon or can cause significant or permanent harm;

(iv) Has an effect on a disease or diseases through one or more of the following factors:

(A) The name of the product;

(B) A statement about the formulation of the product, including a claim that the product contains an ingredient (other than an ingredient that is an article included in the definition of "dietary supplement" under 21 U.S.C. 321(ff)(3)) that has been regulated by FDA as a drug and is well known to consumers for its use or claimed use in preventing or treating a disease;

(C) Citation of a publication or reference, if the citation refers to a disease use, and if, in the context of the labeling as a whole, the citation implies treatment or prevention of a disease, e.g., through placement on the immediate product label or packaging, inappropriate prominence, or lack of relationship to the product's express claims;

(D) Use of the term "disease" or "diseased," except in general statements about disease prevention that do not refer explicitly or implicitly to a specific disease or class of diseases or to a specific product or ingredient; or

(E) Use of pictures, vignettes, symbols, or other means;

(v) Belongs to a class of products that is intended to diagnose, mitigate, treat, cure, or prevent a disease;

(vi) Is a substitute for a product that is a therapy for a disease;

(vii) Augments a particular therapy or drug action that is intended to diagnose, mitigate, treat, cure, or prevent a disease or class of diseases;

(viii) Has a role in the body's response to a disease or to a vector of disease;

(ix) Treats, prevents, or mitigates adverse events associated with a therapy for a disease, if the adverse events constitute diseases; or

(x) Otherwise suggests an effect on a disease or diseases.

[62 FR 49886, Sept. 23, 1997, as amended at 62 FR 49867, Sept. 23, 1997; 65 FR 1050, Jan. 6, 2000; 66 FR 17358, Mar. 30, 2001; 66 FR 56035, Nov. 6, 2001]

Appendix B to Part 101–Graphic Enhancements Used by the FDA

Examples of Graphic Enhancements used by the FDA

A. Overall

1. Nutrition Facts Label is boxed with all black or one color type printed on a white or neutral ground.

B. Typeface and size

1. The "Nutrition Facts" label uses 6 point or larger Helvetica Black and/or Helvetica Regular type. In order to fit some formats the typography may be kerned as much as -4, (tighter kerning reduces legibility).

2. Key nutrients & their % Daily Value are set in 8 point Helvetica Black (but "%" is set in Helvetica Regular).

3. "Nutrition Facts" is set in either Franklin Gothic Heavy or Helvetica Black to fit the width of the label flush left and flush right.

4. "Serving Size" and "Servings per container" are set in 8 point Helvetica Regular with 1 point of leading.

5. The table labels (for example; "Amount per Serving") are set 6 point Helvetica Black.

6. Absolute measures of nutrient content (for example; "1g") and nutrient subgroups are set in 8 point Helvetica Regular with 4 points of leading.

7. Vitamins and minerals are set in 8 point Helvetica Regular, with 4 points of leading, separated by 10 point bullets.

8. All type that appears under vitamins and minerals is set in 6 point Helvetica regular with 1 point of leading.

C. Rules

1. A 7 point rule separates large groupings as shown in example. A 3 point rule separates calorie information from the nutrient information.

2. A hairline rule or 1/4 point rule separates individual nutrients, as shown in the example. Descenders do not touch rule. The top half of the label (nutrient information) has 2 points of leading between the type and the rules, the bottom half of the label (footnotes) has 1 point of leading between the type and the rules.

D. Box

1. All labels are enclosed by 1/2 point box rule within 3 points of text measure.

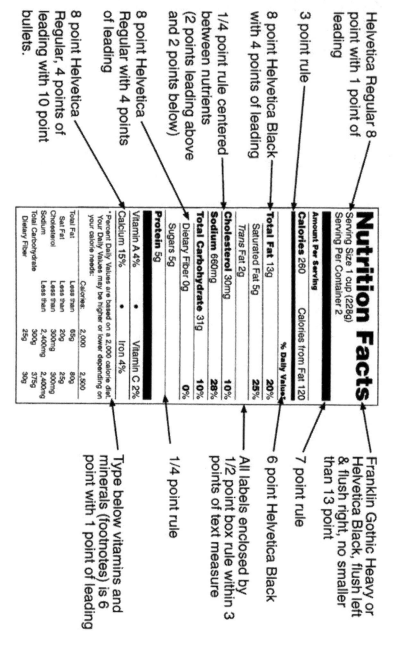

Examples of Graphic Enhancements used by the FDA

Helvetica Regular 8
point with 1 point of
leading

3 point rule

8 point Helvetica Black
with 4 points of leading

1/4 point rule centered
between nutrients
(2 points leading above
and 2 points below)

8 point Helvetica
Regular with 4 points
of leading

8 point Helvetica
Regular, 4 points of
leading with 10 point
bullets.

Franklin Gothic Heavy or
Helvetica Black, flush left
& flush right, no smaller
than 13 point

6 point Helvetica Black

7 point rule

All labels enclosed by
1/2 point box rule within 3
points of text measure

1/4 point rule

Type below vitamins and
minerals (footnotes) is 6
point with 1 point of leading

Nutrition Facts

Amount Per Serving

Serving Size 1 cup (228g)
Serving Per Container 2

Calories 260   Calories from Fat 120

% Daily Value*

Total Fat 13g   20%

Saturated Fat 5g   25%

Trans Fat 2g

Cholesterol 30mg   10%

Sodium 660mg   28%

Total Carbohydrate 31g   10%

Dietary Fiber 0g   0%

Sugars 5g

Protein 5g

Vitamin A 4%   •   Vitamin C 2%

Calcium 15%   •   Iron 4%

*Percent Daily Values are based on a 2,000 calorie diet.
Your Daily Values may be higher or lower depending on
your calorie needs:

	Calories:	2,000	2,500
Total Fat	Less than	65g	80g
Sat Fat	Less than	20g	25g
Cholesterol	Less than	300mg	300mg
Sodium	Less than	2,400mg	2,400mg
Total Carbohydrate		300g	375g
Dietary Fiber		25g	30g

[58 FR 17332, Apr. 2, 1993, as amended at 68 FR 41506, July 11, 2003]

21CFR

Part 111
Current Good Manufacturing Practice in Manufacturing, Packaging, Labeling, or Holding Operations for Dietary Supplements

[Code of Federal Regulations]
[Title 21, Volume 2]
[Revised as of April 1, 2017]
[CITE: 21CFR111]

Title 21–Food and Drugs
Chapter I–Food and Drug Administration
Department of Health and Human Services
Subchapter B–Food for Human Consumption
Part 111–Current Good Manufacturing Practice in Manufacturing, Packaging, Labeling, or Holding Operations for Dietary Supplements[1]

Subpart A–General Provisions

Sec. 111.1 Who is subject to this part?

(a) Except as provided by paragraph (b) of this section, you are subject to this part if you manufacture, package, label, or hold a dietary supplement, including:

   (1) A dietary supplement you manufacture but that is packaged or labeled by another person; and

   (2) A dietary supplement imported or offered for import in any State or territory of the United States, the District of Columbia, or the Commonwealth of Puerto Rico.

(b) The requirements pertaining to holding dietary supplements do not apply to you if you are holding those dietary supplements at a retail establishment for the sole purpose of direct retail sale to individual consumers. A retail establishment does not include a warehouse or other storage facility for a retailer or a warehouse or other storage facility that sells directly to individual consumers.

Sec. 111.3 What definitions apply to this part?

The definitions and interpretations of terms in section 201 of the Federal Food, Drug, and

---

1   21CFR§111 is available on the FDA website at https://www.accessdata.fda.gov/scripts/cdrh/cfdocs/cfcfr/CFRSearch.cfm

Cosmetic Act (the act) apply to such terms when used in this part. For the purpose of this part, the following definitions also apply:

Actual yield means the quantity that is actually produced at any appropriate step of manufacture or packaging of a particular dietary supplement.

Batch means a specific quantity of a dietary supplement that is uniform, that is intended to meet specifications for identity, purity, strength, and composition, and that is produced during a specified time period according to a single manufacturing record during the same cycle of manufacture.

Batch number, lot number, or control number means any distinctive group of letters, numbers, or symbols, or any combination of them, from which the complete history of the manufacturing, packaging, labeling, and/or holding of a batch or lot of dietary supplements can be determined.

Component means any substance intended for use in the manufacture of a dietary supplement, including those that may not appear in the finished batch of the dietary supplement. Component includes dietary ingredients (as described in section 201(ff) of the act) and other ingredients.

Contact surface means any surface that contacts a component or dietary supplement, and those surfaces from which drainage onto the component or dietary supplement, or onto surfaces that contact the component or dietary supplement, occurs during the normal course of operations. Examples of contact surfaces include containers, utensils, tables, contact surfaces of equipment, and packaging.

Ingredient means any substance that is used in the manufacture of a dietary supplement and that is intended to be present in the finished batch of the dietary supplement. An ingredient includes, but is not necessarily limited to, a dietary ingredient as defined in section 201(ff) of the act.

In-process material means any material that is fabricated, compounded, blended, ground, extracted, sifted, sterilized, derived by chemical reaction, or processed in any other way for use in the manufacture of a dietary supplement.

Lot means a batch, or a specific identified portion of a batch, that is uniform and that is intended to meet specifications for identity, purity, strength, and composition; or, in the case of a dietary supplement produced by continuous process, a specific identified amount produced in a specified unit of time or quantity in a manner that is uniform and that is intended to meet specifications for identity, purity, strength, and composition.

Microorganisms means yeasts, molds, bacteria, viruses, and other similar microscopic organisms having public health or sanitary concern. This definition includes species that:

(1) May have public health significance;

(2) May cause a component or dietary supplement to decompose;

(3) Indicate that the component or dietary supplement is contaminated with filth; or

(4) Otherwise may cause the component or dietary supplement to be adulterated.

Must is used to state a requirement.

Pest means any objectionable insect or other animal including birds, rodents, flies, mites, and larvae.

Physical plant means all or any part of a building or facility used for or in connection with manufacturing, packaging, labeling, or holding a dietary supplement.

Product complaint means any communication that contains any allegation, written, electronic, or oral, expressing concern, for any reason, with the quality of a dietary supplement, that could be related to current good manufacturing practice. Examples of product complaints are: Foul odor, off taste, illness or injury, disintegration time, color variation, tablet size or size variation, under-filled container, foreign material in a dietary supplement container, improper packaging, mislabeling, or dietary supplements that are superpotent, subpotent, or contain the wrong ingredient, or contain a drug or other contaminant (e.g., bacteria, pesticide, mycotoxin, glass, lead).

Quality means that the dietary supplement consistently meets the established specifications for identity, purity, strength, and composition, and limits on contaminants, and has been manufactured, packaged, labeled, and held under conditions to prevent adulteration under section 402(a)(1), (a)(2), (a)(3), and (a)(4) of the act.

Quality control means a planned and systematic operation or procedure for ensuring the quality of a dietary supplement.

Quality control personnel means any person, persons, or group, within or outside of your organization, who you designate to be responsible for your quality control operations.

Representative sample means a sample that consists of an adequate number of units that are drawn based on rational criteria, such as random sampling, and that are intended to ensure that the sample accurately portrays the material being sampled.

Reprocessing means using, in the manufacture of a dietary supplement, clean, uncontaminated components or dietary supplements that have been previously removed from manufacturing and that have been made suitable for use in the manufacture of a dietary supplement.

Reserve sample means a representative sample of product that is held for a designated period of time.

Sanitize means to adequately treat cleaned equipment, containers, utensils, or any other cleaned contact surface by a process that is effective in destroying vegetative cells of microorganisms of public health significance, and in substantially reducing numbers of other microorganisms, but without adversely affecting the product or its safety for the consumer.

Theoretical yield means the quantity that would be produced at any appropriate step of manufacture or packaging of a particular dietary supplement, based upon the quantity of components or packaging to be used, in the absence of any loss or error in actual production.

Water activity (aw) is a measure of the free moisture in a component or dietary supplement and is the quotient of the water vapor pressure of the substance divided by the vapor pressure of pure water at the same temperature.

We means the U.S. Food and Drug Administration (FDA).

You means a person who manufactures, packages, labels, or holds dietary supplements.

Sec. 111.5 Do other statutory provisions and regulations apply?

In addition to this part, you must comply with other applicable statutory provisions and regulations under the act related to dietary supplements. For importers of dietary supplements and dietary supplement components, the regulation on foreign supplier verification programs can be found in subpart L of part 1 of this chapter.

[72 FR 34942, June 25, 2007, as amended at 80 FR 74352, Nov. 27, 2015]
Authority: 21 U.S.C. 321, 342, 343, 371, 374, 381, 393; 42 U.S.C. 264.
Source: 72 FR 34942, June 25, 2007, unless otherwise noted.

Subpart B–Personnel

Sec. 111.8 What are the requirements under this subpart B for written procedures?

You must establish and follow written procedures for fulfilling the requirements of this subpart.

Sec. 111.10 What requirements apply for preventing microbial contamination from sick or infected personnel and for hygienic practices?

(a) Preventing microbial contamination. You must take measures to exclude from any operations any person who might be a source of microbial contamination, due to a health condition, where such contamination may occur, of any material, including components, dietary supplements, and contact surfaces used in the manufacture, packaging, labeling, or holding of a dietary supplement. Such measures include the following:

(1) Excluding from working in any operations that may result in contamination any person who, by medical examination, the person's acknowledgement, or supervisory observation, is shown to have, or appears to have, an illness, infection, open lesion, or any other abnormal source of microbial contamination, that could result in

microbial contamination of components, dietary supplements, or contact surfaces, until the health condition no longer exists; and

(2) Instructing your employees to notify their supervisor(s) if they have or if there is a reasonable possibility that they have a health condition described in paragraph (a) (1) of this section that could result in microbial contamination of any components, dietary supplements, or any contact surface.

(b) Hygienic practices. If you work in an operation during which adulteration of the component, dietary supplement, or contact surface could occur, you must use hygienic practices to the extent necessary to protect against such contamination of components, dietary supplements, or contact surfaces. These hygienic practices include the following:

(1) Wearing outer garments in a manner that protects against the contamination of components, dietary supplements, or any contact surface;

(2) Maintaining adequate personal cleanliness;

(3) Washing hands thoroughly (and sanitizing if necessary to protect against contamination with microorganisms) in an adequate hand-washing facility:

    (i) Before starting work; and

    (ii) At any time when the hands may have become soiled or contaminated;

(4) Removing all unsecured jewelry and other objects that might fall into components, dietary supplements, equipment, or packaging, and removing hand jewelry that cannot be adequately sanitized during periods in which components or dietary supplements are manipulated by hand. If hand jewelry cannot be removed, it must be covered by material that is maintained in an intact, clean, and sanitary condition and that effectively protects against contamination of components, dietary supplements, or contact surfaces;

(5) Maintaining gloves used in handling components or dietary supplements in an intact, clean, and sanitary condition. The gloves must be of an impermeable material;

(6) Wearing, where appropriate, in an effective manner, hair nets, caps, beard covers, or other effective hair restraints;

(7) Not storing clothing or other personal belongings in areas where components, dietary supplements, or any contact surfaces are exposed or where contact surfaces are washed;

(8) Not eating food, chewing gum, drinking beverages, or using tobacco products in areas where components, dietary supplements, or any contact surfaces are exposed, or where contact surfaces are washed; and

(9) Taking any other precautions necessary to protect against the contamination of components, dietary supplements, or contact surfaces with microorganisms, filth, or any other extraneous materials, including perspiration, hair, cosmetics, tobacco, chemicals, and medicines applied to the skin.

Sec. 111.12 What personnel qualification requirements apply?

(a) You must have qualified employees who manufacture, package, label, or hold dietary supplements.

(b) You must identify who is responsible for your quality control operations. Each person who is identified to perform quality control operations must be qualified to do so and have distinct and separate responsibilities related to performing such operations from those responsibilities that the person otherwise has when not performing such operations.

(c) Each person engaged in manufacturing, packaging, labeling, or holding, or in performing any quality control operations, must have the education, training, or experience to perform the person's assigned functions.

Sec. 111.13 What supervisor requirements apply?

(a) You must assign qualified personnel to supervise the manufacturing, packaging, labeling, or holding of dietary supplements.

(b) Each supervisor whom you use must be qualified by education, training, or experience to supervise.

Sec. 111.14 Under this subpart B, what records must you make and keep?

(a) You must make and keep records required under this subpart B in accordance with subpart P of this part.

(b) You must make and keep the following records:

(1) Written procedures for fulfilling the requirements of this subpart B; and

(2) Documentation of training, including the date of the training, the type of training, and the person(s) trained.

Authority: 21 U.S.C. 321, 342, 343, 371, 374, 381, 393; 42 U.S.C. 264.
Source: 72 FR 34942, June 25, 2007, unless otherwise noted.

Subpart C–Physical Plant and Grounds

Sec. 111.15 What sanitation requirements apply to your physical plant and grounds?

(a) Grounds. You must keep the grounds of your physical plant in a condition that protects against the contamination of components, dietary supplements, or contact surfaces. The methods for adequate ground maintenance include:

(1) Properly storing equipment, removing litter and waste, and cutting weeds or grass within the immediate vicinity of the physical plant so that it does not attract pests, harbor pests, or provide pests a place for breeding;

(2) Maintaining roads, yards, and parking lots so that they do not constitute a source of contamination in areas where components, dietary supplements, or contact surfaces are exposed;

(3) Adequately draining areas that may contribute to the contamination of components, dietary supplements, or contact surfaces by seepage, filth or any other extraneous materials, or by providing a breeding place for pests;

PART

111

(4) Adequately operating systems for waste treatment and disposal so that they do not constitute a source of contamination in areas where components, dietary supplements, or contact surfaces are exposed; and

(5) If your plant grounds are bordered by grounds not under your control, and if those other grounds are not maintained in the manner described in this section, you must exercise care in the plant by inspection, extermination, or other means to exclude pests, dirt, and filth or any other extraneous materials that may be a source of contamination.

(b) Physical plant facilities.

(1) You must maintain your physical plant in a clean and sanitary condition; and

(2) You must maintain your physical plant in repair sufficient to prevent components, dietary supplements, or contact surfaces from becoming contaminated.

(c) Cleaning compounds, sanitizing agents, pesticides, and other toxic materials.

(1) You must use cleaning compounds and sanitizing agents that are free from microorganisms of public health significance and that are safe and adequate under the conditions of use.

(2) You must not use or hold toxic materials in a physical plant in which components, dietary supplements, or contact surfaces are manufactured or exposed, unless those materials are necessary as follows:

(i) To maintain clean and sanitary conditions;

(ii) For use in laboratory testing procedures;

(iii) For maintaining or operating the physical plant or equipment; or

(iv) For use in the plant's operations.

(3) You must identify and hold cleaning compounds, sanitizing agents, pesticides, pesticide chemicals, and other toxic materials in a manner that protects against contamination of components, dietary supplements, or contact surfaces.

(d) Pest control.

(1) You must not allow animals or pests in any area of your physical plant. Guard or guide

dogs are allowed in some areas of your physical plant if the presence of the dogs will not result in contamination of components, dietary supplements, or contact surfaces;

(2) You must take effective measures to exclude pests from the physical plant and to protect against contamination of components, dietary supplements, and contact surfaces on the premises by pests; and

(3) You must not use insecticides, fumigants, fungicides, or rodenticides, unless you take precautions to protect against the contamination of components, dietary supplements, or contact surfaces.

(e) Water supply.

(1) You must provide water that is safe and sanitary, at suitable temperatures, and under pressure as needed, for all uses where water does not become a component of the dietary supplement.

(2) Water that is used in a manner such that the water may become a component of the dietary supplement, e.g., when such water contacts components, dietary supplements, or any contact surface, must, at a minimum, comply with applicable Federal, State, and local requirements and not contaminate the dietary supplement.

(f) Plumbing. The plumbing in your physical plant must be of an adequate size and design and be adequately installed and maintained to:

(1) Carry sufficient amounts of water to required locations throughout the physical plant;

(2) Properly convey sewage and liquid disposable waste from your physical plant;

(3) Avoid being a source of contamination to components, dietary supplements, water supplies, or any contact surface, or creating an unsanitary condition;

(4) Provide adequate floor drainage in all areas where floors are subject to flooding-type cleaning or where normal operations release or discharge water or other liquid waste on the floor; and

(5) Not allow backflow from, or cross connection between, piping systems that discharge waste water or sewage and piping systems that carry water used for manufacturing dietary supplements, for cleaning contact surfaces, or for use in bathrooms or hand-washing facilities.

(g) Sewage disposal. You must dispose of sewage into an adequate sewage system or through other adequate means.

(h) Bathrooms. You must provide your employees with adequate, readily accessible bathrooms. The bathrooms must be kept clean and must not be a potential source of contamination to components, dietary supplements, or contact surfaces.

(i) Hand-washing facilities. You must provide hand-washing facilities that are designed to ensure that an employee's hands are not a source of contamination of components, dietary supplements, or any contact surface, by providing facilities that are adequate, convenient, and furnish running water at a suitable temperature.

(j) Trash disposal. You must convey, store, and dispose of trash to:

   (1) Minimize the development of odors;

   (2) Minimize the potential for the trash to attract, harbor, or become a breeding place for pests;

   (3) Protect against contamination of components, dietary supplements, any contact surface, water supplies, and grounds surrounding your physical plant; and

   (4) Control hazardous waste to prevent contamination of components, dietary supplements, and contact surfaces.

(k) Sanitation supervisors. You must assign one or more employees to supervise overall sanitation. Each of these supervisors must be qualified by education, training, or experience to develop and supervise sanitation procedures.

Sec. 111.16 What are the requirements under this subpart C for written procedures?

You must establish and follow written procedures for cleaning the physical plant and for pest control.

Sec. 111.20 What design and construction requirements apply to your physical plant?

Any physical plant you use in the manufacture, packaging, labeling, or holding of dietary supplements must:

   (a) Be suitable in size, construction, and design to facilitate maintenance, cleaning, and sanitizing operations;

   (b) Have adequate space for the orderly placement of equipment and holding of materials as is necessary for maintenance, cleaning, and sanitizing operations and to prevent contamination and mixups of components and dietary supplements during manufacturing, packaging, labeling, or holding;

   (c) Permit the use of proper precautions to reduce the potential for mixups or contamination of components, dietary supplements, or contact surfaces, with microorganisms, chemicals, filth, or other extraneous material. Your physical plant must have, and you must use, separate or defined areas of adequate size or other control systems, such as computerized inventory controls or automated systems of separation, to prevent contamination and mixups of components and dietary supplements during the following operations:

   (1) Receiving, identifying, holding, and withholding from use, components, dietary supplements, packaging, and labels that will be used in or during the manufacturing, packaging, labeling, or holding of dietary supplements;

(2) Separating, as necessary, components, dietary supplements, packaging, and labels that are to be used in manufacturing from components, dietary supplements, packaging, or labels that are awaiting material review and disposition decision, reprocessing, or are awaiting disposal after rejection;

(3) Separating the manufacturing, packaging, labeling, and holding of different product types including different types of dietary supplements and other foods, cosmetics, and pharmaceutical products;

(4) Performing laboratory analyses and holding laboratory supplies and samples;

(5) Cleaning and sanitizing contact surfaces;

(6) Packaging and label operations; and

(7) Holding components or dietary supplements.

(d) Be designed and constructed in a manner that prevents contamination of components, dietary supplements, or contact surfaces.

(1) The design and construction must include:

(i) Floors, walls, and ceilings that can be adequately cleaned and kept clean and in good repair;

(ii) Fixtures, ducts, and pipes that do not contaminate components, dietary supplements, or contact surfaces by dripping or other leakage, or condensate;

(iii) Adequate ventilation or environmental control equipment such as airflow systems, including filters, fans, and other air-blowing equipment, that minimize odors and vapors (including steam and noxious fumes) in areas where they may contaminate components, dietary supplements, or contact surfaces;

(iv) Equipment that controls temperature and humidity, when such equipment is necessary to ensure the quality of the dietary supplement; and

(v) Aisles or working spaces between equipment and walls that are adequately unobstructed and of adequate width to permit all persons to perform their duties and to protect against contamination of components, dietary supplements, or contact surfaces with clothing or personal contact.

(2) When fans and other air-blowing equipment are used, such fans and equipment must be located and operated in a manner that minimizes the potential for microorganisms and particulate matter to contaminate components, dietary supplements, or contact surfaces;

(e) Provide adequate light in:

(1) All areas where components or dietary supplements are examined, processed, or held;

(2) All areas where contact surfaces are cleaned; and

(3) Hand-washing areas, dressing and locker rooms, and bathrooms.

(f) Use safety-type light bulbs, fixtures, skylights, or other glass or glass-like materials when the light bulbs, fixtures, skylights or other glass or glass-like materials are suspended over exposed components or dietary supplements in any step of preparation, unless your physical plant is otherwise constructed in a manner that will protect against contamination of components or dietary supplements in case of breakage of glass or glass-like materials.

(g) Provide effective protection against contamination of components and dietary supplements in bulk fermentation vessels, by, for example:

(1) Use of protective coverings;

(2) Placement in areas where you can eliminate harborages for pests over and around the vessels;

(3) Placement in areas where you can check regularly for pests, pest infestation, filth or any other extraneous materials; and

(4) Use of skimming equipment.

(h) Use adequate screening or other protection against pests, where necessary.

Sec. 111.23 Under this subpart C, what records must you make and keep?

(a) You must make and keep records required under this subpart C in accordance with subpart P of this part.

(b) You must make and keep records of the written procedures for cleaning the physical plant and for pest control.

(c) You must make and keep records that show that water, when used in a manner such that the water may become a component of the dietary supplement, meets the requirements of 111.15(e)(2).

Authority: 21 U.S.C. 321, 342, 343, 371, 374, 381, 393; 42 U.S.C. 264.
Source: 72 FR 34942, June 25, 2007, unless otherwise noted.

Subpart D—Equipment and Utensils

Sec. 111.25 What are the requirements under this subpart D for written procedures?

You must establish and follow written procedures for fulfilling the requirements of this subpart D, including written procedures for:

(a) Calibrating instruments and controls that you use in manufacturing or testing a component or dietary supplement;

(b) Calibrating, inspecting, and checking automated, mechanical, and electronic equipment; and

(c) Maintaining, cleaning, and sanitizing, as necessary, all equipment, utensils, and any other contact surfaces that are used to manufacture, package, label, or hold components or dietary supplements.

Sec. 111.27 What requirements apply to the equipment and utensils that you use?

(a) You must use equipment and utensils that are of appropriate design, construction, and workmanship to enable them to be suitable for their intended use and to be adequately cleaned and properly maintained.

(1) Equipment and utensils include the following:

(i) Equipment used to hold or convey;

(ii) Equipment used to measure;

(iii) Equipment using compressed air or gas;

(iv) Equipment used to carry out processes in closed pipes and vessels; and

(v) Equipment used in automated, mechanical, or electronic systems.

(2) You must use equipment and utensils of appropriate design and construction so that use will not result in the contamination of components or dietary supplements with:

(i) Lubricants;

(ii) Fuel;

(iii) Coolants;

(iv) Metal or glass fragments;

(v) Filth or any other extraneous material;

(vi) Contaminated water; or

(vii) Any other contaminants.

(3) All equipment and utensils you use must be:

(i) Installed and maintained to facilitate cleaning the equipment, utensils, and all adjacent spaces;

(ii) Corrosion-resistant if the equipment or utensils contact components or dietary supplements;

(iii) Made of nontoxic materials;

(iv) Designed and constructed to withstand the environment in which they are used, the action of components or dietary supplements, and, if applicable, cleaning compounds and sanitizing agents; and

(v) Maintained to protect components and dietary supplements from being contaminated by any source.

(4) Equipment and utensils you use must have seams that are smoothly bonded or maintained to minimize accumulation of dirt, filth, organic material, particles of components or dietary supplements, or any other extraneous materials or contaminants.

(5) Each freezer, refrigerator, and other cold storage compartment you use to hold components or dietary supplements:

(i) Must be fitted with an indicating thermometer, temperature-measuring device, or temperature-recording device that indicates and records, or allows for recording by hand, the temperature accurately within the compartment; and

(ii) Must have an automated device for regulating temperature or an automated alarm system to indicate a significant temperature change in a manual operation.

(6) Instruments or controls used in the manufacturing, packaging, labeling, or holding of a dietary supplement, and instruments or controls that you use to measure, regulate, or record temperatures, hydrogen-ion concentration (pH), water activity, or other conditions, to control or prevent the growth of microorganisms or other contamination must be:

(i) Accurate and precise;

(ii) Adequately maintained; and

(iii) Adequate in number for their designated uses.

(7) Compressed air or other gases you introduce mechanically into or onto a component, dietary supplement, or contact surface or that you use to clean any contact surface must be treated in such a way that the component, dietary supplement, or contact surface is not contaminated.

(b) You must calibrate instruments and controls you use in manufacturing or testing a component or dietary supplement. You must calibrate:

(1) Before first use; and

(2) At the frequency specified in writing by the manufacturer of the instrument and control; or

(3) At routine intervals or as otherwise necessary to ensure the accuracy and precision of the instrument and control.

(c) You must repair or replace instruments or controls that cannot be adjusted to agree with the reference standard.

(d) You must maintain, clean, and sanitize, as necessary, all equipment, utensils, and any other contact surfaces used to manufacture, package, label, or hold components or dietary supplements.

(1) Equipment and utensils must be taken apart as necessary for thorough maintenance, cleaning, and sanitizing.

(2) You must ensure that all contact surfaces, used for manufacturing or holding low-moisture components or dietary supplements, are in a dry and sanitary condition when in use. When the surfaces are wet-cleaned, they must be sanitized, when necessary, and thoroughly dried before subsequent use.

(3) If you use wet processing during manufacturing, you must clean and sanitize all contact surfaces, as necessary, to protect against the introduction of microorganisms into components or dietary supplements. When cleaning and sanitizing is necessary, you must clean and sanitize all contact surfaces before use and after any interruption during which the contact surface may have become contaminated. If you use contact surfaces in a continuous production operation or in consecutive operations involving different batches of the same dietary supplement, you must adequately clean and sanitize the contact surfaces, as necessary.

(4) You must clean surfaces that do not come into direct contact with components or dietary supplements as frequently as necessary to protect against contaminating components or dietary supplements.

(5) Single-service articles (such as utensils intended for one-time use, paper cups, and paper towels) must be:

(i) Stored in appropriate containers; and

(ii) Handled, dispensed, used, and disposed of in a manner that protects against contamination of components, dietary supplements, or any contact surface.

(6) Cleaning compounds and sanitizing agents must be adequate for their intended use and safe under their conditions of use;

(7) You must store cleaned and sanitized portable equipment and utensils that have contact surfaces in a location and manner that protects them from contamination.

[72 FR 34942, June 25, 2007, as amended at 73 FR 13124, Mar. 12, 2008]

Sec. 111.30 What requirements apply to automated, mechanical, or electronic equipment?

For any automated, mechanical, or electronic equipment that you use to manufacture, package, label, or hold a dietary supplement, you must:

(a) Design or select equipment to ensure that dietary supplement specifications are consistently met;

(b) Determine the suitability of the equipment by ensuring that your equipment is capable of operating satisfactorily within the operating limits required by the process;

(c) Routinely calibrate, inspect, or check the equipment to ensure proper performance. Your quality control personnel must periodically review these calibrations, inspections, or checks;

(d) Establish and use appropriate controls for automated, mechanical, and electronic equipment (including software for a computer controlled process) to ensure that any changes to the manufacturing, packaging, labeling, holding, or other operations are approved by quality control personnel and instituted only by authorized personnel; and

(e) Establish and use appropriate controls to ensure that the equipment functions in accordance with its intended use. These controls must be approved by quality control personnel.

Sec. 111.35 Under this subpart D, what records must you make and keep?

(a) You must make and keep records required under this subpart D in accordance with subpart P of this part.

(b) You must make and keep the following records:

(1) Written procedures for fulfilling the requirements of this subpart, including written procedures for:

(i) Calibrating instruments and controls that you use in manufacturing or testing a component or dietary supplement;

(ii) Calibrating, inspecting, and checking automated, mechanical, and electronic equipment; and

(iii) Maintaining, cleaning, and sanitizing, as necessary, all equipment, utensils, and any other contact surfaces that are used to manufacture, package, label, or hold components or dietary supplements;

(2) Documentation, in individual equipment logs, of the date of the use, maintenance, cleaning, and sanitizing of equipment, unless such documentation is kept with the batch record;

(3) Documentation of any calibration, each time the calibration is performed, for instruments and controls that you use in manufacturing or testing a component or dietary supplement. In your documentation, you must:

(i) Identify the instrument or control calibrated;

(ii) Provide the date of calibration;

(iii) Identify the reference standard used including the certification of accuracy of the known reference standard and a history of recertification of accuracy;

(iv) Identify the calibration method used, including appropriate limits for accuracy and precision of instruments and controls when calibrating;

(v) Provide the calibration reading or readings found;

(vi) Identify the recalibration method used, and reading or readings found, if accuracy or precision or both accuracy and precision limits for instruments and controls were not met; and

(vii) Include the initials of the person who performed the calibration and any recalibration.

(4) Written records of calibrations, inspections, and checks of automated, mechanical, and electronic equipment;

(5) Backup file(s) of current software programs (and of outdated software that is necessary to retrieve records that you are required to keep in accordance with subpart P of this part, when current software is not able to retrieve such records) and of data entered into computer systems that you use to manufacture, package, label, or hold dietary supplements.

(i) Your backup file (e.g., a hard copy of data you have entered, diskettes, tapes, microfilm, or compact disks) must be an exact and complete record of the data you entered.

(ii) You must keep your backup software programs and data secure from alterations, inadvertent erasures, or loss; and

(6) Documentation of the controls that you use to ensure that equipment functions in accordance with its intended use.

Authority: 21 U.S.C. 321, 342, 343, 371, 374, 381, 393; 42 U.S.C. 264.
Source: 72 FR 34942, June 25, 2007, unless otherwise noted.

Subpart E—Requirement to Establish a Production and Process Control System

Sec. 111.55 What are the requirements to implement a production and process control system?

You must implement a system of production and process controls that covers all stages of manufacturing, packaging, labeling, and holding of the dietary supplement to ensure the quality of the dietary supplement and that the dietary supplement is packaged and labeled as specified in the master manufacturing record.

Sec. 111.60 What are the design requirements for the production and process control system?

(a) Your production and in-process control system must be designed to ensure that the dietary supplement is manufactured, packaged, labeled, and held in a manner that will ensure the quality of the dietary supplement and that the dietary supplement is packaged and labeled as specified in the master manufacturing record; and

(b) The production and in-process control system must include all requirements of subparts E through L of this part and must be reviewed and approved by quality control personnel.

Sec. 111.65 What are the requirements for quality control operations?

You must implement quality control operations in your manufacturing, packaging, labeling, and holding operations for producing the dietary supplement to ensure the quality of the dietary supplement and that the dietary supplement is packaged and labeled as specified in the master manufacturing record.

Sec. 111.70 What specifications must you establish?

(a) You must establish a specification for any point, step, or stage in the manufacturing process where control is necessary to ensure the quality of the dietary supplement and that the dietary supplement is packaged and labeled as specified in the master manufacturing record.

(b) For each component that you use in the manufacture of a dietary supplement, you must establish component specifications as follows:

    (1) You must establish an identity specification;

    (2) You must establish component specifications that are necessary to ensure that specifications for the purity, strength and composition of dietary supplements manufactured using the components are met; and

    (3) You must establish limits on those types of contamination that may adulterate or may lead to adulteration of the finished batch of the dietary supplement to ensure the quality of the dietary supplement.

(c) For the in-process production:

    (1) You must establish in-process specifications for any point, step, or stage in the master manufacturing record where control is necessary to help ensure that specifications are met for the identity, purity, strength, and composition of the dietary supplements and, as necessary, for limits on those types of contamination that may adulterate or may lead to adulteration of the finished batch of the dietary supplement;

    (2) You must provide adequate documentation of your basis for why meeting the in-process specifications, in combination with meeting component specifications, will help ensure that the specifications are met for the identity, purity, strength, and composition of the dietary supplements and for limits on those types of contamination that may adulterate or may lead to adulteration of the finished batch of the dietary supplement; and

    (3) Quality control personnel must review and approve the documentation that you provide under paragraph (c)(2) of this section.

(d) You must establish specifications for dietary supplement labels (label specifications) and for packaging that may come in contact with dietary supplements (packaging specifications). Packaging that may come into contact with dietary supplements must be safe and suitable for its intended use and must not be reactive or absorptive or otherwise affect the safety or quality of the dietary supplement.

(e) For each dietary supplement that you manufacture you must establish product specifications for the identity, purity, strength, and composition of the finished batch of the dietary supplement, and for limits on those types of contamination that may adulterate, or that may lead to adulteration of, the finished batch of the dietary supplement to ensure the quality of the dietary supplement.

(f) If you receive a product from a supplier for packaging or labeling as a dietary supplement (and for distribution rather than for return to the supplier), you must establish specifications to provide sufficient assurance that the product you receive is adequately identified and is consistent with your purchase order.

(g) You must establish specifications for the packaging and labeling of the finished packaged and labeled dietary supplements, including specifications that ensure that you used the specified packaging and that you applied the specified label.

Sec. 111.73 What is your responsibility for determining whether established specifications are met?

You must determine whether the specifications you establish under 111.70 are met.

Sec. 111.75 What must you do to determine whether specifications are met?

(a) Before you use a component, you must:

(1)(i) Conduct at least one appropriate test or examination to verify the identity of any component that is a dietary ingredient, unless you petition the agency under paragraph (a)(1)(ii) of this section and the agency exempts you from such testing;

(ii) You may submit a petition, under 21 CFR 10.30, to request an exemption from the testing requirements in paragraph (a)(1)(i) of this section. The petition must set forth the scientific rationale, and must be accompanied by the supporting data and information, for proposed alternative testing that will demonstrate that there is no material diminution of assurance, compared to the assurance provided by 100 percent identity testing, of the identity of the dietary ingredient before use when the dietary ingredient is obtained from one or more suppliers identified in the petition. If FDA grants the petition, you must conduct the tests and examinations for the dietary ingredient, otherwise required under 111.75(a)(1)(i), under the terms specified by FDA when the petition is granted; and

(2) Confirm the identity of other components and determine whether other applicable component specifications established in accordance with 111.70(b) are met. To do so, you must either:

(i) Conduct appropriate tests or examinations; or

(ii) Rely on a certificate of analysis from the supplier of the component that you receive, provided that:

   (A) You first qualify the supplier by establishing the reliability of the supplier's certificate of analysis through confirmation of the results of the supplier's tests or examinations;

   (B) The certificate of analysis includes a description of the test or examination method(s) used, limits of the test or examinations, and actual results of the tests or examinations;

   (C) You maintain documentation of how you qualified the supplier;

   (D) You periodically re-confirm the supplier's certificate of analysis; and

   (E) Your quality control personnel review and approve the documentation setting forth the basis for qualification (and re-qualification) of any supplier.

(b) You must monitor the in-process points, steps, or stages where control is necessary to ensure the quality of the finished batch of dietary supplement to:

   (1) Determine whether the in-process specifications are met; and

   (2) Detect any deviation or unanticipated occurrence that may result in a failure to meet specifications.

(c) For a subset of finished dietary supplement batches that you identify through a sound statistical sampling plan (or for every finished batch), you must verify that your finished batch of the dietary supplement meets product specifications for identity, purity, strength, composition, and for limits on those types of contamination that may adulterate or that may lead to adulteration of the finished batch of the dietary supplement. To do so:

   (1) You must select one or more established specifications for identity, purity, strength, composition, and the limits on those types of contamination that may adulterate or that may lead to adulteration of the dietary supplement that, if tested or examined on the finished batches of the dietary supplement, would verify that the production and process control system is producing a dietary supplement that meets all product specifications (or only those product specifications not otherwise exempted from this provision by quality control personnel under paragraph (d) of this section);

   (2) You must conduct appropriate tests or examinations to determine compliance with the specifications selected in paragraph (c)(1) of this section;

   (3) You must provide adequate documentation of your basis for determining that compliance with the specification(s) selected under paragraph (c)(1) of this section, through the use of appropriate tests or examinations conducted under paragraph (c)(2) of this section, will ensure that your finished batch of the dietary supplement meets all product specifications for identity, purity, strength, and composition, and the limits on those types of contamination that may adulterate, or that may lead to the adulteration of, the dietary supplement; and

PART 111

(4) Your quality control personnel must review and approve the documentation that you provide under paragraph (c)(3) of this section.

(d)(1) You may exempt one or more product specifications from verification requirements in paragraph (c)(1) of this section if you determine and document that the specifications you select under paragraph (c)(1) of this section for determination of compliance with specifications are not able to verify that the production and process control system is producing a dietary supplement that meets the exempted product specification and there is no scientifically valid method for testing or examining such exempted product specification at the finished batch stage. In such a case, you must document why, for example, any component and in-process testing, examination, or monitoring, and any other information, will ensure that such exempted product specification is met without verification through periodic testing of the finished batch; and

(2) Your quality control personnel must review and approve the documentation that you provide under paragraph (d)(1) of this section.

(e) Before you package or label a product that you receive for packaging or labeling as a dietary supplement (and for distribution rather than for return to the supplier), you must visually examine the product and have documentation to determine whether the specifications that you established under 111.70 (f) are met.

(f)(1) Before you use packaging, you must, at a minimum, conduct a visual identification of the containers and closures and review the supplier's invoice, guarantee, or certification to determine whether the packaging specifications are met; and

(2) Before you use labels, you must, at a minimum, conduct a visual examination of the label and review the supplier's invoice, guarantee, or certification to determine whether label specifications are met.

(g) You must, at a minimum, conduct a visual examination of the packaging and labeling of the finished packaged and labeled dietary supplements to determine whether you used the specified packaging and applied the specified label.

(h)(1) You must ensure that the tests and examinations that you use to determine whether the specifications are met are appropriate, scientifically valid methods.

(2) The tests and examinations that you use must include at least one of the following:

(i) Gross organoleptic analysis;

(ii) Macroscopic analysis;

(iii) Microscopic analysis;

(iv) Chemical analysis; or

(v) Other scientifically valid methods.

(i) You must establish corrective action plans for use when an established specification is not met.

[72 FR 34942, June 25, 2007, as amended at 72 FR 34968, June 25, 2007; 73 FR 27727, May 14, 2008]

Sec. 111.77 What must you do if established specifications are not met?

(a) For specifications established under 111.70(a), (b)(2), (b)(3), (c), (d), (e), and (g) that you do not meet, quality control personnel, in accordance with the requirements in subpart F of this part, must reject the component, dietary supplement, package or label unless such personnel approve a treatment, an in-process adjustment, or reprocessing that will ensure the quality of the finished dietary supplement and that the dietary supplement is packaged and labeled as specified in the master manufacturing record. No finished batch of dietary supplements may be released for distribution unless it complies with 111.123(b).

(b) For specifications established under 111.70(b)(1) that you do not meet, quality control personnel must reject the component and the component must not be used in manufacturing the dietary supplement.

(c) For specifications established under 111.70(f) that you do not meet, quality control personnel must reject the product and the product may not be packaged or labeled for distribution as a dietary supplement.

Sec. 111.80 What representative samples must you collect?

The representative samples that you must collect include:

(a) Representative samples of each unique lot of components, packaging, and labels that you use to determine whether the components, packaging, and labels meet specifications established in accordance with 111.70(b) and (d), and as applicable, 111.70(a) (and, when you receive components, packaging, or labels from a supplier, representative samples of each unique shipment, and of each unique lot within each unique shipment);

(b) Representative samples of in-process materials for each manufactured batch at points, steps, or stages, in the manufacturing process as specified in the master manufacturing record where control is necessary to ensure the identity, purity, strength, and composition of dietary supplements to determine whether the in-process materials meet specifications established in accordance with 111.70(c), and as applicable, 111.70(a);

(c) Representative samples of a subset of finished batches of each dietary supplement that you manufacture, which you identify through a sound statistical sampling plan (or otherwise every finished batch), before releasing for distribution to verify that the finished batch of dietary supplement meets product specifications established in accordance with 111.70(e), and as applicable, 111.70(a);

(d) Representative samples of each unique shipment, and of each unique lot within each unique shipment, of product that you receive for packaging or labeling as a dietary supplement (and for distribution rather than for return to the supplier) to determine whether the received product meets specifications established in accordance with 111.70(f), and as applicable, 111.70(a); and

PART
111

(e) Representative samples of each lot of packaged and labeled dietary supplements to determine whether the packaging and labeling of the finished packaged and labeled dietary supplements meet specifications established in accordance with 111.70(g), and as applicable, 111.70(a).

Sec. 111.83 What are the requirements for reserve samples?

(a) You must collect and hold reserve samples of each lot of packaged and labeled dietary supplements that you distribute.

(b) The reserve samples must:

(1) Be held using the same container-closure system in which the packaged and labeled dietary supplement is distributed, or if distributing dietary supplements to be packaged and labeled, using a container-closure system that provides essentially the same characteristics to protect against contamination or deterioration as the one in which it is distributed for packaging and labeling elsewhere;

(2) Be identified with the batch, lot, or control number;

(3) Be retained for 1 year past the shelf life date (if shelf life dating is used), or for 2 years from the date of distribution of the last batch of dietary supplements associated with the reserve sample, for use in appropriate investigations; and

(4) Consist of at least twice the quantity necessary for all tests or examinations to determine whether or not the dietary supplement meets product specifications.

Sec. 111.87 Who conducts a material review and makes a disposition decision?

Quality control personnel must conduct all required material reviews and make all required disposition decisions.

Sec. 111.90 What requirements apply to treatments, in-process adjustments, and reprocessing when there is a deviation or unanticipated occurrence or when a specification established in accordance with 111.70 is not met?

(a) You must not reprocess a rejected dietary supplement or treat or provide an in-process adjustment to a component, packaging, or label to make it suitable for use in the manufacture of a dietary supplement unless:

(1) Quality control personnel conduct a material review and make a disposition decision to approve the reprocessing, treatment, or in-process adjustment; and

(2) The reprocessing, treatment, or in-process adjustment is permitted by 111.77;

(b) You must not reprocess any dietary supplement or treat or provide an in-process adjustment to a component to make it suitable for use in the manufacture of a dietary supplement, unless:

(1) Quality control personnel conduct a material review and make a disposition decision that is based on a scientifically valid reason and approves the reprocessing, treatment, or in-process adjustment; and

(2) The reprocessing, treatment or in-process adjustment is permitted by 111.77;

(c) Any batch of dietary supplement that is reprocessed, that contains components that you have treated, or to which you have made in-process adjustments to make them suitable for use in the manufacture of the dietary supplement must be approved by quality control personnel and comply with 111.123(b) before releasing for distribution.

Sec. 111.95 Under this subpart E, what records must you make and keep?

(a) You must make and keep records required under this subpart E in accordance with subpart P of this part.

(b) Under this subpart E, you must make and keep the following records:

(1) The specifications established;

(2) Documentation of your qualification of a supplier for the purpose of relying on the supplier's certificate of analysis;

(3) Documentation for why meeting in-process specifications, in combination with meeting component specifications, helps ensure that the dietary supplement meets the specifications for identity, purity, strength, and composition; and for limits on those types of contamination that may adulterate or may lead to adulteration of the finished batch of the dietary supplement; and

(4) Documentation for why the results of appropriate tests or examinations for the product specifications selected under 111.75(c)(1) ensure that the dietary supplement meets all product specifications;

(5) Documentation for why any component and in-process testing, examination, or monitoring, and any other information, will ensure that a product specification that is exempted under 111.75(d) is met without verification through periodic testing of the finished batch, including documentation that the selected specifications tested or examined under 111.75 (c)(1) are not able to verify that the production and process control system is producing a dietary supplement that meets the exempted product specification and there is no scientifically valid method for testing or examining such exempted product specification at the finished batch stage.

(6) Documentation of FDA's response to a petition submitted under 111.75(a)(1)(ii) providing for an exemption from the provisions of 111.75(a)(1)(i).

[72 FR 34942, June 25, 2007, as amended at 72 FR 34968, June 25, 2007]
Authority: 21 U.S.C. 321, 342, 343, 371, 374, 381, 393; 42 U.S.C. 264.
Source: 72 FR 34942, June 25, 2007, unless otherwise noted.

Subpart F–Production and Process Control System: Requirements for Quality Control

Sec. 111.103 What are the requirements under this subpart F for written procedures?

PART
111

You must establish and follow written procedures for the responsibilities of the quality control operations, including written procedures for conducting a material review and making a disposition decision, and for approving or rejecting any reprocessing.

Sec. 111.105 What must quality control personnel do?

Quality control personnel must ensure that your manufacturing, packaging, labeling, and holding operations ensure the quality of the dietary supplement and that the dietary supplement is packaged and labeled as specified in the master manufacturing record. To do so, quality control personnel must perform operations that include:

(a) Approving or rejecting all processes, specifications, written procedures, controls, tests, and examinations, and deviations from or modifications to them, that may affect the identity, purity, strength, or composition of a dietary supplement;

(b) Reviewing and approving the documentation setting forth the basis for qualification of any supplier;

(c) Reviewing and approving the documentation setting forth the basis for why meeting in-process specifications, in combination with meeting component specifications, will help ensure that the identity, purity, strength, and composition of the dietary supplement are met;

(d) Reviewing and approving the documentation setting forth the basis for why the results of appropriate tests or examinations for each product specification selected under 111.75(c)(1) will ensure that the finished batch of the dietary supplement meets product specifications;

(e) Reviewing and approving the basis and the documentation for why any product specification is exempted from the verification requirements in 111.75(c)(1), and for why any component and in-process testing, examination, or monitoring, or other methods will ensure that such exempted product specification is met without verification through periodic testing of the finished batch;

(f) Ensuring that required representative samples are collected;

(g) Ensuring that required reserve samples are collected and held;

(h) Determining whether all specifications established under 111.70(a) are met; and

(i) Performing other operations required under this subpart.

Sec. 111.110 What quality control operations are required for laboratory operations associated with the production and process control system?

Quality control operations for laboratory operations associated with the production and process control system must include:

(a) Reviewing and approving all laboratory control processes associated with the production and process control system;

(b) Ensuring that all tests and examinations required under 111.75 are conducted; and

(c) Reviewing and approving the results of all tests and examinations required under 111.75.

Sec. 111.113 What quality control operations are required for a material review and disposition decision?

(a) Quality control personnel must conduct a material review and make a disposition decision if:

(1) A specification established in accordance with 111.70 is not met;

(2) A batch deviates from the master manufacturing record, including when any step established in the master manufacturing record is not completed and including any deviation from specifications;

(3) There is any unanticipated occurrence during the manufacturing operations that adulterates or may lead to adulteration of the component, dietary supplement, or packaging, or could lead to the use of a label not specified in the master manufacturing record;

(4) Calibration of an instrument or control suggests a problem that may have resulted in a failure to ensure the quality of a batch or batches of a dietary supplement; or

(5) A dietary supplement is returned.

(b)(1) When there is a deviation or unanticipated occurrence during the production and in-process control system that results in or could lead to adulteration of a component, dietary supplement, or packaging, or could lead to the use of a label not specified in the master manufacturing record, quality control personnel must reject the component, dietary supplement, packaging, or label unless it approves a treatment, an in-process adjustment, or reprocessing to correct the applicable deviation or occurrence.

(2) When a specification established in accordance with 111.70 is not met, quality control personnel must reject the component, dietary supplement, package or label, unless quality control personnel approve a treatment, an in-process adjustment, or reprocessing, as permitted in 111.77.

(c) The person who conducts a material review and makes the disposition decision must, at the time of performance, document that material review and disposition decision.

Sec. 111.117 What quality control operations are required for equipment, instruments, and controls?

Quality control operations for equipment, instruments, and controls must include:

(a) Reviewing and approving all processes for calibrating instruments and controls;

(b) Periodically reviewing all records for calibration of instruments and controls;

(c) Periodically reviewing all records for calibrations, inspections, and checks of automated, mechanical, or electronic equipment; and

(d) Reviewing and approving controls to ensure that automated, mechanical, or electronic equipment functions in accordance with its intended use.

Sec. 111.120 What quality control operations are required for components, packaging, and labels before use in the manufacture of a dietary supplement?

Quality control operations for components, packaging, and labels before use in the manufacture of a dietary supplement must include:

(a) Reviewing all receiving records for components, packaging, and labels;

(b) Determining whether all components, packaging, and labels conform to specifications established under 111.70 (b) and (d);

(c) Conducting any required material review and making any required disposition decision;

(d) Approving or rejecting any treatment and in-process adjustments of components, packaging, or labels to make them suitable for use in the manufacture of a dietary supplement; and

(e) Approving, and releasing from quarantine, all components, packaging, and labels before they are used.

Sec. 111.123 What quality control operations are required for the master manufacturing record, the batch production record, and manufacturing operations?

(a) Quality control operations for the master manufacturing record, the batch production record, and manufacturing operations must include:

(1) Reviewing and approving all master manufacturing records and all modifications to the master manufacturing records;

(2) Reviewing and approving all batch production-related records;

(3) Reviewing all monitoring required under subpart E;

(4) Conducting any required material review and making any required disposition decision;

(5) Approving or rejecting any reprocessing;

(6) Determining whether all in-process specifications established in accordance with 111.70(c) are met;

(7) Determining whether each finished batch conforms to product specifications established in accordance with 111.70(e); and

(8) Approving and releasing, or rejecting, each finished batch for distribution, including any reprocessed finished batch.

(b) Quality control personnel must not approve and release for distribution:

(1) Any batch of dietary supplement for which any component in the batch does not meet its identity specification;

(2) Any batch of dietary supplement, including any reprocessed batch, that does not meet all product specifications established in accordance with 111.70(e);

(3) Any batch of dietary supplement, including any reprocessed batch, that has not been manufactured, packaged, labeled, and held under conditions to prevent adulteration under section 402(a)(1), (a)(2), (a)(3), and (a)(4) of the act; and

(4) Any product received from a supplier for packaging or labeling as a dietary supplement (and for distribution rather than for return to the supplier) for which sufficient assurance is not provided to adequately identify the product and to determine that the product is consistent with your purchase order.

Sec. 111.127 What quality control operations are required for packaging and labeling operations?

Quality control operations for packaging and labeling operations must include:

(a) Reviewing the results of any visual examination and documentation to ensure that specifications established under 111.70(f) are met for all products that you receive for packaging and labeling as a dietary supplement (and for distribution rather than for return to the supplier);

(b) Approving, and releasing from quarantine, all products that you receive for packaging or labeling as a dietary supplement (and for distribution rather than for return to the supplier) before they are used for packaging or labeling;

(c) Reviewing and approving all records for packaging and label operations;

(d) Determining whether the finished packaged and labeled dietary supplement conforms to specifications established in accordance with 111.70(g);

(e) Conducting any required material review and making any required disposition decision;

(f) Approving or rejecting any repackaging of a packaged dietary supplement;

(g) Approving or rejecting any relabeling of a packaged and labeled dietary supplement; and

(h) Approving for release, or rejecting, any packaged and labeled dietary supplement (including a repackaged or relabeled dietary supplement) for distribution.

Sec. 111.130 What quality control operations are required for returned dietary supplements?

Quality control operations for returned dietary supplements must include:

(a) Conducting any required material review and making any required disposition decision; including:

(1) Determining whether tests or examination are necessary to determine compliance with product specifications established in accordance with 111.70(e); and

(2) Reviewing the results of any tests or examinations that are conducted to determine compliance with product specifications established in accordance with 111.70(e);

(b) Approving or rejecting any salvage and redistribution of any returned dietary supplement;

(c) Approving or rejecting any reprocessing of any returned dietary supplement; and

(d) Determining whether the reprocessed dietary supplement meets product specifications and either approving for release, or rejecting, any returned dietary supplement that is reprocessed.

Sec. 111.135 What quality control operations are required for product complaints?

Quality control operations for product complaints must include reviewing and approving decisions about whether to investigate a product complaint and reviewing and approving the findings and followup action of any investigation performed.

Sec. 111.140 Under this subpart F, what records must you make and keep?

(a) You must make and keep the records required under this subpart F in accordance with subpart P of this part.

(b) You must make and keep the following records:

(1) Written procedures for the responsibilities of the quality control operations, including written procedures for conducting a material review and making a disposition decision and written procedures for approving or rejecting any reprocessing;

(2) Written documentation, at the time of performance, that quality control personnel performed the review, approval, or rejection requirements by recording the following:

(i) Date that the review, approval, or rejection was performed; and

(ii) Signature of the person performing the review, approval, or rejection; and

(3) Documentation of any material review and disposition decision and followup. Such documentation must be included in the appropriate batch production record and must include:

(i) Identification of the specific deviation or the unanticipated occurrence;

(ii) Description of your investigation into the cause of the deviation from the specification or the unanticipated occurrence;

(iii) Evaluation of whether or not the deviation or unanticipated occurrence has resulted in or could lead to a failure to ensure the quality of the dietary supplement or a failure to package and label the dietary supplement as specified in the master manufacturing record;

(iv) Identification of the action(s) taken to correct, and prevent a recurrence of, the deviation or the unanticipated occurrence;

(v) Explanation of what you did with the component, dietary supplement, packaging, or label;

(vi) A scientifically valid reason for any reprocessing of a dietary supplement that is rejected or any treatment or in-process adjustment of a component that is rejected; and

(vii) The signature of the individual(s) designated to perform the quality control operation, who conducted the material review and made the disposition decision, and of each qualified individual who provides information relevant to that material review and disposition decision.

Authority: 21 U.S.C. 321, 342, 343, 371, 374, 381, 393; 42 U.S.C. 264.
Source: 72 FR 34942, June 25, 2007, unless otherwise noted.

Subpart G–Production and Process Control System: Requirements for Components, Packaging, and Labels and for Product That You Receive for Packaging or Labeling as a Dietary Supplement

Sec. 111.153 What are the requirements under this subpart G for written procedures?

You must establish and follow written procedures for fulfilling the requirements of this subpart G.

Sec. 111.155 What requirements apply to components of dietary supplements?

(a) You must visually examine each immediate container or grouping of immediate containers in a shipment that you receive for appropriate content label, container damage, or broken seals to determine whether the container condition may have resulted in contamination or deterioration of the components;

(b) You must visually examine the supplier's invoice, guarantee, or certification in a shipment you receive to ensure the components are consistent with your purchase order;

(c) You must quarantine components before you use them in the manufacture of a dietary supplement until:

(1) You collect representative samples of each unique lot of components (and, for components that you receive, of each unique shipment, and of each unique lot within each unique shipment);

(2) Quality control personnel review and approve the results of any tests or examinations conducted on components; and

(3) Quality control personnel approve the components for use in the manufacture of a dietary supplement, including approval of any treatment (including in-process adjustments) of components to make them suitable for use in the manufacture of a dietary supplement, and releases them from quarantine.

(d)(1) You must identify each unique lot within each unique shipment of components that you receive and any lot of components that you produce in a manner that allows you to trace the lot to the supplier, the date received, the name of the component, the status of the component (e.g., quarantined, approved, or rejected); and to the dietary supplement that you manufactured and distributed.

(2) You must use this unique identifier whenever you record the disposition of each unique lot within each unique shipment of components that you receive and any lot of components that you produce.

(e) You must hold components under conditions that will protect against contamination and deterioration, and avoid mixups.

Sec. 111.160 What requirements apply to packaging and labels received?

(a) You must visually examine each immediate container or grouping of immediate containers in a shipment for appropriate content label, container damage, or broken seals to determine whether the container condition may have resulted in contamination or deterioration of the packaging and labels.

(b) You must visually examine the supplier's invoice, guarantee, or certification in a shipment to ensure that the packaging or labels are consistent with your purchase order.

(c) You must quarantine packaging and labels before you use them in the manufacture of a dietary supplement until:

(1) You collect representative samples of each unique shipment, and of each unique lot within each unique shipment, of packaging and labels and, at a minimum, conduct a visual identification of the immediate containers and closures;

(2) Quality control personnel review and approve the results of any tests or examinations conducted on the packaging and labels; and

(3) Quality control personnel approve the packaging and labels for use in the manufacture of a dietary supplement and release them from quarantine.

(d)(1) You must identify each unique lot within each unique shipment of packaging and labels in a manner that allows you to trace the lot to the supplier, the date received, the name of the packaging and label, the status of the packaging and label (e.g., quarantined, approved, or rejected); and to the dietary supplement that you distributed; and

(2) You must use this unique identifier whenever you record the disposition of each unique lot within each unique shipment of packaging and labels.

(e) You must hold packaging and labels under conditions that will protect against contamination and deterioration, and avoid mixups.

PART

111

Sec. 111.165 What requirements apply to a product received for packaging or labeling as a dietary supplement (and for distribution rather than for return to the supplier)?

(a) You must visually examine each immediate container or grouping of immediate containers in a shipment of product that you receive for packaging or labeling as a dietary supplement (and for distribution rather than for return to the supplier) for appropriate content label, container damage, or broken seals to determine whether the container condition may have resulted in contamination or deterioration of the received product.

(b) You must visually examine the supplier's invoice, guarantee, or certification in a shipment of the received product to ensure that the received product is consistent with your purchase order.

(c) You must quarantine the received product until:

(1) You collect representative samples of each unique shipment, and of each unique lot within each unique shipment, of received product;

(2) Quality control personnel review and approve the documentation to determine whether the received product meets the specifications that you established under 111.70(f); and

(3) Quality control personnel approve the received product for packaging or labeling as a dietary supplement and release the received product from quarantine.

(d)(1) You must identify each unique lot within each unique shipment of received product in a manner that allows you to trace the lot to the supplier, the date received, the name of the received product, the status of the received product (e.g., quarantined, approved, or rejected), and to the product that you packaged or labeled and distributed as a dietary supplement.

(2) You must use this unique identifier whenever you record the disposition of each unique lot within each unique shipment of the received product.

(e) You must hold the received product under conditions that will protect against contamination and deterioration, and avoid mixups.

Sec. 111.170 What requirements apply to rejected components, packaging, and labels, and to rejected products that are received for packaging or labeling as a dietary supplement?

You must clearly identify, hold, and control under a quarantine system for appropriate disposition any component, packaging, and label, and any product that you receive for packaging or labeling as a dietary supplement (and for distribution rather than for return to the supplier), that is rejected and unsuitable for use in manufacturing, packaging, or labeling operations.

Sec. 111.180 Under this subpart G, what records must you make and keep?

(a) You must make and keep records required under this subpart G in accordance with subpart P of this part.

(b) You must make and keep the following records:

(1) Written procedures for fulfilling the requirements of this subpart.

(2) Receiving records (including records such as certificates of analysis, suppliers' invoices, and suppliers' guarantees) for components, packaging, and labels and for products that you receive for packaging or labeling as a dietary supplement (and for distribution rather than for return to the supplier); and

(3) Documentation that the requirements of this subpart were met.

(i) The person who performs the required operation must document, at the time of performance, that the required operation was performed.

(ii) The documentation must include:

(A) The date that the components, packaging, labels, or products that you receive for packaging or labeling as a dietary supplement were received;

(B) The initials of the person performing the required operation;

(C) The results of any tests or examinations conducted on components, packaging, or labels, and of any visual examination of product that you receive for packaging or labeling as a dietary supplement; and

(D) Any material review and disposition decision conducted on components, packaging, labels, or products that you receive for packaging or labeling as a dietary supplement.

Authority: 21 U.S.C. 321, 342, 343, 371, 374, 381, 393; 42 U.S.C. 264.
Source: 72 FR 34942, June 25, 2007, unless otherwise noted.

Subpart H–Production and Process Control System: Requirements for the Master Manufacturing Record

Sec. 111.205 What is the requirement to establish a master manufacturing record?

(a) You must prepare and follow a written master manufacturing record for each unique formulation of dietary supplement that you manufacture, and for each batch size, to ensure uniformity in the finished batch from batch to batch.

(b) The master manufacturing record must:

    (1) Identify specifications for the points, steps, or stages in the manufacturing process where control is necessary to ensure the quality of the dietary supplement and that the dietary supplement is packaged and labeled as specified in the master manufacturing record; and

    (2) Establish controls and procedures to ensure that each batch of dietary supplement that you manufacture meets the specifications identified in accordance with paragraph (b)(1) of this section.

(c) You must make and keep master manufacturing records in accordance with subpart P of this part.

Sec. 111.210 What must the master manufacturing record include?

The master manufacturing record must include:

(a) The name of the dietary supplement to be manufactured and the strength, concentration, weight, or measure of each dietary ingredient for each batch size;

(b) A complete list of components to be used;

(c) An accurate statement of the weight or measure of each component to be used;

(d) The identity and weight or measure of each dietary ingredient that will be declared on the Supplement Facts label and the identity of each ingredient that will be declared on the ingredients list of the dietary supplement;

(e) A statement of any intentional overage amount of a dietary ingredient;

(f) A statement of theoretical yield of a manufactured dietary supplement expected at each point, step, or stage of the manufacturing process where control is needed to ensure the quality of the dietary supplement, and the expected yield when you finish manufacturing the dietary supplement, including the maximum and minimum percentages of theoretical yield beyond which a deviation investigation of a batch is necessary and material review is conducted and disposition decision is made;

(g) A description of packaging and a representative label, or a cross-reference to the physical location of the actual or representative label;

(h) Written instructions, including the following:

(1) Specifications for each point, step, or stage in the manufacturing process where control is necessary to ensure the quality of the dietary supplement and that the dietary supplement is packaged and labeled as specified in the master manufacturing record;

(2) Procedures for sampling and a cross-reference to procedures for tests or examinations;

(3) Specific actions necessary to perform and verify points, steps, or stages in the manufacturing process where control is necessary to ensure the quality of the dietary supplement and that the dietary supplement is packaged and labeled as specified in the master manufacturing record.

(i) Such specific actions must include verifying the weight or measure of any component and verifying the addition of any component; and

(ii) For manual operations, such specific actions must include:

(A) One person weighing or measuring a component and another person verifying the weight or measure; and

(B) One person adding the component and another person verifying the addition.

(4) Special notations and precautions to be followed; and

(5) Corrective action plans for use when a specification is not met.

Authority: 21 U.S.C. 321, 342, 343, 371, 374, 381, 393; 42 U.S.C. 264.

Source: 72 FR 34942, June 25, 2007, unless otherwise noted.

Subpart I–Production and Process Control System: Requirements for the Batch Production Record

Sec. 111.255 What is the requirement to establish a batch production record?

(a) You must prepare a batch production record every time you manufacture a batch of a dietary supplement;

(b) Your batch production record must include complete information relating to the production and control of each batch;

(c) Your batch production record must accurately follow the appropriate master manufacturing record and you must perform each step in the production of the batch; and

(d) You must make and keep batch production records in accordance with subpart P of this part.

Sec. 111.260 What must the batch record include?

The batch production record must include the following:

(a) The batch, lot, or control number:

    (1) Of the finished batch of dietary supplement; and

    (2) That you assign in accordance with 111.415(f) for the following:

        (i) Each lot of packaged and labeled dietary supplement from the finished batch of dietary supplement;

        (ii) Each lot of dietary supplement, from the finished batch of dietary supplement, that you distribute to another person for packaging or labeling;

(b) The identity of equipment and processing lines used in producing the batch;

(c) The date and time of the maintenance, cleaning, and sanitizing of the equipment and processing lines used in producing the batch, or a cross-reference to records, such as individual equipment logs, where this information is retained;

(d) The unique identifier that you assigned to each component (or, when applicable, to a product that you receive from a supplier for packaging or labeling as a dietary supplement), packaging, and label used;

(e) The identity and weight or measure of each component used;

(f) A statement of the actual yield and a statement of the percentage of theoretical yield at appropriate phases of processing;

(g) The actual results obtained during any monitoring operation;

(h) The results of any testing or examination performed during the batch production, or a cross-reference to such results;

(i) Documentation that the finished dietary supplement meets specifications established in accordance with 111.70(e) and (g);

(j) Documentation, at the time of performance, of the manufacture of the batch, including:

    (1) The date on which each step of the master manufacturing record was performed; and

    (2) The initials of the persons performing each step, including:

        (i) The initials of the person responsible for weighing or measuring each component used in the batch;

        (ii) The initials of the person responsible for verifying the weight or measure of each component used in the batch;

        (iii) The initials of the person responsible for adding the component to the batch; and

        (iv) The initials of the person responsible for verifying the addition of components to the batch;

(k) Documentation, at the time of performance, of packaging and labeling operations, including:

(1) The unique identifier that you assigned to packaging and labels used, the quantity of the packaging and labels used, and, when label reconciliation is required, reconciliation of any discrepancies between issuance and use of labels;

(2) An actual or representative label, or a cross-reference to the physical location of the actual or representative label specified in the master manufacturing record; and

(3) The results of any tests or examinations conducted on packaged and labeled dietary supplements (including repackaged or relabeled dietary supplements), or a cross-reference to the physical location of such results;

(l) Documentation at the time of performance that quality control personnel:

(1) Reviewed the batch production record, including:

(i) Review of any monitoring operation required under subpart E of this part; and

(ii) Review of the results of any tests and examinations, including tests and examinations conducted on components, in-process materials, finished batches of dietary supplements, and packaged and labeled dietary supplements;

(2) Approved or rejected any reprocessing or repackaging; and

(3) Approved and released, or rejected, the batch for distribution, including any reprocessed batch; and

(4) Approved and released, or rejected, the packaged and labeled dietary supplement, including any repackaged or relabeled dietary supplement.

(m) Documentation at the time of performance of any required material review and disposition decision.

(n) Documentation at the time of performance of any reprocessing.

Authority: 21 U.S.C. 321, 342, 343, 371, 374, 381, 393; 42 U.S.C. 264.

Source: 72 FR 34942, June 25, 2007, unless otherwise noted.

Subpart J–Production and Process Control System: Requirements for Laboratory Operations

Sec. 111.303 What are the requirements under this subpart J for written procedures?

You must establish and follow written procedures for laboratory operations, including written procedures for the tests and examinations that you conduct to determine whether specifications are met.

Sec. 111.310 What are the requirements for the laboratory facilities that you use?

You must use adequate laboratory facilities to perform whatever testing and examinations are necessary to determine whether:

(a) Components that you use meet specifications;

(b) In-process specifications are met as specified in the master manufacturing record; and

(c) Dietary supplements that you manufacture meet specifications.

PART

111

Sec. 111.315 What are the requirements for laboratory control processes?

You must establish and follow laboratory control processes that are reviewed and approved by quality control personnel, including the following:

(a) Use of criteria for establishing appropriate specifications;

(b) Use of sampling plans for obtaining representative samples, in accordance with subpart E of this part, of:

(1) Components, packaging, and labels;

(2) In-process materials;

(3) Finished batches of dietary supplements;

(4) Product that you receive for packaging or labeling as a dietary supplement (and for distribution rather than for return to the supplier); and

(5) Packaged and labeled dietary supplements.

(c) Use of criteria for selecting appropriate examination and testing methods;

(d) Use of criteria for selecting standard reference materials used in performing tests and examinations; and

(e) Use of test methods and examinations in accordance with established criteria.

Sec. 111.320 What requirements apply to laboratory methods for testing and examination?

(a) You must verify that the laboratory examination and testing methodologies are appropriate for their intended use.

(b) You must identify and use an appropriate scientifically valid method for each established specification for which testing or examination is required to determine whether the specification is met.

Sec. 111.325 Under this subpart J, what records must you make and keep?

(a) You must make and keep records required under this subpart J in accordance with subpart P of this part.

(b) You must make and keep the following records:

(1) Written procedures for laboratory operations, including written procedures for the tests and examinations that you conduct to determine whether specifications are met;

(2) Documentation that laboratory methodology established in accordance with this subpart J is followed.

(i) The person who conducts the testing and examination must document, at the time of performance, that laboratory methodology established in accordance with this subpart J is followed.

(ii) The documentation for laboratory tests and examinations must include the results of the testing and examination.

Authority: 21 U.S.C. 321, 342, 343, 371, 374, 381, 393; 42 U.S.C. 264.

Source: 72 FR 34942, June 25, 2007, unless otherwise noted.

Subpart K–Production and Process Control System: Requirements for Manufacturing Operations

Sec. 111.353 What are the requirements under this subpart K for written procedures?

You must establish and follow written procedures for manufacturing operations.

Sec. 111.355 What are the design requirements for manufacturing operations?

You must design or select manufacturing processes to ensure that product specifications are consistently met.

Sec. 111.360 What are the requirements for sanitation?

You must conduct all manufacturing operations in accordance with adequate sanitation principles.

Sec. 111.365 What precautions must you take to prevent contamination?

You must take all the necessary precautions during the manufacture of a dietary supplement to prevent contamination of components or dietary supplements. These precautions include:

(a) Performing manufacturing operations under conditions and controls that protect against the potential for growth of microorganisms and the potential for contamination;

(b) Washing or cleaning components that contain soil or other contaminants;

(c) Using water that, at a minimum, complies with the applicable Federal, State, and local requirements and does not contaminate the dietary supplement when the water may become a component of the finished batch of dietary supplement;

(d) Performing chemical, microbiological, or other testing, as necessary to prevent the use of contaminated components;

(e) Sterilizing, pasteurizing, freezing, refrigerating, controlling hydrogen-ion concentration (pH), controlling humidity, controlling water activity (aw), or using any other effective means to remove, destroy, or prevent the growth of microorganisms and prevent decomposition;

(f) Holding components and dietary supplements that can support the rapid growth of microorganisms of public health significance in a manner that prevents the components and dietary supplements from becoming adulterated;

(g) Identifying and holding any components or dietary supplements, for which a material review and disposition decision is required, in a manner that protects components or dietary supplements that are not under a material review against contamination and mixups with those that are under a material review;

(h) Performing mechanical manufacturing steps (such as cutting, sorting, inspecting, shredding, drying, grinding, blending, and sifting) by any effective means to protect the dietary supplements against contamination, by, for example:

(1) Cleaning and sanitizing contact surfaces;

(2) Using temperature controls; and

(3) Using time controls.

(i) Using effective measures to protect against the inclusion of metal or other foreign material in components or dietary supplements, by, for example:

(1) Filters or strainers,

(2) Traps,

(3) Magnets, or

(4) Electronic metal detectors.

(j) Segregating and identifying all containers for a specific batch of dietary supplements to identify their contents and, when necessary, the phase of manufacturing; and

(k) Identifying all processing lines and major equipment used during manufacturing to indicate their contents, including the name of the dietary supplement and the specific batch or lot number and, when necessary, the phase of manufacturing.

Sec. 111.370 What requirements apply to rejected dietary supplements?

You must clearly identify, hold, and control under a quarantine system for appropriate disposition any dietary supplement that is rejected and unsuitable for use in manufacturing, packaging, or labeling operations.

Sec. 111.375 Under this subpart K, what records must you make and keep?

(a) You must make and keep records required under this subpart K in accordance with subpart P of this part.

(b) You must make and keep records of the written procedures for manufacturing operations.

Authority: 21 U.S.C. 321, 342, 343, 371, 374, 381, 393; 42 U.S.C. 264.

Source: 72 FR 34942, June 25, 2007, unless otherwise noted.

Subpart L—Production and Process Control System: Requirements for Packaging and Labeling Operations

Sec. 111.403 What are the requirements under this subpart L for written procedures?

You must establish and follow written procedures for packaging and labeling operations.

Sec. 111.410 What requirements apply to packaging and labels?

(a) You must take necessary actions to determine whether packaging for dietary supplements meets specifications so that the condition of the packaging will ensure the quality of your dietary supplements;

(b) You must control the issuance and use of packaging and labels and reconciliation of any issuance and use discrepancies. Label reconciliation is not required for cut or rolled labels if a 100-percent examination for correct labels is performed by appropriate electronic or electromechanical equipment during or after completion of finishing operations; and

(c) You must examine, before packaging and labeling operations, packaging and labels for each batch of dietary supplement to determine whether the packaging and labels conform to the master manufacturing record; and

(d) You must be able to determine the complete manufacturing history and control of the packaged and labeled dietary supplement through distribution.

Sec. 111.415 What requirements apply to filling, assembling, packaging, labeling, and related operations?

You must fill, assemble, package, label, and perform other related operations in a way that ensures the quality of the dietary supplement and that the dietary supplement is packaged and labeled as specified in the master manufacturing record. You must do this using any effective means, including the following:

(a) Cleaning and sanitizing all filling and packaging equipment, utensils, and dietary supplement packaging, as appropriate;

(b) Protecting manufactured dietary supplements from contamination, particularly airborne contamination;

(c) Using sanitary handling procedures;

(d) Establishing physical or spatial separation of packaging and label operations from operations on other components and dietary supplements to prevent mixups;

(e) Identifying, by any effective means, filled dietary supplement containers that are set aside and held in unlabeled condition for future label operations, to prevent mixups;

(f) Assigning a batch, lot, or control number to:

(1) Each lot of packaged and labeled dietary supplement from a finished batch of dietary supplement; and,

(2) Each lot of dietary supplement, from a finished batch of dietary supplement, that you distribute to another person for packaging or labeling.

(g) Examining a representative sample of each batch of the packaged and labeled dietary supplement to determine whether the dietary supplement meets specifications established in accordance with 111.70(g); and

(h) Suitably disposing of labels and packaging for dietary supplements that are obsolete or incorrect to ensure that they are not used in any future packaging and label operations.

Sec. 111.420 What requirements apply to repackaging and relabeling?

(a) You may repackage or relabel dietary supplements only after quality control personnel have approved such repackaging or relabeling.

(b) You must examine a representative sample of each batch of repackaged or relabeled dietary supplements to determine whether the repackaged or relabeled dietary supplements meet all specifications established in accordance with 111.70(g).

(c) Quality control personnel must approve or reject each batch of repackaged or relabeled dietary supplement prior to its release for distribution.

Sec. 111.425 What requirements apply to a packaged and labeled dietary supplement that is rejected for distribution?

You must clearly identify, hold, and control under a quarantine system for appropriate disposition any packaged and labeled dietary supplement that is rejected for distribution.

Sec. 111.430 Under this subpart L, what records must you make and keep?

(a) You must make and keep records required under this subpart L in accordance with subpart P of this part.

(b) You must make and keep records of the written procedures for packaging and labeling operations.

Authority: 21 U.S.C. 321, 342, 343, 371, 374, 381, 393; 42 U.S.C. 264.

Source: 72 FR 34942, June 25, 2007, unless otherwise noted.

PART

111

Subpart M—Holding and Distributing

Sec. 111.453 What are the requirements under this subpart for M written procedures?

You must establish and follow written procedures for holding and distributing operations.

Sec. 111.455 What requirements apply to holding components, dietary supplements, packaging, and labels?

(a) You must hold components and dietary supplements under appropriate conditions of temperature, humidity, and light so that the identity, purity, strength, and composition of the components and dietary supplements are not affected.

(b) You must hold packaging and labels under appropriate conditions so that the packaging and labels are not adversely affected.

(c) You must hold components, dietary supplements, packaging, and labels under conditions that do not lead to the mixup, contamination, or deterioration of components, dietary supplements, packaging, and labels.

Sec. 111.460 What requirements apply to holding in-process material?

(a) You must identify and hold in-process material under conditions that protect against mixup, contamination, and deterioration.

(b) You must hold in-process material under appropriate conditions of temperature, humidity, and light.

Sec. 111.465 What requirements apply to holding reserve samples of dietary supplements?

(a) You must hold reserve samples of dietary supplements in a manner that protects against contamination and deterioration. This includes:

    (1) Holding the reserve samples under conditions consistent with product labels or, if no storage conditions are recommended on the label, under ordinary storage conditions; and

    (2) Using the same container-closure system in which the packaged and labeled dietary supplement is distributed, or if distributing dietary supplements to be packaged and labeled, using a container-closure system that provides essentially the same characteristics to protect against contamination or deterioration as the one in which you distribute the dietary supplement for packaging and labeling elsewhere.

(b) You must retain reserve samples for 1 year past the shelf life date (if shelf life dating is used), or for 2 years from the date of distribution of the last batch of dietary supplements associated with the reserve samples, for use in appropriate investigations.

Sec. 111.470 What requirements apply to distributing dietary supplements?

You must distribute dietary supplements under conditions that will protect the dietary supplements against contamination and deterioration.

Sec. 111.475 Under this subpart M, what records must you make and keep?

(a) You must make and keep records required under this subpart M in accordance with subpart P of this part.

(b) You must make and keep the following records:

(1) Written procedures for holding and distributing operations; and

(2) Records of product distribution.

Authority: 21 U.S.C. 321, 342, 343, 371, 374, 381, 393; 42 U.S.C. 264.

Source: 72 FR 34942, June 25, 2007, unless otherwise noted.

Subpart N—Returned Dietary Supplements

Sec. 111.503 What are the requirements under this subpart N for written procedures?

You must establish and follow written procedures to fulfill the requirements of this subpart.

Sec. 111.510 What requirements apply when a returned dietary supplement is received?

You must identify and quarantine returned dietary supplements until quality control personnel conduct a material review and make a disposition decision.

Sec. 111.515 When must a returned dietary supplement be destroyed, or otherwise suitably disposed of?

You must destroy, or otherwise suitably dispose of, any returned dietary supplement unless the outcome of a material review and disposition decision is that quality control personnel do the following:

(a) Approve the salvage of the returned dietary supplement for redistribution or

(b) Approve the returned dietary supplement for reprocessing.

Sec. 111.520 When may a returned dietary supplement be salvaged?

You may salvage a returned dietary supplement only if quality control personnel conduct a material review and make a disposition decision to allow the salvage.

Sec. 111.525 What requirements apply to a returned dietary supplement that quality control personnel approve for reprocessing?

(a) You must ensure that any returned dietary supplements that are reprocessed meet all product specifications established in accordance with 111.70(e); and

(b) Quality control personnel must approve or reject the release for distribution of any returned dietary supplement that is reprocessed.

Sec. 111.530 When must an investigation be conducted of your manufacturing processes and other batches?

If the reason for a dietary supplement being returned implicates other batches, you must conduct an investigation of your manufacturing processes and each of those other batches to determine compliance with specifications.

Sec. 111.535 Under this subpart N, what records must you make and keep?

(a) You must make and keep records required under this subpart N in accordance with subpart P of this part.

(b) You must make and keep the following records:

(1) Written procedures for fulfilling the requirements of this subpart N.

(2) Any material review and disposition decision on a returned dietary supplement;

(3) The results of any testing or examination conducted to determine compliance with product specifications established under 111.70(e); and,

(4) Documentation of the reevaluation by quality control personnel of any dietary supplement that is reprocessed and the determination by quality control personnel of whether the reprocessed dietary supplement meets product specifications established in accordance with 111.70(e).

Authority: 21 U.S.C. 321, 342, 343, 371, 374, 381, 393; 42 U.S.C. 264.
Source: 72 FR 34942, June 25, 2007, unless otherwise noted.

Subpart O—Product Complaints

Sec. 111.553 What are the requirements under this subpart O for written procedures?

You must establish and follow written procedures to fulfill the requirements of this subpart O.

Sec. 111.560 What requirements apply to the review and investigation of a product complaint?

(a) A qualified person must:

(1) Review all product complaints to determine whether the product complaint involves a possible failure of a dietary supplement to meet any of its specifications, or any other requirements of this part 111, including those specifications and other requirements that, if not met, may result in a risk of illness or injury; and

(2) Investigate any product complaint that involves a possible failure of a dietary supplement to meet any of its specifications, or any other requirements of this part, including those specifications and other requirements that, if not met, may result in a risk of illness or injury.

(b) Quality control personnel must review and approve decisions about whether to investigate a product complaint and review and approve the findings and followup action of any investigation performed.

(c) The review and investigation of the product complaint by a qualified person, and the review by quality control personnel about whether to investigate a product complaint, and the findings and followup action of any investigation performed, must extend to all relevant batches and records.

Sec. 111.570 Under this subpart O, what records must you make and keep?

(a) You must make and keep the records required under this subpart O in accordance with subpart P of this part.

(b) You must make and keep the following records:

(1) Written procedures for fulfilling the requirements of this subpart,

(2) A written record of every product complaint that is related to good manufacturing practice,

(i) The person who performs the requirements of this subpart must document, at the time of performance, that the requirement was performed.

(ii) The written record of the product complaint must include the following:

(A) The name and description of the dietary supplement;

(B) The batch, lot, or control number of the dietary supplement, if available;

(C) The date the complaint was received and the name, address, or telephone number of the complainant, if available;

(D) The nature of the complaint including, if known, how the product was used;

(E) The reply to the complainant, if any; and

PART 111: CURRENT GOOD MANUFACTURING PRACTICE IN MANUFACTURING, PACKAGING, LABELING, OR HOLDING
OPERATIONS FOR DIETARY SUPPLEMENTS

(F) Findings of the investigation and followup action taken when an
investigation is performed.

Authority: 21 U.S.C. 321, 342, 343, 371, 374, 381, 393; 42 U.S.C. 264.
Source: 72 FR 34942, June 25, 2007, unless otherwise noted.

PART
111

Subpart P—Records and Recordkeeping

Sec. 111.605 What requirements apply to the records that you make and keep?

(a) You must keep written records required by this part for 1 year past the shelf life date, if
shelf life dating is used, or 2 years beyond the date of distribution of the last batch of
dietary supplements associated with those records.

(b) Records must be kept as original records, as true copies (such as photocopies, microfilm,
microfiche, or other accurate reproductions of the original records), or as electronic
records.

(c) All electronic records must comply with part 11 of this chapter.

Sec. 111.610 What records must be made available to FDA?

(a) You must have all records required under this part, or copies of such records, readily
available during the retention period for inspection and copying by FDA when requested.

(b) If you use reduction techniques, such as microfilming, you must make suitable reader and
photocopying equipment readily available to FDA.

Authority: 21 U.S.C. 321, 342, 343, 371, 374, 381, 393; 42 U.S.C. 264.
Source: 72 FR 34942, June 25, 2007, unless otherwise noted.

Part 119
Dietary Supplements that Present a Significant or Unreasonable Risk

[Code of Federal Regulations]
[Title 21, Volume 2]
[Revised as of April 1, 2017]
[CITE: 21CFR119]

Title 21–Food And Drugs

Chapter I–Food And Drug Administration

Department Of Health And Human Services

Subchapter B–Food For Human Consumption

Part 119–Dietary Supplements That Present A Significant Or Unreasonable Risk[1]

Sec. 119.1 Dietary supplements containing ephedrine alkaloids.

Dietary supplements containing ephedrine alkaloids present an unreasonable risk of illness or injury under conditions of use recommended or suggested in the labeling, or if no conditions of use are recommended or suggested in the labeling, under ordinary conditions of use. Therefore, dietary supplements containing ephedrine alkaloids are adulterated under section 402(f)(1)(A) of the Federal Food, Drug, and Cosmetic Act.

[69 FR 6853, Feb. 11, 2004]
Authority: 21 U.S.C. 321, 342, 343, 371.

---

1   21CFR§119 is available on the FDA website at https://www.accessdata.fda.gov/scripts/cdrh/cfdocs/cfcfr/CFRSearch.cfm

[Code of Federal Regulations]
[Title 21, Volume 3]
[Revised as of April 1, 2017]
[CITE: 21CFR190]

Title 21—Food and Drugs

Chapter I—Food and Drug Administration

Department of Health and Human Services

Subchapter B—Food For Human Consumption (Continued)

Part 190: Dietary Supplements[1]

Subpart A [Reserved]

Subpart B—New Dietary Ingredient Notification

Sec. 190.6 Requirement for premarket notification.

(a) At least 75 days before introducing or delivering for introduction into interstate commerce a dietary supplement that contains a new dietary ingredient that has not been present in the food supply as an article used for food in a form in which the food has not been chemically altered, the manufacturer or distributor of that supplement, or of the new dietary ingredient, shall submit to the Office of Nutritional Products, Labeling and Dietary Supplements (HFS-820), Center for Food Safety and Applied Nutrition, Food and Drug Administration, 5001 Campus Dr., College Park, MD 20740, information including any citation to published articles that is the basis on which the manufacturer or distributor has concluded that a dietary supplement containing such dietary ingredient will reasonably be expected to be safe. An original and two copies of this notification shall be submitted.

(b) The notification required by paragraph (a) of this section shall include:

    (1) The name and complete address of the manufacturer or distributor of the dietary supplement that contains a new dietary ingredient, or of the new dietary ingredient;

---

1   21CFR§190 is available on the FDA website at https://www.accessdata.fda.gov/scripts/cdrh/cfdocs/cfcfr/CFRSearch.cfm?CFRPart=190

(2) The name of the new dietary ingredient that is the subject of the premarket notification, including the Latin binomial name (including the author) of any herb or other botanical;

(3) A description of the dietary supplement or dietary supplements that contain the new dietary ingredient including:

(i) The level of the new dietary ingredient in the dietary supplement; and

(ii) The conditions of use recommended or suggested in the labeling of the dietary supplement, or if no conditions of use are recommended or suggested in the labeling of the dietary supplement, the ordinary conditions of use of the supplement;

(4) The history of use or other evidence of safety establishing that the dietary ingredient, when used under the conditions recommended or suggested in the labeling of the dietary supplement, will reasonably be expected to be safe, including any citation to published articles or other evidence that is the basis on which the distributor or manufacturer of the dietary supplement that contains the new dietary ingredient has concluded that the new dietary supplement will reasonably be expected to be safe. Any reference to published information offered in support of the notification shall be accompanied by reprints or photostatic copies of such references. If any part of the material submitted is in a foreign language, it shall be accompanied by an accurate and complete English translation; and

(5) The signature of the person designated by the manufacturer or distributor of the dietary supplement that contains a new dietary ingredient.

(c) FDA will acknowledge its receipt of a notification made under section 413 of the Federal Food, Drug, and Cosmetic Act (the act) and will notify the submitter of the date of receipt of such a notification. The date that the agency receives the notification submitted under paragraph (a) of this section is the filing date for the notification. For 75 days after the filing date, the manufacturer or distributor of a dietary supplement that contains a new dietary ingredient shall not introduce, or deliver for introduction, into interstate commerce the dietary supplement that contains the new dietary ingredient.

(d) If the manufacturer or distributor of a dietary supplement that contains a new dietary ingredient, or of the new dietary ingredient, provides additional information in support of the new dietary ingredient notification, the agency will review all submissions pertaining to that notification, including responses made to inquiries from the agency, to determine whether they are substantive and whether they require that the 75-day period be reset. If the agency determines that the new submission is a substantive amendment, FDA will assign a new filing date. FDA will acknowledge receipt of the additional information and, when applicable, notify the manufacturer of the new filing date, which is the date of receipt by FDA of the information that constitutes the substantive amendment.

(e) FDA will not disclose the existence of, or the information contained in, the new dietary ingredient notification for 90 days after the filing date of the notification. After the 90th day, all information in the notification will be placed on public display, except for any information that is trade secret or otherwise confidential commercial information.

(f) Failure of the agency to respond to a notification does not constitute a finding by the agency that the new dietary ingredient or the dietary supplement that contains the new dietary ingredient is safe or is not adulterated under section 402 of the act.

[62 FR 49891, Sept. 23, 1997, as amended at 66 FR 17359, Mar. 30, 2001, 81 FR 49897, July 29, 2016]

Authority: Secs. 201(ff), 301, 402, 413, 701 of the Federal Food, Drug, and Cosmetic Act (21 U.S.C. 321(ff), 331, 342, 350b, 371).

Source: 62 FR 49891, Sept. 23, 1997, unless otherwise noted.

PART
190

LEGISLATIVE ACTS & SIGNIFICANT AMENDMENTS

Chapter 8

Dietary Supplement Health and Education Act of 1994

An Act

To amend the Federal Food, Drug, and Cosmetic Act to establish standards with respect to dietary supplements, and for other purposes.[1]

Be it enacted by the Senate and House of Representatives of the United States of America in Congress assembled,

Section 1. Short Title; Reference; Table of Contents.

(a) Short Title.

This Act may be cited as the ``Dietary Supplement Health and Education Act of 1994''.

(b) Reference.

Whenever in this Act an amendment or repeal is expressed in terms of an amendment to, or repeal of, a section or other provision, the reference shall be considered to be made to a section or other provision of the Federal Food, Drug, and Cosmetic Act.

(c) Table of Contents.

The table of contents of this Act is as follows:

---

1   S.784 — 103rd Congress (1993-1994) is available online at https://www.congress.gov/bill/103rd-congress/senate-bill/784/text

Sec. 2. Findings.

Congress finds that—

(1) improving the health status of United States citizens ranks at the top of the national priorities of the Federal Government;

(2) the importance of nutrition and the benefits of dietary supplements to health promotion and disease prevention have been documented increasingly in scientific studies;

(3)(A) there is a link between the ingestion of certain nutrients or dietary supplements and the prevention of chronic diseases such as cancer, heart disease, and osteoporosis; and

(B) clinical research has shown that several chronic diseases can be prevented simply with a healthful diet, such as a diet that is low in fat, saturated fat, cholesterol, and sodium, with a high proportion of plant-based foods;

(4) healthful diets may mitigate the need for expensive medical procedures, such as coronary bypass surgery or angioplasty;

(5) preventive health measures, including education, good nutrition, and appropriate use of safe nutritional supplements will limit the incidence of chronic diseases, and reduce long-term health care expenditures;

(6)(A) promotion of good health and healthy lifestyles improves and extends lives while reducing health care expenditures; and

(B) reduction in health care expenditures is of paramount importance to the future of the country and the economic well-being of the country;

(7) there is a growing need for emphasis on the dissemination of information linking nutrition and long-term good health;

(8) consumers should be empowered to make choices about preventive health care programs based on data from scientific studies of health benefits related to particular dietary supplements;

(9) national surveys have revealed that almost 50 percent of the 260,000,000 Americans regularly consume dietary supplements of vitamins, minerals, or herbs as a means of improving their nutrition;

(10) studies indicate that consumers are placing increased reliance on the use of nontraditional health care providers to avoid the excessive costs of traditional medical services and to obtain more holistic consideration of their needs;

(11) the United States will spend over $1,000,000,000,000 on health care in 1994, which is about 12 percent of the Gross National Product of the United States, and this amount and percentage will continue to increase unless significant efforts are undertaken to reverse the increase;

(12)(A) the nutritional supplement industry is an integral part of the economy of the United States;

(B) the industry consistently projects a positive trade balance; and

(C) the estimated 600 dietary supplement manufacturers in the United States produce approximately 4,000 products, with total annual sales of such products alone reaching at least $4,000,000,000;

(13) although the Federal Government should take swift action against products that are unsafe or adulterated, the Federal Government should not take any actions to impose unreasonable regulatory barriers limiting or slowing the flow of safe products and accurate information to consumers;

(14) dietary supplements are safe within a broad range of intake, and safety problems with the supplements are relatively rare; and

(15)(A) legislative action that protects the right of access of consumers to safe dietary supplements is necessary in order to promote wellness; and

(B) a rational Federal framework must be established to supersede the current ad hoc, patchwork regulatory policy on dietary supplements.

Sec. 3. Definitions.

(a) **Definition of Certain Foods as Dietary supplements**.–Section 201 (21 U.S.C. 321) is amended by adding at the end the following:

``(ff) The term `dietary supplement'–

``(1) means a product (other than tobacco) intended to supplement the diet that bears or contains one or more of the following dietary ingredients:

``(A) a vitamin;

``(B) a mineral;

``(C) an herb or other botanical;

``(D) an amino acid;

``(E) a dietary substance for use by man to supplement the diet by increasing the total dietary intake; or

``(F) a concentrate, metabolite, constituent, extract, or combination of any ingredient described in clause (A), (B), (C), (D), or (E);

``(2) means a product that–

``(A)(i) is intended for ingestion in a form described in section 411(c)(1)(B)(i); or

``(ii) complies with section 411(c)(1)(B)(ii);

``(B) is not represented for use as a conventional food or as a sole item of a meal or the diet; and

D
S
H
E
A

``(C) is labeled as a dietary supplement; and

``(3) does–

``(A) include an article that is approved as a new drug under section 505, certified as an antibiotic under section 507, or licensed as a biologic under section 351 of the Public Health Service Act (42 U.S.C. 262) and was, prior to such approval, certification, or license, marketed as a dietary supplement or as a food unless the Secretary has issued a regulation, after notice and comment, finding that the article, when used as or in a dietary supplement under the conditions of use and dosages set forth in the labeling for such dietary supplement, is unlawful under section 402(f); and

``(B) not include–

``(i) an article that is approved as a new drug under section 505, certified as an antibiotic under section 507, or licensed as a biologic under section 351 of the Public Health Service Act (42 U.S.C. 262), or

``(ii) an article authorized for investigation as a new drug, antibiotic, or biological for which substantial clinical investigations have been instituted and for which the existence of such investigations has been made public, which was not before such approval, certification, licensing, or authorization marketed as a dietary supplement or as a food unless the Secretary, in the Secretary's discretion, has issued a regulation, after notice and comment, finding that the article would be lawful under this Act.

Except for purposes of section 201(g), a dietary supplement shall be deemed to be a food within the meaning of this Act.''.

(b) **Exclusion From Definition of Food Additive**.–Section 201(s) (21 U.S.C. 321(s)) is amended–

(1) by striking ``or'' at the end of subparagraph (4);

(2) by striking the period at the end of subparagraph (5) and inserting ``; or''; and

(3) by adding at the end the following new subparagraph:

``(6) an ingredient described in paragraph (ff) in, or intended for use in, a dietary supplement.''.

(c) **Form of Ingestion**.–Section 411(c)(1)(B) (21 U.S.C. 350(c)(1)(B)) is amended–

(1) in clause (i), by inserting ``powder, softgel, gelcap,'' after ``capsule,''; and

(2) in clause (ii), by striking ``does not simulate and''.

Sec. 4. Safety of Dietary Supplements and Burden of Proof on FDA.

Section 402 (21 U.S.C. 342) is amended by adding at the end the following:

``(f)(1) If it is a dietary supplement or contains a dietary ingredient that–

    ``(A) presents a significant or unreasonable risk of illness or injury under–

        ``(i) conditions of use recommended or suggested in labeling, or

        ``(ii) if no conditions of use are suggested or recommended in the labeling, under ordinary conditions of use;

    ``(B) is a new dietary ingredient for which there is inadequate information to provide reasonable assurance that such ingredient does not present a significant or unreasonable risk of illness or injury;

    ``(C) the Secretary declares to pose an imminent hazard to public health or safety, except that the authority to make such declaration shall not be delegated and the Secretary shall promptly after such a declaration initiate a proceeding in accordance with sections 554 and 556 of title 5, United States Code, to affirm or withdraw the declaration; or

    ``(D) is or contains a dietary ingredient that renders it adulterated under paragraph (a) (1) under the conditions of use recommended or suggested in the labeling of such dietary supplement.

    In any proceeding under this subparagraph, the United States shall bear the burden of proof on each element to show that a dietary supplement is adulterated. The court shall decide any issue under this paragraph on a de novo basis.

``(2) Before the Secretary may report to a United States attorney a violation of paragraph (1) (A) for a civil proceeding, the person against whom such proceeding would be initiated shall be given appropriate notice and the opportunity to present views, orally and in writing, at least 10 days before such notice, with regard to such proceeding.''.

Sec. 5. Dietary Supplement Claims.

Chapter IV (21 U.S.C. 341 et seq.) is amended by inserting after section 403A the following new section:

``DIETARY SUPPLEMENT LABELING EXEMPTIONS

``Sec. 403B.

(a) **In General**.–A publication, including an article, a chapter in a book, or an official abstract of a peer-reviewed scientific publication that appears in an article and was prepared by the author or the editors of the publication, which is reprinted in its entirety, shall not be defined as labeling when used in connection with the sale of a dietary supplement to consumers when it–

``(1) is not false or misleading;

``(2) does not promote a particular manufacturer or brand of a dietary supplement;

``(3) is displayed or presented, or is displayed or presented with other such items on the same subject matter, so as to present a balanced view of the available scientific information on a dietary supplement;

``(4) if displayed in an establishment, is physically separate from the dietary supplements; and

``(5) does not have appended to it any information by sticker or any other method.

``(b) **Application**.–Subsection (a) shall not apply to or restrict a retailer or wholesaler of dietary supplements in any way whatsoever in the sale of books or other publications as a part of the business of such retailer or wholesaler.

``(c) **Burden of Proof**.–In any proceeding brought under subsection (a), the burden of proof shall be on the United States to establish that an article or other such matter is false or misleading.''.

Sec. 6. Statements of Nutritional Support.

Section 403(r) (21 U.S.C. 343(r)) is amended by adding at the end the following:

``(6) For purposes of paragraph (r)(1)(B), a statement for a dietary supplement may be made if–

``(A) the statement claims a benefit related to a classical nutrient deficiency disease and discloses the prevalence of such disease in the United States, describes the role of a nutrient or dietary ingredient intended to affect the structure or function in humans, characterizes the documented mechanism by which a nutrient or dietary ingredient acts to maintain such structure or function, or describes general well-being from consumption of a nutrient or dietary ingredient,

``(B) the manufacturer of the dietary supplement has substantiation that such statement is truthful and not misleading, and

``(C) the statement contains, prominently displayed and in boldface type, the following: `This statement has not been evaluated by the Food and Drug Administration. This product is not intended to diagnose, treat, cure, or prevent any disease.'.

A statement under this subparagraph may not claim to diagnose, mitigate, treat, cure, or prevent a specific disease or class of diseases. If the manufacturer of a dietary supplement proposes to make a statement described in the first sentence of this subparagraph in the labeling of the dietary supplement, the manufacturer shall notify the Secretary no later than 30 days after the first marketing of the dietary supplement with such statement that such a statement is being made.''.

Sec. 7. Dietary Supplement Ingredient Labeling and Nutrition Information Labeling.

(a) **Misbranded Supplements.**–Section 403 (21 U.S.C. 343) is amended by adding at the end the following:

``(s) If–

``(1) it is a dietary supplement; and

``(2)(A) the label or labeling of the supplement fails to list–

``(i) the name of each ingredient of the supplement that is described in section 201(ff); and

``(ii)(I) the quantity of each such ingredient; or

``(II) with respect to a proprietary blend of such ingredients, the total quantity of all ingredients in the blend;

``(B) the label or labeling of the dietary supplement fails to identify the product by using the term `dietary supplement', which term may be modified with the name of such an ingredient;

``(C) the supplement contains an ingredient described in section 201(ff)(1)(C), and the label or labeling of the supplement fails to identify any part of the plant from which the ingredient is derived;

``(D) the supplement–

``(i) is covered by the specifications of an official compendium;

``(ii) is represented as conforming to the specifications of an official compendium; and

``(iii) fails to so conform; or

``(E) the supplement–

``(i) is not covered by the specifications of an official compendium; and

``(ii)(I) fails to have the identity and strength that the supplement is represented to have; or

``(II) fails to meet the quality (including tablet or capsule disintegration), purity, or compositional specifications, based on validated assay or other appropriate methods, that the supplement is represented to meet.''.

(b) **Supplement Listing on Nutrition Labeling**.–Section 403(q)(5)(F)(21 U.S.C. 343(q)(5)(F)) is amended to read as follows:

``(F) A dietary supplement product (including a food to which section 411 applies) shall comply with the requirements of subparagraphs (1) and (2) in a manner which is appropriate for the product and which is specified in regulations of the Secretary

D
S
H
E
A

which shall provide that–

``(i) nutrition information shall first list those dietary ingredients that are present in the product in a significant amount and for which a recommendation for daily consumption has been established by the Secretary, except that a dietary ingredient shall not be required to be listed if it is not present in a significant amount, and shall list any other dietary ingredient present and identified as having no such recommendation;

``(ii) the listing of dietary ingredients shall include the quantity of each such ingredient (or of a proprietary blend of such ingredients) per serving;

``(iii) the listing of dietary ingredients may include the source of a dietary ingredient; and

``(iv) the nutrition information shall immediately precede the ingredient information required under subclause (i), except that no ingredient identified pursuant to subclause (i) shall be required to be identified a second time.''.

(c) **Percentage Level Claims**.–Section 403(r)(2) (21 U.S.C. 343(r)(2)) is amended by adding after clause (E) the following:

``(F) Subclause (i) clause (A) does not apply to a statement in the labeling of a dietary supplement that characterizes the percentage level of a dietary ingredient for which the Secretary has not established a reference daily intake, daily recommended value, or other recommendation for daily consumption.''.

(d) **Vitamins and Minerals**.–Section 411(b)(2) (21 U.S.C. 350(b)(2)) is amended–

(1) by striking ``vitamins or minerals'' and inserting ``dietary supplement ingredients described in section 201(ff)'';

(2) by striking ``(2)(A)'' and inserting ``(2)''; and

(3) by striking subparagraph (B).

(e) **Effective Date**.–Dietary supplements–

(1) may be labeled after the date of the enactment of this Act in accordance with the amendments made by this section, and

(2) shall be labeled after December 31, 1996, in accordance with such amendments.

Sec. 8. New Dietary Ingredients.

Chapter IV of the Federal Food, Drug, and Cosmetic Act is amended by adding at the end the following:

``NEW DIETARY INGREDIENTS

``Sec. 413.

(a) **In General**.—A dietary supplement which contains a new dietary ingredient shall be deemed adulterated under section 402(f) unless it meets one of the following requirements:

> ``(1) The dietary supplement contains only dietary ingredients which have been present in the food supply as an article used for food in a form in which the food has not been chemically altered.

> ``(2) There is a history of use or other evidence of safety establishing that the dietary ingredient when used under the conditions recommended or suggested in the labeling of the dietary supplement will reasonably be expected to be safe and, at least 75 days before being introduced or delivered for introduction into interstate commerce, the manufacturer or distributor of the dietary ingredient or dietary supplement provides the Secretary with information, including any citation to published articles, which is the basis on which the manufacturer or distributor has concluded that a dietary supplement containing such dietary ingredient will reasonably be expected to be safe.

> The Secretary shall keep confidential any information provided under paragraph (2) for 90 days following its receipt. After the expiration of such 90 days, the Secretary shall place such information on public display, except matters in the information which are trade secrets or otherwise confidential, commercial information.

``(b) **Petition**.—Any person may file with the Secretary a petition proposing the issuance of an order prescribing the conditions under which a new dietary ingredient under its intended conditions of use will reasonably be expected to be safe. The Secretary shall make a decision on such petition within 180 days of the date the petition is filed with the Secretary. For purposes of chapter 7 of title 5, United States Code, the decision of the Secretary shall be considered final agency action.

``(c) **Definition**.—For purposes of this section, the term `new dietary ingredient' means a dietary ingredient that was not marketed in the United States before October 15, 1994 and does not include any dietary ingredient which was marketed in the United States before October 15, 1994.''.

D
S
H
E
A

Sec. 9. Good Manufacturing Practices.

Section 402 (21 U.S.C. 342), as amended by section 4, is amended by adding at the end the following:

``(g)(1) If it is a dietary supplement and it has been prepared, packed, or held under conditions that do not meet current good manufacturing practice regulations, including regulations requiring, when necessary, expiration date labeling, issued by the Secretary under subparagraph (2).

``(2) The Secretary may by regulation prescribe good manufacturing practices for dietary supplements. Such regulations shall be modeled after current good manufacturing practice regulations for food and may not impose standards for which there is no current and generally available analytical methodology. No standard of current good manufacturing practice may be imposed unless such standard is included in a regulation promulgated after notice and opportunity for comment in accordance with chapter 5 of title 5, United States Code.''.

Sec. 10. Conforming Amendments.

(a) **Section** 201.–The last sentence of section 201(g)(1) (21 U.S.C. 321(g)(1)) is amended to read as follows: ``A food or dietary supplement for which a claim, subject to sections 403(r)(1)(B) and 403(r)(3) or sections 403(r)(1)(B) and 403(r)(5)(D), is made in accordance with the requirements of section 403(r) is not a drug solely because the label or the labeling contains such a claim. A food, dietary ingredient, or dietary supplement for which a truthful and not misleading statement is made in accordance with section 403(r)(6) is not a drug under clause (C) solely because the label or the labeling contains such a statement.''.

(b) **Section** 301.–Section 301 (21 U.S.C. 331) is amended by adding at the end the following:

``(u) The introduction or delivery for introduction into interstate commerce of a dietary supplement that is unsafe under section 413.''.

(c) **Section** 403.–Section 403 (21 U.S.C. 343), as amended by section 7, is amended by adding after paragraph (s) the following:

``A dietary supplement shall not be deemed misbranded solely because its label or labeling contains directions or conditions of use or warnings.''.

Sec. 11. Withdrawal of the Regulations and Notice.

The advance notice of proposed rulemaking concerning dietary supplements published in the Federal Register of June 18, 1993 (58 FR 33690-33700) is null and void and of no force or effect insofar as it applies to dietary supplements. The Secretary of Health and Human Services shall publish a notice in the Federal Register to revoke the item declared to be null and void and of no force or effect under subsection (a).

Sec. 12. Commission on Dietary Supplement Labels.

(a) **Establishment.**–There shall be established as an independent agency within the executive branch a commission to be known as the Commission on Dietary Supplement Labels (hereafter in this section referred to as the ``Commission'').

(b) **Membership.**–

(1) **Composition.**–The Commission shall be composed of 7 members who shall be appointed by the President.

(2) **Expertise requirement.**–The members of the Commission shall consist of individuals with expertise and experience in dietary supplements and in the manufacture, regulation, distribution, and use of such supplements. At least three of the members of the Commission shall be qualified by scientific training and experience to evaluate the benefits to health of the use of dietary supplements and one of such three members shall have experience in pharmacognosy, medical botany, traditional herbal medicine, or other related sciences. Members and staff of the Commission shall be without bias on the issue of dietary supplements.

(c) **Functions of the Commission.**–The Commission shall conduct a study on, and provide recommendations for, the regulation of label claims and statements for dietary supplements, including the use of literature in connection with the sale of dietary supplements and procedures for the evaluation of such claims. In making such recommendations, the Commission shall evaluate how best to provide truthful, scientifically valid, and not misleading information to consumers so that such consumers may make informed and appropriate health care choices for themselves and their families.

(d) **Administrative Powers of the Commission.**–

(1) **Hearings.**–The Commission may hold hearings, sit and act at such times and places, take such testimony, and receive such evidence as the Commission considers advisable to carry out the purposes of this section.

(2) **Information from federal agencies.**–The Commission may secure directly from any Federal department or agency such information as the Commission considers necessary to carry out the provisions of this section.

(3) **Authorization of appropriations.**–There are authorized to be appropriated such sums as may be necessary to carry out this section.

(e) **Reports and Recommendations.**–

(1) **Final report required.**–Not later than 24 months after the date of enactment of this Act, the Commission shall prepare and submit to the President and to the Congress a final report on the study required by this section.

(2) **Recommendations.**–The report described in paragraph (1) shall contain such recommendations, including recommendations for legislation, as the Commission deems appropriate.

D
S
H
E
A

(3) **Action on recommendations**.–Within 90 days of the issuance of the report under paragraph (1), the Secretary of Health and Human Services shall publish in the Federal Register a notice of any recommendation of Commission for changes in regulations of the Secretary for the regulation of dietary supplements and shall include in such notice a notice of proposed rulemaking on such changes together with an opportunity to present views on such changes. Such rulemaking shall be completed not later than 2 years after the date of the issuance of such report. If such rulemaking is not completed on or before the expiration of such 2 years, regulations of the Secretary published in 59 FR 395-426 on January 4, 1994, shall not be in effect.

Sec. 13. Office of Dietary Supplements.

(a) **In General**.–Title IV of the Public Health Service Act is amended by inserting after section 485B (42 U.S.C. 287c-3) the following:

``Subpart 4–Office of Dietary Supplements

``Sec. 485C. Dietary Supplements.

``(a) **Establishment**.–The Secretary shall establish an Office of Dietary Supplements within the National Institutes of Health.

``(b) **Purpose**.–The purposes of the Office are–

``(1) to explore more fully the potential role of dietary supplements as a significant part of the efforts of the United States to improve health care; and

``(2) to promote scientific study of the benefits of dietary supplements in maintaining health and preventing chronic disease and other health-related conditions.

``(c) **Duties**.–The Director of the Office of Dietary Supplements shall–

``(1) conduct and coordinate scientific research within the National Institutes of Health relating to dietary supplements and the extent to which the use of dietary supplements can limit or reduce the risk of diseases such as heart disease, cancer, birth defects, osteoporosis, cataracts, or prostatism;

``(2) collect and compile the results of scientific research relating to dietary supplements, including scientific data from foreign sources or the Office of Alternative Medicine;

``(3) serve as the principal advisor to the Secretary and to the Assistant Secretary for Health and provide advice to the Director of the National Institutes of Health, the Director of the Centers for Disease Control and Prevention, and the Commissioner of Food and Drugs on issues relating to dietary supplements including–

``(A) dietary intake regulations;

``(B) the safety of dietary supplements;

``(C) claims characterizing the relationship between–

   ``(i) dietary supplements; and

   ``(ii)(I) prevention of disease or other health-related conditions; and

     ``(II) maintenance of health; and

``(D) scientific issues arising in connection with the labeling and composition of dietary supplements;

``(4) compile a database of scientific research on dietary supplements and individual nutrients; and

``(5) coordinate funding relating to dietary supplements for the National Institutes of Health.

``(d) **Definition**.–As used in this section, the term `dietary supplement' has the meaning given the term in section 201(ff) of the Federal Food, Drug, and Cosmetic Act.

``(e) **Authorization of Appropriations**.–There are authorized to be appropriated to carry out this section $5,000,000 for fiscal year 1994 and such sums as may be necessary for each subsequent fiscal year.''.

(b) **Conforming Amendment**.–Section 401(b)(2) of the Public Health Service Act (42 U.S.C. 281(b)(2)) is amended by adding at the end the following:

``(E) The Office of Dietary Supplements.''.

D
S
H
E
A

Chapter 9

Dietary Supplement and Nonprescription Drug Consumer Protection Act

An Act[1]

To amend the Federal Food, Drug, and Cosmetic Act with respect to serious adverse event reporting for dietary supplements and nonprescription drugs, and for other purposes.

Be it enacted by the Senate and House of Representatives of the United States of America in Congress assembled

Sec. 1. Short Title.

This Act may be cited as the ``Dietary Supplement and Nonprescription Drug Consumer Protection Act''.

Sec. 2. Serious Adverse Event Reporting For Nonprescription Drugs.

(a) **In General.**–Chapter VII of the Federal Food, Drug, and Cosmetic Act (21 U.S.C. 371 et seq.) is amended by adding at the end the following:

``Subchapter H–Serious Adverse Event Reports

``**Sec. 760. Serious Adverse Event Reporting for Nonprescription Drugs.**

``(a) **Definitions.**–In this section:

``(1) **Adverse event.**–The term `adverse event' means any health-related event associated with the use of a nonprescription drug that is adverse, including–

``(A) an event occurring from an overdose of the drug, whether accidental or intentional;

``(B) an event occurring from abuse of the drug;

``(C) an event occurring from withdrawal from the drug; and

``(D) any failure of expected pharmacological action of the drug.

---

1   Public Law 109-462, 109th Congress. [DOCID: f:publ462.109] is available online at https://www.gpo.gov/fdsys/pkg/PLAW-109publ462/html/PLAW-109publ462.htm.

``(2) **Nonprescription drug**.–The term `nonprescription drug' means a drug that is–

  ``(A) not subject to section 503(b); and

  ``(B) not subject to approval in an application submitted under section 505.

``(3) **Serious adverse event**.–The term `serious adverse event' is an adverse event that–

  ``(A) results in–

    ``(i) death;

    ``(ii) a life-threatening experience;

    ``(iii) inpatient hospitalization;

    ``(iv) a persistent or significant disability or incapacity; or

    ``(v) a congenital anomaly or birth defect; or

  ``(B) requires, based on reasonable medical judgment, a medical or surgical intervention to prevent an outcome described under subparagraph (A).

``(4) **Serious adverse event report**.–The term `serious adverse event report' means a report that is required to be submitted to the Secretary under subsection (b).

``(b) **Reporting Requirement**.–

  ``(1) **In General**.–The manufacturer, packer, or distributor whose name (pursuant to section 502(b)(1)) appears on the label of a nonprescription drug marketed in the United States (referred to in this section as the `responsible person') shall submit to the Secretary any report received of a serious adverse event associated with such drug when used in the United States, accompanied by a copy of the label on or within the retail package of such drug.

  ``(2) **Retailer**.–A retailer whose name appears on the label described in paragraph (1) as a distributor may, by agreement, authorize the manufacturer or packer of the nonprescription drug to submit the required reports for such drugs to the Secretary so long as the retailer directs to the manufacturer or packer all adverse events associated with such drug that are reported to the retailer through the address or telephone number described in section 502(x).

``(c) **Submission of Reports**.–

  ``(1) **Timing of Reports**.–The responsible person shall submit to the Secretary a serious adverse event report no later than 15 business days after the report is received through the address or phone number described in section 502(x).

  ``(2) **New Medical Information**.–The responsible person shall submit to the Secretary any new medical information, related to a submitted serious adverse event report that is received by the responsible person within 1 year of the initial report, no later than 15 business days after the new information is received by the responsible person.

``(3) **Consolidation of Reports**.–The Secretary shall develop systems to ensure that duplicate reports of, and new medical information related to, a serious adverse event shall be consolidated into a single report.

``(4) **Exemption**.–The Secretary, after providing notice and an opportunity for comment from interested parties, may establish an exemption to the requirements under paragraphs (1) and (2) if the Secretary determines that such exemption would have no adverse effect on public health.

``(d) **Contents of Reports**.–Each serious adverse event report under this section shall be submitted to the Secretary using the MedWatch form, which may be modified by the Secretary for nonprescription drugs, and may be accompanied by additional information.

``(e) **Maintenance and Inspection of Records**.–

``(1) **Maintenance**.–The responsible person shall maintain records related to each report of an adverse event received by the responsible person for a period of 6 years.

``(2) **Records Inspection**.–

``(A) **In General**.–The responsible person shall permit an authorized person to have access to records required to be maintained under this section, during an inspection pursuant to section 704.

``(B) **Authorized Person**.–For purposes of this paragraph, the term `authorized person' means an officer or employee of the Department of Health and Human Services who has–

``(i) appropriate credentials, as determined by the Secretary; and

``(ii) been duly designated by the Secretary to have access to the records required under this section.

``(f) **Protected Information**.–A serious adverse event report submitted to the Secretary under this section, including any new medical information submitted under subsection (c)(2), or an adverse event report voluntarily submitted to the Secretary shall be considered to be–

``(1) a safety report under section 756 and may be accompanied by a statement, which shall be a part of any report that is released for public disclosure, that denies that the report or the records constitute an admission that the product involved caused or contributed to the adverse event; and

``(2) a record about an individual under section 552a of title 5, United States Code (commonly referred to as the `Privacy Act of 1974') and a medical or similar file the disclosure of which would constitute a violation of section 552 of such title 5 (commonly referred to as the `Freedom of Information Act'), and shall not be publicly disclosed unless all personally identifiable information is redacted.

``(g) **Rule of Construction**.–The submission of any adverse event report in compliance with this section shall not be construed as an admission that the nonprescription drug involved caused or contributed to the adverse event.

D
S
N
D
C
P
A

``(h) **Preemption**.–

    ``(1) **In General**.–No State or local government shall establish or continue in effect any law, regulation, order, or other requirement, related to a mandatory system for adverse event reports for nonprescription drugs, that is different from, in addition to, or otherwise not identical to, this section.

    ``(2) **Effect Of Section**.–

        ``(A) **In General**.–Nothing in this section shall affect the authority of the Secretary to provide adverse event reports and information to any health, food, or drug officer or employee of any State, territory, or political subdivision of a State or territory, under a memorandum of understanding between the Secretary and such State, territory, or political subdivision.

        ``(B) **Personally-Identifiable Information**.–Notwithstanding any other provision of law, personally-identifiable information in adverse event reports provided by the Secretary to any health, food, or drug officer or employee of any State, territory, or political subdivision of a State or territory, shall not–

            ``(i) be made publicly available pursuant to any State or other law requiring disclosure of information or records; or

            ``(ii) otherwise be disclosed or distributed to any party without the written consent of the Secretary and the person submitting such information to the Secretary.

        ``(C) **Use of Safety Reports**.–Nothing in this section shall permit a State, territory, or political subdivision of a State or territory, to use any safety report received from the Secretary in a manner inconsistent with subsection (g) or section 756.

            ``(i) **Authorization of Appropriations**.–There are authorized to be appropriated to carry out this section such sums as may be necessary.''.

(b) **Modifications**.–The Secretary of Health and Human Services may modify requirements under the amendments made by this section in accordance with section 553 of title 5, United States Code, to maintain consistency with international harmonization efforts over time.

(c) **Prohibited Act**.–Section 301(e) of the Federal Food, Drug, and Cosmetic Act (21 U.S.C. 331(e)) is amended by–

    (1) striking ``, or 704(a);'' and inserting ``, 704(a), or 760;''; and

    (2) striking ``, or 564'' and inserting ``, 564, or 760''.

(d) **Misbranding**.–Section 502 of the Federal Food, Drug, and Cosmetic Act (21 U.S.C. 352) is amended by adding at the end the following:

    ``(x) If it is a nonprescription drug (as defined in section 760) that is marketed in the United States, unless the label of such drug includes a domestic address or domestic phone number through which the responsible person (as described in section 760) may receive a report of a serious adverse event (as defined in section 760) with such drug.''.

(e) **Effective Dates.**–

(1) **In General**.–Except as provided in paragraph (2), the amendments made by this section shall take effect 1 year after the date of enactment of this Act.

(2) **Misbranding**.–Section 502(x) of the Federal Food, Drug, and Cosmetic Act (as added by this section) shall apply to any nonprescription drug (as defined in such section 502(x)) labeled on or after the date that is 1 year after the date of enactment of this Act.

(3) **Guidance**.–Not later than 270 days after the date of enactment of this Act, the Secretary of Health and Human Services shall issue guidance on the minimum data elements that should be included in a serious adverse event report described under the amendments made by this Act.

Sec. 3. Serious Adverse Event Reporting for Dietary Supplements.

(a) **In General**.–Chapter VII of the Federal Food, Drug, and Cosmetic Act (21 U.S.C. 371 et seq.) is amended by adding at the end the following:

``**Sec. 761. Serious Adverse Event Reporting for Dietary Supplements.**

``(a) **Definitions**.–In this section:

``(1) **Adverse event**.–The term `adverse event' means any health-related event associated with the use of a dietary supplement that is adverse.

``(2) **Serious adverse event**.–The term `serious adverse event' is an adverse event that–

``(A) results in–

``(i) death;

``(ii) a life-threatening experience;

``(iii) inpatient hospitalization;

``(iv) a persistent or significant disability or incapacity; or

``(v) a congenital anomaly or birth defect; or

``(B) requires, based on reasonable medical judgment, a medical or surgical intervention to prevent an outcome described under subparagraph (A).

``(3) **Serious adverse event report**.–The term `serious adverse event report' means a report that is required to be submitted to the Secretary under subsection (b).

``(b) **Reporting Requirement**.–

``(1) **In General**.–The manufacturer, packer, or distributor of a dietary supplement whose name (pursuant to section 403(e)(1)) appears on the label of a dietary supplement marketed in the United States (referred to in this section as the `responsible

D
S
N
D
C
P
A

person') shall submit to the Secretary any report received of a serious adverse event associated with such dietary supplement when used in the United States, accompanied by a copy of the label on or within the retail packaging of such dietary supplement.

``(2) **Retailer**.–A retailer whose name appears on the label described in paragraph (1) as a distributor may, by agreement, authorize the manufacturer or packer of the dietary supplement to submit the required reports for such dietary supplements to the Secretary so long as the retailer directs to the manufacturer or packer all adverse events associated with such dietary supplement that are reported to the retailer through the address or telephone number described in section 403(y).

``(c) **Submission of Reports**.–

``(1) **Timing of reports**.–The responsible person shall submit to the Secretary a serious adverse event report no later than 15 business days after the report is received through the address or phone number described in section 403(y).

``(2) **New medical information**.–The responsible person shall submit to the Secretary any new medical information, related to a submitted serious adverse event report that is received by the responsible person within 1 year of the initial report, no later than 15 business days after the new information is received by the responsible person.

``(3) **Consolidation of reports**.–The Secretary shall develop systems to ensure that duplicate reports of, and new medical information related to, a serious adverse event shall be consolidated into a single report.

``(4) **Exemption**.–The Secretary, after providing notice and an opportunity for comment from interested parties, may establish an exemption to the requirements under paragraphs (1) and (2) if the Secretary determines that such exemption would have no adverse effect on public health.

``(d) **Contents of Reports**.–Each serious adverse event report under this section shall be submitted to the Secretary using the MedWatch form, which may be modified by the Secretary for dietary supplements, and may be accompanied by additional information.

``(e) **Maintenance and Inspection of Records**.–

``(1) **Maintenance**.–The responsible person shall maintain records related to each report of an adverse event received by the responsible person for a period of 6 years.

``(2) **Records inspection**.–

``(A) **In general**.–The responsible person shall permit an authorized person to have access to records required to be maintained under this section during an inspection pursuant to section 704.

``(B) **Authorized person**.–For purposes of this paragraph, the term `authorized person' means an officer or employee of the Department of Health and Human Services, who has–

``(i) appropriate credentials, as determined by the Secretary; and

``(ii) been duly designated by the Secretary to have access to the records required under this section.

``(f) **Protected Information.**–A serious adverse event report submitted to the Secretary under this section, including any new medical information submitted under subsection (c)(2), or an adverse event report voluntarily submitted to the Secretary shall be considered to be–

``(1) a safety report under section 756 and may be accompanied by a statement, which shall be a part of any report that is released for public disclosure, that denies that the report or the records constitute an admission that the product involved caused or contributed to the adverse event; and

``(2) a record about an individual under section 552a of title 5, United States Code (commonly referred to as the `Privacy Act of 1974') and a medical or similar file the disclosure of which would constitute a violation of section 552 of such title 5 (commonly referred to as the `Freedom of Information Act'), and shall not be publicly disclosed unless all personally identifiable information is redacted.

``(g) **Rule of Construction.**–The submission of any adverse event report in compliance with this section shall not be construed as an admission that the dietary supplement involved caused or contributed to the adverse event.

``(h) **Preemption.**–

``(1) **In general.**–No State or local government shall establish or continue in effect any law, regulation, order, or other requirement, related to a mandatory system for adverse event reports for dietary supplements, that is different from, in addition to, or otherwise not identical to, this section.

``(2) **Effect of section.**–

``(A) **In general.**–Nothing in this section shall affect the authority of the Secretary to provide adverse event reports and information to any health, food, or drug officer or employee of any State, territory, or political subdivision of a State or territory, under a memorandum of understanding between the Secretary and such State, territory, or political subdivision.

``(B) **Personally-identifiable information.**–Notwithstanding any other provision of law, personally-identifiable information in adverse event reports provided by the Secretary to any health, food, or drug officer or employee of any State, territory, or political subdivision of a State or territory, shall not–

``(i) be made publicly available pursuant to any State or other law requiring disclosure of information or records; or

``(ii) otherwise be disclosed or distributed to any party without the written consent of the Secretary and the person submitting such information to the Secretary.

D
S
N
D
C
P
A

``(C) USE OF SAFETY REPORTS.–Nothing in this section shall permit a State, territory, or political subdivision of a State or territory, to use any safety report received from the Secretary in a manner inconsistent with subsection (g) or section 756.

``(i) Authorization of Appropriations.–There are authorized to be appropriated to carry out this section such sums as may be necessary.''.

(b) **Prohibited Act**.–Section 301(e) of the Federal Food, Drug, and Cosmetic Act (21 U.S.C. 331(e)) is amended by–

(1) striking ``, or 760;'' and inserting ``, 760, or 761;''; and

(2) striking ``, or 760'' and inserting ``, 760, or 761''.

(c) **Misbranding**.–Section 403 of the Federal Food, Drug, and Cosmetic Act (21 U.S.C. 343) is amended by adding at the end the following:

``(y) If it is a dietary supplement that is marketed in the United States, unless the label of such dietary supplement includes a domestic address or domestic phone number through which the responsible person (as described in section 761) may receive a report of a serious adverse event with such dietary supplement.''.

(d) **Effective Date**.–

(1) **In general**.–Except as provided in paragraph (2), the amendments made by this section shall take effect 1 year after the date of enactment of this Act.

(2) **Misbranding**.–Section 403(y) of the Federal Food, Drug, and Cosmetic Act (as added by this section) shall apply to any dietary supplement labeled on or after the date that is 1 year after the date of enactment of this Act.

(3) **Guidance**.–Not later than 270 days after the date of enactment of this Act, the Secretary of Health and Human Services shall issue guidance on the minimum data elements that should be included in a serious adverse event report as described under the amendments made by this Act.

Sec. 4. Prohibition of Falsification of Reports.

(a) **In General**.–Section 301 of the Federal Food, Drug, and Cosmetic Act (21 U.S.C. 331) is amended by adding at the end the following:

``(ii) The falsification of a report of a serious adverse event submitted to a responsible person (as defined under section 760 or 761) or the falsification of a serious adverse event report (as defined under section 760 or 761) submitted to the Secretary.''.

(b) **Effective Date**.–The amendment made by this section shall take effect 1 year after the date of enactment of this Act.

Sec. 5. Importation of Certain Nonprescription Drugs and Dietary Supplements.

(a) **In General.**–Section 801 of the Federal Food, Drug, and Cosmetic Act (21 U.S.C. 381) is amended–

    (1) in subsection (a), by inserting after the third sentence the following: ``If such article is subject to a requirement under section 760 or 761 and if the Secretary has credible evidence or information indicating that the responsible person (as defined in such section 760 or 761) has not complied with a requirement of such section 760 or 761 with respect to any such article, or has not allowed access to records described in such section 760 or 761, then such article shall be refused admission, except as provided in subsection (b) of this section.''; and

    (2) in the second sentence of subsection (b)–

        (A) by inserting ``(1)'' before ``an article included'';

        (B) by inserting before ``final determination'' the following: ``or (2) with respect to an article included within the provision of the fourth sentence of subsection (a), the responsible person (as defined in section 760 or 761) can take action that would assure that the responsible person is in compliance with section 760 or 761, as the case may be,''; and

        (C) by inserting ``, or, with respect to clause (2), the responsible person,'' before ``to perform''.

(b) **Effective Date.**–The amendments made by this section shall take effect 1 year after the date of enactment of this Act.

Approved December 22, 2006.

GUIDANCE & ASSOCIATED DOCUMENTS

⇛ IMPORTANT NOTE ⇚

GUIDANCE DOCUMENTS

Guidance documents represent the Agency's current thinking on a particular subject. These documents are prepared for FDA review staff and drug sponsors to provide guidelines for the processing, content, and evaluation of applications, and for the design, production, manufacturing, and testing of regulated products. They also provide consistency in the Agency's regulation, inspection and enforcement procedures.

Because guidances are not regulations or laws, they are not enforceable. They do not create or confer any rights for or on any person and do not operate to bind FDA or the public. An alternative approach may be used if it satisfies the requirements of the applicable statute, regulations, or both. If you want to discuss an alternative approach, contact the appropriate FDA staff responsible for implementing this guidance. To identify the appropriate FDA staff, refer to the FDA website.

Chapter 10

Current Good Manufacturing Practice
Guidance

Contains Nonbinding Recommendations
December 2010

Guidance for Industry: Current Good Manufacturing Practice in Manufacturing, Packaging, Labeling, or Holding Operations for Dietary Supplements; Small Entity Compliance Guide[1]

I. Introduction[2]

On June 25, 2007, FDA published in the *Federal Register* a final rule that established a regulation (21 CFR part 111) entitled Current Good Manufacturing Practice (CGMP) In Manufacturing, Packaging, Labeling, Or Holding Operations For Dietary Supplements (72 FR 34752). The Dietary Supplement (DS) CGMP rule in 21 CFR part 111 ("the DS CGMP rule") requires persons who manufacture, package, label, or hold a dietary supplement to establish and follow current good manufacturing practice to ensure the quality of the dietary supplement and to ensure that the dietary supplement is packaged and labeled as specified in the master manufacturing record.

In the same issue of the *Federal Register* (72 FR 34959), FDA also issued an interim final rule (the identity testing interim final rule) setting forth a procedure for requesting an exemption from a requirement of the DS CGMP rule for the manufacturer to conduct at least one appropriate test or examination to verify the identity of any dietary ingredient that is a component of a dietary supplement. The provisions of the identity testing interim final rule have the full force of law, but FDA provided a 90-day comment period on those provisions through September 24, 2007. On September 17, 2007, FDA published a notice in the *Federal Register* to extend the comment period to October 24, 2007.

The DS CGMP rule and the identity testing interim final rule were effective as of August 24, 2007. The compliance dates are described below.

FDA has prepared this Small Entity Compliance Guide in accordance with section 212 of the Small Business Regulatory Enforcement Fairness Act (Public Law 104-121). This guidance document

---

1   This guidance is available on the FDA website http://www.fda.gov/FoodGuidances
2   This guidance has been prepared by the Division of Dietary Supplement Programs in the Center for Food Safety and Applied Nutrition at the U.S. Food and Drug Administration.

restates in plain language the legal requirements set forth in the DS CGMP rule (21 CFR part 111). The DS CGMP rule is binding and has the full force and effect of law.

FDA's guidance documents, including this guidance, do not establish legally enforceable responsibilities. Instead, guidances describe the Agency's current thinking on a topic and should be viewed only as recommendations, unless specific regulatory or statutory requirements are cited. The use of the word should in Agency guidances means that something is suggested or recommended, but not required.

II. Discussion

A. Compliance Dates for the Dietary Supplement Current Good Manufacturing Practice Rule (DS CGMP Rule) and the Interim Final Rule

1. What were the compliance dates for the DS CGMP rule?

As shown in Table 1, the compliance dates were based on how many full-time equivalent employees (FTEs) you employ.

Table 1—Compliance Dates Based on the Size of Your Organization	
If you employ …	**The DS CGMP rule required you to comply by …**
500 or more FTEs	June 25, 2008
At least 20 but fewer than 500 FTEs	June 25, 2009
Fewer than 20 FTEs	June 25, 2010

B. Organization of the DS CGMP Rule

1. How is the DS CGMP rule organized?

The DS CGMP rule is organized as a series of "subparts," which each cover a different aspect of current good manufacturing practice. We list these subparts in Table 2.

Table 2—Subparts of the DS CGMP Rule	
Subpart	**Subject of Subpart**
A	General Provisions (including coverage and definitions)
B	Personnel
C	Physical Plant and Grounds
D	Equipment and Utensils
E	Requirements to Establish a Production and Process Control System
F	Production and Process Control System: Requirements for Quality Control
G	Production and Process Control System: Requirements for Components, Packaging, Labels and for Product that You Receive for Packaging or Labeling as a Dietary Supplement

Table 2—Subparts of the DS CGMP Rule	
H	Production and Process Control System: Requirements for the Master Manufacturing Record
I	Production and Process Control System: Requirements for the Batch Production Record
J	Production and Process Control System: Requirements for Laboratory Operations
K	Production and Process Control System: Requirements for Manufacturing Operations
L	Production and Process Control System: Requirements for Packaging and Labeling Operations
M	Holding and Distributing
N	Returned Dietary Supplements
O	Product Complaints
P	Records and Recordkeeping

III. Subpart A – General Provisions

A. Coverage of the DS CGMP Rule

1. Who is subject to the DS CGMP rule?

You are subject to the DS CGMP rule if you manufacture, package, label, or hold a dietary supplement.

(21 CFR 111.1(a))

In our answers to questions in sections III.A, III.B, III.C and XIX of this document, we address some specific examples of firms who do, or do not, fall within the coverage of the DS CGMP rule.

2. Am I subject to the DS CGMP rule if I am a foreign firm?

Yes. The DS CGMP rule applies to you if you manufacture, package, label, or hold a dietary supplement imported or offered for import in any State or Territory of the United States, the District of Columbia, or the Commonwealth of Puerto Rico.

(21 CFR 111.1(a)(2))

3. Am I subject to the DS CGMP rule if my product is sold only within my state?

You may be subject to the DS CGMP rule for products sold only within your state. FDA may consider its jurisdiction over such products under the Public Health Service Act, the Federal Food, Drug, and Cosmetic Act, or both, depending on the circumstances of the situation. (72 FR 34752 at 34785)

CH
10

4. Am I subject to the holding requirements established in the DS CGMP rule if I am a retailer who is holding dietary supplements at a retail establishment for the sole purpose of direct retail sale to individual consumers?

No. Importantly, a retail establishment does not include a warehouse or other storage facility for a retailer or a warehouse or other storage facility that sells directly to individual consumers. (21 CFR 111.1(b); 72 FR 34792)

5. Am I subject to the holding requirements established in the DS CGMP rule if I am a retailer who operates a warehouse or storage facility?

Yes. The "retail exemption" does not apply to you, because a retail establishment does not include a warehouse or other storage facility for a retailer or a warehouse or other storage facility that sells directly to individual consumers (21 CFR 111.1(b); 72 FR 34752 at 34792).

6. Do the requirements of the DS CGMP rule apply to all types of dietary supplements (e.g., for botanical dietary supplements and for vitamin/mineral dietary supplements)?

Yes. (72 FR 34752 at 34913)

B. How the DS CGMP Rule Applies to Specific Types of Operations

1. Am I subject to the DS CGMP rule if I package, label, or distribute a dietary supplement manufactured by another firm?

Yes. The DS CGMP rule requires you to comply with those provisions directly applicable to the operations you perform.

For example, if you are a labeler, the DS CGMP rule:

- Requires you to comply with the requirement in 21 CFR 111.255 to establish a batch production record;
- Requires you to comply with other applicable requirements, such as requirements for personnel, physical plant and grounds, equipment and utensils, and holding operations;
- Does not require you to comply with the requirement of 21 CFR 111.260(e) to include the identity and weight or measure of each component used, because you would be starting from packages that already had been filled rather than from individual components.

As another example, if you are a distributor who purchases a packaged and labeled dietary supplement and then holds the product in a warehouse for distribution to another physical location, the DS CGMP rule:

- Requires you to comply with requirements for holding and distributing; and
- Requires you to comply with other applicable requirements, such as requirements for personnel, the physical plant and grounds.

(21 CFR 111.1(a) and (a)(1); 72 FR 34752 at 34790 and 34886)

2. Am I subject to the DS CGMP rule if I manufacture a dietary ingredient (or a "pre-mix" of dietary ingredients) used by another manufacturer to make a dietary supplement?

   Whether you are subject to the DS CGMP rule depends on the totality of your business operation (72 FR 34752 at 34791). For example:

   - You are not subject to the DS CGMP rule if your only customers are other manufacturers who further process the dietary ingredient to make a dietary supplement (72 FR 34752 at 34791). However, we encourage firms who only supply dietary ingredients to other firms for further processing as part of the manufacture of a dietary supplement to adhere to the applicable provisions established in the DS CGMP rule that apply to their operations (72 FR 34752 at 34805).

   - You would be subject to the DS CGMP rule if you sell a dietary ingredient to a firm who simply packages the dietary ingredient for sale as a dietary supplement, or labels your packaged dietary ingredient for sale as a dietary supplement, because in this circumstance you are manufacturing a dietary supplement that another firm is simply packaging or labeling without further processing into a dietary supplement (72 FR 34752 at 34791). In other words, you would have acted as a manufacturer whose finished product is simply repackaged or relabeled.

   - You would be subject to the DS CGMP rule if you supply a dietary ingredient directly to consumers (72 FR 34752 at 34791); you would be considered a dietary supplement manufacturer in such a situation.

3. Am I subject to the DS CGMP rule if I manufacture a dietary supplement that is packaged or labeled by another firm – e.g., if I sell my dietary supplement to another firm for packaging and labeling and do not sell my dietary supplement directly to consumers?

   Yes. The DS CGMP rule requires you to comply with those provisions directly applicable to the operations you perform (21 CFR 111.1(a)(1); 72 FR 34752 at 34790). For example, you are required to make and keep records of product distribution (21 CFR 111.475).

4. Am I subject to the DS CGMP rule if I harvest, store, or distribute raw agricultural commodities that will be incorporated into a dietary supplement by others?

   No. If you simply supply a raw agricultural commodity that another person will process into a dietary supplement, you are not considered to be engaging in the manufacture, packing, labeling, or holding of a dietary supplement.. However, if you simply supply bulk material to someone who packages it in smaller packages or you sell agricultural commodities to the consumer as a dietary supplement, you would be considered the manufacturer. (21 CFR 111.1(a); 72 FR 34752 at 34792)

5. Am I responsible for the oversight of a packager/labeler if I am a manufacturer and I sell my dietary supplement to the packager/labeler?

   No. You would not be responsible for the oversight of the packager/labeler, because:

CH 10

- The packager/labeler is not under your control; and
- The packager/labeler (rather than you) has control over the release of the packaged and labeled dietary supplement

(72 FR 34752 at 34790)

6. When am I subject to the specific requirements applying to product received for packaging or labeling as a dietary supplement (and for distribution rather than for return to the supplier)?

You are subject to the specific requirements (such as those in 21 CFR 111.70(f), 111.75(e), 111.127(a) and (b), and 111.165) applying to product received for packaging or labeling as a dietary supplement (and for distribution rather than for return to the supplier) if you will distribute the dietary supplement that you package or label rather than return it to the person who supplied it to you. This means that you are subject to those specific requirements if the product that you will package or label has left the control of the firm who supplied it to you (e.g., because you purchased the product). (72 FR 34752 at 34844)

7. When am I not subject to the specific requirements applying to product received for packaging or labeling as a dietary supplement (and for distribution rather than for return to the supplier)?

You are not subject to the specific requirements (such as those in 21 CFR 111.70(f), 111.75(e), 111.127(a) and (b), and 111.165) applying to product received for packaging or labeling as a dietary supplement (and for distribution rather than for return to the supplier) if you package or label a dietary supplement under contract to a firm who supplied the product to you, and then return it to that firm rather than distribute it yourself. For the purposes of the DS CGMP rule, this situation is no different than a situation in which the packaging or labeling of the dietary supplement is done by the firm who manufactured the product, because the product remains under the control of the firm who arranged for your services under contract. (72 FR 34752 at 34844)

8. Am I subject to the DS CGMP rule if I am a practitioner (such as an herbalist, acupuncturist, naturopath, or other related health care provider)?

Yes. Practitioners such as herbalists, acupuncturists, naturopaths, and other related health care providers are subject to the DS CGMP rule. However, we believe that it would be appropriate to consider the exercise of our enforcement discretion in certain circumstances (see example which follows in the next question). (72 FR 34752 at 34793)

9. How does FDA expect to apply the DS CGMP rule to practitioners?

FDA expects to exercise enforcement discretion, on a case-by-case basis, in determining whether to apply the DS CGMP rule to practitioners such as herbalists, acupuncturists, naturopaths, and other related health care providers. For example:

- We expect to exercise discretion in the case of a one-on-one consultation by a practitioner who is adequately trained in his or her profession. We believe such a case may not necessitate the same types of controls as we established in the DS CGMP rule for manufacturing activities on a larger scale. Such a practitioner may make some formulations in advance of the consultation and still make the formulations in very limited quantities for the individual client.

- We are not considering exercising our enforcement discretion with respect to practitioners who prepare batches of dietary supplements and sell them to individual consumers without determining whether the dietary supplement is appropriate for each consumer's needs in a one-on-one personal consultation.

- We are not considering exercising our enforcement discretion with respect to practitioners who prepare batches of a dietary supplement for which there is a known or suspected safety concern.

- We do not expect the number of practitioners subject to the consideration of our enforcement discretion to be very large. Many products manufactured by practitioners would not necessarily be considered to be dietary supplements (e.g., certain products used by traditional Asian medicine practitioners).

(72 FR 34752 at 34793)

C. How the DS CGMP Rule Applies to Contractors

1. Does the DS CGMP rule apply to a contractor who provides a service to a firm who is subject to the DS CGMP rule?

   Yes. Contractors who provide a particular service (such as packaging, labeling or both packaging and labeling) to a firm who is subject to the DS CGMP rule must comply with those regulations directly applicable to the operations they perform for the firm who contracted with them (72 FR 34752 at 34790). For example, if a contractor is a labeler, the DS CGMP rule:

   - Requires the contractor to comply with the requirement in 21 CFR 111.255 to establish a batch production record;

   - Requires the contractor to comply with other applicable requirements, such as requirements for personnel, physical plant and grounds, equipment and utensils, and holding operations;

   - Does not require the contractor to comply with the requirement of 21 CFR 111.260(e) to include the identity and weight or measure of each component used, because the contractor would be starting from packages that already had been filled rather than from individual components.

2. What are some examples of how the requirements of the DS CGMP rule apply under contractual relationships?

   Below, we provide three examples of how the requirements of the DS CGMP rule apply under contractual relationships. Importantly, it is not practical to list all possible

CH 10

contractual relationships that persons may enter into in the manufacture of a dietary supplement, or to list all businesses or practices that may be subject to the requirements of the DS CGMP rule.

- Example 1. A manufacturer who contracts with a person to do packaging and labeling, but who later distributes the packaged and labeled product, is ultimately responsible for the dietary supplement it releases for distribution. The manufacturer would be responsible for the CGMP requirements for the operations it performs, including those related to the release of the product for distribution. For example, the manufacturer would determine whether the packaged and labeled dietary supplement it receives from the packager/labeler conforms to applicable specifications (21 CFR 111.127(d)), and is responsible for approving the release of the packaged and labeled dietary supplement for distribution (21 CFR 111.127(h)). Although the manufacturer is not performing the specific activities related to the packaging and labeling operations done by another person, the manufacturer has an obligation to know what and how such activities are performed so that it can make decisions related to whether the packaged and labeled product conforms to applicable specifications and whether to approve and release the product for distribution.

- Example 2. A manufacturer who hires a contractor to perform specific operations within the scope of the manufacturer's responsibilities under the DS CGMP rule is responsible for complying with the requirements related to the contracted operation. For example, a manufacturer who hires a contractor to calibrate its equipment is responsible for complying with the requirements of the DS CGMP rule related to calibrating equipment, even though it is the contractor who is performing that job task.

- Example 3. A distributor who contracts with a manufacturer to manufacture a dietary supplement, which the distributor then distributes under its own label, has an obligation to know what and how manufacturing activities are performed so that the distributor can make decisions related to whether the packaged and labeled product conforms to its established specifications and whether to approve and release the product for distribution.

(72 FR 34752 at 34790)

D. Terms Used in the DS CGMP Rule and In This Document

1. What terms does the DS CGMP rule define?

The DS CGMP rule defines the following terms:
- Actual yield;
- Batch;
- Batch number, lot number, or control number;
- Component;
- Contact surface;

- Ingredient;
- In-process material;
- Lot;
- Microorganisms;
- Pest;
- Physical plant;
- Product complaint;
- Quality;
- Quality control;
- Quality control personnel;
- Representative sample;
- Reprocessing;
- Reserve sample;
- Sanitize;
- Theoretical yield; and
- Water activity.

The DS CGMP rule also explains how we use the following terms:

- Must;
- We; and
- You.

The text of these definitions is available in 21 CFR 111.3.

2. What definitions from the DS CGMP rule did we copy to this document?

We copied the definitions of the terms "quality" and "product complaint" (other than the examples in such definition) to this document.

3. How does the DS CGMP rule define "quality"?

The DS CGMP rule defines "quality" to mean "that the dietary supplement consistently meets the established specifications for identity, purity, strength, and composition and limits on contaminants, and has been manufactured, packaged, labeled, and held under conditions to prevent adulteration under sections 402(a)(1), (a)(2), (a)(3), and (a)(4) of the act" [referring to the Federal Food, Drug, and Cosmetic Act] (see 21 CFR 111.3).

4. How does the DS CGMP rule define "product complaint"?

The DS CGMP rule defines "product complaint" to mean "any communication that contains any allegation, written, electronic, or oral, expressing concern, for any reason, with the quality of a dietary supplement, that could be related to current good manufacturing practice (see 21 CFR 111.3).

5. What does this document mean when it uses the terms "received product" or "product received for packaging or labeling as a dietary supplement"?

For the purposes of this document, we use the terms "received product" and "product received for packaging or labeling as a dietary supplement" to mean product you receive for packaging or labeling as a dietary supplement (and for distribution rather than for return to the supplier).

6. What does this document mean when it uses the term "food CGMP"?

For the purposes of this document, we use the term "food CGMP" to mean the CGMP requirements, in 21 CFR part 110, established for all food.

7. What does this document mean when it uses the term "required specifications"?

For the purposes of this document, we use the term "required specifications" to mean specifications that you are required to establish in accordance with 21 CFR 111.70.

8. What does this document mean when it uses the term "Certificate of Analysis"?

For the purposes of this document, we use the term "certificate of analysis" to mean a document, provided by the supplier of a component prior to or upon receipt of the component, that documents certain characteristics and attributes of the component. (72 FR 34752 at 34834)

9. What does this document mean when it uses the term "scientifically valid method"?

For the purposes of this document, we use the term "scientifically valid method" to mean a scientific method that is accurate, precise, and specific for its intended purpose. In other words, we use the term "scientifically valid method" to mean a scientific method that consistently does what it is intended to do. (72 FR 34752 at 34893)

E. Other Applicable Statutory Provisions and Regulations

1. Do other statutory provisions and regulations apply to persons who manufacture, package, label or hold dietary supplements?

Yes. You must comply with other applicable statutory provisions and regulations under the Federal Food, Drug, and Cosmetic Act related to dietary supplements. (21 CFR 111.5)

2. How does the DS CGMP rule relate to the food CGMP rule in 21 CFR part 110?

In establishing 21 CFR part 111, we:

- Duplicated those requirements in the food CGMP rule (i.e., 21 CFR part 110) that we found to be common to most dietary supplements;
- Did not duplicate those requirements in the food CGMP rule that were not common to most dietary supplements.

3. What is an example of a requirement in the food CGMP rule that FDA did not duplicate in the DS CGMP rule?

CH 10

An example of a requirement in the food CGMP rule that we did not duplicate in the DS CGMP rule is 21 CFR 110.80(b)(4), which requires that food that relies on the control of water activity for preventing the growth of microorganisms be processed to, and maintained at, a safe moisture level. We did not duplicate this requirement because we concluded that it may not be applicable to most dietary supplements. However, to the extent that this requirement is applicable to a particular dietary supplement, a manufacturer would be expected to comply with it.

4. What should I do if a provision of the DS CGMP rule conflicts with an analogous provision in the food CGMP rule?

To the extent that the DS CGMP rule conflicts with the food CGMP rule, you would comply with the DS CGMP rule. (72 FR 34752 at 34764)

IV. Written Procedures Required by the DS CGMP Rule

1. Does the DS CGMP rule require me to establish and follow written procedures?

Yes. The DS CGMP rule requires you to establish and follow the written procedures shown in Table 3.

Subpart	Written Procedures That the DS CGMP rule Requires You to Establish and Follow
	Table 3—Requirements for Written Procedures
B	Fulfilling the requirements for personnel (21 CFR 111.8)
C	Cleaning the physical plant and pest control (21 CFR 111.16)
D	Fulfilling the requirements for equipment and utensils, including calibrating instruments and controls you use in manufacturing or testing a component or dietary supplement; calibrating, inspecting, and checking automated, mechanical, and electronic equipment; and maintaining, cleaning, and sanitizing, as necessary, all equipment, utensils, and any other contact surfaces that are used to manufacture, package, label, or hold components or dietary supplements (21 CFR 111.25)
F	The responsibilities of quality control personnel, including written procedures for conducting a material review and making a disposition decision, and for approving or rejecting any reprocessing (21 CFR 111.103)
G	Fulfilling the requirements for components, packaging, and labels and for product that you receive for packaging or labeling as a dietary supplement (21 CFR 111.153)
J	Laboratory operations, including written procedures for the tests and examinations you conduct to determine whether specifications are met (21 CFR 111.303)
K	Manufacturing operations (21 CFR 111.353)
L	Packaging and labeling operations (21 CFR 111.403)
M	Holding and distributing operations (21 CFR 111.453)
N	Fulfilling the requirements for returned dietary supplements (21 CFR 111.503)
O	Fulfilling the requirements for product complaints (21 CFR 111.553)

CH
10

2. Does the DS CGMP rule require me to establish and follow written procedures for product recalls?

No. However, we encourage you to refer to our "Guidance for Industry: Product Recalls, Including Removals and Corrections" (Ref. 1) (72 FR 34752 at 34774).

V. Records Required by the DS CGMP Rule

1. What records does the DS CGMP rule require me to make and keep?

The DS CGMP rule requires you to make and keep the records shown in Table 4.

Table 4—Records the DS CGMP rule Requires You to Make and Keep	
Subpart	**Required Records**
B	<ul><li>Written procedures (21 CFR 111.14(b)(1))</li><li>Documentation of training, including the date of the training, the type of training, and the person(s) trained (21 CFR 111.14(b)(2))</li></ul>
C	<ul><li>Written procedures (21 CFR 111.23(b))</li><li>Records that show that water, when used in a manner such that the water may become a component of the dietary supplement, meets the requirements of 21 CFR 111.15(e)(2) of the DS CGMP rule (21 CFR 111.23(c))</li></ul>
D	<ul><li>Written procedures (21 CFR 111.35(b)(1))</li><li>Documentation, either in individual equipment logs or in the batch record (see § 111.260(c) for batch record requirements), of the date of the use, maintenance, cleaning, and sanitizing of equipment, unless such documentation is kept with the batch record (see § 111.260(c) for batch record requirements) (21 CFR 111.35(b)(2))</li><li>Documentation of any calibration, each time the calibration is performed, for instruments and controls that you use in manufacturing or testing a component or dietary supplement (21 CFR 111.35(b)(3)). The DS CGMP rule establishes specific requirements for what must be in this documentation. You should refer to 21 CFR 111.35(b)(3) for the complete requirements.</li><li>Written records of calibrations, inspections, and checks of automated, mechanical, and electronic equipment (21 CFR 111.35(b)(4))</li></ul>
D	<ul><li>Backup file(s) of current software programs (and of outdated software that is necessary to retrieve records that you are required to keep in accordance with subpart P, when current software is not able to retrieve such records) and of data entered into computer systems that you use to manufacture, package, label, or hold dietary supplements (21 CFR 111.35(b)(5)). The DS CGMP rule establishes specific requirements for these backup files. You should refer to 21 CFR 111.35(b)(5) for the complete requirements.</li><li>Documentation of the controls that you use to ensure that equipment functions in accordance with its intended use (21 CFR 111.35(b)(6))</li></ul>

Table 4—Records the DS CGMP rule Requires You to Make and Keep	
Subpart	**Required Records**
E	□ Documentation of the specifications established (21 CFR 111.95(b)(1)) □ Documentation of your qualification of a supplier for the purpose of relying on the supplier's certificate of analysis (21 CFR 111.95(b)(2)) □ Documentation for why meeting in-process specifications, in combination with meeting component specifications, helps ensure that the dietary supplement meets the specifications for identity, purity, strength, and composition; and for limits on those types of contamination that may adulterate or may lead to adulteration of the finished batch of the dietary supplement (21 CFR 111.95(b)(3)) □ Documentation for why the results of appropriate tests or examinations for the product specifications that you selected for testing ensure that the dietary supplement meets all product specifications (21 CFR 111.95(b)(4)) □ Documentation for why any component and in-process testing, examination, or monitoring, and any other information, will ensure that a product specification that is exempted under 21 CFR 111.75(d) is met without verification through periodic testing of the finished batch, including documentation that the selected specifications tested or examined under 21 CFR 111.75 (c)(1) are not able to verify that the production and process control system is producing a dietary supplement that meets the exempted product specification and there is no scientifically valid method for testing or examining such exempted product specification at the finished batch stage (21 CFR 111.95(b)(5)) □ If you submit a petition to FDA under 21 CFR 111,75(a)(ii), documentation, under the identity testing interim final rule, of FDA's response to a petition submitted under 21 CFR 111.75(a)(1)(ii) providing for an exemption from the provisions of 21 CFR 111.75(a)(1)(i)
F	□ Written procedures (21 CFR 111.140(b)(1)) □ Written documentation, at the time of performance, that quality control personnel performed the review, approval, or rejection requirements by recording the date that the review, approval, or rejection was performed and the signature of the person performing the review, approval, or rejection (21 CFR 111.140(b)(2)) □ Documentation of any material review and disposition decision and follow-up (21 CFR 111.140(b)(3)). The DS CGMP rule establishes specific requirements for this documentation. You should refer to 21 CFR 111.140(b)(3) for the complete requirements.
G	□ Written procedures (21 CFR 111.180(b)(1)) □ Receiving records (including records such as certificates of analysis, suppliers' invoices, and suppliers' guarantees) for components, packaging, and labels and for products that you receive for packaging or labeling as a dietary supplement (21 CFR 111.180(b)(2)) □ Documentation, at time of performance, that the requirements for components, packaging, labels, and product that is received for packaging or labeling as a dietary supplement were performed (21 CFR 111.180(b)(3)).
G	□ The DS CGMP rule establishes specific requirements for this documentation. You should refer to 21 CFR 111.180(b)(3) for the complete requirements.

CH
10

Table 4—Records the DS CGMP rule Requires You to Make and Keep	
Subpart	**Required Records**
H	□ The master manufacturing record (21 CFR 111.210). The DS CGMP rule establishes specific requirements for this documentation. You should refer to 21 CFR 111.210 for the complete requirements.
I	□ The batch production record (21 CFR 111.260). The DS CGMP rule establishes specific requirements for this documentation. You should refer to 21 CFR 111.260 for the complete requirements.
J	□ Written procedures (21 CFR 111.325(b)(1)) □ Documentation, at time of performance, that laboratory methodology is followed, and the results of testing and examination (21 CFR 111.325(b)(2))
K	□ Written procedures (21 CFR 111.375(b))
L	□ Written procedures (21 CFR 111.430(b))
M	□ Written procedures (21 CFR 111.475(b)(1)) □ Records of product distribution (21 CFR 111.475(b)(2))
N	□ Written procedures (21 CFR 111.535(b)(1)) □ Any material review and disposition decision on a returned dietary supplement (21 CFR 111.535(b)(2)) □ The results of any testing or examination conducted on a returned dietary supplement to determine compliance with product specifications (21 CFR 111.535(b)(3)) □ Documentation of the reevaluation by quality control personnel of any dietary supplement that is reprocessed and the determination by quality control personnel of whether the reprocessed dietary supplement meets product specifications (21 CFR 111.535(b)(4))
O	□ Written procedures (21 CFR 111.570(b)(1)) □ A written record of every product complaint that is related to good manufacturing practice (21 CFR 111.570(b)(2)). □ The DS CGMP rule establishes specific requirements for this documentation. You should refer to 21 CFR 111.570 for the complete requirements.

VI. Subpart B - Personnel

1. What does the DS CGMP rule require me to do to prevent microbial contamination from sick or infected personnel?

The DS CGMP rule requires you to take measures to exclude from any operations any person who might be a source of microbial contamination of any material used in the manufacture, packaging, labeling, or holding of a dietary supplement, and establishes several specific measures for you to take. (21 CFR 111.10(a))

2. What factors should I consider when determining whether a sick or infected employee may be permitted to work?

In addition to the obvious potential sources of microbial contamination, you should consider possibilities for indirect contamination (e.g., whether contamination could spread to areas through common air handling units or ducts). (72 FR 34752 at 34808)

3. What does the DS CGMP rule require regarding hygienic practices?

The DS CGMP rule requires employees who work in an operation during which adulteration of the component, dietary supplement, or a contact surface could occur must use hygienic practices to the extent necessary to protect against such contamination of components, dietary supplements, or contact surfaces. (21 CFR 111.10(b))

4. What hygienic practices does the DS CGMP rule identify for me to use to protect against contamination of components, dietary supplements, or contact surfaces?

Below, we list the specific hygienic practices identified in the DS CGMP rule. You should refer to 21 CFR 111.10(b) for the complete description associated with each of the items in the list.

- Wearing outer garments;
- Maintaining adequate personal cleanliness;
- Washing and sanitizing hands;
- Removing unsecured jewelry (and other unsecured objects);
- Using gloves made of an impermeable material and maintaining them in an intact, clean and sanitary condition;
- Wearing effective hair restraints;
- Not storing clothing or other personal belongings in areas where components, dietary supplements, or any contact surfaces are exposed or where contact surfaces are washed;
- Not eating food, chewing gum, drinking beverages, or using tobacco products in areas where components, dietary supplements, or any contact surfaces are exposed, or where contact surfaces are washed; and
- Taking any other precautions necessary to protect against the contamination of components, dietary supplements, or contact surfaces with microorganisms, filth, or any other extraneous materials.

5. What does the DS CGMP rule require regarding personnel?

The DS CGMP rule requires that:

- You have qualified employees who manufacture, package, label, or hold dietary supplements (21 CFR 111.12(a));
- You identify who is responsible for your quality control operations. Each person who is identified to perform quality control operations must be qualified to do so and

such responsibilities must be distinct and separate from other responsibilities (21 CFR 111.12(b)); and

- Each person engaged in manufacturing, packaging, labeling, or holding, or in performing any quality control operations, to have the education, training, or experience to perform the person's assigned functions (21 CFR 111.12(c)).

6. What does the DS CGMP rule require regarding supervisors?

The DS CGMP rule requires that:

- You assign qualified personnel to supervise the manufacturing, packaging, labeling, or holding of dietary supplements (21 CFR 111.13(a)); and

- Each supervisor whom you use to be qualified by education, training, or experience to supervise (21 CFR 111.13(b)).

7. May individuals who I identify to perform quality control operations also perform other functions, such as production functions?

Yes. However, the DS CGMP rule requires that each person who is identified to perform quality control operations have distinct and separate responsibilities related to performing such operations from those responsibilities that the person otherwise has when not performing such operations (21 CFR 111.12(b)).

We recommend that, whenever practical, the person performing a given quality control operation be a different person than the person who performed the operation subject to quality control oversight (72 FR 34752 at 34867).

VII. Subpart C - Physical Plant And Grounds

1. What does the DS CGMP rule require regarding the physical plant and grounds?

The DS CGMP rule:

- Requires you to keep the grounds of your physical plant in a condition that protects against the contamination of components, dietary supplements, or contact surfaces, and establishes several specific measures for you to take to do this (21 CFR 111.15(a));

- Requires you to maintain your physical plant in a clean and sanitary condition, and in repair sufficient to prevent components, dietary supplements, or contact surfaces from becoming contaminated (21 CFR 111.15(b)); and

- Establishes specific requirements for:

  □ Cleaning compounds, sanitizing agents, pesticides, and other toxic materials (21 CFR 111.15(c));

  □ Pest control (21 CFR 111.15(d));

  □ Plumbing and sewage (21 CFR 111.15(f) and (g));

  □ Bathrooms and hand washing facilities (21 CFR 111.15(h) and (i));

- Trash disposal (21 CFR 111.15(j));
- Sanitation supervisors (21 CFR 111.15)(k));
- The design and construction of the physical plant (21 CFR 111.20); and
- The water supply (see 21 CFR 111.15(e) and Questions 2 through 7 in section VIII of this document).

2. What does the DS CGMP rule require regarding the water supply when the water does not become a component of a dietary supplement?

The DS CGMP rule requires you to provide water that is safe and sanitary, at suitable temperatures, and under pressure as needed, for all uses where water does not become a component of the dietary supplement. (21 CFR 111.15(e)(1))

3. What is an example of water that does not become a component of the dietary supplement?

Water used to wash floors does not become a component of a dietary supplement. (72 FR 34752 at 34816)

4. What does the DS CGMP rule require regarding the water supply when the water may become a component of a dietary supplement?

The DS CGMP rule requires that, at a minimum, water used in a manner such that the water may become a component of the dietary supplement comply with applicable Federal, State, and local requirements and not contaminate the dietary supplement. (21 CFR 111.15(e)(2))

5. What are examples of water that may become a component of a dietary supplement?

Examples of water that may become a component of a dietary supplement include water that contacts components, dietary supplements, or any contact surface. (72 FR 34752 at 34816)

6. What steps should I take if I use a municipal water supply?

If you use a municipal water supply, you should take steps to ensure that you are at all times aware of problems, such as an acute problem with microbial contamination or a long-term problem associated with lead pipes present in some parts of the city water supply, that may not be reflected in the municipal water report. (72 FR 34752 at 34821)

7. What does the CGMP rule require regarding water from a private source, such as a well, used in a manner such that the water may become a component of the dietary supplement?

The DS CGMP rule requires that water from a private source, used in a manner such that the water may become a component of the dietary supplement, comply with any State and local requirements and not contaminate the dietary supplement. Satisfying this requirement may involve performing appropriate water treatment procedures, including filtration, sedimentation, and chlorination). (21 CFR 111.15(e)(2); 72 FR 34752 at 34817)

CH 10

VIII. Subpart D - Equipment And Utensils

1. What kinds of equipment and utensils are covered by the DS CGMP rule?

   Equipment and utensils used in manufacturing, packaging, labeling or holding operations that are covered by the DS CGMP rule include:

   - Equipment used to hold or convey;
   - Equipment used to measure;
   - Equipment using compressed air or gas;
   - Equipment used to carry out processes in closed pipes and vessels; and
   - Equipment used in automated, mechanical, or electronic systems (21 CFR 111.27(a)(1))

2. What requirements does the DS CGMP rule establish regarding equipment and utensils?

   The DS CGMP rule establishes requirements for:

   - The design, construction, installation, use and maintenance of equipment and utensils, including specific requirements for the seams of equipment and utensils, cold storage compartments, instruments or controls used to measure or record, and compressed air or other gases (21 CFR 111.27(a)); and
   - Calibrating equipment and controls (21 CFR 111.27(b)).

3. What does the DS CGMP rule require regarding automated, mechanical, or electronic equipment that you use to manufacture, package, label or hold a dietary supplement?

   For any automated, mechanical, or electronic equipment that you use to manufacture, package, label, or hold a dietary supplement, the DS CGMP rule requires you to:

   - Design or select equipment to ensure that dietary supplement specifications are consistently met (21 CFR 111.30(a));
   - Determine the suitability of the equipment by ensuring that your equipment is capable of operating satisfactorily within the operating limits required by the process (21 CFR 111.30(b));
   - Routinely calibrate, inspect, or check the equipment to ensure proper performance. Your quality control personnel must periodically review these calibrations, inspections, or checks (21 CFR 111.30(c));
   - Establish and use appropriate controls for automated, mechanical, and electronic equipment (including software for a computer controlled process) to ensure that any changes to the manufacturing, packaging, labeling, holding, or other operations are approved by quality control personnel and instituted only by authorized personnel (21 CFR 111.30(d)); and
   - Establish and use appropriate controls to ensure that the equipment functions in accordance with its i ntended use. These controls must be approved by quality control personnel (21 CFR 111.30(e)).

IX. Subpart E - Requirement To Establish A Production And Process Control System

A. General Requirements of Subpart E

1. What does Subpart E of the DS CGMP rule require regarding the design and implementation of a production and process control system?

Subpart E of the DS CGMP rule requires you to design (21 CFR 111.60(a)) and implement (21 CFR 111.55) a system of production and process controls covering all stages of manufacturing, packaging, labeling, and holding of the dietary supplement to ensure the quality of the dietary supplement and to ensure that the dietary supplement is packaged and labeled as specified in the master manufacturing record.

2. Does the DS CGMP rule require quality control personnel to review and approve all aspects of the production and process control system?

Yes. (21 CFR 111.60(b))

3. What does Subpart E of the DS CGMP rule require regarding quality control operations?

Subpart E of the DS CGMP rule requires you to implement quality control operations in your manufacturing, packaging, labeling, and holding operations for producing the dietary supplement to ensure the quality of the dietary supplement and that the dietary supplement is packaged and labeled as specified in the master manufacturing record. (21 CFR 111.65)

B. Requirements to Establish Specifications

1. What specifications does the DS CGMP rule require me to establish?

- The DS CGMP rule requires you to establish:
- A specification for any point, step, or stage in the manufacturing process where control is necessary to ensure the quality of the dietary supplement and that the dietary supplement is packaged and labeled as specified in the master manufacturing record (21 CFR 111.70(a));
- Specifications for components you use in the manufacture of a dietary supplement (21 CFR 111.70(b));
- Specifications for the in-process production (21 CFR 111.70(c));
- Specifications for dietary supplement labels and packaging (21 CFR 111.70(d));
- Product specifications for the finished batch of the dietary supplement (21 CFR 111.70(e));
- Specifications for product you receive from a supplier for packaging or labeling as a dietary supplement (21 CFR 111.70(f)); and
- Specifications for the packaging and labeling of the finished packaged and labeled dietary supplements (21 CFR 111.70g)).

CH
10

2. Does the DS CGMP rule require me to establish specifications for parameters such as dissolution, disintegration, and bioavailability?

> No. (72 FR 34752 at 34851)

3. Does the DS CGMP rule require me to establish an "expiration date" (or a "shelf date" or "best if used by" date)?

> No. (72 FR 34752 at 34855)

C. Requirements to Determine Whether Specifications Are Met

1. Does the DS CGMP rule require me to determine whether required specifications are met?

> Yes. The DS CGMP rule requires you to determine whether each of the following required specifications are met:
>
> - Specifications for components (21 CFR 111.75(a));
> - Specifications for the in-process production (21 CFR 111.75(b));
> - Specifications for the finished batch of the dietary supplement (21 CFR 111.75(c) and (d));
> - Specifications for product you receive from a supplier for packaging or labeling as a dietary supplement (21 CFR 111.75(e));
> - Specifications for dietary supplement labels and packaging (21 CFR 111.75(f)); and
> - Specifications for the packaging and labeling of the finished packaged and labeled dietary supplements (21 CFR 111.75(g)).

2. Should I have data to support any specifications I establish for parameters such as dissolution, disintegration, and bioavailability?

> Yes. Although the DS CGMP rule does not require you to establish specifications for parameters such as dissolution, disintegration, and bioavailability, if you establish such specifications you should have data to support that such specifications are met. (72 FR 34752 at 34851)

3. Should I have data to support any expiration date (or "shelf date" or "best if used by" date) that I will place on a product label?

> Yes. Although the DS CGMP rule does not require you to establish an "expiration date" (or a "shelf date" or "best if used by" date), you should have data to support any such date that you place on a product label. (72 FR 34752 at 34855)

4. What does the DS CGMP rule require regarding the tests and examinations I use to determine whether specifications are met?

The DS CGMP rule requires that:

You ensure that the tests and examinations you use to determine whether the specifications are met are appropriate, scientifically valid methods (21 CFR 111.75(h)(1)); and

The tests and examinations you use include at least one of the following (21 CFR 111.75(h)(2)):

- Gross organoleptic analysis (21 CFR 111.75(h)(2)(i));
- Macroscopic analysis (21 CFR 111.75(h)(2)(ii));
- Microscopic analysis (21 CFR 111.75(h)(2)(iii));
- Chemical analysis (21 CFR 111.75(h)(2)(iv)); or
- Other scientifically valid methods (21 CFR 111.75(h)(2)(v)).

5. Does the DS CGMP rule require any verification that a finished batch of dietary supplement meets product specifications?

Yes. The DS CGMP rule requires you to verify that a subset of finished dietary supplement batches (which you identify through a sound statistical sampling plan) meets product specifications (i.e., specifications that the DS CGMP rule requires you to establish under 21 CFR 111.70(e)), unless you choose to verify that product specifications are met for every finished batch (21 CFR 111.75(c)). To do so, the DS CGMP rule requires that:

- You select one or more established specifications for identity, purity, strength, composition, and the limits on those types of contamination that may adulterate or that may lead to adulteration of the dietary supplement that, if determined to be in compliance with specifications by testing or examination of the finished batch of the dietary supplement, would verify that the production and process control system is producing a dietary supplement that meets all product specifications (with the exception of those product specifications that are exempted from this requirement) (21 CFR 111.75(c)(1) and 21 CFR 111.75(d));
- You conduct appropriate tests or examinations to determine compliance with these specifications (21 CFR 111.75(c)(2));
- You provide adequate documentation of your basis for determining that compliance with the selected specification(s), through the use of appropriate tests or examinations, will ensure that your finished batch of the dietary supplement meets all product specifications established under 21 CFR 111.70(e) (21 CFR111.75(c)(3)); and
- Your quality control personnel review and approve this documentation (21 CFR 111.75(c)(4)).

CH 10

6. Is there any exemption from the requirement of the DS CGMP rule regarding verification that a finished batch of dietary supplement meets product specifications?

Yes (21 CFR 111.75(d)). We realize that there may well be some specifications that you may not be able to test for at the finished batch stage. For example, you may determine that you could not verify, by testing for compliance with the specifications for identity and composition, that the purity specification is met, and there may be no scientifically valid method for testing or examining the finished batch to evaluate the purity in the finished batch of dietary supplement. In such a case, the DS CGMP rule provides that you can document why, for example, any component and in-process testing, examination, or monitoring, and any other information, will ensure that this product specification is met without verification through periodic testing of the finished batch, provided your quality control personnel review and approve that documentation (21 CFR 111.75(d)). For example, you could exempt the specification for purity from the requirement in 21 CFR 111.75(c)(1) through, for example, documentation that meeting component and specifications for strength is sufficient, or through documentation that in-process monitoring is sufficient, provided your quality control personnel review and approve such documentation (21 CFR 111.75(d)). (72 FR 34752 at 34850)

7. Does the DS CGMP rule require me to establish a corrective action plan for use when an established specification is not met?

Yes. (21 CFR 111.75(i))

8. What are the consequences of not meeting a specification that I must establish under 21 CFR 111.70?

The consequences of not meeting a specification that the DS CGMP rule requires you to establish under 21 CFR 111.70 depend on which specification is not met (21 CFR 111.77). Table 5 shows these consequences.

Table 5—Consequences of Not Meeting an Established Specification		
Specification Provision	Description of Specification	Consequence of Not Meeting the Established Specification
21 CFR 111.70(a)	Any point, step, or stage in the manufacturing process where control is necessary to ensure the quality of the dietary supplement and that the dietary supplement is packaged and labeled as specified in the master manufacturing record	Reject the finished batch of the dietary supplement and not package or label the dietary supplement for distribution unless quality control personnel approve a treatment, an in-process adjustment, or reprocessing (21 CFR 111.77(a))
21 CFR 111.70(b)(1)	Identity of a Component	Reject the component and not use it in the manufacture of a dietary supplement (21 CFR 111.77(b))

Table 5—Consequences of Not Meeting an Established Specification		
Specification Provision	**Description of Specification**	**Consequence of Not Meeting the Established Specification**
21 CFR 111.70(b)(2)	Component specifications necessary to ensure that specifications for the purity, strength and composition of the dietary supplement are met	Reject the finished batch of the dietary supplement and not package or label the dietary supplement for distribution unless quality control personnel approve a treatment, an in-process adjustment, or reprocessing (21 CFR 111.77(a))
21 CFR 111.70(b)(3)	Limits on contaminants	Reject the finished batch of the dietary supplement and not package or label the dietary supplement for distribution unless quality control personnel approve a treatment, an in-process adjustment, or reprocessing (21 CFR 111.77(a))
21 CFR 111.70(c)	In-process production	Reject the finished batch of the dietary supplement and not package or label the dietary supplement for distribution unless quality control personnel approve a treatment, an in-process adjustment, or reprocessing (21 CFR 111.77(a))
21 CFR 111.70(d)	Dietary supplement labels and packaging	Reject the finished batch of the dietary supplement and not package or label the dietary supplement for distribution unless quality control personnel approve a treatment, an in-process adjustment, or reprocessing (21 CFR 111.77(a))
21 CFR 111.70(e)	Product specifications	Reject the finished batch of the dietary supplement and not package or label the dietary supplement for distribution unless quality control personnel approve a treatment, an in-process adjustment, or reprocessing (21 CFR 111.77(a))
21 CFR 111.70(f)	Product received from a supplier for packaging or labeling as a dietary supplement (and for distribution rather than for return to the supplier)	Reject the product and not package or label it for distribution as a dietary supplement (21 CFR 111.77(c))
21 CFR 111.70(g)	Packaging and labeling of the finished batch of the dietary supplement	Reject the finished batch of the dietary supplement and not package or label the dietary supplement for distribution unless quality control personnel approve a treatment, an in-process adjustment, or reprocessing (21 CFR 111.77(a))

CH
10

9. What does the DS CGMP rule require regarding treatments, in-process adjustments, and reprocessing when there is a deviation or unanticipated occurrence or when a specification is not met?

The DS CGMP rule requires that:

- You not reprocess a rejected dietary supplement, or treat or provide an in-process adjustment to a component, packaging, or label to make it suitable for use in the manufacture of a dietary supplement unless quality control personnel conduct a material review and make a disposition decision to approve the reprocessing, treatment, or in-process adjustment (21 CFR 111.90(a));

- You not reprocess any dietary supplement, or treat or provide an in-process adjustment to a component to make it suitable for use in the manufacture of a dietary supplement, unless quality control personnel conduct a material review and make a disposition decision based on a scientifically valid reason and approves the reprocessing, treatment, or in-process adjustment (21 CFR 111.90(b)); and

- Any batch of dietary supplement that is reprocessed (or that contains components that you have treated, or to which you have made in-process adjustments to make them suitable for use in the manufacture of the dietary supplement) must meet requirements in 21 CFR 111.123(b) and be approved by quality control personnel before releasing for distribution (21 CFR 111.90(c)).

D. Specific Requirements Regarding Specifications for Dietary Ingredients and Other Components

1. What does the DS CGMP rule require me to do to verify the identity of each dietary ingredient that I use in the manufacture of a dietary supplement?

The DS CGMP rule requires you to conduct at least one appropriate test or examination to verify the identity of any dietary ingredient, unless you petition us to exempt you from this requirement and we approve your petition (21 CFR 111.75(a)(1)). It is up to you to determine the appropriate test(s) or examination(s) necessary to verify the identity of a dietary ingredient. In some cases, a single test or examination may be all that is needed to verify the identity of a dietary ingredient; in other cases, it may be necessary to conduct more than one test or examination (72 FR 34752 at 34847).

2. Is there an alternative to the requirement of 21 CFR 111.75(a)(1) for me to verify the identity of each dietary ingredient that I use in the manufacture of a dietary supplement?

Yes. You may petition us for an alternative to the required 100 percent identity testing of components that are dietary ingredients (see 21 CFR 111.75(a)(1)(ii) of the identity testing interim final rule). You would submit the petition as a citizen petition in accordance with the provisions of 21 CFR 10.30 (21 CFR 111.75(a)(1)(ii)).

Your petition must set forth the scientific rationale, and be accompanied by the supporting data and information, for proposed alternative testing that will demonstrate that there is no material diminution of assurance, compared to the assurance provided by 100 percent identity testing, of the identity of the dietary ingredient before use when the dietary ingredient is obtained from one or more suppliers identified in the petition (21 CFR 111.75(a)(1)(ii)).

If FDA grants the petition, you would conduct the tests and examinations for the dietary ingredient, otherwise required under 21 CFR 111.75(a)(1)(i), under the terms specified by FDA when the petition is granted (21 CFR 111.75(a)(1)(ii)).

3. What does the DS CGMP rule require me to do to ensure that specifications are met for components that I use in the manufacture of a dietary supplement?

The DS CGMP rule requires you to confirm the identity of components, and determine whether other specifications for components (including dietary ingredients), are met, either by conducting appropriate tests or examinations or by relying on a certificate of analysis from the supplier of the component. (21 CFR 111.75(a)(2))

4. What does the CGMP rule require me to do if I rely on a Certificate of Analysis from a supplier to confirm the identity of a component other than a dietary ingredient, or to determine whether any other component specifications are met?

The DS CGMP rule requires that:

- You first qualify the supplier by establishing the reliability of the supplier's certificate of analysis through confirmation of the results of the supplier's tests or examinations (21 CFR 111.75(a)(2)(ii)(A)).
- The certificate of analysis include a description of the test or examination method(s) used, limits of the test or examinations, and actual results of the tests or examinations (21 CFR 111.75(a)(2)(ii)(B)).
- You maintain documentation of how you qualified the supplier (21 CFR 111.75(a)(2)(ii)(C)).
- You periodically re-confirm the supplier's certificate of analysis (21 CFR 111.75(a)(2)(ii)(D)).
- Your quality control personnel review and approve the documentation setting forth the basis for qualification (and re-qualification) of any supplier (21 CFR 111.75(a)(2)(ii)(E)).

CH 10

E. Requirements for Representative and Reserve Samples

1. What representative samples does the DS CGMP rule require me to collect?

The DS CGMP rule requires you to collect representative samples of the following materials:

- Each unique lot of components, packaging, and labels that you use (21 CFR 111.80(a));

- In-process materials for each manufactured batch at points, steps, or stages, in the manufacturing process as specified in the master manufacturing record where control is necessary to ensure the identity, purity, strength, and composition of dietary supplements (21 CFR 111.80(b));

- A subset of finished batches of each dietary supplement that you manufacture, which you identify through a sound statistical sampling plan (or otherwise every finished batch), before releasing for distribution (21 CFR 111.80(c));

- Each unique shipment, and each unique lot within each unique shipment, of product that you receive for packaging or labeling as a dietary supplement (and for distribution rather than for return to the supplier (21 CFR 111.80(d)); and

- Each lot of packaged and labeled dietary supplements (21 CFR 111.80(e)).

2. Why does the DS CGMP rule require me to collect and to hold representative samples?

The DS CGMP rule requires you to collect representative samples to determine whether applicable specifications are met. (21 CFR 111.80)

3. What reserve samples does the DS CGMP rule require me to collect and hold?

The DS CGMP rule requires you to collect and hold reserve samples of each lot of packaged and labeled dietary supplements that you distribute. This would include dietary supplements that you package and label in bulk. (21 CFR 111.83(a))

4. Why does the DS CGMP rule require me to collect and to hold reserve samples of packaged and labeled dietary supplements?

The DS CGMP rule requires you to collect and hold reserve samples of packaged and labeled dietary supplements for use in appropriate investigations, such as consumer complaint investigations. (21 CFR 111.83(b)(3) and 21 CFR 111.465(b))

5. How many reserve samples does the DS CGMP rule require me to collect and hold?

The DS CGMP rule requires that the amount of reserve samples you collect and hold consist of at least twice the quantity necessary for all tests or examinations to determine whether or not the dietary supplement meets product specifications. (21 CFR 111.83(b)(4))

6. How does the DS CGMP rule require me to identify reserve samples of packaged and labeled dietary supplements?

The DS CGMP rule requires you to identify reserve samples with the batch, lot, or control number. (21 CFR 111.83(b)(2))

7. What container-closure system does the DS CGMP rule require me to use to hold reserve samples of packaged and labeled dietary supplements?

The DS CGMP rule requires you to use the following container-closure systems to hold reserve samples of dietary supplements:

- If you are distributing a packaged and labeled dietary supplement, the DS CGMP rule requires you to keep the reserve samples in a container-closure system that is the same as the container-closure system in which the dietary supplement is distributed.

- If you are distributing a dietary supplement for packaging and labeling, the DS CGMP rule requires you to keep the reserve samples in a container-closure system that provides essentially the same characteristics to protect against contamination or deterioration as the one in which you distributed the dietary supplement for packaging and labeling elsewhere. For example, if you distribute product in bulk using a polyethylene bottle that can hold 50 kilograms of the product, and there is an air space above the product, you would hold the reserve samples in a polyethylene bottle with an air space. However, you would use a bottle sized to fit the smaller amount you are holding in reserve.

(21 CFR 111.83(b)(1); 72 FR 34752 at 34904)

8. How long does the DS CGMP rule require me to hold reserve samples of packaged and labeled dietary supplements?

The DS CGMP rule requires you to hold reserve samples of packaged and labeled dietary supplements for:

- One year past the shelf life date (if shelf life dating is used); or

- Two years from the date of distribution of the last batch of dietary supplements associated with the reserve sample.

(21 CFR 111.83(b)(3); 72 FR 34752 at 34905)

CH 10

X. Subpart F – Production and Process Control: Requirements For Quality Control

1. What does the DS CGMP rule require quality control personnel to do?

The DS CGMP rule requires quality control personnel to ensure that your manufacturing, packaging, labeling, and holding operations ensure the quality of the dietary supplement and that the dietary supplement is packaged and labeled as specified in the master manufacturing record. (21 CFR 111.105)

2. What operations does the DS CGMP rule require quality control personnel to perform?

The DS CGMP rule requires quality control personnel to perform operations that include:

- Approving or rejecting all processes, specifications, written procedures, controls, tests, and examinations, and deviations from or modifications to them, that may affect the identity, purity, strength, or composition of a dietary supplement (21 CFR 111.105(a));

- Reviewing and approving the documentation setting forth the basis for qualification of any supplier (21 CFR 111.105(b));

- Reviewing and approving the documentation setting forth the basis for why meeting in-process specifications, in combination with meeting component specifications, will help ensure that the identity, purity, strength, and composition of the dietary supplement are met (21 CFR 111.105(c));

- Reviewing and approving the documentation setting forth the basis for why the results of appropriate tests or examinations for each product specification selected under 21 CFR 111.75(c)(1) will ensure that the finished batch of the dietary supplement meets product specifications (21 CFR 111.105(d));

- Reviewing and approving the basis and the documentation for why any product specification is exempted from the verification requirements in 21 CFR 111.75(c)(1), and for why any component and in-process testing, examination, or monitoring, or other methods will ensure that such exempted product specification is met without verification through periodic testing of the finished batch (21 CFR 111.105(e));

- Ensuring that all representative samples are collected (21 CFR 111.105(f));

- Ensuring that all reserve samples are collected and held (21 CFR 111.105(g));

- Determining whether all specifications established under 21 CFR 111.70(a) are met (21 CFR 111.105(h));

- Laboratory operations (21 CFR 111.110);

- Operations regarding material review and disposition decisions (21 CFR 111.113);

- Operations regarding equipment, instruments, and controls (21 CFR 111.117);

- Operations regarding components, packaging, and labels before use in the manufacture of a dietary supplement (21 CFR 111.120);

- Operations regarding the master manufacturing record, the batch production record, and manufacturing operations (21 CFR 111.123);

- Packaging and labeling operations (21 CFR 111.127);

- Operations regarding returned dietary supplements (21 CFR 111.130); and

- Operations regarding product complaints (21 CFR 111.135).

3. Who conducts a material review and disposition decision?

Quality control personnel conduct all required material reviews and make all required disposition decisions (21 CFR 111.87). However, qualified individuals who are not assigned as quality control personnel may participate in the material review, e.g., by providing relevant information or analysis (72 FR 34752 at 34865).

4. When does the DS CGMP rule require quality control personnel to do to conduct a material review and disposition decision?

The DS CGMP rule identifies five circumstances when quality control personnel must conduct a material review and make a disposition decision (21 CFR 111.113(a)):

- A specification established in accordance with 21 CFR 111.70 is not met (21 CFR 111.113(a)(1));

- A batch deviates from the master manufacturing record, including when any step established in the master manufacturing record is not completed and including any deviation from specifications (21 CFR 111.113(a)(2));

- There is any unanticipated occurrence during the manufacturing operations that adulterates or may lead to adulteration of the component, dietary supplement, or packaging, or could lead to the use of a label not specified in the master manufacturing record (21 CFR 111.113(a)(3));

- Calibration of an instrument or control suggests a problem that may have resulted in a failure to ensure the quality of a batch or batches of a dietary supplement (21 CFR 111.113(a)(4)); or

- A dietary supplement is returned (21 CFR 111.113(a)(5)).

5. When does the DS CGMP rule require quality control personnel to reject a component, dietary supplement, packaging or label?

The DS CGMP rule requires quality control personnel to reject a component, dietary supplement, packaging, or label when:

- There is a deviation or unanticipated occurrence during the production and in-process control system that results in or could lead to adulteration of a component, dietary supplement, or packaging, or could lead to the use of a label not specified in the master manufacturing record (unless quality control personnel approve a treatment, an in-process adjustment, or reprocessing to correct the applicable deviation or occurrence) (21 CFR 111.113(b)(1)).

- When a specification that you are required to establish is not met (unless quality control personnel approve a treatment, an in-process adjustment, or reprocessing, as permitted in 21 CFR 111.77) (21 CFR 111.113(b)(2)).

6. When does the DS CGMP rule require documentation of a material review and disposition decision?

The DS CGMP rule requires the person who conducts a material review and makes the disposition decision to document the material review and disposition decision at the time of performance. (21 CFR 111.113(c))

CH 10

XI. Subpart G–Production and Process Control System; Requirements for Components, Packaging, and Labels and for Product That Is Received for Packaging or Labeling as a Dietary Supplement

A. Requirements for Components

1. What visual examinations does the DS CGMP rule require me to conduct for components of dietary supplements?

   The DS CGMP rule requires you to visually examine the supplier's invoice, guarantee, or certification, and each immediate container or grouping of immediate containers, in a shipment of components. (21 CFR 111.155(a) and (b))

2. How long does the DS CGMP rule require me to quarantine components?

   The DS CGMP rule requires you to quarantine components until:

   - You collect representative samples (21 CFR 111.155(c)(1));

   - Quality control personnel review and approve the results of any tests or examinations conducted on the representative samples (21 CFR 111.155(c)(2));

   - Quality control personnel approve the components for use in the manufacture of a dietary supplement (21 CFR 111.155(c)(3)); and

   - Quality control personnel release the components from quarantine (21 CFR 111.155(c)(3)).

3. Does the DS CGMP rule require me to assign a unique identifier to components?

   Yes. The DS CGMP rule requires you to identify each unique lot within each unique shipment of components you receive (and any lot of components you produce) in a manner that allows you to trace the lot to the supplier, the date received, the name of the component, the status of the component (e.g., quarantined, approved, or rejected), and to the dietary supplement that you manufactured and distributed. (21 CFR 111.155(d)(1))

4. When does the DS CGMP rule require me to use the unique identifier that I assign to components?

   The DS CGMP rule requires you to use this unique identifier whenever you record the disposition of each unique lot within each unique shipment of components you receive and any lot of components you produce. (21 CFR 111.155(d)(2))

5. How does the DS CGMP rule require me to hold components?

   The DS CGMP rule requires you to hold components under conditions that will protect against contamination and deterioration, and avoid mix-ups. (21 CFR 111.155(e))

CH 10

6. What does the DS CGMP rule require to be included in a Certificate of Analysis that accompanies a component?

   The DS CGMP rule requires a certificate of analysis to include:

   - A description of the test or examination method(s) used;

   - Limits of the test or examinations; and

   - Actual results of the tests or examinations.

   (21 CFR 111.75(a)(2)(ii)(B))

7. Does the DS CGMP rule establish any requirements specific to animal-derived ingredients?

   No. However, you are responsible to comply with any other regulations applying to foods containing animal-derived ingredients. For example, if you manufacture a dietary supplement containing cattle-derived material, you would be responsible to comply with the requirements for cattle-derived material established in 21 CFR 189.5. As another example, if you manufacture a dietary supplement containing ingredients derived from fish, you would be responsible to comply with applicable requirements for fish and fishery products in 21 CFR part 123. (72 FR 34752 at 34838)

B. Requirements for Packaging and Labels

1. What visual examinations does the DS CGMP rule require me to conduct for packaging and labels?

   The DS CGMP rule requires you to visually examine the supplier's invoice, guarantee, or certification, and each immediate container or grouping of immediate containers, in a shipment. (21 CFR 111.160(a) and (b))

2. How long does the DS CGMP rule require me to quarantine packaging and labels?

   The DS CGMP rule requires you to quarantine packaging and labels until:

   - You collect representative samples and, at a minimum, conduct a visual identification of the immediate containers and closures (21 CFR 111.160(c)(1));

   - Quality control personnel review and approve the results of any tests or examinations conducted on the packaging and labels (21 CFR 111.160(c)(2));

   - Quality control personnel approve the packaging and labels for use in the manufacture of a dietary supplement (21 CFR 111.160(c)(3)); and

   - Quality control personnel release the packaging and labels from quarantine (21 CFR 111.160(c)(3)).

3. Does the DS CGMP rule require me to assign a unique identifier to packaging and labels?

   Yes. The DS CGMP rule requires you to identify each unique lot within each unique shipment of packaging and labels in a manner that allows you to trace the lot to the

CH 10

supplier, the date received, the name of the packaging and label, the status of the packaging and label (e.g., quarantined, approved, or rejected), and to the dietary supplement that you distributed. (21 CFR 111.160(d)(1))

4. When does the DS CGMP rule require me to use the unique identifier that I assign to packaging and labels?

The DS CGMP rule requires you to use this unique identifier whenever you record the disposition of each unique lot within each unique shipment of packaging and labels. (21 CFR 111.160(d)(2))

5. How does the DS CGMP rule require me to hold packaging and labels?

The DS CGMP rule requires you to hold packaging and labels under conditions that will protect against contamination and deterioration, and avoid mix-ups. (21 CFR 111.160(e))

C. Requirements for Received Product

1. What visual examinations does the DS CGMP rule require me to conduct for received product (i.e., product that I receive for packaging and labeling as a dietary supplement (and for distribution rather than for return to the supplier))?

The DS CGMP rule requires you to visually examine the supplier's invoice, guarantee, or certification, and each immediate container or grouping of immediate containers, in a shipment. (21 CFR 111.165(a) and (b))

2. How long does the DS CGMP rule require me to quarantine received product?

The DS CGMP rule requires you to quarantine received product until:

- You collect representative samples (21 CFR 111.165 (c)(1));
- Quality control personnel review and approve the documentation to determine whether the received product meets specifications (21 CFR 111.165(c)(2));
- Quality control personnel approve the received product for packaging or labeling as a dietary supplement (21 CFR 111.165(c)(3)); and
- Quality control personnel release the received product from quarantine (21 CFR 111.165(c)(3)).

3. Does the DS CGMP rule require me to assign a unique identifier to received product?

Yes. The DS CGMP rule requires you to identify each unique lot within each unique shipment of received product in a manner that allows you to trace the lot to the supplier, the date received, the name of the received product, the status of the received product (e.g., quarantined, approved, or rejected), and to the product you packaged or labeled and distributed as a dietary supplement. (21 CFR 111.165(d)(1))

CH 10

4. When does the DS CGMP rule require me to use the unique identifier that I assign to received product?

The DS CGMP rule requires you to use this unique identifier whenever you record the disposition of each unique lot within each unique shipment of the received product. (21 CFR 111.165(d)(2))

5. How does the DS CGMP rule require me to hold received product?

The DS CGMP rule requires you to hold received product under conditions that will protect against contamination and deterioration, and avoid mix-ups. (21 CFR 111.165(e))

D. Requirements for Rejected Components, Packaging, Labels and Received Product

1. What does the DS CGMP rule require me to do with rejected components, packaging, and labels, and with rejected products received for packaging or labeling as a dietary supplement?

The DS CGMP rule requires you to clearly identify, hold, and control under a quarantine system for appropriate disposition any component, packaging, and label, and any product you receive for packaging or labeling as a dietary supplement, that is rejected and unsuitable for use in manufacturing, packaging, or labeling operations. (21 CFR 111.170)

XII. Subpart H – Production and Process Control System: Requirements for a Master Manufacturing Record

1. Does the DS CGMP rule require me to establish a master manufacturing record?

Yes. The DS CGMP rule requires you to prepare and follow a written master manufacturing record for each unique formulation of dietary supplement that you manufacture, and for each batch size, to ensure uniformity in the finished batch from batch to batch (21 CFR 111.205(a)). The master manufacturing record must establish controls and procedures to ensure that each batch of dietary supplement you manufacture meets those specifications (21 CFR 111.205(b)(2)).

2. What specifications does the DS CGMP rule require the master manufacturing record to identify?

The DS CGMP rule requires the master manufacturing record to identify specifications for the points, steps, or stages in the manufacturing process where control is necessary to ensure the quality of the dietary supplement and that the dietary supplement is packaged and labeled as specified in the master manufacturing record.

(21 CFR 111.205(b))

3. What does the DS CGMP rule require the master manufacturing record to include?

The DS CGMP rule requires the master manufacturing record to include:

- The name of the dietary supplement to be manufactured and the strength, concentration, weight, or measure of each dietary ingredient for each batch size (21 CFR 111.210(a));

- A complete list of components to be used (21 CFR 111.210(b));

- An accurate statement of the weight or measure of each component to be used (21 CFR 111.210(c));

- The identity and weight or measure of each dietary ingredient that will be declared on the Supplement Facts label and the identity of each ingredient that will be declared on the ingredients list of the dietary supplement (21 CFR 111.210(d));

- A statement of any intentional overage amount of a dietary ingredient (21 CFR 111.210(e)) (the amount of overage should be limited to the amount needed to meet the weight or measure of each dietary ingredient that will be declared on the Supplement Facts label of the dietary supplement) (72 FR 34752 at 34884);

- A statement of theoretical yield of a manufactured dietary supplement expected at each point, step, or stage of the manufacturing process where control is needed to ensure the quality of the dietary supplement, and the expected yield when you finish manufacturing the dietary supplement, including the maximum and minimum percentages of theoretical yield beyond which a deviation investigation of a batch is necessary and material review is conducted and disposition decision is made (21 CFR 111.210(f));

- A description of packaging and a representative label, or a cross-reference to the physical location of the actual or representative label (21 CFR 111.210(g)); and

- Written instructions, including the following:

  □ Specifications for each point, step, or stage in the manufacturing process where control is necessary to ensure the quality of the dietary supplement and that the dietary supplement is packaged and labeled as specified in the master manufacturing record (21 CFR 111.210(h)(1));

  □ Procedures for sampling and a cross-reference to procedures for tests or examinations (21 CFR 111.210(h)(2));

  □ Specific actions necessary to perform and verify points, steps, or stages in the manufacturing process where control is necessary to ensure the quality of the dietary supplement and that the dietary supplement is packaged and labeled as specified in the master manufacturing record (21 CFR 111.210(h)(3));

    ▪ Such specific actions must include verifying the weight or measure of any component and verifying the addition of any component (21 CFR 111.210(h)(3)(i)); and

- ▪ For manual operations, such specific actions must include one person weighing or measuring a component and another person verifying the weight or measure, and one person adding the component and another person verifying the addition (21 CFR 111.210(h)(3)(ii));
  - ▫ Special notations and precautions to be followed (21 CFR 111.210(h)(4)); and
  - ▫ Corrective action plans for use when a specification is not met (21 CFR 111.210(h)(5)).

XIII. Subpart I – Production and Process Control System: Requirements for a Batch Production Record

1. Does the DS CGMP rule require me to establish a batch production record?

Yes. The DS CGMP rule requires you to prepare a batch production record every time you manufacture a batch of a dietary supplement. (21 CFR 111.255(a))

2. What does the DS CGMP rule require regarding the batch production record?

The DS CGMP rule requires that:

- ▫ Your batch production record accurately follow the appropriate master manufacturing record; and
- ▫ You perform each step in the production of the batch.

(21 CFR 111.255(c))

3. What does the DS CGMP rule require the batch production record to include?

The DS CGMP rule requires the batch production record to include complete information relating to the production and control of each batch (21 CFR 111.255(b)). Specifically, the DS CGMP rule requires the batch production record to include:

- The batch, lot, or control number of the finished batch of dietary supplement, each lot of packaged and labeled dietary supplement from the finished batch of dietary supplement, and each lot of dietary supplement, from the finished batch of dietary supplement, that you distribute to another person for packaging or labeling (21 CFR 111.260(a));
- The identity of equipment and processing lines used in producing the batch (21 CFR 111.260(b));
- The date and time of the maintenance, cleaning, and sanitizing of the equipment and processing lines used in producing the batch, or a cross-reference to records, such as individual equipment logs, where this information is retained (21 CFR 111.260(c));
- The unique identifier you assigned to each component (or, when applicable, to a product that you receive from a supplier for packaging or labeling as a dietary supplement), packaging, and label used (21 CFR 111.260(d));

CH 10

- The identity and weight or measure of each component used (21 CFR 111.260(e));

- A statement of the actual yield and a statement of the percentage of theoretical yield at appropriate phases of processing (21 CFR 111.260(f));

- The actual results obtained during any monitoring operation (21 CFR 111.260(g));

- The results of any testing or examination performed during the batch production, or a cross-reference to such results (21 CFR 111.260(h));

- Documentation that the finished dietary supplement meets specifications established in accordance with 21 CFR 111.70(e) and (g) (21 CFR 111.260(i));

- Documentation, at the time of performance, of the manufacture of the batch, including the date on which each step of the master manufacturing record was performed and the initials of the persons performing each step (21 CFR 111.260(j));

- Documentation, at the time of performance, of packaging and labeling operations, including:

  □ The unique identifier you assigned to packaging and labels used, the quantity of the packaging and labels used, and, when label reconciliation is required, reconciliation of any discrepancies between issuance and use of labels (21 CFR 111.260(k)(1));

  □ An actual or representative label, or a cross-reference to the physical location of the actual or representative label specified in the master manufacturing record (21 CFR 111.260(k)(2)); and

  □ The results of any tests or examinations conducted on packaged and labeled dietary supplements (including repackaged or relabeled dietary supplements), or a cross-reference to the physical location of such results (21 CFR 111.260(k)(1));

- Documentation at the time of performance that quality control personnel reviewed the batch production record, approved or rejected any reprocessing or repackaging, approved and released (or rejected) the batch for distribution, and approved and released (or rejected) the packaged and labeled dietary supplement, including any repackaged or relabeled dietary supplement (21 CFR 111.260(l));

- Documentation at the time of performance of any required material review and disposition decision (21 CFR 111.260(m)); and

- Documentation at the time of performance of any reprocessing (21 CFR 111.260(n)).

XIV. Subpart J – Production and Process Control System: Requirements for Laboratory Operations

1. What does the DS CGMP rule require regarding facilities to perform testing and examinations?

   The DS CGMP rule requires you to use adequate laboratory facilities to perform testing and examinations. (21 CFR 111.310)

2. What laboratory control processes does the DS CGMP rule require me to establish and follow?

   The DS CGMP rule requires you to establish and follow laboratory control processes that include:

   - Use of criteria for establishing appropriate specifications (21 CFR 111.315(a));
   - Use of sampling plans for obtaining representative samples (21 CFR 111.315(b));
   - Use of criteria for selecting appropriate examination and testing methods (21 CFR 111.315(c));
   - Use of criteria for selecting standard reference materials used in performing tests and examinations (21 CFR 111.315(d)); and
   - Use of test methods and examinations in accordance with established criteria (21 CFR 111.315(e)).

3. Does the DS CGMP rule require quality control personnel to review and approve the laboratory control processes I establish and follow?

   Yes. (21 CFR 111.315)

4. How should I determine which reference materials to use in performing tests and examinations?

   Reference materials should be appropriate to the assay procedure for which they are used. We recommend that you use compendia reference standards whenever possible. If no compendia reference standard exists, we recommend that you establish appropriately characterized in-house materials prepared from representative lots. Such in-house materials should be of the highest purity that can be obtained by reasonable effort and should be thoroughly characterized to ensure their identity, purity, quality, and strength. (72 FR 34752 at 34892)

5. What does the DS CGMP rule require me to do regarding laboratory methods I use for testing and examination?

   The DS CGMP rule requires you to:

   - Verify that the laboratory examination and testing methodologies are appropriate for their intended use (21 CFR 111.320(a)); and

CH

10

- Identify and use an appropriate scientifically valid method for each established specification for which testing or examination is required to determine whether the specification is met (21 CFR 111.320(b)).

6. What is an example of a scientifically valid method?

An example of a scientifically valid method can be one that is based on scientific data or results published in, for example, scientific journals, references, text books, or proprietary research. (72 FR 34752 at 34893)

7. Does the DS CGMP rule require me to use a "validated" scientific method to perform tests or examinations?

No, it requires you to use a scientifically "valid" method. However, we recommend that you use a "validated" scientific method whenever one is available. (72 FR 34752 at 34893)

8. What does "validating" a scientific method involve?

In general, "validating" a scientific method involves evaluating the method on multiple occasions or in multiple test facilities. Official methods are validated in collaborative studies using several laboratories under identical conditions. Other method validations are conducted in a single laboratory by repeating the same test multiple times. Typical validation characteristics include accuracy, precision, specificity, detection limit, quantitation limit, linearity, range, and robustness. (72 FR 34752 at 34893)

9. Where can I find validated methods?

Validated methods can be found in official references, such as AOAC International, United States Pharmacopoeia (USP), and others (72 FR 34752 at 34893)

10. What should I do if I modify a validated method?

If you modify an officially validated method, you should:

- Document the reason for the modification;
- Have data to show that the modified method produces results that are at least as accurate and reliable as the established method for the material being tested; and
- Have complete records of any testing and standardization of laboratory reference standards, reagents, and standard solutions you use in your laboratory operations.

(72 FR 34752 at 34894)

XV. Subpart K – Production and Process Control System: Requirements for Manufacturing Operations

1. How does the DS CGMP rule require me to design or select manufacturing processes?

The DS CGMP rule requires you to design or select manufacturing processes to ensure that product specifications are consistently met. (21 CFR 111.355)

2. How does the DS CGMP rule require me to conduct manufacturing operations?

The DS CGMP rule requires you to conduct all manufacturing operations in accordance with adequate sanitation principles. (21 CFR 111.360)

3. What precautions does the DS CGMP rule require me to take to prevent contamination during manufacturing operations?

The DS CGMP rule requires you to take all necessary precautions during the manufacture of a dietary supplement to prevent contamination of components or dietary supplements, including the following specific precautions:

- Performing manufacturing operations under conditions and controls that protect against the potential for growth of microorganisms and the potential for contamination (21 CFR 111.365(a));

- Washing or cleaning components that contain soil or other contaminants (21 CFR 111.365(b));

- Using water that, at a minimum, complies with the applicable Federal, State, and local requirements and does not contaminate the dietary supplement when the water may become a component of the finished batch of dietary supplement (21 CFR 111.365(c));

- Performing chemical, microbiological, or other testing, as necessary to prevent the use of contaminated components (21 CFR 111.365(d));

- Sterilizing, pasteurizing, freezing, refrigerating, controlling hydrogen-ion concentration (pH), controlling humidity, controlling water activity (aw), or using any other effective means to remove, destroy, or prevent the growth of microorganisms and prevent decomposition (21 CFR 111.365(e));

- Holding components and dietary supplements that can support the rapid growth of microorganisms of public health significance in a manner that prevents the components and dietary supplements from becoming adulterated (21 CFR 111.365(f));

- Identifying and holding any components or dietary supplements, for which a material review and disposition decision is required, in a manner that protects components or dietary supplements that are not under a material review against contamination and mix-ups with those that are under a material review (21 CFR 111.365(g));

- Performing mechanical manufacturing steps (such as cutting, sorting, inspecting, shredding, drying, grinding, blending, and sifting) by any effective means to protect the dietary supplements against contamination (21 CFR 111.365(h));

- Using effective measures to protect against the inclusion of metal or other foreign material in components or dietary supplements (21 CFR 111.365(i));

- Segregating and identifying all containers for a specific batch of dietary supplements

CH 10

to identify their contents and, when necessary, the phase of manufacturing (21 CFR 111.365(j)); and

- Identifying all processing lines and major equipment used during manufacturing to indicate their contents, including the name of the dietary supplement and the specific batch or lot number and, when necessary, the phase of manufacturing (21 CFR 111.365(k)).

4. What does the DS CGMP rule require me to do with a rejected dietary supplement?

The DS CGMP rule requires you to clearly identify, hold, and control under a quarantine system for appropriate disposition any dietary supplement that is rejected and unsuitable for use in manufacturing, packaging, or labeling operations. (21 CFR 111.370)

XVI. Subpart L – Production and Process Control System: Requirements for Packaging and Labeling Operations

1. What does the DS CGMP rule require me to do regarding packaging and labels?

The DS CGMP rule requires you to:

- Take necessary actions to determine whether the packaging for a given dietary supplement meets specifications so that the condition of the packaging will ensure the quality of your product (21 CFR 111.410(a));

- Control the issuance and use of packaging and labels and reconciliation of any issuance and use discrepancies; however, label reconciliation is not required for cut or rolled labels if a 100 percent examination for correct labels is performed by appropriate electronic or electromechanical equipment during or after completion of finishing operations (21 CFR 111.410(b));

- Examine packaging and labels for each batch of dietary supplement, before conducting packaging and labeling operations, to determine whether the packaging and labels conform to the master manufacturing record (21 CFR 111.410(c)); and

- Be able to determine the complete manufacturing history and control of the packaged and labeled dietary supplement through distribution (21 CFR 111.410(d)).

2. Does the DS CGMP rule require me to place a batch, lot, or control number on the packaged and labeled dietary supplement?

No. Putting a batch, lot, or control number on the packaged and labeled dietary supplement is one way to satisfy the requirement in 21 CFR 111.410(d) that you be able to determine the complete manufacturing history and control of the packaged and labeled dietary supplement through distribution. However, you have flexibility to develop and use other mechanisms to satisfy this requirement. For example, if you make one type of product that you distribute to a select few customers, you may be able to trace the dietary supplement using dates on distribution records to such customers, by using different containers, or by labeling other than a batch, lot, or control number affixed to the label. (72 FR 34752 at 34900)

3. What does the DS CGMP rule require me to do regarding filling, assembling, packaging, labeling, and related operations?

The DS CGMP rule requires you to fill, assemble, package, label, and perform other related operations in a way that ensures the quality of the dietary supplement and that the dietary supplement is packaged and labeled as specified in the master manufacturing record, using any effective means, including:

- Cleaning and sanitizing all filling and packaging equipment, utensils, and dietary supplement packaging, as appropriate (21 CFR 111.415(a));

- Protecting manufactured dietary supplements from contamination, particularly airborne contamination (21 CFR 111.415(b));

- Using sanitary handling procedures (21 CFR 111.415(c));

- Establishing physical or spatial separation of packaging and label operations from operations on other components and dietary supplements to prevent mix-ups (21 CFR 111.415(d));

- Identifying, by any effective means, filled dietary supplement containers that are set aside and held in unlabeled condition for future label operations, to prevent mix-ups (21 CFR 111.415(e));

- Assigning a batch, lot, or control number to each lot of packaged and labeled dietary supplement from a finished batch of dietary supplement and each lot of dietary supplement, from a finished batch of dietary supplement, that you distribute to another person for packaging or labeling (21 CFR 111.415(f));

- Examining a representative sample of each batch of the packaged and labeled dietary supplement to determine whether the dietary supplement meets specifications established in accordance with 21 CFR 111.70(g) (21 CFR 111.415(g)); and

- Suitably disposing of labels and packaging for dietary supplements that are obsolete or incorrect to ensure that they are not used in any future packaging and label operations (21 CFR 111.415(h)).

4. When may I repackage or relabel a dietary supplement?

You may repackage or relabel a dietary supplement only after quality control personnel have approved such repackaging or relabeling. (21 CFR 111.420(a))

5. What does the DS CGMP rule require me to do regarding repackaging and relabeling?

The DS CGMP rule requires that:

- You examine a representative sample of each batch of repackaged or relabeled dietary supplements to determine whether the repackaged or relabeled dietary supplements meet all required specifications (21 CFR 111.420(b)); and

- Quality control personnel approve or reject each batch of repackaged or relabeled dietary supplement prior to its release for distribution (21 CFR 111.420(c)).

CH 10

6. What does the DS CGMP rule require me to do with a packaged and labeled dietary supplement that is rejected for distribution?

The DS CGMP rule requires you to clearly identify, hold, and control under a quarantine system for appropriate disposition any packaged and labeled dietary supplement that is rejected for distribution. (21 CFR 111.425)

XVII. Subpart M - Holding and Distributing

1. What does the DS CGMP rule require me to do when holding components, dietary supplements, packaging, and labels?

The DS CGMP rule requires you to:

- Hold components and dietary supplements under appropriate conditions of temperature, humidity, and light so that the identity, purity, strength, and composition of the components and dietary supplements are not affected (21 CFR 111.455(a));

- Hold packaging and labels under appropriate conditions so that the packaging and labels are not adversely affected (21 CFR 111.455(b));

- Hold components, dietary supplements, packaging, and labels under conditions that do not lead to the mix-up, contamination, or deterioration of components, in-process materials, dietary supplements, packaging, and labels (21 CFR 111.455(c));

2. What does the DS CGMP rule require me to do when holding in-process materials?

The DS CGMP rule requires you to:

- Identify and hold in-process material under conditions that protect against mix-up, contamination, and deterioration (21 CFR 111.460(a)); and

- Hold in-process material under appropriate conditions of temperature, humidity, and light (21 CFR 111.460(b)).

3. What container-closure system does the DS CGMP rule require me to use to hold reserve samples of packaged and labeled dietary supplements?

The DS CGMP rule requires you to use the following container-closure systems to hold reserve samples of dietary supplements:

- If you are distributing a packaged and labeled dietary supplement, the DS CGMP rule requires you to keep the reserve samples in a container-closure system that is the same as the container-closure system in which the dietary supplement is distributed.

- If you are distributing a dietary supplement for packaging and labeling, the DS CGMP rule requires you to keep the reserve samples in a container-closure system that provides essentially the same characteristics to protect against contamination or deterioration as the one in which you distributed the dietary supplement for packaging and labeling elsewhere. For example, if you distribute product in bulk using a polyethylene bottle that can hold 50 kilograms of the product, and there is an air space above the product, you would hold the reserve samples in a polyethylene bottle with an air space. However, you would use a bottle sized to fit the smaller amount you are holding in reserve.

(21 CFR 111.83(b)(1); 21 CFR 111.465(a)(2); 72 FR 34752 at 34904)

4. How does the DS CGMP rule require me to hold reserve samples of packaged and labeled dietary supplements?

The DS CGMP rule requires you to hold reserve samples under conditions consistent with product labels or, if no storage conditions are recommended on the label, under ordinary storage conditions. For example, if the product label states "Keep this product refrigerated," you would store the reserve sample in a refrigerator. (21 CFR 111.465(a)(1))

5. How long does the DS CGMP rule require me to hold reserve samples of packaged and labeled dietary supplements?

The DS CGMP rule requires you to hold reserve samples of packaged and labeled dietary supplements for:

- One year past the shelf life date (if shelf life dating is used); or
- Two years from the date of distribution of the last batch of dietary supplements associated with the reserve sample.

(21 CFR 111.83(b)(3) and 111.465(b))

6. What does the DS CGMP rule require me to do when distributing dietary supplements?

The DS CGMP rule requires you to distribute dietary supplements under conditions that will protect the dietary supplements against contamination and deterioration. (21 CFR 111.470)

XVIII. Subpart N - Returned Dietary Supplements

1. What does the DS CGMP rule require me to do with a returned dietary supplement?

The DS CGMP rule requires you to identify and quarantine a returned dietary supplement until quality control personnel conduct a material review and make a disposition decision. (21 CFR 111.510)

2. When does the DS CGMP rule require me to destroy, or otherwise suitably dispose of, a returned dietary supplement?

The DS CGMP rule requires you to destroy, or otherwise suitably dispose of, any returned dietary supplement unless the outcome of a material review and disposition decision is that quality control personnel approve the salvage of the returned dietary supplement for redistribution, or approve the returned dietary supplement for reprocessing. (21 CFR 111.515)

CH 10

3. When may I salvage a returned dietary supplement?

You may salvage a returned dietary supplement only if quality control personnel conduct a material review and make a disposition decision to allow the salvage. (21 CFR 111.520)

4. What does the DS CGMP rule require me to do with a returned dietary supplement that quality control personnel approve for reprocessing?

The DS CGMP rule requires that:

- You ensure that any returned dietary supplements that are reprocessed meet all product specifications established for the finished batch to ensure the quality of the dietary supplement(21 CFR 111.525(a)); and

- Quality control personnel approve or reject the release for distribution of any returned dietary supplement that is reprocessed (21 CFR 111.525(b)).

5. When does the DS CGMP rule require me to conduct an investigation of my manufacturing processes and other batches following the return of a product?

The DS CGMP rule requires you to conduct an investigation of your manufacturing processes and each of those other batches to determine compliance with specifications if the reason for a dietary supplement being returned implicates other batches. (21 CFR 111.530)

XIX. Subpart O - Product Complaints

1. What are some examples of product complaints?

Examples of product complaints are: foul odor, off taste, illness or injury, disintegration time, color variation, tablet size or size variation, under-filled container, foreign material in a dietary supplement container, improper packaging, mislabeling, or dietary supplements that are superpotent, subpotent, or contain the wrong ingredient, or contain a drug or other contaminant (e.g., bacteria, pesticide, mycotoxin, glass, lead). (21 CFR 111.3)

2. Does the DS CGMP rule establish requirements for handling complaints about the inherent safety of a dietary supplement?

No (72 FR 34752 at 34763 and 34765). However, we encourage firms to investigate all complaints in a consistent way, regardless of whether the complaints relate to the quality of the dietary supplement or to the inherent safety of a dietary ingredient (72 FR 34752 at 34910). We also note that manufacturers, packers, and distributors whose names appear on the label of dietary supplements marketed in the United States are required to submit to FDA any report received of a serious adverse event associated with such dietary supplement when used in the United States (section 761 of the Federal Food, Drug and Cosmetic Act (the Act) (21 U.S.C. 379aa-1)) (see also question 8 below).

3. What does the DS CGMP rule require me to do during the review and investigation of a product complaint?

The DS CGMP rule requires that:

- A qualified person review all product complaints to determine whether the product complaint involves a possible failure of a dietary supplement to meet any of its specifications, or any other requirements of part 111, including those specifications and other requirements that, if not met, may result in a risk of illness or injury (21 CFR 111.560(a)(1));

- A qualified person investigate the product complaint if it is determined that the product complaint does involve such a failure (21 CFR 111.560(a)(2));

- Quality control personnel review and approve decisions about whether to investigate a product complaint and review and approve the findings and follow-up action of any investigation performed (21 CFR 111.560(b)); and

- The review and investigation of the product complaint extend to all relevant batches and records (21 CFR 111.560(c)).

4. Am I subject to the requirements for product complaints if I am a packager, labeler, or distributor rather than a manufacturer?

Yes. The DS CGMP rule requires any person in the manufacturing chain who receives a product complaint to comply with the requirements for product complaints (21 CFR 111.1; 72 FR 34752 at 34909). This is true regardless of the source of the product complaint – i.e., regardless of whether you receive the complaint from a consumer or from another firm in the manufacturing chain (72 FR 34752 at 34909).

5. What should I do if I am a packager, labeler, or distributor and I conclude that the problem in a product complaint is unrelated to any process under my control?

We recommend that you contact the manufacturer so that the manufacturer can determine whether the product complaint involves a possible failure of a dietary supplement to meet any of its specifications, or any other requirements of part 111, including those specifications and other requirements that, if not met, may result in a risk of illness or injury. (72 FR 34752 at 34909)

6. Am I subject to the requirements for product complaints if I manufacture dietary ingredients rather than dietary supplements?

You are not subject to the requirements for product complaints if you manufacture dietary ingredients and do not sell the dietary ingredients directly to consumers (72 FR 34752 at 34791). However, if you are a manufacturer of dietary ingredients, and you receive complaints about a dietary supplement, we recommend that you share those complaints with those in the manufacturing chain associated with that dietary supplement's manufacture so others may take corrective action as needed (72 FR 34752 at 34798). In addition, we encourage you to evaluate the complaint to determine if it may involve a problem with the manufacture of the dietary ingredient (72 FR 34752 at 34792).

7. Does the DS CGMP rule require me to report any product complaints to FDA?

CH 10

No. The DS CGMP rule addresses the internal processes and controls that persons who manufacture, package, label, or hold dietary supplements must follow rather than any procedures for reporting any product complaints to us (72 FR 34752 at 34909). However, we recommend that firms who receive product complaints notify us about any illness or injury, because, for example, we may have additional expertise or data that may be helpful in investigating the complaint or determining whether the problem applies to more than one product. We encourage you to include this recommendation in the written procedures you develop for handling product complaints (72 FR 34752 at 34909). Information about how to notify us about a product complaint is available on our Internet site (Ref. 2).

8. What should I do if I receive a product complaint involving serious illness or injury?

We encourage firms who receive a product complaint involving serious illness or injury to consult with a health care provider and to include such a consultation in its written procedures for handling product complaints (72 FR 34752 at 34909). In addition, be advised that in 2006 Congress enacted the "Dietary Supplement and Non-Prescription Drug Consumer Protection Act" (Pub. L. 109-462), which established a new statutory requirement for mandatory reporting to FDA of serious adverse events (section 761 of the Act (21 U.S.C. 379aa-1)). This law defines "serious adverse events" as those adverse events that result in death, a life-threatening experience, an inpatient hospitalization, a persistent or significant disability or incapacity, or a congenital anomaly or birth defect, or that require medical or surgical intervention to prevent such serious outcomes (based on reasonable medical judgment). Among other things, this law also has specific provisions for how serious adverse event reports are to be submitted to FDA and recordkeeping requirements relating to adverse event reports. We encourage firms who are unsure as to whether an adverse event should be reported to FDA to contact us for assistance (72 FR 34752 at 34909). FDA has also published guidance for industry about mandatory dietary supplement adverse event reporting and recordkeeping requirements, entitled "Questions and Answers Regarding Adverse Event Reporting and Recordkeeping for Dietary Supplements as Required by the Dietary Supplement and Nonprescription Drug Consumer Protection Act," (Ref. 3).

XX. Subpart P – Records and Recordkeeping

1. What does the DS CGMP rule require regarding the records that I make and keep?

The DS CGMP rule requires that:

- You keep written records for one year past the shelf life date (if shelf life dating is used), or for 2 years beyond the date of distribution of the last batch of dietary supplements associated with those records (21 CFR 111.605(a));

- Records be kept as original records, as true copies (such as photocopies, microfilm, microfiche, or other accurate reproductions of the original records), or as electronic records (21 CFR 111.605(b)); and

- All electronic records comply with 21 CFR part 11 (21 CFR 111.605(c)).

2. What does the DS CGMP rule require me to do to make records available to FDA?

The DS CGMP rule requires you to:

- Have all required records, or copies of such records, readily available during the retention period for inspection and copying by FDA when requested (21 CFR 111.610(a)); and

- Make suitable reader and photocopying equipment readily available to FDA if you use reduction techniques, such as microfilming (21 CFR 111.610(b)).

XXI. References

We have placed the following references on display in the Division of Dockets Management, Food and Drug Administration, 5630 Fishers Lane, rm. 1061, Rockville, MD 20852. You may see them at that location between 9 a.m. and 4 p.m., Monday through Friday. As of November 9, 2010, FDA had verified the Web site address for the references it makes available as hyperlinks from the Internet copy of this guidance.

1. FDA. Guidance for Industry: Product Recalls, Including Removals and Corrections.

2. FDA. Report a Problem. How to Report Problems With Products Regulated by FDA.

3. FDA. Questions and Answers Regarding Adverse Event Reporting and Recordkeeping for Dietary Supplements as Required by the Dietary Supplement and Nonprescription Drug Consumer Protection Act.

**CH
10**

Dietary Supplement Current Good Manufacturing Practices (CGMPs) and Interim Final Rule (IFR) Facts[1]

CGMP Final Rule:

- The U.S. Food and Drug Administration issued the final rule establishing regulations to require current good manufacturing practices (CGMPs) for dietary supplements.

- The current good manufacturing practices (CGMPs) final rule will require that proper controls are in place for dietary supplements so that they are processed in a consistent manner, and meet quality standards.

- The CGMPs apply to all domestic and foreign companies that manufacture, package, label or hold dietary supplements, including those involved with the activities of testing, quality control, packaging and labeling, and distributing them in the U.S.

- The rule establishes CGMPs for industry-wide use that are necessary to require that dietary supplements are manufactured consistently as to identity, purity, strength, and composition.

- The requirements include provisions related to:

    o the design and construction of physical plants that facilitate maintenance,

    o cleaning,

    o proper manufacturing operations,

    o quality control procedures,

    o testing final product or incoming and inprocess materials,

    o handling consumer complaints, and

    o maintaining records.

- To limit any disruption for dietary supplements produced by small businesses, the rule has a staggered three-year phase-in for small businesses. The final CGMPs is effective in June 2008 for large companies. Companies with less than 500 employees have until June 2009 and companies with fewer than 20 employees have until June 2010 to comply with the regulations.

---

1   http://wayback.archive-it.org/7993/20170111070358/http://www.fda.gov/Food/GuidanceRegulation/ CGMP/ucm110858.htm

Interim Final Rule:

- The interim final rule (IFR) establishes a petition process for a manufacturer to apply for exemption from the 100 percent identity testing requirements for dietary ingredients used in manufacturing dietary supplements.

- If a manufacturer is granted an exemption, the manufacturer would still be responsible for ensuring the quality of the final dietary supplement product.

- The manufacturer would have to provide data in its petition demonstrating that less than 100% identity testing does not materially diminish assurance that the dietary ingredient is the correct dietary ingredient.

- The IFR is effective in June 2008 when the CGMP final rule becomes effective. However, there is a 90-day comment period. Based on the comments received, the IFR may be revised.

Consumer Benefits:

- Consumers should have access to dietary supplements that meet quality standards and that are free from contamination and are accurately labeled.

- The rule will give consumers greater confidence that the dietary supplement they use has been manufactured to ensure its identity, purity, strength, and composition.

- The rule addresses the quality of manufacturing processes for dietary supplements and the accurate listing of supplement ingredients. It does not limit consumers' access to dietary supplements, or address the safety of their ingredients, or their effects on health when proper manufacturing techniques are used.

CH
10

Manufacturers:

- Under the Dietary Supplement Health and Education Act (DSHEA), manufacturers have an essential responsibility to substantiate the safety of their products and for determining that any representations or claims made about their products are substantiated by adequate evidence to show that they are not false or misleading.

- The CGMPs will help to ensure manufacturers produce unadulterated and properly labeled dietary supplements.

- Under the CGMP rule, manufacturers are required to:
    - o Employ qualified employees and supervisors;
    - o Design and construct their physical plant in a manner to protect dietary ingredients and dietary supplements from becoming adulterated during manufacturing, packaging, labeling and holding;
    - o Use equipment and utensils that are of appropriate design, construction, and workmanship for the intended use;

- o Establish and use master manufacturing and batch production records;
- o Establish procedures for quality control operations;
- o Hold and distribute dietary supplements and materials used to manufacture dietary supplements under appropriate conditions of temperature, humidity, light, and sanitation so that the quality of the dietary supplement is not affected;
- o Keep a written record of each product complaint related to CGMPs; and
- o Retain records for 1 year past the shelf life date, if shelf life dating is used, or 2 years beyond the date of distribution of the last batch of dietary supplements associated with those records.

- Examples of product quality problems that the rule will help prevent are:
  - o dietary supplements that contain ingredients in amounts that are greater than those listed on the label dietary supplements that contain ingredients in amounts that are less than those listed on the label
  - o wrong ingredient,
  - o other contaminant (e.g., bacteria, pesticide, glass, lead),
  - o foreign material in a dietary supplement container,
  - o improper packaging, and
  - o mislabeled

- The interim final rule allows manufacturers to petition FDA for an exemption from the requirement of 100 percent identity testing of one or more dietary ingredients used in manufacturing the dietary supplement. The manufacturer would provide data to demonstrate that its proposed reduced frequency of identity testing does not materially diminish assurance that the dietary ingredient is the correct dietary ingredient. Each petition will be considered on a case by case basis.

Federal Register, June 25, 2007:

Final Rule: Current Good Manufacturing Practice in Manufacturing, Packaging, Labeling, or Holding Operations for Dietary Supplements

Interim Final Rule: Petition to Request Exemption from 100 Percent Identity Testing of Dietary Ingredients: Current Good Manufacturing Practice in Manufacturing, Packaging, Labeling, or Holding Operations for Dietary Supplements

Provided for Reference Purposes Only
July 2005

Responses to Questions about Codex and Dietary Supplements[1]

In July of 2005, the Codex Alimentarius Commission adopted the Guidelines for Vitamin and Mineral Food Supplements. Some U.S. citizens have expressed concern that these Guidelines will restrict consumers' access to the wide range of vitamin and mineral supplements of varying potencies legally sold in the United States. Others are concerned that the Guidelines will limit the amount and type of information on the labels of dietary supplements sold in the United States. Still others believe that the Guidelines will require dietary supplements to be sold as drugs in the United States.

- ➲ What is Codex?
- ➲ What work has Codex undertaken on vitamin and mineral supplements?
- ➲ What is the scope and content of these Guidelines?
- ➲ What has been the U.S. position on these Guidelines?
- ➲ Why won't these Guidelines restrict U.S. consumers' access to vitamin and mineral supplements?
- ➲ The Guidelines also include packaging and labeling provisions for vitamin and mineral food supplement products. Would vitamin and mineral supplements sold in the U.S. be required to comply with these?
- ➲ If the U.S. is not trying to harmonize its regulatory framework for dietary supplements with Codex, what are the benefits of our country participating in the process of developing these Codex Guidelines?
- ➲ How can I keep abreast of the work of Codex?

CH 10

What is Codex?

The Codex Alimentarius Commission, or Codex, was created in 1963 by two U.N. organizations, the Food and Agriculture Organization and the World Health Organization. Its main purpose is to protect the health of consumers and to ensure fair practices in international trade in food through the development of food standards, codes of practice, guidelines and other recommendations. Codex standards and guidelines are developed by committees, which are open to all member countries. Member countries review and provide comments on Codex

---

1   http://wayback.archive-it.org/7993/20170111070451/http://www.fda.gov/Food/GuidanceRegulation/
GuidanceDocumentsRegulatoryInformation/DietarySupplements/ucm113860.htm#what

standards and related texts at several stages in the development process. In the United States, public meetings are held to receive comments on Codex drafts and comments are invited from all interested parties (See U.S. Codex Office web site). Codex standards and related texts are voluntary; member countries are not bound by or required to adopt them.

You can obtain more information about Codex at the Rome Codex web site.[2]

You can also obtain information about U.S. Codex activities at the U.S. Codex Office web site.[3]

What work has Codex undertaken on vitamin and mineral supplements?

In the early 1990's, the Codex Committee on Nutrition and Foods for Special Dietary Uses (CCNFSDU) began discussions on guidelines for vitamin and mineral supplements. This Committee is responsible for studying nutritional issues referred by the Codex Alimentarius Commission; drafting provisions, as appropriate, on the nutritional aspects of all foods; and developing standards, guidelines, or related texts for foods for special dietary uses. Germany is the host government for the Committee, which has met either every year or every other year since 1966.

At the 26 th CCNFSDU session (Bonn, November 1-5, 2004), the Committee completed work on Draft Guidelines for Vitamin and Mineral Food Supplements and submitted them for adoption by the Codex Alimentarius Commission (CAC). The Guidelines were adopted at the 28 th CAC Session that was held in Rome on July 4-9, 2005.

What is the scope and content of these Guidelines?

The Guidelines apply only to supplements that contain vitamins and/or minerals, where these products are regulated as foods.

The Guidelines address the composition of vitamin and mineral supplements, including the safety, purity, and bioavailability of the sources of vitamins and minerals.

The Guidelines do not specify upper limits for vitamins and minerals in supplements. Instead, they provide criteria for establishing maximum amounts of vitamins and minerals per daily portion of supplement consumed, as recommended by the manufacturer. The criteria specify that maximum amounts should be established by scientific risk assessment based on generally accepted scientific data and taking into consideration, as appropriate, the varying degrees of sensitivity of different consumer groups.

The Guidelines also address the packaging and labeling of vitamin and mineral supplements.

We encourage you to read the complete text of the Guidelines, which is found in Appendix II of the report of the most recent session of the CCNFSDU. See ALINORM 5/28/26 on the Codex website (see "Reports" under the "Meetings and Events" pull down menu).

---

2   Current information about the Codex Alimentarius is avaiable through the Food and Agriculture Organization of the United Nations at http://www.fao.org/fao-who-codexalimentarius/about-codex/en/

3   U.S Codex & Codex Alimentarius information is available on the USDA website at https://www.fsis.usda.gov/wps/portal/fsis/topics/international-affairs/us-codex-alimentarius

What has been the U.S. position on these Guidelines?

The U.S. supports consumer choice and access to dietary supplements that are safe and labeled in a truthful and non-misleading manner. The Dietary Supplement Health and Education Act of 1994 (DSHEA) ensures that a broad array of dietary supplements are available to U.S. consumers. The Codex Guidelines for Vitamin and Mineral Food Supplements do not, in any way, affect the availability of supplement products to U.S. consumers. On the contrary, the absence of science-based Codex guidelines could adversely affect the ability of U.S. manufacturers to compete in the international marketplace.

Why won't these Guidelines restrict U.S. consumers' access to vitamin and mineral supplements?

Some consumers mistakenly believe that with the adoption of the Guidelines on Vitamin and Mineral Food Supplements, the U.S. is required to automatically change its laws and regulations to comply with the international standard. Some have expressed concerns that the World Trade Organization (WTO) and its trade dispute settlement panels may place pressure on the U.S. to change its laws because of international trade agreements such as the Agreement on the Application of Sanitary and Phytosanitary Measures (SPS Agreement), which references Codex as the international organization for food safety standards.

We see no basis for these concerns. First, the DSHEA covers a much broader range of dietary supplements than the vitamin and mineral supplements that are the subject of the Codex Guidelines. Moreover, for supplements covered by these Guidelines, we note the following:

CH 10

The SPS Agreement does not require a country to adopt any international standard. Rather, the SPS Agreement provides that members may base their Sanitary and Phytosanitary measures either on international standards, guidelines or recommendations, where they exist, or may establish measures that result in a higher level of protection if there is a scientific justification, or if a country determines it to be appropriate in accord with provisions of the SPS Agreement (SPS Agreement, Article 3(1) and (3)).

WTO and WTO dispute panels do not have the power to change U.S. law. If a WTO decision in response to a dispute settlement panel is adverse to the U.S., only Congress and the Administration can decide whether to implement the panel recommendation, and, if so, how to implement it.

For dietary supplements, it is unlikely that another country will accuse the U.S. of imposing a trade barrier for the importation of supplement products into the U.S. marketplace because the U.S. laws and regulations are generally broader in scope and less restrictive than the international standard.

However, other countries with more restrictive laws and regulations for dietary supplement products than the U.S. may create trade barriers to the importation of products manufactured by the U.S. dietary supplement industry. Thus, the U.S. government's involvement in the setting of international standards can help minimize the potential of trade barriers to U.S products in international trade.

Further, there is no basis for the concern that the Codex Guidelines on Vitamin and Mineral Food Supplements would require dietary supplements be sold as prescription drugs in the United States. First, there is nothing in the Guidelines that suggests that supplements be sold as drugs requiring a prescription. Second, U.S. regulatory agencies are bound by the laws established by Congress, not by Codex standards. Third, because of our generally less restrictive standards, it is unlikely that the trade dispute would be brought against the U.S.

In summary, U.S. consumers' access to a broad array of dietary supplements under DSHEA would not be changed in any way by Codex's adoption of guidelines on vitamin and mineral food supplements.

The Guidelines also include packaging and labeling provisions for vitamin and mineral food supplement products. Would vitamin and mineral supplements sold in the U.S. be required to comply with these?

All Codex standards and related texts are voluntary, and vitamin and mineral food supplement products sold in the U.S. would not be required to comply with provisions that are more restrictive than U.S. law (i.e., DSHEA).

If the U.S. is not trying to harmonize its regulatory framework for dietary supplements with Codex, what are the benefits of our country participating in the process of developing these Codex Guidelines?

Our participation in the Codex process is important to encourage the development of guidelines on vitamin and mineral supplements that are based on sound science and not on arbitrary criteria. For example, encouraging the use of science-based risk assessment for determining the maximum levels of vitamins and minerals in supplements reduces the chance that arbitrary standards will be used for determining maximum levels.

How can I keep abreast of the work of Codex?

To keep abreast of U.S. Codex activities, you may want to periodically access the U.S. Codex Office website.

You can also obtain the agenda and reference documents for Commission and committee meetings and final reports from these meetings from the Rome Codex website.[4]

The appendices to the committee reports provide the latest draft versions following a committee meeting of some of the Codex standards that are being developed or revised by the Committee.[5]

---

4   Current information about the Codex Alimentarius is avaiable through the Food and Agriculture Organization of the United Nations at http://www.fao.org/fao-who-codexalimentarius/about-codex/en/

5   U.S Codex & Codex Alimentarius information is available on the USDA website at https://www.fsis.usda.gov/wps/portal/fsis/topics/international-affairs/us-codex-alimentarius

Chapter 11

Labeling of Dietary Supplements
Guidance

Contains Nonbinding Recommendations
December 2007;
Revised December 2008
and September 2009

Guidance for Industry: Questions and Answers Regarding the Labeling of Dietary Supplements as Required by the Dietary Supplement and Nonprescription Drug Consumer Protection Act1

I. Introduction

This document provides guidance to the dietary supplement industry for complying with the labeling requirements prescribed for dietary supplement manufacturers, packers, and distributors by the Dietary Supplement and Nonprescription Drug Consumer Protection Act (Pub. L. 109-462, 120 Stat. 3469). The guidance covers the following topics:

(1) what "domestic address" means for purposes of the dietary supplement labeling requirements in section 403(y) of the Federal Food, Drug, and Cosmetic Act (FD&C Act);

(2) FDA's recommendation for the use of an introductory statement before the domestic address or phone number that is required to appear on the product label under section 403(y);

(3) when FDA intends to begin enforcing the labeling requirements of section 403(y).

FDA's guidance documents, including this document, do not establish legally enforceable responsibilities. Instead, guidance documents describe the Agency's current thinking on a topic and should be viewed only as recommendations, unless specific regulatory or statutory requirements are cited. The use of the word should in Agency guidance means that something is suggested or recommended, but not required.

---

1   This guidance is available on the FDA website at https://www.fda.gov/Food/GuidanceRegulation/ GuidanceDocumentsRegulatoryInformation/ucm179018.htm

II. Background

On December 22, 2006, the President signed into law the Dietary Supplement and Nonprescription Drug Consumer Protection Act. This law amends the FD&C Act with respect to adverse event reporting and recordkeeping for dietary supplements and non-prescription drugs marketed without an approved application. This guidance document contains questions and answers relating to the new labeling requirements for dietary supplements under the Dietary Supplement and Nonprescription Drug Consumer Protection Act.

III. Questions and Answers

What information must be included on the label of a dietary supplement to enable consumers to report serious adverse events associated with the use of the dietary supplement?

Section 403(y) of the FD&C Act (21 U.S.C. 343(y)) requires the label of a dietary supplement being marketed in the United States to include "a domestic address or domestic phone number through which the responsible person ... may receive a report of a serious adverse event with such dietary supplement." If the label does not include the required domestic address or phone number, the dietary supplement is misbranded.

When the responsible person chooses to provide a domestic address (rather than a phone number) for adverse event reporting, FDA concludes that the statute requires the product label to bear a full U.S. mailing address that includes the street address or P.O. box, city, state, and zip code of the responsible person (i.e., the manufacturer, packer, distributor, or retailer identified on the dietary supplement label). FDA finds that Congress's use of the term "domestic address" in section 403(y) is a clear and unambiguous directive that dietary supplement labels include all information necessary to enable a serious adverse event report to reach the responsible person. This reading of section 403(y) is supported by dictionary definitions of "address," which include "the indication of destination, as on mail or parcels" and "the location at which a person or an organization may be reached" *(Ref. 1)*. Indeed, an address does not serve its intended purpose unless it includes all the information necessary to enable mail to reach its destination.

Similarly, when the responsible person chooses to provide a domestic phone number for adverse event reporting, FDA concludes that the statute requires the phone number on the product label to include an area code (e.g., a toll-free area code such as 800 or a local area code such as 301). Without the area code, the phone number is incomplete and does not serve its intended purpose of enabling the consumer to contact the responsible person to report a serious adverse event.

Congress's use of the phrase "through which the responsible person ... may receive a report" to modify "domestic address or domestic phone number" further supports FDA's conclusion that "domestic address or domestic phone number" means a complete address or phone number (see section 403(y) of the FD&C Act (21 U.S.C. 343(y))). This phrase shows Congress's intent that the domestic address or phone number on the label be

CH
11

sufficient to ensure that the responsible person will actually receive the serious adverse event reports that consumers submit. If the address provided on the product label for adverse event reporting is incomplete (e.g., no street address or P.O. box), some of the serious adverse event reports that are submitted to the responsible person by mail likely will not be received. In addition, when consumers notice the incomplete address, they may decide not to submit a report to the responsible person because they believe it will not be received. Similarly, a phone number without an area code would be useless to consumers except for those who happen to be in the same area code as the responsible person.

The use of the term "domestic address" in section 403(y) contrasts with Congress's use of a different term, "place of business," in section 403(e) of the FD&C Act (21 U.S.C. 343(e)). Section 403(e) provides that foods, including dietary supplements, are misbranded unless the product label bears the name and place of business of the manufacturer, packer, or distributor of the food. FDA's regulations interpret "place of business" to require only the firm's city, state, and zip code to appear on the product label, as long as the firm's street address is listed in a current telephone directory or other city directory (21 C.F.R. 101.5(d)). The use of the term "domestic address" in section 403(y) demonstrates Congress's intent to require the responsible person's full address, including the street address or P.O. box, to appear on dietary supplement labels when the responsible person has opted to receive serious adverse event reports by mail. If Congress had considered the less complete address already required under the "place of business" labeling regulation to be adequate for serious adverse event reporting, there would have been no need to impose a new, more specific requirement in section 403(y) for the responsible person's "domestic address" to appear on dietary supplement labels.

Should the label of a dietary supplement also include language indicating that the purpose of the domestic address or phone number is to report serious adverse events associated with use of the dietary supplement?

Although section 403(y) does not require a label to include anything other than a domestic address or domestic phone number for the responsible person, FDA recommends that the label also bear a clear, prominent statement informing consumers that they may report serious adverse events to the domestic address or domestic phone number on the label.

FDA would have no objection to a firm's combining the recommended statement with language informing consumers that the domestic address or phone number on the label may also be used for other purposes, as long as the information provided is not false or misleading. The responsible person can also clarify that a doctor should be called for medical advice. For example, a multi-purpose label statement might be "You should call your doctor for medical advice about serious adverse events. To report a serious adverse event or obtain product information, contact..." or other similar language.

Responsible persons may also provide on the product label an email address or website to which reports may be made, provided that such email address or website is in addition to the domestic phone number or domestic address required by Section 403(y) of the FD&C Act (21 U.S.C. 343(y)).

CH
11

When do the labeling requirements in section 403(y) become effective?

Under section 3(d)(2) of the Dietary Supplement and Nonprescription Drug Consumer Protection Act, the labeling requirements of section 403(y) of the FD&C Act apply to all dietary supplements labeled on or after December 22, 2007. Therefore, these labeling requirements are already in effect. However, FDA intends to exercise enforcement discretion for the new labeling requirements until September 30, 2010.

Congress provided one year after the Dietary Supplement and Nonprescription Drug Consumer Protection Act was signed into law on December 22, 2006, for affected firms to comply with its new requirements. However, due to competing priorities, FDA was not able to consider, develop and finalize guidance on the labeling requirements of Section 403(y) until now. As a result, firms did not have the benefit of FDA's guidance on how to comply with the new labeling requirements when the requirements went into effect. Although the December 2008 revised draft guidance notified industry that the agency intended to exercise enforcement discretion for the new labeling requirements until January 1, 2010, this final guidance sets forth FDA's intention to exercise enforcement discretion for the new labeling requirements for dietary supplements labeled on or after September 30, 2010, approximately one year after this final guidance issues. This period of enforcement discretion should be adequate to enable all firms to meet the new labeling requirements for dietary supplements. FDA intends to begin enforcing the requirements of 403(y) for dietary supplements labeled on or after September 30, 2010.

IV. Paperwork Reduction Act of 1995

This guidance contains information collection provisions that are subject to review by the Office of Management and Budget (OMB) under the Paperwork Reduction Act of 1995 (44 U.S.C. 3501-3520).

The time required to complete this information collection is estimated to average 8 hours per response, including the time to review instructions, search existing data sources, gather the data needed, and complete and review the information collection. Send comments regarding this burden estimate or suggestions for reducing this burden to:

Office of Nutrition, Labeling, and Dietary Supplements
Division of Dietary Supplement Programs, HFS-810
Center for Food Safety and Applied Nutrition
Food and Drug Administration
5001 Campus Drive
College Park, MD 20740

An agency may not conduct or sponsor, and a person is not required to respond to, a collection of information unless it displays a currently valid OMB control number. The OMB control number for this information collection is 0910-0642 (expires 08/31/2012).

References:

1. Webster's II New Riverside University Dictionary (Houghton Mifflin 1984), p.77.

Guidance for Industry[1]
Contains Nonbinding Recommendations
April 2005

Guidance for Industry: A Dietary Supplement Labeling Guide[2]

Introduction

The Food and Drug Administration (FDA) receives many questions about the labeling of dietary supplements. These questions are a consequence of the activity in this area over the past several years. Some of the important events relating to the labeling of dietary supplements include:

- The Nutrition Labeling and Education Act of 1990 amended the Federal Food, Drug, and Cosmetic Act (the act) in a number of important ways. Notably, by requiring that most foods, including dietary supplements, bear nutrition labeling.

- The Dietary Supplement Health and Education Act of 1994 (the DSHEA) amended the act, in part, by defining "dietary supplements," adding specific labeling requirements for dietary supplements, and providing for optional labeling statements.

- On September 23, 1997 (62 FR 49826), we implemented the DSHEA by publishing several key regulations on the statement of identity, nutrition labeling, ingredient labeling, and nutrient content and health claims for dietary supplements. On June 5, 1998 (63 FR 30615), we amended the regulations pertaining to the nutrition labeling of extracts used in dietary supplements.

- On January 15, 1997 (62 FR 2218), we published regulations that require a label warning statement on dietary supplements with added iron. These regulations also required the unit-dose packaging of supplements containing 30 milligrams or more, but this requirement has been eliminated as a result of a court challenge in January, 2003.

- On July 11, 2003 (68 FR 41434), we published a final regulation that amended the labeling requirements for dietary supplements, as well as for conventional foods, that would make the declaration of trans fat mandatory in nutrition labeling. This regulation requires that, when present at 0.5 g or more, trans fat be listed in the Supplement Facts panel of dietary supplements on a separate line under the listing of saturated fat by January 1, 2006.

We have prepared this guide to help assure that the dietary supplements sold in the United Stated (U.S.) are properly labeled. This guide applies to dietary supplements produced domestically as well as those produced in foreign countries. Under our regulations, label approval is not required to import or distribute a dietary supplement.

CH 11

---

1   This guidance has been prepared by the Office of Nutritional Products, Labeling and Dietary Supplements (ONPLDS) in the Center for Food Safety and Applied Nutrition (CFSAN) at the U.S. Food and Drug Administration.
2   This guidance is available on the FDA website at https://www.fda.gov/Food/GuidanceRegulation/ GuidanceDocumentsRegulatoryInformation/DietarySupplements/ucm2006823.htm

We have included the most frequently raised questions about the labeling of dietary supplements using a "question and answer" format. If you have a question not addressed in this guide, please contact an FDA District Office (see Appendix A of this guide) or the:

> Division of Dietary Supplement Programs (HFS-810)
> Office of Nutritional Products, Labeling, and Dietary Supplements
> Center for Food Safety and Applied Nutrition
> Food and Drug Administration
> 5001 Campus Drive
> College Park, MD 20740-3835

Please be advised that you must comply with any requirements for dietary supplements that may publish after this booklet is issued. New regulations are published in the Federal Register prior to their effective date and are compiled annually in Title 21, Part 101 of the Code of Federal Regulations (21 CFR 101). Summaries of our new regulations (proposed regulations and final regulations) are posted on our Internet Website (http://www.fda.gov).

FDA's guidance documents, including this guidance, do not establish legally enforceable responsibilities. Instead, guidances describe the agency's current thinking on a topic and should be viewed only as recommendations, unless specific regulatory or statutory requirements are cited. The use of the word "should" in agency guidances means that something is suggested or recommended, but not required.

Chapter I. General Dietary Supplement Labeling

1. How are dietary supplements defined?

Dietary supplements are defined, in part, as products (other than tobacco) intended to supplement the diet that bear or contain one or more of the following dietary ingredients:

- A vitamin;
- A mineral;
- An herb or other botanical;
- An amino acid;
- A dietary substance for use by man to supplement the diet by increasing the total dietary intake; or
- A concentrate, metabolite, constituent, extract, or a combination of any ingredient mentioned above.

Further, dietary supplements are products intended for ingestion, are not represented for use as a conventional food or as a sole item of a meal or the diet, and are labeled as dietary supplements. The complete statutory definition is found in section 201(ff) of Federal Food, Drug, and Cosmetic Act (the act) (21 U.S.C. 321).

2. What label statements are required on the containers and packages of dietary supplements?

CH
11

Five statements are required:

1) the statement of identity (name of the dietary supplement),

2) the net quantity of contents statement (amount of the dietary supplement),

3) the nutrition labeling,

4) the ingredient list, and

5) the name and place of business of the manufacturer, packer, or distributor.

[21 CFR 101.3(a), 21 CFR 101.105(a), 21 CFR 101.36, 21 CFR 101.4(a)(1), and 21 CFR 101.5]

3. Where do I place the required label statements?

You must place all required label statements either on the front label panel (the principal display panel) or on the information panel (usually the label panel immediately to the right of the principal display panel, as seen by the consumer when facing the product), unless otherwise specified by regulation (i.e., exemptions). [21 CFR 101.2(b) and (d), 21 CFR 101.9(j)(13) and (j)(17), 21 CFR 101.36(g), (i)(2) and (i)(5)]

4. What label statements must I place on the principal display panel?

You must place the statement of identity and the net quantity of contents statement on the principal display panel. Where packages bear alternate principal display panels, you must place this information on each alternate principal display panel. [21 CFR 101.1, 21 CFR 101.3(a) and 21 CFR 101.105(a)]

5. How do I locate the principal display panel?

The principal display panel of the label is the portion of the package that is most likely to be seen by the consumer at the time of display for retail purchase. Many containers are designed with two or more different surfaces that are suitable for use as the principal display panel. These are alternate principal display panels. [21 CFR 101.1]

6. What label statements must I place on the information panel?

You must place the "Supplement Facts" panel, the ingredient list, and the name and place of business of the manufacturer, packer, or distributor on the information panel if such information does not appear on the principal display panel, except that if space is insufficient, you may use the special provisions on the "Supplement Facts" panel in 21 CFR 101.36(i)(2)(iii) and (i)(5). See questions 46 and 56 in Chapter IV for more details. [21 CFR 101.2(b) and (d), 101.36(i)(2)(iii) and (i)(5), 101.5, 101.9(j)(13)(i)(A) and (j)(17)]

7. Where is the information panel?

The information panel is located immediately to the right of the principal display panel as the product is displayed to the consumer. If this panel is not usable, due to package design and construction (e.g. folded flaps), the panel immediately contiguous and to the right of this part may be used for the information panel. The information panel may be any adjacent panel when the top of a container is the principal display panel. [21 CFR 101.2(a)]

8. What name and address must I list on the label of my product?

You must list the street address if it is not listed in a current city directory or telephone book, the city or town, the state, and zip code. You may list the address of the principal place of business in lieu of the actual address. [21 CFR 101.5]

9. May I place intervening material on the information panel?

No. You may not place intervening material, which is defined as label information that is not required (e.g., UPC bar code), between label information that is required on the information panel. [21 CFR 101.2(e)]

10. What type size, prominence and conspicuousness am I required to use on the principal display panel and the information panel?

You are required to use a print or type size that is prominent, conspicuous and easy to read. The letters must be at least one-sixteenth (1/16) inch in height based on the lower case letter "o," and not be more than three times as high as they are wide, unless you petition for an exemption in accordance with 21 CFR 101.2(f). The lettering must contrast sufficiently (it does not need to be black and white) with the background so as to be easy to read. See Chapter IV for the type size requirements for the nutrition label. [21 CFR 101.2(c) and (f), 21 CFR 101.15, and 21 CFR 101.105(h)]

11. Do I need to specify the country of origin if my product, or the ingredients in my product, is not from the United States?

Yes. Unless excepted by law, the Tariff Act requires that every article of foreign origin (or its container) imported into the United States conspicuously indicate the English name of the country of origin of the article. Section 304, Tariff Act of 1930, as amended (19 U.S.C. 304)

12. Who regulates the statement "Made in the U. S. A."?

FDA does not have regulatory authority over such statements. The U.S. Customs Service regulates country of origin marking (i.e., "Made in the U.S.A.") as authorized by the Tariff Act of 1930. Their website is www.customs.ustreas.gov.

13. How do I obtain a UPC bar code?

The UPC bar code may be obtained from the Uniform Code Council. Their website is www. uc-council.org. Click on the button that says "I Need a UPC Bar Code."

14. Must expiration dating be included on the label of dietary supplements?

No. However, a firm may include this information if it is supported by valid data demonstrating that it is not false or misleading.

Chapter II. Identity Statement

1. What is the statement of identity for a dietary supplement and where must I place it?

The statement of identity for a dietary supplement is the name that appears on the label of the dietary supplement. As a general matter, the statement of identity of a food (including dietary supplements) is the name specified by federal law or regulation, or, if no such name is specified, the common or usual name of the food. If the food has no common or usual name and the nature of the food is not obvious, the statement of identity must be an appropriately descriptive term. In the case of dietary supplements, both the Federal Food, Drug, and Cosmetic Act and FDA's regulations specify that the statement of identity must include the term "dietary supplement," except that the word "dietary" may be replaced with a description of the type of dietary ingredient(s) in the product (e.g., "herbal supplement") or the names of one or more dietary ingredients in the product (e.g., "bee pollen supplement"). You must place the statement of identity on the principal display panel of the dietary supplement and on any alternate principal display panels. Brand names are not considered to be statements of identity and should not be unduly prominent compared to the statement of identity. [21 U.S.C. 321(ff)(2)(C), 21 U.S.C. 343(s) (2)(B), 21 CFR 101.1 and 21 CFR 101.3]

2. How am I required to identify a dietary supplement?

You must identify a dietary supplement by using the term "dietary supplement" in the statement of identity, except that you may delete the word "dietary" and replace it with the name of the dietary ingredient(s) in the product (e.g., "calcium supplement") or an appropriately descriptive term indicating the type of dietary ingredient(s) in your dietary supplement product (e.g., "herbal supplement with vitamins"). [21 U.S.C. 321(ff)(2)(C), 21 U.S.C. 343(s)(2)(B) and 21 CFR 101.3(g)]

3. Can the term "dietary supplement" by itself be considered the statement of identity?

Yes. This term describes the basic nature of a dietary supplement and therefore is an "appropriately descriptive term" that can be used as the product's statement of identity. The statement of identity for a dietary supplement may therefore consist simply of the term "dietary supplement," or "dietary supplement" may be part of a longer statement of identity (e.g., "cod liver oil liquid dietary supplement"). In either case, the word "dietary" may be deleted and replaced by another appropriately descriptive term identifying the contents of the product, such as "calcium supplement," "herbal supplement", or "herbal supplement with vitamins." [21 CFR 101.3(g)]

4. Should I make the statement of identity stand out?

Yes. You must make the statement of identity one of the most important features on the principal display panel. To do this, you must use bold type and a type size reasonably related to the most prominent printed matter on the front panel of your label. [21 CFR 101.3(d)]

CH 11

5. How should I place the statement of identity on the principal display panel?

You must place the statement of identity of your dietary supplement product in lines generally parallel to the base of the package. [21 CFR 101.3(d)]

Chapter III. Net Quantity of Contents

1. What is the net quantity of contents statement for a dietary supplement?

The net quantity of contents statement for a dietary supplement is the statement that informs consumers of the amount of dietary supplement that is in the container or package. [21 CFR 101.105(a)]

2. Where must I locate the net quantity of contents statement on my label?

You must locate the net quantity of contents statement on your product label as a distinct item in the bottom 30 percent of the principal display panel, in lines generally parallel with the base of the container. If the principal display panel of your product is 5 square inches or less, the requirement for placement within the bottom 30 percent does not apply when the declaration of net quantity of contents meets the other requirements of 21 CFR 101. [21 CFR 101.105(f)]

3. How must I express the net quantity of contents statement on my label?

You must express the net quantity of contents statement in either weight, measure, numerical count or a combination of numerical count and weight or measure. When you express this quantity as a weight or measure, you must specify both metric (grams, kilograms, milliliters, or liters) and U.S. Customary System (ounces, pounds, or fluid ounces) terms. [Public Law 102-329, August 3, 1992 and 21 CFR 101.105]

4. Why must I calculate the area of the principal display panel?

You must calculate the area of the principal display panel (calculated in square inches or square centimeters) to determine the minimum type size that is permitted for the net quantity of contents statement. [21 CFR 101.1]

5. How do I calculate the area of the principal display panel?

You may calculate the area of the principal display panel for rectangular or square shaped packages by multiplying the height by the width (both in inches or both in centimeters), and for cylindrical shaped packages by multiplying 40% of the circumference by the height. For example, a rectangular package that is 8 inches high and 6 inches wide would have a principal display panel of 48 square inches. A cylindrical package having a circumference of 10 inches and a height of 2 inches would have a principal display panel of 8 square inches. [21 CFR 101.1]

6. Am I required to place the net quantity of contents statement conspicuously and prominently on my product labels?

Yes. You are required to use a print style that is prominent, conspicuous, and easy to read, with letters not more than three times as high as wide. Use letters that contrast sufficiently with the background. [21 CFR 101.15 and 21 CFR 101.105(h)]

7. What is the minimum type size that I can use for the net quantity of contents statements?

The smallest type size permitted for the net quantity of contents statement is based on the size of the principal display panel. You may determine the height of the type by measuring the height of upper case letters, when only upper case letters are used, or the height of a lower case letter "o," or its equivalent, when mixed upper and lower case letters are used. The table below sets out the minimum type size in inches (in.), with metric equivalents (millimeters (mm) and centimeters (cm)) in parentheses.

Minimum Type Size	Area of Principal Display Panel
1/16 in.	(1.6 mm) 5 sq. in. (32 sq. cm.) or less
1/8 in. (3.2 mm)	More than 5 sq. in. (32 sq. cm.) but not more than 25 sq. in. (161 sq. cm.)
3/16 in. (4.8 mm)	More than 25 sq. in. (161 sq. cm.) but not more than 100 sq. in. (645 sq. cm.)
1/4 in. (6.4 mm)	More than 100 sq. in. (645 sq. cm.) but not more than 400 sq. in. (2580 sq. cm.)
1/2 in. (12.7 mm)	Over 400 sq. in. (2580 sq. cm.)

[21 CFR 101.105(h) and (i)]

8. What must I include in a weight-based net quantity of contents statement?

You must include only the quantity of the dietary supplement in a container, and not the weight of the container, wrappers and packing materials, except that in the case of dietary supplements packed in containers designed to deliver the dietary supplement under pressure, the propellant is included in the net quantity declaration. [21 CFR 101.105(g)]

9. What must I include in a numerical count-based net quantity statement?

You must include the number of units in a container, e.g. "100 tablets." 21 CFR 101.105(a)

10. May I use qualifying phrases in the net quantity of contents statement?

No. You may not use qualifying phrases that qualify a unit or weight, measure, or count (such as "jumbo quart" and "full gallon") in the net quantity of contents statement because they tend to exaggerate the amount of the dietary supplement in the container. [21 CFR 101.105(f)]

Chapter IV. Nutrition Labeling

General

1. What is the nutrition label for a dietary supplement called?

The nutrition label for a dietary supplement is called a "Supplement Facts" panel (see sample labels at the end of this chapter). [21 CFR 101.36(b)(1)(i)]

2. How does "Supplement Facts" differ from "nutrition facts?"

The major differences between "Supplement Facts" panel and "Nutrition Facts" panel are as follows:

a. You must list dietary ingredients without RDIs or DRVs in the "Supplement Facts" panel for dietary supplements. You are not permitted to list these ingredients in the "Nutrition Facts" panel for foods.

b. You may list the source of a dietary ingredient in the "Supplement Facts" panel for dietary supplements. You cannot list the source of a dietary ingredient in the "Nutrition Facts" panel for foods.

c. You are not required to list the source of a dietary ingredient in the ingredient statement for dietary supplements if it is listed in the "Supplement Facts" panel.

d. You must include the part of the plant from which a dietary ingredient is derived in the "Supplement Facts" panel for dietary supplements. You are not permitted to list the part of a plant in the "Nutrition Facts" panel for foods.

e. You are not permitted to list "zero" amounts of nutrients in the "Supplement Facts" panel for dietary supplements. You are required to list "zero" amounts of nutrients in the "Nutrition Facts" panel for food.

[21 CFR 101.36(b)(3) and (b)(2)(i), 21 CFR 101.4(h), 21 CFR 101.36(d) and (d)(1), and 21 CFR 101.9]

3. What information must I list in the "Supplement Facts" panel?

You must list the names and quantities of dietary ingredients present in your product, the "Serving Size" and the "Servings Per Container." However, the listing of "Servings Per Container" is not required when it is the same information as in the net quantity of contents statement. For example, when the net quantity of contents statement is 100 tablets and the "Serving Size" is one tablet, the "Serving Per Container" also would be 100 tablets and would not need to be listed. [21 CFR 101.36(b)]

Serving Size

4. What is the serving size for a dietary supplement?

One serving of a dietary supplement equals the maximum amount recommended, as appropriate, on the label for consumption per eating occasion, or in the absence of recommendations, 1 unit (e.g., tablet, capsule, packet, teaspoonful, etc). For example, if the directions on your label say to take 1-3 tablets with breakfast, the serving size would be 3 tablets. 21 CFR 101.12(b) Table 2 in the Miscellaneous Category

5. May I use flexibility in the wording for "Serving Size?"

No. You must use the term "Serving Size." [21 CFR 101.36(b)(1)]

Nutrient Declaration

6. What nutrients am I required to list in the "Supplement Facts" panel?

Total calories, calories from fat, total fat, saturated fat, cholesterol, sodium, total carbohydrate, dietary fiber, sugars, protein, vitamin A, vitamin C, calcium, and iron must be listed when they are present in measurable amounts. A measurable amount is an amount that exceeds the amount that can be declared as "zero" in the nutrition label of conventional foods, as specified in 21 CFR 101.9(c). If present in a measurable amount, trans fat must be listed on a separate line underneath the listing of saturated fat by January 1, 2006.

Calories from saturated fat and the amount of polyunsaturated fat, monounsaturated fat, soluble fiber, insoluble fiber, sugar alcohol, and other carbohydrate may be declared, but they must be declared when a claim is made about them. [21 CFR 101.36(b)(2)(i) (see 68 FR 41434 at 41505, July 11, 3003)]

7. Must I declare vitamins and minerals (other than vitamin A, vitamin C, calcium, and iron) listed in 21 CFR 101. 9(c)(8)(iv) and (c)(9)?

No. You are only required to declare them when they are added to the product for purposes of supplementation, or if you make a claim about them. [21 CFR 101.36(b)(2)(i)]

8. Am I required to list any other nutrients if I make a claim about them?

Yes. When you make a claim about calories from saturated fat, insoluble fiber, polyunsaturated fat, sugar alcohol, monounsaturated fat, other carbohydrate, and soluble fiber, you must list that nutrient. [21 CFR 101.36(b)(2)(i)]

9. May I declare dietary ingredients not having Daily Values (i.e., RDIs or DRVs)?

Yes. Dietary ingredients for which no daily values have been established must be listed by their common or usual names when they are present in a dietary supplement. They must be identified as having no Daily Values by use of a symbol in the column for "% Daily Value" that refers to the footnote "Daily Value Not Established." [21 CFR 101.36(b)(2)(iii)(F) and (b)(3)]

10. If I use a magnesium salt as a binder, where must I declare it?

You must list the specific magnesium salt in the ingredient statement below the "Supplement Facts" panel, not in the "Nutrition Facts" panel. Ingredients in dietary supplements that are not dietary ingredients, such as binders, excipients, fillers, must be included in the ingredient statement. [21 CFR 101.4(g)]

11. Must I declare vitamin E when it occurs naturally in my product and I make no claim for it?

No. Because Vitamin E is not one of the 14 mandatory dietary ingredients, it does not need to be declared when it occurs naturally. [21 CFR 101.36(b)(2)(i)]

12. May I declare protein on the label if my product contains only individual amino acids?

No. You may not declare protein on your products that contain only amino acids. [21 CFR 101.36(b)(2)(i)]

13. Must I list the dietary ingredients in my products in a specified order?

Yes. You must list the dietary ingredients that have Daily Values in the same order as for the labels of conventional foods, except that vitamins, minerals and electrolytes are grouped together. This results in the following order for vitamins and minerals: Vitamin A, vitamin C, vitamin D, vitamin E, vitamin K, thiamin, riboflavin, niacin, vitamin B6, folate, vitamin B12, biotin, pantothenic acid, calcium, iron, phosphorus, iodine, magnesium, zinc, selenium, copper, manganese, chromium, molybdenum, chloride, sodium, and potassium. [21 CFR 101.36(b)(2)(i)(B)]

14. May I use synonyms for my dietary ingredients?

Yes. You may use the following synonyms in parentheses after your dietary ingredients: Vitamin C (ascorbic acid), thiamin (vitamin B1), riboflavin (vitamin B2), folate (folacin or folic acid), and calories (energy). Alternatively, you may list "folic acid" or "folacin" without parentheses in place of "folate." You may also express energy content parenthetically in kilojoules immediately following the caloric content. [21 CFR 101.36(b)(2)(i)(B)(2)]

CH 11

Amounts

15. If the calcium carbonate in my product supplies calcium , should I list the weight of the entire salt or just of the calcium?

You must list the weight of calcium, rather than the weight of the calcium carbonate, the source ingredient, in the "Supplement Facts" panel. [21 CFR 101.36(b)(2)(ii)]

16. May I list the amount of my dietary ingredient in a separate column?

Yes. You may place the amount of your dietary ingredient in a separate column or immediately following the name of your dietary ingredient. [21 CFR 101.36(b)(2)(ii)]

17. When I use a separate column for amounts, can the heading "Amount per Serving" be placed over the column of amounts?

Yes. [21 CFR 101.36(b)(2)(i)(A)]

18. May I use language other than the term "Amount Per Serving?"

Yes. Language consistent with the declaration of the serving size, such as "Each Tablet Contains" or "Amount Per 2 Tablets" may be used in place of the heading "Amount Per Serving." You may also use terms, such as capsule, packet, or teaspoonful. [21 CFR 101.36(b)(2)(i)(A)]

19. May I present information on the "Amount Per Unit" basis?

Yes. You may declare information on a "per unit" basis in addition to the required "per serving" basis. [21 CFR 101.36(b)(2)(iv)]

20. May I present information on more than one serving?

Yes. You may use additional columns when you have a product with different servings, such as one tablet in the morning and two at night. You must label the columns appropriately, e.g., "Amount per 1 Tablet" and "Amount per 2 Tablets." [21 CFR 101.36(b)(2)(i)(A)]

21. Am I required to use the units of measurement specified for use in the "Nutrition Facts" panel?

Yes. For example, the amount of fat would be listed in terms of grams in both the "Nutrition Facts" and "Supplement Facts" panels. However, units of measurement for amounts of vitamins and minerals are not specified for use in the "Nutrition Facts" panel because they must be listed by % Daily Value, not by weight. You should use the units of measurement given in 21 CFR 101.9(c)(8)(iv) for the Daily Values of vitamins and minerals when listing these nutrients in "Supplement Facts" (e.g., the amount of vitamin C must be listed in terms of milligrams because its Daily Value is stated in milligrams). [21 CFR 101.36(b)(2)(ii)(B) and 101.9(c)]

Percent Of Daily Value (% DV)

22. What is the % DV?

The % DV is the percent of the Daily Value (i.e., Reference Daily Intakes or Daily Reference Value) of a dietary ingredient that is in a serving of the product. [21 CFR 101.36(b)(2)(ii)(B) and 21 CFR 101.9(c)(8) and (9)]

23. Do I need to list the % DV on my label?

The % DV must be declared for all dietary ingredients for which FDA has established Daily Values, except that 1) the percent for protein may be omitted, and 2) on the labels of dietary supplements to be used by infants, children less than 4 years of age, or pregnant or lactating women, you must not list any percent for total fat, saturated fat, cholesterol, total carbohydrate, dietary fiber, vitamin K, selenium, manganese, chromium, molybdenum, chloride, sodium, or potassium. See Appendix B for the daily values to be used for adults and children 4 or more years of age and Appendix C for the daily values to be used for infants, children less than 4 years of age, or pregnant or lactating women. [21 CFR 101.36(b)(2)(iii)]

24. How do I calculate the % DV?

You calculate the % DV by dividing the quantitative amount by weight by the established Daily Value for the specified dietary ingredient and multiplying by 100 (except that the % DV for protein must be calculated in accordance with 21 CFR 101.9(c)(7)(iii)). In this calculation, you must use as the quantitative amount the unrounded amount, except that for total fat, saturated fat, cholesterol, sodium, potassium, total carbohydrate, and dietary fiber, you may use the quantitative amount by weight declared on the label (i.e., the rounded amount). For example, the % DV for 60 mg of vitamin C is 100 (60 mg divided by the Daily Value for vitamin C, multiplied by 100). [21 CFR 101.36(b)(2)(iii)(B) and 21 CFR 101.9(c)(7)(iii)]

25. What rounding rules must I use for expressing the % DV?

You must express the percentages to the nearest whole percent, except that "Less than 1 %" or "< 1 %" must be used when the amount present is big enough to be listed, but so small that the % DV when rounded to the nearest percent is zero. For example, a product containing 1 gram of total carbohydrate would list the % DV as "Less than 1 %" or "< 1 %." [21 CFR 101.36(b)(2)(iii)(C)]

26. What if the amount of a dietary ingredient present in my product is high enough to declare, but so low that the % DV rounds to zero?

You must declare "Less than 1%" or "< 1%" because your label might confuse consumers if you declare 5 mg and list 0% DV. For example, if a product contains 5 mg of potassium, the % DV calculates to 0.14 percent (5 mg divided by 3,500 mg), which you would round to zero. In this case, you would declare "Less than 1%" or "< 1%" for the % DV.

Note: This does not pertain to dietary ingredients having RDIs because they may not be listed when present at less than 2 percent of the RDI. [21 CFR 101.36(b)(2)(iii)(C) and 101.36(b)(2)(i)]

27. Can I show more than one column for % DVs?

Yes. You may show more than one column. FDA has established four sets of Daily Values for many nutrients. Appendix B shows the Daily Values to be used for adults and children 4 or more years of age and Appendix C has the Daily Values to be used for children under 4 years of age, for infants, and for pregnant and lactating women. When you show more than one column, you must clearly identify each column (e.g., % Daily Value for Children Under 4 Years of Age). [21 CFR 101.36(b)(2)(iii)(E) and (e)(10)(ii)]

Other Dietary Ingredients

28. What are "other dietary ingredients?"

"Other dietary ingredients" are those dietary ingredients that do not have Daily Values (i.e. RDIs or DRVs) such as phosphatidylserine. [21 CFR 101.36(b)(3)(i)]

29. Where must I list "other dietary ingredients?"

You must list "other dietary ingredients" in the "Supplement Facts" panel following the listing of dietary ingredients having Daily Values. [21 CFR 101.36(b)(3)(i)]

30. How must I list "other dietary ingredients?"

You must list "other dietary ingredients" by common or usual name in a column or linear display. FDA has not specified an order that you must follow. You must list the quantitative amount by weight per serving immediately following the name of the dietary ingredient or in a separate column. You must place a symbol in the column for "% Daily Value" that refers to the footnote "Daily Value Not Established," except that the symbol must follow the weight when you do not use the column format. [21 CFR 101.36(b)(3)]

31. How must I list liquid extracts?

You must list liquid extracts using the volume or weight of the total extract and the condition of the starting material prior to extraction when it was fresh. You may include information on the concentration of the dietary ingredient and the solvent used, e.g., "fresh dandelion root extract, x (y:z) in 70% ethanol," where "x" is the number of mL or mg of the entire extract, "y" is the weight of the starting material, and "z" is the volume (mL) of solvent. You must identify the solvent in either the nutrition label or ingredient list. [21 CFR 101.36(b)(3)(ii)(B)]

CH 11

32. How must I list dried extracts?

For dietary ingredients that are extracts from which the solvent has been removed, you must list the weights of the dried extracts. [21 CFR 101.36(b)(3)(ii)(C)]

33. May I list constituents of a dietary ingredient?

Yes. You may list constituents of a dietary ingredient indented under the dietary ingredient and followed by their quantitative amounts by weight per serving. You may declare the constituents in a column or in a linear display. [21 CFR 101.36(b)(3)(iii)]

34. How must I list proprietary blends?

You must identify proprietary blends by use of the term "Proprietary Blend" or an appropriately descriptive term or fanciful name. On the same line, you must list the total weight of all "other dietary ingredients" contained in the blend. Indented underneath the name of the blend, you must list the "other dietary ingredients" in the blend, either in a column or linear fashion, in descending order of predominance by weight. These ingredients should be followed by a symbol referring to the footnote "Daily Value Not Established." Dietary ingredients having RDIs or DRVs must be listed separately and the individual weights declared. [21 CFR 101.36(b)(2) and (c)]

Format

35. How must I display the "Supplement Facts" panel?

The "Supplement Facts" nutrition information (referred to as a panel) must be enclosed in a box by using hairlines. The title, "Supplement Facts," must be larger than all other print in the panel and, unless impractical, must be set full width of the panel. The title and all headings must be bolded to distinguish them from other information. [21 CFR 101.36(e)]

36. How must I present the information in the "Supplement Facts" panel?

You must present all information using the following:

a. A single easy-to-read type style;

b. All black or one color type, printed on a white or neutral contrasting background, whenever practical;

c. Upper- and lowercase letters, except that you may use all uppercase lettering on small packages (i.e., packages having a total surface area available to bear labeling of less than 12 square inches);

d. At least one point leading (i.e., space between lines of text); and

e. Letters that do not touch.

[21 CFR 101.36(e)]

37. What are the type size requirements for the "Supplement Facts" panel?

Except as provided for small and intermediate-sized packages, you must set information other than the title, headings, and footnotes in uniform type size no smaller than 8 point. You also must use a type size larger than all other print size in the nutrition label for the title "Supplement Facts." You may set the column headings and footnotes in type no smaller than 6 point type. See the section on "Special Labeling Provisions" for the exceptions for small and intermediate-sized packages. [21 CFR 101.36(e)]

38. Must I use hairlines in the Supplement Facts panel?

Except for small and intermediate-sized packages, you must use a hairline rule that is centered between the lines of text to separate each dietary ingredient from the dietary ingredient above and beneath it. FDA has provided an exception for certain packages with space constraints. See the section on "Special Labeling Provisions" for the exceptions for small and intermediate-sized packages. [21 CFR 101.36(e)]

39. How closely must I follow the "Examples of graphic enhancements used by the FDA" in appendix B to Part 101?

You are not required to follow Appendix B to Part 101. Appendix B and its specifications are a model, which FDA has suggested in the interest of uniformity of presentation. For example, 21 CFR 101.36(e)(3)(i) requires the use of an "easy-to-read" type style, not specifically Helvetica type, as suggested in Appendix B. [21 CFR 101.36(e)(9)]

40. How do I provide nutrition labeling when my product contains two or more packets of supplements (e.g., a packet of capsules for the morning and a different packet for the evening)?

You may present the information for each packet (e.g., a packet of capsules for the morning and a different packet for the evening) in an individual nutrition label or you may use an aggregate nutrition label. For two packets, this would consist of five columns. List all of the dietary ingredients in the first column. List the amounts and percents of the morning packet in the second and third columns and similar information for the evening packet in the fourth and fifth columns (see the illustration of aggregate nutrition labeling in 21 CFR 101.36(e)(10)(iii)). [21 CFR 101.36(e)(8)]

Compliance

41. What kind of samples will FDA collect to determine compliance with 21 CFR 101.36?

FDA will collect a composite of 12 subsamples (consumer packages) or 10 percent of the number of packages in the same inspection lot, whichever is smaller. FDA will randomly select these packages. [21 CFR 101.36(f)(1)]

**CH
11**

42. What if it is not technically feasible for me to comply with the nutrition labeling requirements?

FDA may permit you to use an alternative means of compliance or additional exemptions in accordance with 21 CFR 101.9(g)(9). If your firm needs such special allowances, you must make your request in writing to the Office of Nutritional Products, Labeling, and Dietary Supplements (HFS-800), Food and Drug Administration, 5100 Paint Branch Parkway, College Park, Maryland 20740-3835. [21 CFR 101.36(f)(2)]

43. Must dietary ingredients that I have added to my products be present at 100% of the amount that I declare?

For dietary ingredients that are specifically added, your product must contain 100% of the volume or weight that you have declared on the label, with the exception of a deviation that is attributable to the analytical method. Products that contain less than this amount of such a dietary ingredient would be misbranded and in violation of the law. Dietary ingredients that are naturally-occurring must be present at 80% of the declared value. For example, if you add vitamin C that was isolated from a natural source or made synthetically to your dietary supplement product, it would be subject to the 100% rule. However, if you added rose hips to your product, the vitamin C in the rose hips is naturally-occurring and must be present at least 80% of the declared value. [21 CFR 101.9(g)(3) and (g)(4)]

Exemptions

44. What are the circumstances in which my dietary supplement products would be exempt from the nutrition labeling requirements?

Your dietary supplement product is not required to have a "Supplement Facts" panel if:

a. Your firm is a small business that has not more than $50,000 gross sales made or business done in sales of food to consumers or not more than $500,000 per year from total sales in accordance with 21 CFR 101.36(h)(1);

b. You sell less than 100,000 units of the product annually, your firm has fewer than 100 full-time equivalent employees in accordance with 21 CFR 101.36(h)(2) and you file an annual notification with FDA as specified in 21 CFR 101.9(j)(18)(iv); or

c. You ship the product in bulk form, do not distribute it to consumers in such form, and you supply it for use in the manufacture of other dietary supplements in accordance with 21 CFR 101.36(h)(3).

The two exemptions for small businesses and low-volume products (a. and b. above) are available to you only if your products' labels bear no claims or other nutrition information [21 CFR 101.36(h)(1) - (3)]

Special Labeling Provisions

45. What are small packages?

Small packages are those packages having less than 12 square inches of total surface area available to bear labeling. [21 CFR 101.36(i)(2) and 21 CFR 101.9(j)(13)]

46. What is the telephone provision for small packages?

In lieu of a "Supplement Facts" panel, you may print labels for small packages with a telephone number or address that consumers can use to obtain nutrition information. You may use a telephone number or an address in place of the "Supplement Facts" panel only if you place no claims or other nutrition information on the product label. [21 CFR 101.36(i)(2) and 21 CFR 101.9(j)(13)(i)]

47. What is the minimum type size that I may use for small packages?

You may use a type size no smaller than 4.5 point for the "Supplement Facts" panel on the labels of small packages. [21 CFR 101.36(i)(2)(i)]

48. May I use a tabular or linear format for the "Supplement Facts" panel on a small package?

Yes. You may use a tabular format on small packages. You also may present "Supplement Facts" information in a linear (i.e., string) fashion if the label will not accommodate the "Supplement Facts" panel in a tabular format. (See 21 CFR 101.9(j)(13)(ii)(A)(1) for an illustration of a tabular display and 21 CFR 101.9(j)(13)(ii)(A)(2) for an illustration of a linear display. [21 CFR 101.36(i)(2) and 21 CFR 101.9(j)(13)(ii)(A)]

49. What are intermediate-sized packages?

Intermediate-sized packages are those packages having from 12 to 40 square inches of total surface area available to bear labeling. [21 CFR 101.36(i)(2)(ii)]

50. What is the minimum type size for intermediate-sized packages?

The "Supplement Facts" panel on the labels of intermediate-sized packages must use type size no smaller than 6 point, except that type no smaller than 4.5 point may be used on packages that have 20 to 40 square inches that list more than 16 dietary ingredients. Also, 4.5 point type may be used on packages with less than 20 square inches that list more than 8 dietary ingredients.

Furthermore, the type size used in the "Supplement Facts" panel on an inner container may be as small as needed to accommodate all required information if the "Supplement Facts" on the outer container meets these type size requirements. [21 CFR 101.36(i)(2)(ii) and (i)(2)(iv)]

CH 11

51. May I use a tabular or linear format for the "Supplement Facts" panel on an intermediate-sized package?

You may use a tabular format on an intermediate-sized package if the package shape or size cannot accommodate vertical columns. You may use a linear format if the label will not accommodate a tabular format. (See 21 CFR 101.9(j)(13)(ii)(A)(1) for an illustration of a tabular display and 21 CFR 101.9(j)(13)(ii)(A)(2) for an illustration of a linear display). [21 CFR 101.36(i)(2) and 21 CFR 101.9(j)(13)(ii)(A)]

52. May I abbreviate on the labels of intermediate- sized packages?

You may use the abbreviations in 21 CFR 101.9(j)(13)(ii)(B) in the "Supplement Facts" panel for small and intermediate-sized packages, e.g, "Serv size" for "Serving Size" and "Servings" for "Servings Per Container." [21 CFR 101.9(j)(13)(ii)(B)]

53. Must I always use hairlines on the labels of intermediate-sized packages?

No. You may use a row of dots connecting the columns containing the name of each dietary ingredient and the quantitative amount (by weight and as a percent of Daily Value) in the "Supplement Facts" panel on a small or an intermediate-sized package if you use the minimum type size and there is not sufficient space for you to use hairlines. [21 CFR 101.36(i)(2)(v)]

54. Are there special requirements that I must follow for the labeling of dietary supplements for children?

Yes. On products for children less than 2 years of age, other than infant formula, you must not declare calories from fat, calories from saturated fat, saturated fat, polyunsaturated fat, monounsaturated fat, and cholesterol. Also, on products for children less than 4 years of age, you may not include % DVs for total fat, saturated fat, cholesterol, total carbohydrate, dietary fiber, vitamin K, selenium, manganese, chromium, molybdenum, chloride, sodium, or potassium. [21 CFR 101.36(b)(2)(iii) and (i)(1)]

55. Must I include a footnote comparing a 2,000 calorie diet to a 2,500 calorie diet in the "Supplement Facts" panel of my product?

No. You are not required to place the footnote on dietary supplements that is required by 21 CFR 101.9(d)(9) on conventional foods. However, you are required to include the footnote "Percent Daily Values are based on a 2,000 calorie diet" when you declare total fat, saturated fat, total carbohydrate, dietary fiber, or protein. [21 CFR 101.36(b)(2)(iii)(D)]

56. May I locate the "Supplement Facts" panel on other than the information panel?

Yes. If there is insufficient space for the "Supplement Facts" panel on the information panel or the principal display panel, you may locate it on other panels that can readily be seen by consumers in accordance with 21 CFR 101.9(j)(17). [21 CFR 101.36(i)(2)(iii) and (i)

(5) and 21 CFR 101.9(j)(17)]

57. May I omit the "Supplement Facts" panel on individual unit containers in multi-unit retail packs?

Yes. You may omit the "Supplement Facts" panel on individual units if nutrition information is fully provided on the outer package of the multi-unit pack and the unit containers are securely enclosed and are not intended to be separated for retail sale. You must label each individual unit with the statement "This Unit Not Labeled For Retail Sale" in accordance with 21 CFR 101.9(j)(15). [21 CFR 101.36(i)(3) and 21 CFR 101.9(j)(15)]

58. How do I provide the "Supplement Facts" panel if my dietary supplements are sold from bulk containers?

The retailer must display a "Supplement Facts" panel clearly at the point of purchase (e.g. on a counter card, sign, tag affixed to the product, or some other appropriate device). Alternatively, the required information may be placed in a booklet, looseleaf binder, or some other appropriate format that is available at the point of purchase. [21 CFR 101.36(i)(4), 21 CFR 101.9(a)(2) and (j)(16)]

59. Does FDA have sample labels for dietary supplements?

Yes. See sample labels below.

Sample Labels

A) Dietary supplement containing multiple vitamins (see 21 CFR 101.36(e)(10)(i)):

Supplement Facts
Serving Size 1 Tablet

	Amount Per Serving	% Daily Value
Vitamin A (as retinyl acetate and 50% as beta-carotene)	5000 IU	100%
Vitamin C (as ascorbic acid)	60 mg	100%
Vitamin D (as cholecalciferol)	400 IU	100%
Vitamin E (as d-alpha tocopheryl acetate)	30 IU	100%
Thiamin (as thiamin mononitrate)	1.5 mg	100%
Riboflavin	1.7 mg	100%
Niacin (as niacinamide)	20 mg	100%
Vitamin B$_6$ (as pyridoxine hydrochloride)	2.0 mg	100%
Folate (as folic acid)	400 mcg	100%
Vitamin B$_{12}$ (as cyanocobalamin)	6 mcg	100%
Biotin	30 mcg	10%
Pantothenic Acid (as calcium pantothenate)	10 mg	100%

Other ingredients: Gelatin, lactose, magnesium stearate, microcrystalline cellulose, FD&C Yellow No. 6, propylene glycol, propylparaben, and sodium benzoate.

CH 11

B) Dietary supplement containing multiple vitamins for children and adults (see 21 CFR 101.36(e)(10)(ii)):

Supplement Facts

Serving Size 1 Tablet

Amount Per Serving		% Daily Value for Children Under 4 Years of Age	% Daily Value for Adults and Children 4 or more Years of Age
Calories	5		
Total Carbohydrate	1 g	†	< 1%*
Sugars	1 g	†	†
Vitamin A	2500 IU	100%	50%
(50% as beta-carotene)			
Vitamin C	40 mg	100%	67%
Vitamin D	400 IU	100%	100%
Vitamin E	15 IU	150%	50%
Thiamin	1.1 mg	157%	73%
Riboflavin	1.2 mg	150%	71%
Niacin	14 mg	156%	70%
Vitamin B₆	1.1 mg	157%	55%
Folate	300 mcg	150%	75%
Vitamin B₁₂	5 mcg	167%	83%

* Percent Daily Values are based on a 2,000 calorie diet.
† Daily Value not established.

Other ingredients: Sucrose, sodium ascorbate, stearic acid, gelatin, maltodextrins, artificial flavors, d-alpha tocopheryl acetate, niacinamide, magnesium stearate, Yellow 6, artificial colors, stearic acid, palmitic acid, pyridoxine hydrochloride, thiamin mononitrate, vitamin A acetate, beta-carotene, folic acid, cholecalciferol, and cyanocobalamin.

C) Multiple vitamins in packets (see 21 CFR 101.36(e)(10)(iii)):

Supplement Facts

Serving Size 1 Packet
Servings Per Container 10

Amount Per Serving	AM Packet	% Daily Value	PM Packet	% Daily Value
Vitamin A	2500 IU	50%	2500 IU	50%
Vitamin C	60 mg	100%	60 mg	100%
Vitamin D	400 IU	100%		
Vitamin E	30 IU	100%		
Thiamin	1.5 mg	100%	1.5 mg	100%
Riboflavin	1.7 mg	100%	1.7 mg	100%
Niacin	20 mg	100%	20 mg	100%
Vitamin B₆	2.0 mg	100%	2.0 mg	100%
Folic Acid	200 mcg	50%	200 mcg	50%
Vitamin B₁₂	3 mcg	50%	3 mcg	50%
Biotin			30 mcg	10%
Pantothenic Acid	5 mg	50%	5 mg	50%

Ingredients: Sodium ascorbate, ascorbic acid, calcium pantothenate, niacinamide, d-alpha tocopheryl acetate, microcrystalline cellulose, artificial flavors, dextrin, starch, mono- and diglycerides, vitamin A acetate, magnesium stearate, gelatin, FD&C Blue #1, FD&C Red #3, artificial colors, thiamin mononitrate, pyridoxine hydrochloride, citric acid, lactose, sorbic acid, tricalcium phosphate, sodium benzoate, sodium caseinate, methylparaben, potassium sorbate, BHA, BHT, ergocalciferol and cyanocobalamin.

CH 11

D) Dietary supplement containing dietary ingredients with and without RDIs and DRVs (see 21 CFR 101.36(e)(10)(iv):

Supplement Facts

Serving Size 1 Capsule

Amount Per Capsule	% Daily Value
Calories 20	
Calories from Fat 20	
Total Fat 2 g	3%*
Saturated Fat 0.5 g	3%*
Polyunsaturated Fat 1 g	†
Monounsaturated Fat 0.5 g	†
Vitamin A 4250 IU	85%
Vitamin D 425 IU	106%
Omega-3 fatty acids 0.5 g	†

* Percent Daily Values are based on a 2,000 calorie diet.
† Daily Value not established.

Ingredients: Cod liver oil, gelatin, water, and glycerin.

Chapter V. Ingredient Labeling

1. What is an "ingredient"?

The Dietary Supplement Health and Education Act uses the term "ingredient" to refer to the compounds used in the manufacture of a dietary supplement. For instance, when calcium carbonate is used to provide calcium, calcium carbonate is an "ingredient" and calcium is a "dietary ingredient." The term "ingredient" also refers to substances such as binders, colors, excipients, fillers, flavors, and sweeteners. [Public Law 103-417, 60 Federal Register 67194 at 67199 (December 28, 1995)]

CH 11

2. What is unique about the ingredient labeling of dietary supplements?

Ingredients that are sources of dietary ingredients may be listed within the "Supplement Facts" panel, e.g., "Calcium (as calcium carbonate)." When ingredients are listed in this way, they do not have to be listed again in the ingredient statement (also called an ingredient list). [21 CFR 101.36(d)]

3. Do I need an ingredient statement when all of my ingredients are listed in the "Supplement Facts" panel?

No. If you place all source ingredients in the "Supplement Facts" panel and you have no other ingredients, such as excipients or fillers, you do not need an ingredient statement. [21 CFR 101.4(a)(1)]

4. How must I identify the ingredient list?

You must precede the ingredient list by the word "Ingredients," except that you must use the words "Other Ingredients" when you have identified some ingredients (i.e., as sources) within the nutrition label. [21 CFR 101.4(g)]

5. Where must I place the ingredient list on the label?

When present, you must place the ingredient list on dietary supplements immediately below the nutrition label, or if there is insufficient space below the nutrition label, immediately contiguous and to the right of the nutrition label. [21 CFR 101.4(g)]

6. What type size must I use for the ingredient list?

You must display this information prominently and conspicuously, but in no case may the types size be less that 1/16 inch in height as measured by the lower case "o", or its equivalent, in accordance with 21 CFR 101.105(h)(2). [21 CFR 101.2(c), 21 CFR 101.15, and 21 CFR 101.105(h)(1) and (2)]

7. Must I list the ingredients in a specified order?

Yes. You must list the ingredients in descending order of predominance by weight. This means that the ingredient that weighs the most is first and the ingredient that weighs the least is last. [21 CFR 101.4(a)]

8. How must I declare spices, natural flavors, or artificial flavors?

You must declare these ingredients in ingredient lists by using either specific common or usual names or by using the declarations "spice," "natural flavor" or "artificial flavor," or any combination thereof. [21 CFR 101.22(h)(1) and 21 CFR 101.4(a)(1)]

9. Can I indicate that a spice is also a coloring?

Yes. Paprika, turmeric, saffron and other spices that are also colorings, may be declared either by name or the term "spice and coloring." For example, paprika may be listed as "paprika" or as "spice and coloring." [21 CFR 101.22(a)(2)]

10. How must I declare artificial colors?

It depends on whether or not the artificial color is certified. List a certified color by its specific or abbreviated name, e.g., "FD&C Red No. 40" or "Red 40."

A color that is not certified may be listed as an "Artificial Color," "Artificial Color Added," "Color Added,"or by its specific common or usual name. [21 CFR 101.22(k)(1) and (k)(2)]

11. May I use "and/or" labeling for fats and oils?

Yes. When a blend of fats and/or oils is not the predominant ingredient of your product and you vary the makeup of the blend you may use "and/or" labeling or language such as:

INGREDIENTS:...vegetable oil shortening (contains one or more of the following: cottonseed oil, palm oil, soybean oil)."

[21 CFR 101.4(b)(14)]

12. Do I need to list water?

Yes. You must identify the added water in the list of ingredients in descending order of predominance by weight. For example:

"Ingredients: Cod liver oil, gelatin, water, and glycerin"

[21 CFR 101.4(a) and (c) and 21 CFR 101.36(e)(10)(iv)]

13. How do I list a chemical preservative?

You must list the common or usual name of the preservative followed by a description that explains its function e.g., "preservative," "to retard spoilage," "a mold inhibitor," "to help protect flavor," or "to promote color retention." [21 CFR 101.22(j)]

Chapter VI. Claims

Nutrient Content Claims

1. What is a nutrient content claim?

A nutrient content claim expressly or by implication characterizes the level of a nutrient in a dietary supplement. [21 CFR 101.13(b)]

2. What nutrient levels must be present in my dietary supplement products that would permit me to use nutrient content claims on my product labels?

The nutrient levels needed to use nutrient content claims are shown in Appendix D of this labeling guide.

3. May I use a nutrient content claim not included in FDA's regulations on my product label?

No. Only those claims, or their synonyms, that are specifically defined in regulations may be used. [21 CFR 101.13(b)]

4. Where may I find nutrient content claims specifically defined by the FDA?

You may find the regulations for specific claims in 21 CFR 101, Subpart D (Specific Requirements of Nutrient Content Claims) as follows:

§101.54(b) "High" claims

§101.54(c) "Good Source" claims

CH
11

§101.54(e) "More" claims

§101.54(f) "High potency" claims

§101.54(g) "Antioxidant" claims

§101.56 "Light" or "Lite" claims

§101.60 "Calorie or Sugar" claims

§101.61 "Sodium or Salt" claims

§101.62 "Fat, fatty acids, and cholesterol" claims

§101.65 Implied nutrient content claims

§101.65(d) "Healthy" claims

§101.67 Use of nutrient content claims for butter

5. What are the type size requirements for nutrient content claims?

A nutrient content claim may be no larger than twice the type size of the statement of identity (the name of the food) and may not be unduly prominent in style compared to the statement of identity. [21 CFR 101.13(f)]

6. Am I required to provide a "Supplement Facts" panel when I make a claim?

Yes. A "Supplement Facts" panel is required if you make a nutrient content claim. [21 CFR 101.13(n)]

7. What is a disclosure statement?

It is a statement that calls the consumer's attention to one or more nutrients (other than the nutrient that is the subject of the claim) in a dietary supplement (e.g., "See nutrition information for fat content"). [21 CFR 101.13(h)(1)]

8. When am I required to use a disclosure statement?

You must use a disclosure statement when you make a nutrient content claim and your food (including dietary supplements) contains one or more of the following nutrients in excess of the levels listed below per reference amount customarily consumed, per labeled serving, or, for a product with a reference amount of 30 g or less or 2 tablespoons or less, per 50 grams:

Fat	13.0 grams
Saturated Fat	4.0 grams
Cholesterol	60 milligrams
Sodium	480 milligrams

[21 CFR 101.13(h)(1)]

9. How must I present the disclosure statement on my label?

You must present it in easily legible boldface print or type, in distinct contrast to other printed or graphic matter. [21 CFR 101.13(h)(4)(i)]

10. What are the type size requirements for the disclosure statement?

The type requirements for the disclosure statement are the same as those for the net quantity of contents statement in 21 CFR 101.105(i), except where the size of the claim is less than two times the required size of the net quantity of contents statement, in which case the disclosure statement is no less than one-half (1/2) the size of the claim, but no smaller than one-sixteenth (1/16) of an inch. A disclaimer statement of one thirty-second (1/32) of an inch is allowed if your package has less than three square inches of available label space and is an individual serving-size package served with meals in restaurants. [21 CFR 101.105(i) and 21 CFR 101.13(h)(4)(i)]

11. Where must I place the disclosure statement?

You must place the disclosure statement immediately adjacent to (i.e., right next to) the claim with no intervening material (such as vignettes or other art work) other than information in the statement of identity or any other information that is required to be presented with the claim. [21 CFR 101.13(h)(4)(ii)]

12. When can a disclosure statement be omitted from the panel bearing the nutrition information?

You can omit the disclosure statement from the panel bearing the nutrition information when the nutrient content claim appears on more than one panel of a label. [21 CFR 101.13(h)(4)(ii)]

13. Am I required to have a disclosure statement each time I make a claim when I make several claims on one panel?

No. You are only required to have one disclosure statement per panel when you make multiple claims on a panel. The statement is required to be adjacent to the claim printed in the largest type on that panel. [21 CFR 101.13(h)(4)(iii)]

14. When may I make a "high" or "good source" claim?

You may make a "high" claim when your dietary supplement contains at least 20% of the Daily Value (DV) (i.e. the Reference Daily Intake (RDI) or Daily Reference Value (DRV)) of the nutrient that is the subject of the claim per reference amount customarily consumed. You may make a "good source" claim when your dietary supplement contains 10 to 19% of DV. [21 CFR 101.54(b)(1) and (c)(1)]

CH
11

15. Is there any way that I can let consumers know that my product contains nutrients without DVs, such as phosphatidylserine?

You may make a statement about a nutrient for which there is no established Daily Value (DV) so long as the claim specifies only the amount of the nutrient per serving and does not imply that there is a lot or a little of that nutrient in the product (e.g., "x grams of phosphatidylserine"). You must list the dietary ingredient for which there is no DV and the quantitative amount of that dietary ingredient in the "Supplement Facts" panel in the section below the nutrients with DVs. These dietary ingredients must be identified as having no DVs by the use of the footnote "Daily Value Not Established." [21 CFR 101.13(i) (3) and 21 CFR 101.36(b)(3)]

16. May I make statements using the words "contains" and "provides" for nutrients without DVs?

Yes. You may use such statements if, and only if, you include the specific amount of the nutrient (e.g., "Contains x grams of phosphatidylserine per serving" or "Provides x g of phosphatidylserine"). [21 CFR 101.13(i)(3) and 101.54(c)(1)]

17. Is a statement outside of the "Supplement Facts" panel that describes the percentage of the RDI of a vitamin or mineral in my dietary supplement product a nutrient content claim?

Yes. These claims are considered nutrient content claims and are not exempt from bearing a disclosure statement when required. [21 CFR 101.13(b)(1), (c) and (i)]

18. Am I permitted to make a "low" or "free" claim when my dietary supplement product is specially processed?

Yes. If a similar dietary supplement is normally expected to contain a nutrient and your dietary supplement is specially processed, altered, formulated, or reformulated as to lower the amount of the nutrient in the food, remove the nutrient in the food, or not include the nutrient, then you are permitted to make a "low" or "free" claim as applicable. [21 CFR 101.13(e)(1)]

19. May I make a "low" or "free" claim for my dietary supplement product if it is normally low in or free of a nutrient, and I use an appropriate disclaimer?

No. However, a claim may be used if you indicate that it refers to all products of that type and not merely to that particular brand. [21 CFR 101.13(e)(2)]

20. Are claims such as "100 percent milk free" and "contains no preservatives" subject to the nutrient content claim requirements?

No. Such statements are not nutrient content claims so long as they are not used in a nutrient context that would make them an implied claim under 21 CFR 101.13(b)(2).

The statement "100 percent milk free" is generally a claim to facilitate avoidance of milk products. "Contains no preservatives" is a claim about a substance that does not have a nutritive function. [21 CFR 101.65(b)(1) and (b)(2)]

21. Is a "no sugar" claim subject to the nutrient content claim requirements?

Yes. Sugar content claims are subject to the nutrient content claim requirements. [21 CFR 101.60(c)(1)]

22. When can the nutrient content claim "no added sugar" be used?

To avoid misleading consumers, the term "no added sugar" should be limited to dietary supplements containing no added sugars that are normally expected to contain them. [21 CFR 101.60(c)(2)(iv)]

23. Must a dietary supplement bearing a "sugar free" claim be labeled "low calorie"?

No. A "low calorie" claim may not be made on dietary supplements, except when an equivalent amount of a dietary supplement that the labeled dietary supplement resembles and for which it substitutes (e.g., another protein supplement), normally exceeds the definition for "low calorie." [21 CFR 101.60(c)(1)(iii)(A)]

Antioxidant Claims

24. What is a nutrient content claim for antioxidants?

It is a nutrient content claim that characterizes the level of one or more antioxidant nutrients present in a dietary supplement. [21 CFR 101.54(g)]

25. Must the nutrient or dietary ingredient have an RDI to qualify for an antioxidant claim?

Yes, except as noted in question #28 below. [21 CFR 101.54(g)(1)]

26. Are there any other requirements for a dietary supplement to qualify for an antioxidant nutrient content claim?

Yes. The nutrients that are the subject of the claim must have recognized antioxidant activity. In addition, the level of each nutrient that is the subject of the claim must be sufficient to qualify for either "high" claims in 21 CFR 101.54(b), "good source" claims in 21 CFR 101.54(c), or "more" claims in 21 CFR 101.54(e). For example, for a product to qualify for a "high in antioxidant vitamin C" claim, it must contain 20 percent or more of the RDI for vitamin C. That is, it must meet the level for "high" defined in §101.54(b). For a product to qualify for a "good source of antioxidant vitamin C" claim it must contain 10 to 19 percent of the RDI for vitamin C. [21 CFR 101.54(g)(2) and (g)(3)]

27. What do you mean by "recognized antioxidant activity"?

Recognized antioxidant activity means that there is scientific evidence that, following absorption from the gastrointestinal tract, the substance participates in physiological, biochemical, or cellular processes that inactivate free radicals or prevent free radical-initiated chemical reactions. [21 CFR 101.54(g)(2)]

28. May beta-carotene, which does not have an RDI, be the subject of an antioxidant claim?

Yes. You may make a claim for beta-carotene when the level of vitamin A present as beta-carotene is sufficient to qualify for the claim. For example, you may make the claim "good source of antioxidant beta-carotene" when 10% or more of the RDI for vitamin A is present as beta-carotene. [21 CFR 101.54(g)(3)]

29. Must I list all antioxidants present in my product when making an antioxidant nutrient content claim?

Yes. The names of the nutrients that are the subject of the claim must be included as part of the claim (e.g., "high in antioxidant vitamins C and E"). Alternatively, you may link the term "antioxidant" or "antioxidants" in a nutrient content claim (as in "high in antioxidants") by a symbol (e.g., an asterisk) that refers to the same symbol that appears elsewhere on the same panel followed by the name or names of the nutrients with recognized antioxidant activity. This list should be in letters at least 1/16 of an inch in height or no smaller than half the type size of the largest nutrient content claim, whichever is larger. [21 CFR 101.54(g)(4)]

30. Can I make other claims that describe the antioxidant properties of my product?

Yes. You may craft a statement, subject to section 403(a) of the act (the false and misleading provisions), that describes how a dietary ingredient that does not have an RDI participates in antioxidant processes. Likewise, structure/function claims may be made about antioxidants as long as such claims are not false or misleading and, if appropriate, are made in accordance with section 403(r)(6) of the act (the provisions for statements of nutritional support). For example, a claim that reads "_____, involved in antioxidant processes" would be acceptable as long as it is:

1) truthful and not misleading; and

2) meets the requirements of section 403(r)(6) of the act (see questions #44 through #51 of this chapter).

[62 FR 49868 at 49873 (September 23, 1997)]

High Potency Claims

31. Can I use the term "high potency" to describe an individual nutrient?

Yes. You may use the term "high potency" on your dietary supplement labels to describe individual vitamins or minerals that are present at 100 percent or more of the RDI per reference amount customarily consumed. [21 CFR 101.54(f)(1)(i)]

32. Can the term "high potency" be used for combination products, such as botanicals with vitamins?

Yes. However, when you use the term "high potency" to describe individual vitamins or minerals in your product that contains other nutrients or dietary ingredients, you must clearly identify which vitamin or mineral you are describing by the term "high potency" (e.g., "Botanical 'X' with high potency vitamin E"). [21 CFR 101.54(f)(1)(ii)]

33. How many nutrients must be present at 100% of the DV for a multinutrient product to qualify for the term "high potency?"

You may use the term "high potency" on your multinutrient product to describe the product if it contains 100 percent or more of the RDI for at least two-thirds of the vitamins and minerals that are listed in 21 CFR 101.9(c)(8)(iv), and that are present in the product at 2 percent or more of the RDI (e.g., "High potency multivitamin, multimineral dietary supplement tablets"). [21 CFR 101.54(f)(2)]

Percentage Claims

34. What is a percentage claim?

It is a statement that characterizes the percentage level of a dietary ingredient for which a reference daily intake (RDI) or daily reference value (DRV) has not been established. You may make a percentage claim on your products without a regulation that specifically defines such a statement. These statements must be accompanied by any disclosure statement required under 21 CFR 101.13(h). There are simple percentage claims and comparative percentage claims. [21 CFR 101.13(q)(3)(ii)]

35. What is a simple percentage claim?

It is a statement that characterizes the percentage level of a dietary ingredient for which there is no RDI or DRV (e.g., omega-3 fatty acids, amino acids, phytochemicals). The statement of the actual amount of the dietary ingredient per serving must be declared next to the percentage statement (e.g., "40 percent omega-3 fatty acids, 10 mg per capsule"). [21 CFR 101.13(q)(3)(ii)(A)]

CH 11

36. What is a comparative percentage claim?

It is a statement that compares the percentage level of a dietary ingredient for which there is no RDI or DRV in a product to the amount of the dietary ingredient in a reference food. The reference food must be clearly identified, the amount of that food must be identified, and the information on the actual amount of dietary ingredient in both the dietary supplement and reference food must be declared (e.g., "twice the omega-3 fatty acids per capsule (80 mg) as in 100 mg of menhaden oil (40 mg)"). [21 CFR 101.13(q)(3)(ii)(B)]

Health Claims

37. What is a health claim?

A health claim is an explicit or implied characterization of a relationship between a substance and a disease or a health-related condition. This type of claim requires significant scientific agreement and must be authorized by FDA. The claim can be a written statement, a "third party" reference, a symbol, or a vignette. [21 CFR 101.14(a)(1) and (c)]

38. How is a health claim different from a structure/function claim?

A health claim describes the effect a substance has on reducing the risk of or preventing a disease, e.g., "calcium may reduce the risk of osteoporosis." A health claim requires FDA evaluation and authorization prior to its use. A structure/function claim describes the role of a substance intended to maintain the structure or function of the body. Structure/function claims do not require preapproval by FDA. [21 CFR 101.14(a)(1) and (c), and 21 CFR 101.93(f)]

39. What health claims can be used on dietary supplement labels?

Appendix E of this guide contains a list of FDA authorized health claims. An updated list is also maintained on the Internet at: A Food Labeling Guide—Appendix C. In addition to these authorized health claims, there are certain "qualified" health claims permitted by FDA. Qualified health claims are listed in Appendix F of this guide and on the Internet

40. What is a qualified health claim?

A qualified health claim is supported by less scientific evidence than an authorized health claim. FDA requires that qualified claims be accompanied by a disclaimer that explains the level of the scientific evidence supporting the relationship.

Unlike authorized health claims, FDA does not issue regulations for qualified health claims.

U.S. Food and Drug Administration, Guidance for Industry, Interim Procedures for Qualified Health Claims in the Labeling of Conventional Human Food and Human Dietary Supplements July 2003.

41. How can I use a qualified health claim if the FDA did not authorize it?

FDA will permit the use of a qualified health claim provided that 1) FDA has issued a letter stating the conditions under which we will consider exercising enforcement discretion for the specific health claim, 2) the qualified claim is accompanied by an agency-approved disclaimer, and 3) the claim meets all the general requirements for health claims in 21 CFR 101.14, except for the requirement that the evidence for the claim meet the validity standard for authorizing a claim, and the requirement that the claim be made in accordance with an authorizing regulation.

U.S. Food and Drug Administration, Guidance for Industry, Interim Procedures for Qualified Health Claims in the Labeling of Conventional Human Food and Human Dietary Supplements July 2003.

42. What is an agency-approved disclaimer?

An agency-approved disclaimer is a statement that discloses the level of scientific evidence used to substantiate the health claim.

FDA Task Force Final Report: Consumer Health Information for Better Nutrition Initiative, Attachment E - Interim Procedures for Qualified Health Claims in the Labeling of Conventional Human Food and Human Dietary Supplements July 2003.

43. How can I use additional health claims?

To use additional health claims, an individual must submit a health claim petition in accordance with 21 CFR 101.70. A new health claim may be used only after FDA issues either an authorizing regulation or a letter stating enforcement discretion conditions for a qualified health claim. [21 CFR 101.14 and 21 CFR 101.70]

Structure/Function Claims

CH 11

44. What types of structure/functure claims may be made under section 403(r)(6) of the act?

You may make the following types of structure/function claims under section 403(r)(6) of the act:

a. A statement that claims a benefit related to a classical nutrient deficiency disease and that discloses the prevalence of such disease in the U.S.;

b. A statement that describes the role of a nutrient or dietary ingredient intended to affect the structure or function in humans, or characterizes the documented mechanism by which a nutrient or dietary ingredient acts to maintain such structure or function; or

c. A statement that describes the general well-being from consumption of a nutrient or dietary ingredient.

[21 U.S.C. 343(r)(6)]

45. What must I do when making structure/function claims in my products' labeling?

You must (1) have substantiation that such statement is truthful and not misleading; (2) include the disclaimer; and (3) notify FDA no later than 30 days after the first marketing of the product that you are making the statement in accordance with 21 CFR 101.93. [21 CFR 101.93]

46. What text must I use for the disclaimer?

You must use the following text for the disclaimer, as appropriate:

a. singular: "This statement has not been evaluated by the Food and Drug Administration. This product is not intended to diagnose, treat, cure, or prevent any disease;" or

b. plural: "These statements have not been evaluated by the Food and Drug Administration. This product is not intended to diagnose, treat, cure, or prevent any disease."

You may not modify the wording of these disclaimers. [21 CFR 101.93(c)]

47. Where must I place the required disclaimer?

You must place the disclaimer immediately adjacent to the claim with no intervening material, or elsewhere on the same panel or page that bears the statement. In the latter case, the disclaimer must be placed in a box and linked to the statement by a symbol (e.g., an asterisk) placed at the end of each statement that refers to an identical symbol placed adjacent to the disclaimer. [21 CFR 101.93(d)]

48. What type size must I use for the required disclaimer?

You must use boldface type in a type size no smaller than one-sixteenth (1/16) inch for the required disclaimer. [21 CFR 101.93(e)]

49. What are the notification procedures for structure/function claims?

The notification procedures require that you as a manufacturer, packer, or distributor making such a statement must:

a. Notify FDA within 30 days of first marketing a product whose label or labeling bears a statement made under section 403(r)(6) of the act;

b. Submit an original and two copies of the notification to the Office of Nutritional Products, Labeling, and Dietary Supplements (HFS-800), Center for Food Safety and Applied Nutrition, Food and Drug Administration, 5100 Paint Branch Parkway, College Park, MD 20740-3835;

c. The notification must be signed by a person who can certify that the information in the notification is complete and accurate, and that the notifying firm has substantiation that the section 403(r)(6) statement is truthful and not misleading.

[21 CFR 101.93(a)(1) and (a)(3)]

50. What form must be used to notify FDA?

There is no official form to use. You may make the notification by a letter containing the required information in any format that is convenient to you.

51. What information must be included in the notification for structure/function claims?

You must include the following information in your notification:

a. The name and address of the manufacturer, packer, or distributor of the dietary supplement that bears the statement;

b. The text of the statement that you are making;

c. The name of the dietary ingredient or supplement that is the subject of the statement, and

d. The name of the dietary supplement (including its brand name) on whose label, or in whose labeling, the statement appears.

[21 CFR 101.93(a)(2)]

Chapter VII. Premarket Notification of New Dietary Ingredients

1. What is a new dietary ingredient?

A new dietary ingredient is a dietary ingredient that was not marketed in the United States before October 15, 1994, and does not include any dietary ingredient which was marketed in the United States before October 15, 1994. [21 U.S.C. 350b(c)]

2. Is premarket notification required for new dietary ingredients?

Yes. The manufacturer or distributor of a new dietary ingredient or of a dietary supplement that contains a new dietary ingredient must submit a notification to FDA at least 75 days before introducing or delivering for introduction into interstate commerce a dietary supplement that contains the new dietary ingredient. [21 U.S.C. 305b(a)]

3. Are there regulations about premarket notification for new dietary ingredients?

Yes. FDA has issued regulations on premarket notification for new dietary ingredients in 21 CFR 190.6. [21 CFR 190.6]

4. Where do I submit my new dietary ingredient premarket notification?

You must send the premarket notification to the Office of Nutritional Products, Labeling, and Dietary Supplements (HFS-800), Center for Food Safety and Applied Nutrition, Food and Drug Administration, 5100 Paint Branch Parkway, College Park, MD 20740-3835. You must submit the original and two copies of the document. [21 CFR 190.6(a)]

5. What information must I include in my premarket notification for a new dietary ingredient?

You must submit the following information:

- The name and complete address of the manufacturer or distributor of a dietary supplement that contains the new dietary ingredient, or of the new dietary ingredient;

- The name of the new dietary ingredient that is the subject of the premarket notification, including the Latin binomial name (including the author) of any herb or other botanical;

- A description of the dietary supplement or dietary supplements that will contain the new dietary ingredient including:

  i. the level of the new dietary ingredient in the dietary supplement; and

  ii. the conditions of use recommended or suggested in the labeling of the dietary supplement, or if no conditions of use are recommended or suggested in the labeling of the dietary supplement, the ordinary conditions of use of the supplement;

- The history of use or other evidence of safety establishing that the dietary ingredient, when used under the conditions recommended or suggested in the labeling of the dietary supplement, will reasonably be expected to be safe, including any citation to published articles or other evidence that is the basis on which you have concluded that the new dietary supplement will reasonably be expected to be safe. You must submit reprints or photostatic copies of published information that you reference in support of the notification material. You must submit an accurate and complete English translation of any material you submit in a foreign language; and

- Your signature, or that of a person you designate.

[21 CFR 190.6(b)]

6. What does FDA do with my premarket notification for a new dietary ingredient?

FDA will acknowledge its receipt of a notification made under section 413 of the act and will notify you of the date of receipt of such a notification. The date that the agency receives the notification is the filing date for the notification. For 75 days after the filing date, you must not introduce, or deliver for introduction, into interstate commerce any dietary supplement that contains the new dietary ingredient. [21 CFR 190.6(c)]

7. What happens if I submit additional information?

If you provide additional information, including responses you make to inquiries from the agency, in support of your new dietary ingredient notification, the agency will review the information to determine whether it is substantive. If the agency determines that the new submission is a substantive amendment, the agency will designate the date of its receipt by FDA as the new filing date. FDA will acknowledge receipt of the additional information and, when applicable, will notify you of the new filing date, which restarts the 75-day period. [21 CFR 190.6(d)]

8. Will FDA maintain the confidentiality of my premarket notification for a new dietary ingredient?

FDA will not disclose the existence of, or the information contained in, a new dietary ingredient notification for 90 days after the filing date of the notification. After the 90th day, FDA will place all information in the notification on public display, except for any information that is trade secret or otherwise confidential commercial information. [21 CFR 190.6(e)]

9. Is no response from FDA to a new dietary ingredient premarket notification an indication that the FDA finds that the product is safe and not adulterated?

No. Failure of the agency to respond to your notification does not constitute a finding by the agency that the new dietary ingredient or the dietary supplement that contains the new dietary ingredient is safe or is not adulterated under section 402 of the act (21 U.S.C. 342). [21 CFR 190.6(f)]

Chapter VIII. Other Labeling Information

1. Are there special labeling requirements for iron-containing dietary supplements?

Yes. You must label any dietary supplement in solid oral dosage form (e.g., tablets or capsules) that contains iron or iron salts for use as an iron source with a specific warning statement. [21 CFR 101.17(e)]

2. What is the text of the warning statement?

The text of the warning statement is as follows:

WARNING: Accidental overdose of iron-containing products is a leading cause of fatal poisoning in children under 6. Keep this product out of reach of children. In case of accidental overdose, call a doctor or poison control center immediately. [21 CFR 101.17(e)(1)]

3. May I deviate from the specified text of the warning statement?

No. You may not make deviations from the specified test. [21 CFR 101.17(e)(1)]

4. Where must I locate the warning statement?

You must place the warning statement prominently and conspicuously on the information

CH
11

panel of the product's immediate container. You must set the warning statement off in a box using hairlines. You must also place it on any labeling that contains warnings. If the immediate container has an outer package, you must also place the warning statement on the outer package. [21 CFR 101.17(e)(2) through(5)]

5. Are there packaging requirements for iron-containing dietary supplements?

No. FDA revoked its regulations on "Packaging of iron-containing dietary supplements" (21 CFR 111.5) on October 17, 2003, in response to a U.S. federal appeals court decision that FDA lacked the authority to require unit-dose packaging of dietary supplements for the purpose of poison prevention. [68 Federal Register 59714; October 17, 2003]

6. Is there a limit on the folic acid content in dietary supplements?

No. FDA does not specify any limit on the folic acid content that may be contained in dietary supplements.

7. Who regulates whether I can make a claim indicating that my product is organic?

Organic claims are regulated by the U.S. Department of Agriculture under the National Organic Program. Their website is www.usda.gov.

Appendixes

Appendix A. FDA District Offices[3]

Appendix B. Daily Values For Adults And Children 4 Or More Years Of Age

These values can be found in Reference Values for Nutrition Labeling of the Food Labeling Guide. Note that the nutrients in the table are listed in the order in which they are required to appear on the labels of conventional foods in accordance with 21 CFR 101.9(c). The order for the labels of dietary supplements (i.e. "Supplement Facts") is given in 21 CFR 101.36(b)(2)(i)(B):

The names of dietary ingredients that are declared under paragraph (b)(2)(i) of this section shall be presented in a column aligned on the left side of the nutrition label in the order and manner of indentation specified in Sec. 101.9(c), except that calcium and iron shall follow pantothenic acid, and sodium and potassium shall follow chloride. This results in the following order for vitamins and minerals: Vitamin A, vitamin C, vitamin D, vitamin E, vitamin K, thiamin, riboflavin, niacin, vitamin B6, folate, vitamin B12, biotin, pantothenic acid, calcium, iron, phosphorus, iodine, magnesium, zinc, selenium, copper, manganese, chromium, molybdenum, chloride, sodium, and potassium.

---

3   No text was available under Appendix A at the time of the publishing of this edition. Contact information is available on the FDA website for the Office of Global Regulatory Operations and Policy (OGR) at https://www.fda.gov/aboutfda/centersoffices/officeofglobalregulatoryoperationsandpolicy/ora/contactora/default.htm

Percent DVs must be based on these values and not on Dietary Reference Intakes (DRIs) established by the National Academy of Sciences.

Appendix C. Daily Values for Infants, Children Less Than 4 Years of Age, and Pregnant and Lactating Women

These values have not been codified, but have been published in the Federal Register to provide guidance to manufacturers for the nutrients listed (58 FR 2206 at 2213; January 6, 1993). The abbreviation "IU" is used for International Units, "mg" for milligrams, and "mcg" for micrograms. The abbreviation "μg" may also be used for micrograms. Also, the agency has modified the units of measure for four nutrients. Calcium and phosphorus values are expressed in mg and biotin and folate values in mcg (60 FR 67164 at 67174).

Vitamin or Mineral	Infants	Less than 4 Years	Pregnant and Lactating Women	Units of Measure
Vitamin A	1,500	2,500	8,000	IU
Vitamin C	35	40	60	mg
Calcium	600	800	1,300	mg
Iron	15	10	18	mg
Vitamin D	400	400	400	IU
Vitamin E	5	10	30	IU
Thiamin	0.5	0.7	1.7	mg
Riboflavin	0.6	0.8	2.0	mg
Niacin	8	9	20	mg
Vitamin B6	0.4	0.7	2.5	mg
Folate	100	200	800	mcg
Vitamin B12	2	3	8	mcg
Biotin	50	150	300	mcg
Pantothenic acid	3	5	10	mg
Phosphorus	500	800	1,300	mg
Iodine	45	70	150	mcg
Magnesium	70	200	450	mg
Zinc	5	8	15	mg
Copper	0.6	1.0	2.0	mg

CH
11

Appendix D. Nutrient Content Claims

Information on nutrient content claims is located in the Food Labeling Guide Appendix A - Definitions of Nutrient Content Claims and Appendix B - Relative (or Comparative) Claims. Note that this information is for foods in general, e.g. the information regarding the use of nutrient content claims to describe meals is not applicable to dietary supplements. Also 21 CFR 101.60(a)(4) provides that "calorie free" and "low calorie" claims can be made for a dietary supplement if it is a substitute for a similar product that has more than 40 calories per serving.

Appendix E. Authorized Health Claims

Information on Authorized Health Claims is located in the Food Labeling Guide Appendix C - Health Claims and on the FDA Modernization Act of 1997 (FDAMA) web page. You can find complete information on the use of these claims in the regulations cited and in the general requirements for health claims in 21 CFR 101.14.

Appendix F. Qualified Health Claims[4]

---

4   For information on Qualified Health Claims, refer to the Chaper entitled Claims. Addtitional information is available on the FDA website at https://www.fda.gov/Food/LabelingNutrition/ucm073992.htm

Index for the Dietary Supplement Labeling Guide

CH 11

Guidance for Industry[1]
Contains Nonbinding Recommendations
January 4, 1999

Statement of Identity, Nutrition Labeling and Ingredient Labeling of Dietary Supplements; Small Entity Compliance Guide[2]

On October 25, 1994, the President signed the Dietary Supplement Health and Education Act (DSHEA). This law defines dietary supplements and requires that dietary supplements be clearly identified. Also, the law requires that nutrition information followed by ingredient information be stated on the labels of dietary supplements. The nutrition information is to list the dietary ingredients present in a supplement and to state the amounts of these ingredients. Additionally, when a supplement contains any material from a plant, the label must identify any part of a plant used.

Previously, only nutrients that have daily recommendations, such as 1000 mg for calcium, could be listed in the nutrition information. The new law allows dietary ingredients for which recommendations have not been established to be listed as long as the label indicates this fact.

Additionally, the new law allows information on sources to be included in the nutrition information. Previously, this information was given in the ingredient list. For example, if calcium is from calcium carbonate, the nutrition information can now state "calcium (as calcium carbonate)." When a source is listed in this manner, it does not have to be listed again in the ingredient information.

In response to DSHEA, FDA has amended its regulations with respect to dietary supplements in the FEDERAL REGISTER of September 23, 1997 (62 FR 49826). Manufacturers may comply immediately, but all labels applied to dietary supplements after March 23, 1999 are to be in compliance with these regulations.

To help consumers identify dietary supplements, the new regulations require that dietary supplement products have the term "supplement" in their name, e.g. vitamin C supplement. Additionally, to highlight the nature of these products, the nutrition information is titled "Supplement Facts."

As provided by DSHEA, the labels of dietary supplements are to list the names and amounts per serving of dietary ingredients. A serving of a dietary supplement is the amount recommended in one eating occasion. This information is stated at the top of the nutrition information following the words "Serving Size." Similar to the labels of conventional foods, FDA is requiring that the nutrients most important to the public health be listed. Other vitamins and minerals may be

CH
11

---

[1]   This guidance has been prepared by the Office of Food Labeling in the Center for Food Safety and Applied Nutrition (CFSAN) at the Food and Drug Administration.

[2]   This guidance is available on the FDA website at https://www.fda.gov/food/guidanceregulation/ guidancedocumentsregulatoryinformation/ucm073168.htm

declared, but they must be declared when they are added for purposes of supplementation or when a claim is made about them. Dietary ingredients are to be listed in the order specified in the regulation and their amounts may immediately follow the names or be in a separate column. For uniformity, amounts are to be declared using the units of measurement specified in the regulation.

In addition to the names and amounts, FDA is requiring that the "% Daily Values" be listed. For example, the recommended daily amount for vitamin C is 60 mg. If a food contains this amount, the "% Daily Value" for vitamin C would be 100%. The "% Daily Values" on labels are intended for adults and children 4 or more years of age, unless stated otherwise.

Following the listing of dietary ingredients that have recommendations, other dietary ingredients not having recommendations may be listed as long as this fact is indicated. Accordingly, the names and amounts of these dietary ingredients may be listed in the next section of the nutrition label with an asterisk in the "% Daily Value" column that refers to the footnote "Daily Value not established." The following sample label is presented for the purpose of illustration:

Supplement Facts

Serving Size 1 Capsule

Amount Per Capsule	% Daily Value
Calories 20	
Calories from Fat 20	
Total Fat 2 g	3%*
Saturated Fat 0.5 g	3%*
Polyunsaturated Fat 1 g	†
Monounsaturated Fat 0.5 g	†
Vitamin A 4250 IU	85%
Vitamin D 425 IU	106%
Omega-3 fatty acids 0.5 g	†

* Percent Daily Values are based on a 2,000 calorie diet.
† Daily Value not established.

Ingredients: Cod liver oil, gelatin, water, and glycerin.

Other dietary ingredients are to be listed by their common names. Botanicals are to be listed in accordance with the standard terminology in the book *Herbs of Commerce*[3]. In most cases, this reference also gives the corresponding Latin binomial for each common name. When the Latin name cannot be obtained from this reference, the label must state the Latin name of the botanical.

DSHEA provides that when the dietary ingredients in a supplement are considered to be a proprietary blend, just the total amount of the blend need be stated. In the absence of individual amounts, FDA requires that the dietary ingredients in a proprietary blend are to be listed in order of predominance by weight. These blends also are to be identified by the term "Proprietary Blend" or other appropriately descriptive term or fanciful name.

CH
11

---

3   *Herbs of Commerce* by Michael McGuffin, John Kartesz, Albert Leung and Arthur Tucker is published by the American Herbal Products Association (AHPA) and is the standard for all common and scientific plant names used for products containing herbs.

With respect to dietary supplements that are extracts, labeling requirements were amended in the FEDERAL REGISTER of June 5, 1998. For liquid extracts, the quantity may be listed by weight or by volume, the listing of starting material to the final volume of solvent is optional, and solvents present may be listed either in the nutrition label or in the ingredient statement. For dry extracts, FDA does not require identification of the solvent used to produce the extract.

FDA is requiring that the nutrition information be presented in a certain format that is similar to the presentation of nutrition information on all foods. Some of the major features of the format include use of the largest type size for the title, a hairline box around the nutrition information, bars that separate parts of the nutrition label, lines that separate the listing of dietary ingredients, a single easy-to-read type style, all black or one color type on a white or other neutral contrasting background (whenever practical), upper and lower case letters except on very small packages, at least one point leading, and letters that do not touch.

With respect to the type size of the information presented in the nutrition label, the minimum size required depends on the total surface area available for labeling. Large packages (those having over 40 square inches) are to have a minimum type size of 8 point, except that no smaller than 6 point may be used for column headings and footnotes. Small packages (those having less than 12 square inches) are to have a minimum type size no smaller than 4.5 point. Intermediate-sized packages (from 12 to 40 square inches) are to have a minimum of 6 point, except that a minimum of 4.5 point may be used on packages that have less than 20 square inches and more than 8 dietary ingredients to be listed and on packages that have 20 to 40 square inches and more than 16 dietary ingredients.

FDA has determined that the compliance requirements in §101.9(g) for conventional foods are generally applicable to dietary supplements. It should be noted that supplements should contain at least the amounts of dietary ingredients that are declared, except that for a dietary ingredient that is naturally-occurring, a label is not considered misbranded when an FDA analysis finds 80% of the amount declared on the label. Reasonable excesses of most dietary ingredients are acceptable within current good manufacturing practice, except that no more than a 20% excess is allowed for calories, sugars, total fat, saturated fat, cholesterol, or sodium.

FDA has three types of exemptions from nutrition labeling that are available for food products whose labels do not make nutrient content or health claims. Dietary supplement products that qualify for these exemptions do not have to have a "Supplement Facts" panel. One type of exemption is for products that are sold by small businesses that meet the criteria in §101.9(j)(1) (under $50,000 worth of food sales or under $500,000 worth of total sales to consumers). Another exemption is for products that are "low-volume" as defined in §101.9(j)(18). The last exemption applies to products shipped in bulk that are not distributed to consumers in such form as described in §101.9(j)(9).

FDA also has special labeling provisions for food products that are applicable to dietary supplements. This final rule states in §101.36(i) that dietary supplements are subject to the special provisions for foods for infants and children, foods in small and intermediate-sized packages, foods in multiunit containers, and foods sold in bulk products in §101.9(j). Firms in need of other special allowances may write to the FDA for permission.

Guidance for Industry[1]
Contains Nonbinding Recommendations
July 18, 2008

Nutrient Content Claims Definition for "High Potency" and Definition for "Antioxidant" for Use in Nutrient Content Claims for Dietary Supplements and Conventional Foods; Small Entity Compliance Guide[2]

I. Introduction

On September 23, 1997, FDA published in the Federal Register a final rule amended regulations concerning certain nutrient content claims. The amended regulations defined the term "High potency" as a nutrient content claim; defined nutrient content claims using the term "antioxidant" (e.g., "good source of antioxidants," "high in antioxidants," "more antioxidants"); and corrected an omission pertaining to the use of "sugar free" claims on dietary supplements (62 FR 49868). FDA took these actions to provide for the use of additional nutrient content claims on labels or in labeling in accordance with provisions of the Nutrition Labeling and Education Act of 1990. The final rule is effective on March 23, 1999. FDA has prepared this Small Entity Compliance Guide in accordance with section 212 of the Small Business Regulatory Enforcement Fairness Act (Public Law 104-121). This guidance document restates in plain language the legal requirements set forth in 21 CFR 101.54(f) and (g) and 21 CFR 101.60(c)(1)(iii)(A) concerning dietary supplement use of certain nutrient content claims. This regulation is binding and has the full force and effect of law.

FDA's guidance documents, including this guidance, do not establish legally enforceable responsibilities. Instead, guidances describe the Agency's current thinking on a topic and should be viewed only as recommendations, unless specific regulatory or statutory requirements are cited. The use of the word should in Agency guidances means that something is suggested or recommended, but not required.

II. Questions and Answers

1. High Potency Claims

1) What is the definition of "high potency?"

The regulation states that the term "high potency" may be used in a claim on the label or in labeling to describe individual vitamins or minerals that are present at

CH
11

---

[1]   This guidance has been prepared by the Division of Dietary Supplement Programs in the Center for Food Safety and Applied Nutrition at the U.S. Food and Drug Administration.

[2]   This guidance is available on the FDA website at https://www.fda.gov/Food/GuidanceRegulation/GuidanceDocumentsRegulatoryInformation/ucm063064.htm

100 percent or more of the Reference Daily Intakes (RDI) per reference amount customarily consumed (21 CFR 101.54(f)(1)(i)). This means a supplement may be labeled as "high potency" for each nutrient(s) that is present at 100% of the RDI per serving.

2) How should the label or labeling describe the nutrients that are the subject of the high potency claim?

When the term "high potency" is used to describe individual vitamins or minerals in a product that contains other nutrients, then the label or labeling must clearly identify which specific vitamins or minerals are being described as "high potency." For example, "Botanical X with high potency vitamin E." (21 CFR 101.54(f)(1)(ii))

3) Can I name an entire product "high potency" when not all ingredients are present at 100% or greater?

The term "high potency" may be used on the label or in labeling of a multi-ingredient product to describe the product (as opposed to describing the level of individual ingredients) if the product contains 100 percent or more of the RDI for at least two-thirds of the vitamins and minerals that are listed in 21 CFR 101.9(c)(8)(iv) and that are present in the product at 2 percent or more of the RDI. For example, "High potency multivitamin, multimineral dietary supplement tablets." (21 CFR 101.54(f)(2))

4) Do any other requirements apply to the use of the term "High potency" in foods?

Yes. If the nutrient that is the subject of a high potency claims is added to a food that is not a dietary supplement, then that fortification must be in accordance with the policy on food fortification in 21 CFR 104.20 (21 CFR 101.54(f)(3)).

2. Antioxidant nutrient content claims

1) Is an antioxidant claim a nutrient content claim?

Yes. A claim that describes the level of antioxidant nutrients present in a food is a nutrient content claim and may be used on the label or in the labeling of a food when the conditions of use in the regulation are met (21 CFR 101.54(g)).

2) Can I make an antioxidant nutrient content claim for any ingredient in a food?

No. An antioxidant nutrient content claim can only be made for nutrients for which there is an RDI established in 21 CFR 101.9 (21 CFR 101.54(g)(1)).

3) Does the claim apply to all nutrients listed in 21 CFR 101.9?

No. The nutrient that is the subject of the claim must have recognized antioxidant activity. That is, there must be scientific evidence that after it is eaten and absorbed from the gastrointestinal tract, the substance participates in physiological, biochemical, or cellular processes that inactivate free radicals or prevent free radical-initiated chemical reactions (21 CFR 101.54(g)(2)).

CH 11

4) How much of the nutrient must be present in each serving in order to use the antioxidant nutrient content claim?

The antioxidant nutrient must meet the requirements for nutrient content claims in 21 CFR 101.54(b), (c), or (e) for "High" claims, "Good source" claims, and "More" claims, respectively. For example, to use a "high" claim, the food would have to contain 20% or more of the Daily Reference Value (DRV) or RDI per serving. For a "good source" claim, the food would have to contain between 10-19% of the DRV or RDI per serving (21 CFR 101.54(g)(3)).

5) What special requirements apply to an antioxidant nutrient content claim for beta-carotene?

Beta-carotene may be the subject of an antioxidant claim when the level of vitamin A present as beta-carotene in the food using the claim is sufficient to qualify for the claim. For example, if the claim is "good source of antioxidant beta-carotene," then at least 10% of the RDI for vitamin A must be present as beta-carotene per serving (21 CFR 101.54(g)(3)).

6) Does the label claim have to include the name of the nutrient that is an antioxidant, or can the claim simply say "antioxidants?"

The names of the nutrients that are the antioxidants must appear in the claim. For example, "high in antioxidant vitamins C and E."

Alternatively, when used as part of a nutrient content claim, the term "antioxidant" or "antioxidants" (such as "high in antioxidants"), may be linked by a symbol (such as an asterisk) that refers to the same symbol that appears elsewhere on the same panel of a product label followed by the name or names of the nutrients with the recognized antioxidant activity. If this is done, the list of nutrients must appear in letters of a type size height no smaller than the larger of one half of the type size of the largest nutrient content claim or 1/16 inch (21 CFR 101.54(g)(4)).

CH
11

3. Sugar-free claims

1) Can dietary supplements include claims on their label such as "sugar free," "free of sugar," "no sugar," "zero sugar," "without sugar," "sugarless," "trivial source of sugar," negligible source of sugar," or "dietarily insignificant source of sugar"?

Yes. A dietary supplement may include claims in labeling such as "sugar free," "no sugar," or other claims described in 21 CFR 101.60(c) provided it meets all of the eligibility criteria set forth in the regulation (21 CFR 101.60(c)(1)(i)-(iii)). Among other requirements, a food must be labeled as "low calorie" or "reduced calorie" or bear a relative claim of special dietary usefulness. However, a dietary supplement that is prohibited from bearing a "low calorie" or "reduced calorie" claim by 21 CFR 101.13(b)(5) and 101.60(a)(4) can still use a sugar-free claim provided it meets the "low calorie" requirement in 21 CFR 101.60(b)(2) (21 CFR 101.60(c)(1)(iii)).

Guidance for Industry[1]
October 17, 2003

Iron-Containing Supplements and Drugs: Label Warning Statements; Small Entity Compliance Guide[2]

Summary

The Food and Drug Administration has prepared this Small Entity Compliance Guide in accordance with section 212 of the Small Business Regulatory Enforcement Fairness Act (Public Law 104-121). This guidance document restates in plain language the legal requirements set forth in sections 101.17(e) and 310.518(a) of Title 21 of the Code of Federal Regulations (21 CFR 101.17(e) and 310.518(a)) concerning label warning statements for iron-containing dietary supplement and drug products in solid oral dosage form. This small entity compliance guide (SECG) is intended to help small entities comply with the regulations that require label warning statements for iron-containing dietary supplement and drug products.

In the Federal Register of January 15, 1997 (62 FR 2218), FDA issued a final rule (1997 final rule) to require (1) label warning statements on iron-containing products taken in solid oral dosage form to supplement the dietary intake of iron or to provide iron for therapeutic purposes, and (2) unit-dose packaging for iron-containing dietary supplement and drug products that contain 30 milligrams (mg) or more of iron per dosage unit. This final rule became effective July 15, 1997. In the Federal Register of December 12, 1997 (62 FR 65432), FDA announced the availability of a small entity compliance guide entitled "Iron-Containing Supplements and Drugs: Label Warning Statements and Unit-Dose Packaging Requirements; Small Entity Compliance Guide" (1997 SECG). The 1997 SECG was prepared in accordance with section 212 of the Small Business Regulatory Enforcement Act (P.L. 104-121).

In the Federal Register of October 17, 2003 (68 FR 59714), FDA withdrew those parts of the 1997 final rule that established regulations requiring unit-dose packaging for iron-containing dietary supplement and drug products that contain 30 milligrams (mg) or more of iron per dosage unit. FDA withdrew the regulations in response to Nutritional Health Alliance v. FDA (318 F.3d 92 (2d Cir. 2003)), in which the United States Court of Appeals for the Second Circuit invalidated the unit-dose packaging regulations based upon its conclusions that the Federal Food, Drug, and Cosmetic Act (the Act) does not provide the FDA with authority to regulate the packaging of iron-containing dietary supplement and drug products for poison prevention purposes. The Court's ruling affects only the unit-dose packaging requirements of the 1997 final rule, and not the label warning statement requirements. On remand, the United States District Court for the Eastern District of

---

1   This guidance has been prepared by the Division of Dietary Supplement Programs in the Center for Food Safety and Applied Nutrition (CFSAN) in cooperation with the Center for Drug Evaluation and Research at the U.S. Food and Drug Administration.
2   This guidance is available on the FDA website at https://www.fda.gov/Food/GuidanceRegulation/GuidanceDocumentsRegulatoryInformation/ucm073014.htm

New York entered final judgment in accordance with the Court's decision, declaring the unit-dose packaging regulations invalid and without legal force or effect (Nutritional Health Alliance v. FDA, No. 97-CV-5042 (E.D.N.Y. filed May 29, 2003)). As a result, the 1997 SECG has been revised in accordance with the Court's ruling and FDA's withdrawal of the unit-dose packaging regulations.

FDA's guidance documents, including this guidance, do not establish legally enforceable responsibilities. Instead, guidances describe the Agency's current thinking on a topic and should be viewed only as recommendations, unless specific regulatory or statutory requirements are cited. The use of the word *should* in Agency guidances means that something is suggested or recommended, but not required.

Requirements

1. Where can I find the regulations requiring label warning statements for iron-containing dietary supplements and drugs?

The regulation requiring a warning statement on the labeling of dietary supplements in solid oral dosage form can be found in 21 CFR 101.17(e). The regulation requiring a warning statement on the labeling of drugs in solid oral dosage form can be found in 21 CFR 310.518(a). You can find these regulations through links in FDA's web site, located at www.fda.gov.

2. What types of dietary supplements and drugs are covered by the regulations?

The regulations apply to all iron-containing dietary supplements and drugs in solid oral dosage form (e.g., tablets, capsules, or caplets), except iron-containing inert tablets supplied in monthly packages of contraceptives. The regulations do not apply to iron-containing products in liquid or powder form.

3. What is the language that must be used in the label warning statement?

The regulations require the following warning statement on the labeling of iron-containing dietary supplements and drugs in solid oral dosage form:

WARNING: Accidental overdose of iron-containing products is a leading cause of fatal poisoning in children under 6. Keep this product out of reach of children. In case of accidental overdose, call a doctor or poison control center immediately.

4. May I use a different warning statement?

No. The regulations do not provide for the use of a warning statement different from the one contained in the regulations.

5. Where must the warning statement appear on the label?

For products that are not packaged in unit-dose packaging (e.g., for tablets packaged in a bottle), the regulations require that the warning statement appear prominently and

CH
11

conspicuously on the information panel of the immediate container label (i.e., on the label of the bottle that holds the tablets).

6. If my product is packaged in unit-dose packaging, where must the warning statement appear on the label?

For products that are packaged in unit-dose packaging (e.g., "blister pack," pouch, or other nonreusable container), the regulations require that the warning statement must appear prominently and conspicuously on the unit-dose packaging itself if the unit-dose packaging bears any printed material. The regulations also require that when the warning statement is placed on unit-dose packaging, it must appear in a way that maximizes the likelihood that it can be read until all the individual dosage units are used. For example, multiple copies of the warning statement may be printed on the unit-dose packaging to increase the chances that at least one complete warning statement will remain intact until all of the individual units are used.

7. If the immediate container or unit-dose packaging is placed inside of another package for retail sale, must the warning statement also appear on the retail packaging?

Yes. In instances when the immediate container (e.g., a bottle or unit-dose packaging) of iron-containing dietary supplements or drugs is placed within another package (e.g., a separate box) for retail sale, the regulations require that the warning statement must appear prominently and conspicuously on the information panel of the retail packaging, in addition to the immediate container label.

8. Is the warning statement required to appear on any other labeling for these iron-containing products?

Yes. The regulations require that the warning statement must appear on any labeling (e.g., package inserts) that contains other product warnings.

9. Are there any special format requirements for the warning statement?

Yes. The regulations require that the warning statement be set off in a printed boxed area.

Federal Register - 68 FR 59714 October 17, 2003: Iron-Containing Supplements and Drugs; Label Warning Statements and Unit-Dose Packaging Requirements; Removal of Regulations for Unit-Dose Packaging Requirements for Dietary Supplements and Drugs

This document supercedes Iron-containing Supplements and Drugs: Label Warning and Unit Dose Packaging Small Entity Compliance Guide (November 1997)

Chapter 12

Liquid Dietary Supplements
Guidance

Contains Nonbinding Recommendations
January 2014

Guidance for Industry:
Distinguishing Liquid Dietary Supplements from Beverages[1]

I. Introduction

We are issuing this guidance to help dietary supplement and beverage manufacturers and distributors determine whether a product in liquid form is properly classified as a dietary supplement or as a beverage. This guidance describes the factors that distinguish liquid products that are dietary supplements from those that are conventional foods. Further, this guidance reminds manufacturers and distributors of dietary supplements and beverages about the requirements of the Federal Food, Drug, and Cosmetic Act (the FD&C Act) regarding their respective ingredients and labeling.

FDA's guidance documents, including this guidance, do not establish legally enforceable responsibilities. Instead, guidance describes the Agency's current thinking on a topic and should be viewed only as recommendations, unless specific regulatory or statutory requirements are cited. The use of the word "should" in Agency guidance means that something is suggested or recommended, but not required.

In this guidance, "we" refers to FDA and "you" refers to manufacturers and distributors of dietary supplements and beverages.

II. Background

We have observed an increase in the marketing of liquid products with a wide array of ingredients and intended uses. Some of these products are marketed as dietary supplements, and others as conventional foods. Some products may be misbranded because their labeling or

---

1   This guidance has been prepared by the Office of Nutrition, Labeling, and Dietary Supplements and the Office of Food Additive Safety in the Center for Food Safety and Applied Nutrition at the U.S. Food and Drug Administration.This guidance is available on the FDA website at https://www.fda.gov/Food/GuidanceRegulation/ GuidanceDocumentsRegulatoryInformation/ucm381189.htm

other representations made about them are inconsistent with the product category under which they are being marketed. In addition, products may be excluded from the dietary supplement category because of representations that they are for use as conventional foods. This guidance is intended to describe the factors to consider when determining whether a liquid product should be marketed as a dietary supplement or a conventional food.

III. Discussion

A. Beverages Are Conventional Foods That May Not Be Marketed as Dietary Supplements

Under section 201(ff)(2)(B) of the FD&C Act (21 U.S.C. 321(ff)(2)(B)), the term "dietary supplement" means a product that, among other requirements, "is not represented for use as a conventional food or as a sole item of a meal or the diet." Beverages are conventional foods under the FD&C Act. Even when the label of a product characterizes it as a dietary supplement, the product may not in fact be a dietary supplement. Products in liquid form can be represented as conventional foods as a result of factors such as their product or brand name, packaging, serving size and total recommended daily intake (i.e., the volume in which they are intended to be consumed), composition, recommendations and directions for use, statements or graphic representations in labeling or advertising, and other marketing practices.

B. Factors that Distinguish Beverages from Liquid Dietary Supplements

The most obvious representations about a product's use are claims made for the product in its labeling and advertising. However, a product's name, packaging, serving size, recommended daily intake and other recommended conditions of use, and composition, as well as marketing practices and representations about the product outside its labeling and advertising, can also be important determinants of whether the product is represented as a conventional food (and, thus, may not be marketed as a dietary supplement). Below, we discuss some of these factors in more detail. Although in some circumstances a single factor may be determinative of whether the product is represented as a conventional food (see, e.g., the discussion below regarding product name), in most circumstances a combination of factors would determine whether the product is represented as a conventional food.

- **Labeling and advertising**. FDA considers statements and graphics on product labels, labeling, and advertising, including Web sites and social media, when the agency evaluates the intended use of the product and how it is represented. For example, a product that bears a Supplement Facts panel may still be a conventional food if it also bears statements that the product is intended to "refresh" or "rehydrate" because such statements represent the product for use as a beverage, i.e., a conventional food. Graphics (e.g., symbols, vignettes, pictorial serving suggestions) can also represent a product as a conventional food. For example, an ad or label with a picture of a liquid product being poured onto a green salad would represent the product as a salad dressing.

- **Product name.** Product or brand names that use conventional food terms such as "beverage," "drink," "water," or "soda" represent the product as a conventional food.

Examples of other terms that generally would be considered to represent a liquid product as a conventional food when used in the product's name are beverage names such as "orange juice," "apple cider," "bottled water," "iced tea," and "coffee." For example, calling a product "bottled water" represents the product as a conventional food because "bottled water" is a term identifying a specific category of conventional food that is defined in a food standard regulation (see 21 Code of Federal Regulations (CFR) 165.100). In some instances, the mere use of such a term in a product name or brand name may be sufficient to establish that a product is represented for use as a conventional food. However, in other situations (e.g., where the term is not associated exclusively with conventional foods), the use of such a term in the product name likely would be evaluated in the broader context of other factors. This would be the case, for example, for products described as teas.

- **Product packaging.** Packaging is used to market a product as well as to contain, hold, and preserve the product. Packaging can convey messages about how the product is to be used. Packaging characteristics that should be considered include the size, shape, color, and design of the container or other packaging, the volume of liquid it holds, whether it is reclosable or designed to be consumed in a single serving, and the similarity of the packaging to packaging used for common beverages. For example, packaging a liquid product in a red twelve-ounce pop-top aluminum can bearing a silver stripe with the name "cola supplement" printed in script on the can could be considered an implied representation that the product is a cola-flavored soft drink that is intended to be consumed in a single serving like other canned soft drinks. However, there may be situations where other factors (such as labeled serving size and recommended daily intake, discussed in next bullet) support a determination that the product is not represented as a conventional food, even if its container is similar to a beverage container.

- **Serving size and recommended daily intake.** Based on data from the 2005-2006 National Health and Nutrition Examination Survey on daily intake of drinking water and other beverages in the United States, we estimate the average total daily drinking fluid intake per person to be about 1.2 liters (1200 ml) (Ref. 1). Liquid products that suggest through their labeled serving size and/or recommended daily intake (e.g., "Drink up to three 16-ounce bottles per day") that they are intended to be consumed in amounts that provide all or a significant part of the entire daily drinking fluid intake of an average person in the United States are effectively being represented as conventional foods. Even if a product is not expressly represented as an alternative to a beverage, when the practical result of the labeled serving size and/or total recommended daily intake is that the product is used as a beverage or replaces beverages that serve as ordinary sources of drinking fluid, FDA would generally consider the product to be represented for use as a conventional food.

- **Recommendations and directions for use.** Dietary supplements are defined as products that, among other requirements, are intended to supplement the diet. (See section 201(ff)(1) of the FD&C Act [21 U.S.C. 321(ff)(1)].) In contrast, beverages generally are

CH 12

intended, for example, to quench thirst or otherwise provide a source of fluids (e.g., water, soda), provide nutritive value (e.g., milk, orange juice), or provide taste and aroma (e.g., hot cocoa). Recommendations or directions to use a product as a thirst quencher can be considered recommendations or directions to use that product as a beverage, replacing other beverages such as fruit juice, water, or soda, and thus represent the product as a conventional food. In contrast, recommendations or directions to use a liquid product to supplement the diet in a manner consistent with other dietary supplements (e.g., by taking one tablespoon three times a day) could be a factor in determining that the product is not represented as a conventional food, even if the packaging is similar to packaging used for beverages.

- **Marketing practices.** Examples of marketing practices that may represent a product in liquid form as a conventional food include labeling, advertising, or other promotional activities that favorably compare the product to a category of beverages (e.g., sodas), market the product as an accompaniment to a meal, or market the product based on typical beverage criteria like taste, refreshment, and thirst-quenching ability; the use of metatags[2] that result in the product's appearing in the results of an electronic search for sodas, juices, or other beverages; and paying for the product to be displayed in the beverage section of retail stores. However, simply recommending that a liquid product be taken with a meal would not generally be considered to represent the product as a conventional food, as many dietary supplements should be taken with food for best absorption. Moreover, promoting a product as a substitute for a beverage would not always represent the product as a conventional food. For example, a labeling or advertising statement promoting a liquid vitamin C supplement as a quick and easy alternative to drinking orange juice would not represent the product as a conventional food because it would be promoting the supplement as a more convenient source of vitamin C, not as a beverage to quench thirst, provide fluids, or wash down a meal.

- **Composition.** FDA recognizes that there are areas of overlap between the ingredients of some dietary supplements and conventional foods. For example, amino acids, proteins, vitamins, water, and certain plant ingredients are commonly used in both. However, in light of Congress's findings in the Dietary Supplement Health and Education Act of 1994 (DSHEA), which focused on the value of dietary supplements in improving nutrition, promoting long-term health and quality of life, and reducing the risk of chronic diet-related diseases, the agency does not believe that Congress intended the overlap in composition between dietary supplements and conventional foods to be total.[3] Moreover, the dietary supplement provisions of the FD&C Act (added by DSHEA) are premised on the concept of dietary supplements as products that are marketed and consumed for nutrition and health benefits, and specifically authorize supplements to be marketed for those purposes (see section 403(r)(6) of the FD&C Act [21 U.S.C. 343(r)(6)]). Given that some conventional foods are consumed primarily for taste rather than

---

2   A metatag is an HTML tag that contains descriptive information about a Web page. Although the metatag does not appear when the Web page is displayed in a browser, searching for a word that is one of the Web page's metatags will cause that Web page to turn up in the search results (Ref. 2).

3   Dietary Supplement Health and Education Act of 1994, Pub. L. No. 103-417, § 2, 108 Stat. 4325, 4325-26.

for nutrition or health-related purposes, it would strain common sense to interpret DSHEA as authorizing the creation of a dietary supplement whenever any dietary ingredient is added to any conventional food. Such an interpretation would make the dietary supplement and conventional food universes co-extensive, differentiated only by labeling, advertising, and other marketing practices. In addition, if a manufacturer could create a dietary supplement simply by adding a dietary ingredient to any pre-existing conventional food and labeling the resulting product as a supplement, firms could easily evade the requirement that ingredients in conventional foods be generally recognized as safe (GRAS) or approved for their intended use (see section III.D.1, below).

When a product marketed as a dietary supplement consists in significant part of conventional food components unrelated to its claimed nutritional or health benefit as a supplement and the product is essentially a copy of a common beverage with a dietary ingredient added, FDA intends to consider whether the composition, along with other factors, represents the product as a conventional food. Merely adding an ingredient listed as a dietary ingredient in section 201(ff)(1) of the FD&C Act to a product universally recognized as a beverage does not by itself transform that beverage into a dietary supplement. For example, adding a botanical such as ginkgo to kool-aid or non-alcoholic eggnog would not automatically create a product that could be marketed as a "ginkgo supplement."

It should be noted that a dietary ingredient that is lawful for addition to dietary supplements may or may not also be lawful for addition to conventional foods. To be lawful for use in a conventional food, the ingredient must be used in conformity with a food or color additive regulation prescribing the conditions of its use in food, be GRAS for its intended use in food, or qualify for one of the other exceptions to the food additive definition. For example, a firm that makes or distributes a liquid dietary supplement containing yohimbe bark extract should not assume that yohimbe bark extract may be added to a carbonated soft drink. Unless the intended use of yohimbe bark extract in the soft drink meets the GRAS eligibility criteria described in the FD&C Act or another exception to the food additive definition applies, this use of yohimbe bark extract would be unlawful without a food or color additive regulation prescribing safe conditions of use.

- **Other representations about a product.** Other representations about a product include, for example, representations in publicly available documents, such as statements made in filings with government agencies such as the U.S. Securities and Exchange Commission or the U.S. Patent and Trademark Office. For example, a filing describing a product as a type of "bottled water" or "coffee drink" would represent the product as a conventional food. However, an isolated representation of this type generally would not be enough for FDA to conclude that the product is not a dietary supplement. FDA intends to consider all relevant factors in context when determining whether a product is represented as a conventional food.

CH 12

C. Powdered Premix Products and Liquid Concentrates May Be Dietary Supplements

Powdered premix products that are intended to be added to water or other liquids have long been marketed as dietary supplements. If properly labeled as a dietary supplement, a product of this type is unlikely to be confused with beverage mixes or used as a substitute for a beverage mix. Powdered premixes may bear directions recommending that the premix be added to a liquid as a convenient delivery system, for other reasons of convenience or stability (e.g., if the ingredients are not stable in aqueous solutions), or to mask the taste of certain ingredients. We generally do not view such products as beverages when they are labeled as dietary supplements, provided that they are not otherwise represented as being for beverage use or as alternatives to beverages. Likewise, we generally would not view liquid concentrates that are added to water or other liquids as beverages when they are labeled as dietary supplements, provided that they are not otherwise represented for beverage use or as alternatives to beverages. An example of a product represented for beverage use would be chocolate syrup labeled with the statement "Delicious in milk or over ice cream." In addition, a product labeled as a powdered lemonade mix would be considered to be a conventional food because lemonade is a beverage.

D. Regulatory Requirements for Ingredients of Beverages and Liquid Dietary Supplements

It is your responsibility to ensure that any beverage or liquid dietary supplement you market complies with all applicable regulatory requirements for substances added to the product.

1. Substances intentionally added to beverages

Many substances intentionally added to beverages are food additives, which require premarket approval by FDA. (See section 409 of the FD&C Act [21 U.S.C. 348] and 21 CFR Part 171.) A substance is exempt from the definition of a food additive, and thus from pre-market approval, if it is generally recognized as safe by qualified experts under the conditions of its intended use in food (see 21 CFR 170.30), or if it falls under another exception to the food additive definition in section 201(s) of the FD&C Act (21 U.S.C. 321(s)).

The "Ingredients, Packaging & Labeling" Web page on the FDA Web site (Ref. 3) includes links to regulatory requirements and recommendations that apply to substances intentionally added to beverages and other conventional foods. A guidance document entitled "Considerations Regarding Substances Added to Foods, Including Beverages and Dietary Supplements" (Ref. 4) is particularly relevant to beverages containing ingredients that have not previously been used in conventional foods, that are now being added to beverages at levels in excess of their traditional use levels, or that are now being added to new beverages.

2. Dietary ingredients in dietary supplements

Substances that are "dietary ingredients" under section 201(ff)(1) of the FD&C Act (21 U.S.C. 321(ff)(1)) must not adulterate the dietary supplement to which they are added (see section 402 of the FD&C Act [21 U.S.C. 342]). In addition, dietary ingredients that were not marketed in the United States before October 15, 1994, are "new dietary ingredients" subject to the requirements of section 413 of the FD&C Act (21 U.S.C. 350b) and 21 CFR 190.6. Our Web pages entitled "Dietary Supplements" (Ref. 5), "New Dietary Ingredients in Dietary Supplements - Background for Industry" (Ref. 6), and "New Dietary Ingredients Notification Process" (Ref. 7) include links to regulatory requirements and recommendations that apply to new dietary ingredients.

3. Substances (other than dietary ingredients) intentionally added to dietary supplements

Section 201(s) of the FD&C Act (21 U.S.C. 321(s)) exempts dietary ingredients used in dietary supplements from the food additive definition. Although a dietary ingredient used in a dietary supplement must not adulterate the supplement under section 402(f) of the FD&C Act (21 U.S.C. 342(f)), it does not have to be GRAS for its intended use in the supplement. However, other ingredients intended for use in dietary supplements, such as binders, excipients, and fillers, are not exempt from the food additive definition and must meet the same requirements as substances added to conventional foods. In other words, non-dietary ingredients added to a dietary supplement must be used in accordance with a food additive regulation or be GRAS for their intended use (unless they qualify for another exception to the food additive definition). See the discussion in section III.D.1 of this guidance and References 3 and 4.

E. Regulatory Requirements for the Labeling of Beverages and Liquid Dietary Supplements

It is your responsibility to ensure that your dietary supplement or beverage complies with all applicable labeling requirements.

1. General prohibition on false or misleading labeling

All claims, statements, and graphics in the labeling of foods, including beverages and liquid dietary supplements, are subject to section 403(a)(1) of the FD&C Act (21 U.S.C. 343(a)(1)), which provides that a food is misbranded if its labeling is false or misleading. The FD&C Act further provides in section 201(n) (21 U.S.C. 321(n)) that affirmative representations are not the only factor relevant to whether labeling is misleading. In determining whether the labeling of an article is misleading, "there shall be taken into account (among other things) ... the extent to which the labeling fails to reveal facts material in the light of such representations or material with respect to consequences which may result from the use of the article to which the labeling relates under the conditions of use prescribed in the labeling thereof or under such conditions of use as are customary or usual." 21 U.S.C. 321(n).

CH 12

2. Health claims

Beverages and liquid dietary supplements may bear health claims, which characterize the relationship between a substance (food or food component) and a disease or health-related condition (see 21 CFR 101.14(a)(1)). For more information about health claims, including procedures for our review of health claims and examples of authorized health claims, we refer you to the following:

- Sections 403(r)(1)(B), (r)(3), (r)(4), and (r)(5) of the FD&C Act (21 U.S.C. 343(r)(1)(B), (r)(3), (r)(4), (r)(5));
- 21 CFR 101.14;
- 21 CFR 101.70;
- 21 CFR 101.72–101.83; and
- References from FDA's Web site
- "Label Claims. General Information" (Ref. 8)
- "Guidance for Industry: Evidence-Based Review System for the Scientific Evaluation of Health Claims"
- (Ref. 9)
- "Qualified Health Claims" (Ref. 10)
- "FDA Modernization Act (FDAMA) Claims" (Ref. 11)
- "Summary of Qualified Health Claims Subject to Enforcement Discretion" (Ref. 12).

3. Nutrient content claims

Liquid dietary supplements and beverages may bear nutrient content claims, which characterize the level of a nutrient in a food (see 21 CFR 101.13(b)). For more information about nutrient content claims, including procedures for our review of nutrient content claims and examples of authorized nutrient content claims, we refer you to the following:

- Sections 403(r)(1)(A), (r)(2), (r)(4), and (r)(5) of the FD&C Act (21 U.S.C. 343(r)(1)(A), (r)(2), (r)(4), (r)(5));
- 21 CFR 101.13;
- 21 CFR 101.69;
- 21 CFR 101.54–101.67; and
- References from FDA's Web site
  - "Label Claims. General Information" (Ref. 8)
  - "FDA Modernization Act (FDAMA) Claims" (Ref. 11).

4. Structure/function claims for conventional foods

Conventional foods, including beverages, may bear certain kinds of claims about effects on the structure or function of the body (structure/function claims). The FD&C Act defines "drug" to include articles intended to affect the structure or function of the body. This provision contains an exception for foods, which affect the structure and function of the body by virtue of providing nutrition to sustain life and health. See section 201(g)(1)(C) of the FD&C Act (21 U.S.C. 321(g)(1)(C)). "Food" is defined in section

201(f) of the FD&C Act (21 U.S.C. 321(f)) as "(1) articles used for food or drink for man or other animals, (2) chewing gum, and (3) articles used for components of any such article."

Consistent with case law interpreting the "other than food" exception as applying to articles consumed primarily for taste, aroma, or nutritive value, FDA does not intend to regulate conventional foods that bear structure/function claims in their labeling as drugs if the claimed structure/function effect derives from the product's character as a food—its taste, aroma, or nutritive value. See Nutrilab v. Schweiker, 713 F.2d 335 (7th Cir. 1983). However, if a structure/function claim promotes a product for a use other than providing taste, aroma, or nutritive value, such as blocking the absorption of carbohydrates in the gut, the claim may cause the product to be a drug under section 201(g)(1)(C) of the FD&C Act by changing its primary use. In other words, because of the use promoted in the claim, the product may no longer be consumed as a food— primarily for taste, aroma, or nutritive value—but rather as a drug for some other physiological effect. Further, if a labeling claim about the effect of a conventional food on the structure or function of the body also states or implies that the product is useful in treating, mitigating, curing, or diagnosing a disease, the claim causes the product to be a drug under section 201(g)(1)(B) of the FD&C Act (21 U.S.C. 321(g)(1)(B)). The same is true for a disease prevention claim in the labeling of a conventional food, unless the claim is an authorized health claim about reducing the risk of a disease or health-related condition.

As with all claims in food labeling, structure/function claims for conventional foods may not be false or misleading. See section 403(a)(1) of the FD&C Act (21 U.S.C. 343(a)(1)).

5. Structure/function claims and related claims for dietary supplements

Structure/function claims in the labeling of dietary supplements are subject to section 403(r)(6) of the FD&C Act (21 U.S.C. 343(r)(6)) and our regulation in 21 CFR 101.93, as are dietary supplement labeling claims about general well-being and benefits related to a classical nutrient deficiency disease. For more information about these claims for dietary supplements, see Ref. 8.

As with conventional foods, if a labeling claim about the effect of a dietary supplement on the structure or function of the body also states or implies that the product is useful in treating, mitigating, curing, or diagnosing a disease, the claim causes the product to be a drug under section 201(g)(1)(B) of the FD&C Act (21 U.S.C. 321(g)(1)(B)); see also 21 CFR 101.93(g). The same is true for a disease prevention claim in the labeling of a dietary supplement, unless the claim is an authorized health claim about reducing the risk of a disease or health-related condition.

6. General food labeling requirements

Mandatory labeling for beverages and other conventional foods differs in many respects from mandatory labeling for dietary supplements. For example, beverages must show nutrition information in the Nutrition Facts format (see 21 CFR 101.9), but dietary

CH 12

supplements must show nutrition information in the Supplement Facts format (see 21 CFR 101.36). Generally, all ingredients in a beverage must be declared in the ingredient statement by their common and usual names,[4] in descending order of predominance; however, for dietary supplements, only ingredients not listed in Supplement Facts have to be listed in the ingredient statement. In addition, a beverage or other conventional food should not be labeled with the FDA disclaimer that is required on dietary supplement labels that bear structure/function claims or other claims described in section 403(r)(6)(A) of the FD&C Act (21 U.S.C. 343(r)(6)(A)).

FDA's general food labeling requirements, including those that apply to dietary supplements, are in 21 CFR Part 101.

IV. References

We have placed the following references on display in the Division of Dockets Management, Food and Drug Administration, 5630 Fishers Lane, rm. 1061, Rockville, MD 20852. You may see them at that location between 9 a.m. and 4 p.m., Monday through Friday.

1. Memorandum from Jannavi Srinivasan, FDA, Center for Food Safety and Applied Nutrition, Office of Food Additive Safety, to Barbara Schneeman, FDA, Center for Food Safety and Applied Nutrition, Office of Nutrition, Labeling, and Dietary Supplements. Daily Drinking Fluid Intake Estimate (Aug. 31, 2009).

2. "Metatag." Dictionary.com . The American Heritage® Science Dictionary. Houghton Mifflin Company. Available at http://dictionary.reference.com/browse/metatag . Accessed May 31, 2013.

3. FDA. Ingredients, Packaging & Labeling . Available at http://www.fda.gov/Food/IngredientsPackagingLabeling/default.htm

4. FDA. Guidance for Industry: Considerations Regarding Substances Added to Foods, Including Beverages and Dietary Supplements (2014). Available at http://www.fda.gov/Food/GuidanceRegulation/GuidanceDocumentsRegulatoryInformation/default.htm

5. FDA. Dietary Supplements . Available at http://www.fda.gov/Food/DietarySupplements/default.htm

6. FDA. New Dietary Ingredients in Dietary Supplements - Background for Industry . Available at http://www.fda.gov/Food/DietarySupplements/ucm109764.htm

7. FDA. New Dietary Ingredients Notification Process . Available at http://www.fda.gov/Food/DietarySupplements/NewDietaryIngredientsNotificationProcess/default.htm

8. FDA. Label Claims. General Information . Available at http://www.fda.gov/Food/IngredientsPackagingLabeling/LabelingNutrition/ucm2006873.htm

CH
12

---

4   There are a few exceptions for ingredients that are exempt from declaration (e.g., processing aids) or that may be declared collectively (e.g., spices and flavorings). See 21 CFR 101.4(b), 101.22, 101.100(a).

9. FDA. Guidance for Industry: Evidence-Based Review System for the Scientific Evaluation of Health Claims (2009). Available at http://www.fda.gov/Food/GuidanceRegulation/GuidanceDocumentsRegulatoryInformation/LabelingNutrition/ucm073332.htm

10. FDA. Qualified Health Claims . Available at http://www.fda.gov/Food/IngredientsPackagingLabeling/LabelingNutrition/ucm2006877.htm

11. FDA. FDA Modernization Act (FDAMA) Claims . Available at http://www.fda.gov/Food/IngredientsPackagingLabeling/LabelingNutrition/ucm2006874.htm

12. FDA. Summary of Qualified Health Claims Subject to Enforcement Discretion . Available at http://www.fda.gov/Food/IngredientsPackagingLabeling/LabelingNutrition/ucm073992.htm

CH
12

Contains Nonbinding Recommendations
Draft - Not for Implementation
December 2009

Draft Guidance for Industry:
Factors that Distinguish Liquid Dietary Supplements from Beverages, Considerations Regarding Novel Ingredients, and Labeling for Beverages and Other Conventional Foods[1]

I. Introduction

FDA is issuing this guidance to assist dietary supplement and beverage manufacturers and distributors in reaching a determination as to whether a liquid product may be labeled and marketed as a dietary supplement. The guidance describes factors that can be used to identify liquid products that are excluded from being dietary supplements because they are represented as conventional foods. Further, this guidance reminds manufacturers and distributors of beverages and other conventional foods, particularly those that contain novel ingredients, about the requirements of the Federal Food, Drug, and Cosmetic Act (the FFDCA) regarding ingredients and labeling.

FDA's guidance documents, including this guidance, do not establish legally enforceable responsibilities. Instead, guidances describe the Agency's current thinking on a topic and should be viewed only as recommendations, unless specific regulatory or statutory requirements are cited. The use of the word should in Agency guidances means that something is suggested or recommended, but not required.

II. Background

The Food and Drug Administration (FDA) has observed and become concerned about two trends in the marketing of beverages. First, we have seen an increase in the marketing of beverages as dietary supplements, in spite of the fact that the packaging and labeling of many liquid products represent the products as conventional foods. Products that are represented as conventional foods do not meet the statutory definition of a dietary supplement in section 201(ff) of the FFDCA (21 U.S.C. 321(ff)) and must meet the regulatory requirements that apply to conventional foods.

Second, FDA has seen a growth in the marketplace of beverages and other conventional foods that contain novel ingredients, such as added botanical ingredients or their extracts. Some of these ingredients have not previously been used in conventional foods and may be unapproved food additives. In addition, ingredients that have been present in the food supply for many

---

1   This guidance is available on the FDA website at https://www.fda.gov/Food/GuidanceRegulation/GuidanceDocumentsRegulatoryInformation/ucm196903.htm

years are now being added to beverages and other conventional foods at levels in excess of their traditional use levels or in new beverages or other conventional foods. This trend raises questions regarding whether these ingredients are unapproved food additives when used at higher levels or under other new conditions of use. Some foods with novel ingredients also bear claims that misbrand the product or otherwise violate the FFDCA.

III. Discussion

A. Beverages Are Conventional Foods That May Not Be Marketed as Dietary Supplements

Under section 201(ff)(2)(B) of the FFDCA (21 U.S.C. 321(ff)(2)(B)), the term "dietary supplement" means a product that, among other requirements, "is not represented for use as a conventional food or as a sole item of a meal or the diet." Beverages are conventional foods under the FFDCA. Even when the label of a liquid product characterizes it as a dietary supplement, the product may not in fact be a dietary supplement. Liquid products can be represented as conventional foods as a result of factors such as their packaging, the volume in which they are intended to be consumed, their product or brand name, and statements about the product in labeling or advertising. For example, the packaging of liquid products in bottles or cans similar to those in which single or multiple servings of beverages like soda, bottled water, fruit juices, and iced tea are sold, suggests that the liquid product is intended for use as a conventional food.

Based on data from the 2005-2006 National Health and Nutrition Examination Survey on daily intake of drinking water and other beverages in the United States, FDA estimates the average total daily drinking fluid intake[2] per person to be about 1.2 liters (1200 ml) (Ref. 1). Liquid products that suggest through their serving size, packaging, or recommended daily intake that they are intended to be consumed in amounts that provide all or a significant part of the entire daily drinking fluid intake of an average person in the U.S., are represented as beverages. In addition, the name of a product can represent the product as a conventional food. Product or brand names that use conventional food terms such as "beverage," "drink," "water," 'juice," or similar terms represent the product as a conventional food.

In sum, FDA considers a liquid product's name, packaging, serving size, and recommended conditions of use, as well as other representations about the product, to be important determinants of whether the product is represented as a conventional food and may not be marketed as a dietary supplement.

B. Ingredients in Beverages and Other Conventional Foods are Subject to the FFDCA's Requirements for Substances Added to Food

Many ingredients intentionally added to beverages and other conventional foods are food additives. Food additives require pre-market approval based on data demonstrating safety submitted to FDA in a food additive petition. The agency issues food additive regulations specifying the conditions under which an additive has been demonstrated to be safe and, therefore, may be lawfully used.

CH
12

---

2   Foods Analysis and Residue Evaluation Program (FARE), Version 8.50, Consumption Analysis: Distribution and Means Analysis based on NHANES 2005-2006.

A substance is exempt from the definition of a food additive and thus, from pre-market approval, if, among other reasons, it is generally recognized as safe (GRAS) by qualified experts under the conditions of intended use. 21 U.S.C. 321(s). Accordingly, for a particular use of a substance to be GRAS, there must be both evidence of safety (the "technical element" of the GRAS standard) and a basis to conclude that this evidence is generally known and accepted by qualified experts. The technical element of the GRAS standard requires that the information about the substance establish that the intended use of the substance is safe; i.e., that there is a reasonable certainty in the minds of competent scientists that the substance is not harmful under its intended conditions of use. 21 CFR 170.3(i). In addition, the data and information to establish the technical element must be generally available, and there must be a basis to conclude that there is consensus among qualified experts about the safety of the substance for its intended use. See 21 CFR 170.30(a)-(c). Any substance added to a beverage or other conventional food that is an unapproved food additive (e.g., because it is not GRAS for its intended use) causes the food to be adulterated under section 402(a)(2)(C) of the FFDCA (21 U.S.C. 342(a)(2)(C)). Adulterated foods cannot be legally imported or marketed in the United States.

FDA is concerned that some of the novel ingredients that are being added to beverages and other conventional foods may cause the food to be adulterated because these added ingredients are not being used in accordance with an approved food additive regulation and may not be GRAS for their intended use. In addition, some ingredients that have been present in the food supply for many years are now being added to beverages and other conventional foods at levels in excess of their traditional use levels or in new beverages or other conventional foods. This trend raises questions regarding whether these higher levels and other new conditions of use are safe.

C. **Beverages and Other Conventional Foods May Not Carry Unauthorized Labeling Claims and Must Carry the Appropriate Mandatory Labeling**

   Labeling Claims

   * **General prohibition on false or misleading labeling**. All claims and statements in the labeling of a food are subject to section 403(a)(1) of the FFDCA (21 U.S.C. 343(a)(1)), which provides that a food is misbranded if its labeling is false or misleading in any particular. The FFDCA further provides in section 201(n) (21 U.S.C. 321(n)) that affirmative representations are not the only factor relevant to whether labeling is misleading. Rather, in determining whether the labeling of an article is misleading, "there shall be taken into account (among other things) ... the extent to which the labeling fails to reveal facts material in the light of such representations or material with respect to consequences which may result from the use of the article to which the labeling relates under the conditions of use prescribed in the labeling thereof or under such conditions of use as are customary or usual." 21 U.S.C. 321(n).

   * **Health claims**. Health claims characterize the relationship between a substance (food or food component) and a disease or health-related condition. 21 C.F.R. 101.14(a)(1). Health claims are limited to claims about reducing the risk of a disease or health-related

CH 12

condition and do not include claims about treating, mitigating, or curing disease, which are drug claims. See Whitaker v. Thompson, 353 F.3d 947 (D.C. Cir.), cert. denied, 125 S. Ct. 310 (2004)). See FDA's website for more information on health claims http://www. fda.gov/Food/LabelingNutrition/LabelClaims/default.htm.

There are three ways in which FDA exercises its oversight in determining which health claims may be used on a label or in labeling for a food:

(1) FDA reviews health claim petitions and issues regulations authorizing health claims that meet the significant scientific agreement standard set forth in the Nutrition Labeling and Education Act of 1990 (Pub. L. 101-535).

(2) FDA reviews health claim notifications under the Food and Drug Administration Modernization Act of 1997, which amended the FFDCA to establish a notification procedure that streamlines the authorization of health claims that are based on an authoritative statement from a scientific body of the United States government with official responsibility for public health protection or research directly related to human nutrition, or from the National Academy of Sciences (now the National Academies) or any of its subdivisions, about the relationship between a nutrient and a disease or health-related condition. Such claims may be used beginning 120 days after submission of a health claim notification to FDA, unless the agency prohibits or modifies the claim by regulation or obtains a court order determining that the statutory requirements for an authoritative statement notification health claim have not been met. See section 403(r)(3)(C)-(D) of the FFDCA (21 U.S.C. 343(r)(3)(C)-(D)).

(3) As a result of court decisions interpreting the First Amendment to the U.S. Constitution, FDA reviews qualified health claim petitions and issues a letter of enforcement discretion when there is credible scientific evidence supporting the claim, but the strength of the evidence falls below the standard for FDA to issue an authorizing regulation. These claims are referred to as "qualified health claims" because they include qualifying language to describe the limitations in the evidence supporting the claim and to convey any other information necessary to prevent the claim from misleading consumers. Although FDA's enforcement discretion letters are issued to the petitioner who requested the qualified health claim, the qualified health claims are available for use on other products that meet the enforcement discretion conditions specified in the letter. See FDA's website for information on the procedures that FDA uses to evaluate and respond to qualified health claim petitions http://www.fda.gov/Food/LabelingNutrition/LabelClaims/QualifiedHealthClaims/default.htm.

CH 12

A beverage or other conventional food bearing a health claim that is not authorized by regulation or by the FFDCA is misbranded under section 403(r)(1)(B) of the FFDCA (21 U.S.C. 343(r)(1)(B)). Currently, the health claims that FDA has authorized by regulation are listed in 21 C.F.R. 101.72 to 101.83. Health claims that have been authorized through the notification procedure are listed on FDA's website at http://www.fda.gov/Food/LabelingNutrition/LabelClaims/FDAModernizationActFDAMAClaims/default.

htm. Qualified health claims for which the agency has issued a letter of enforcement discretion are listed on FDA's website at: http://www.fda.gov/Food/LabelingNutrition/ LabelClaimsQualifiedHealthClaims/ucm073992.htm.

As a legal matter, an unauthorized health claim or a claim that suggests that a beverage or other conventional food is intended to treat, cure or mitigate disease subjects the food to regulation as a drug under section 201(g)(1) of the FFDCA (21 U.S.C. 321(g)(1)). An example of a health claim that meets the significant scientific agreement standard and is authorized by regulation is: "Diets low in sodium may reduce the risk of high blood pressure, a disease associated with many factors" (see 21 C.F.R. 101.74). In comparison, the following are examples of drug claims: "Shrinks tumors, "Kills influenza viruses," and "We've loaded our product with nature's best cold fighters."

* **Nutrient content claims.** A nutrient content claim is a claim characterizing the level of a nutrient in a beverage or other conventional food. 21 C.F.R. 101.13(b). Beverages and other foods may bear authorized nutrient content claims on their labels and in other labeling. Nutrient content claims describe the level of a nutrient in a food using terms such as free, high and low, or they compare the level of a nutrient in a food to that of another food, using terms such as more, reduced and lite.

There are three ways in which FDA exercises its oversight in determining which nutrient content claims may be used on a label or in labeling for a beverage or other conventional food:

(1) FDA reviews petitions for new nutrient content claims and, when appropriate, issues a regulation defining the claim and establishing nutritional criteria that a food must meet to use the claim. See 21 C.F.R. 101.69(m).

(2) FDA reviews petitions to establish a synonym for a nutrient content claim defined by regulation or to authorize the use of an implied nutrient content claim in a brand name and, when appropriate, issues a letter granting the petition. See 21 C.F.R. 101.69(n)-(o).

(3) FDA reviews nutrient content claim notifications under the Food and Drug Administration Modernization Act of 1997, which amended the FFDCA to establish a notification procedure that streamlines the authorization of claims that are based on an authoritative statement from a scientific body of the United States government with official responsibility for public health protection or research directly related to human nutrition, or from the National Academy of Sciences (now the National Academies) or any of its subdivisions, identifying the nutrient level to which the claim refers. Such claims may be used beginning 120 days after submission of a nutrient content claim notification to FDA, unless the agency prohibits or modifies the claim by regulation or obtains a court order determining that the statutory requirements for authorization of the claim have not been met. See section 403(r)(2)(G) of the FFDCA (21 U.S.C. 343(r)(2)(G)).

The requirements that govern the use of nutrient content claims help ensure that descriptive terms, such as high or low, are used consistently for all types of food products and are meaningful to consumers. A beverage or other conventional food bearing an unauthorized nutrient content claim is misbranded under section 403(r)(1)(A) of the FFDCA (21 U.S.C. 343(r)(1)(A)). Currently, the nutrient content claims that FDA has authorized by regulation are listed in 21 C.F.R. 101.13 and 21 C.F.R. 101.54 to 101.67. See FDA's website for information on nutrient claims that have been authorized through the notification procedure. http://www.fda.gov/Food/LabelingNutrition/LabelClaims/FDAModernizationActFDAMAClaims/ default.htm.

Some nutrient content claims, such as "high" and "more," are defined only for substances with an established Reference Daily Intake (RDI) or Daily Reference Value (DRV). A list of nutrients with RDIs can be found at 21 C.F.R. 101.9(c)(8)(iv); a list of nutrients with DRVs can be found at 21 C.F.R. 101.9(c)(9). A food may bear a statement about a nutrient for which there is no established RDI or DRV as long as the claim specifies only the amount of the substance per serving, does not characterize the level of the substance (e.g., by implying that there is a lot or a little of the substance in the product), and is not otherwise false or misleading. 21 C.F.R. 101.13(i)(3).

* **Structure/function claims.** The FFDCA defines "drug" to include articles intended to affect the structure or function of the body. This provision contains an exception for foods, which affect the structure and function of the body by virtue of providing nutrition to sustain life and health. See section 201(g)(1)(C) of the FFDCA (21 U.S.C. 321(g)(1)(C)). "Food" is defined in section 201(f) of the FFDCA (21 U.S.C. 321(f)) as "(1) articles used for food or drink for man or other animals, (2) chewing gum, and (3) articles used for components of any such article." Consistent with case law interpreting the "other than food" exception as applying to articles consumed primarily for taste, aroma, or nutritive value, FDA does not intend to regulate conventional foods that bear structure/function claims in their labeling as drugs as long as the claimed structure/function effect derives from the product's character as a food — its taste, aroma, or nutritive value. See Nutrilab v. Schweiker, 713 F.2d 335 (7th Cir. 1983). However, if a structure/function claim promotes a product for a use other than providing taste, aroma or nutritive value, such as blocking the absorption of carbohydrates in the gut, the claim may cause the product to be a drug by changing its primary use. In other words, because of the use promoted in the claim, the product may no longer be consumed as a food — primarily for taste, aroma, or nutritive value — but rather as a drug for some other physiological effect.

Further, if a labeling claim about the effect of a beverage or other conventional food on the structure or function of the body also states or implies that the product is useful in treating, mitigating, curing, or diagnosing a disease, the claim subjects the product to regulation as a drug under section 201(g)(1)(B) of the FFDCA (21 U.S.C. 321(g)(1)(B)). The same is true for a disease prevention claim in the labeling of a conventional food, unless the claim is an authorized health claim about reducing the risk of a disease or health-related condition.

CH 12

As with all claims in food labeling, structure/function claims for conventional foods may not be false or misleading. See section 403(a)(1) of the FFDCA (21 U.S.C. 343(a)(1)).

Required Labeling for Conventional Foods

Labeling requirements for beverages and other conventional foods differ from those for dietary supplements. For example, beverages and other conventional foods are required to bear nutrition information in the form of Nutrition Facts rather than Supplement Facts, and all ingredients in a beverage and other conventional food must be declared in the ingredient statement by their common and usual names, in descending order of predominance. In addition, a beverage or other conventional food should not be labeled with the FDA disclaimer that is required on dietary supplement labels that bear structure/function claims or other claims described in section 403(r)(6)(A) of the FFDCA (21 U.S.C. 343(r)(6)(A)).

Questions regarding the regulatory status of ingredients that you intend to use in your beverage or other conventional food, and about how to file a GRAS Notice or Food Additive Petition, should be directed to the Office of Food Additive Safety, Center for Food Safety and Applied Nutrition, HFS-200, 5001 Campus Drive, College Park, MD 20740. Questions regarding the labeling requirements for beverages and other conventional foods, and about voluntary labeling claims for these foods, should be directed to the Food Labeling and Standards Staff, Office of Nutrition, Labeling and Dietary Supplements, Center for Food Safety and Applied Nutrition, HFS-810, 5001 Campus Drive, College Park, MD 20740.

FDA's general food labeling requirements are located in Title 21 of the Code of Federal Regulations, Part 101, and additional guidance can be obtained from the Food Labeling Guide http://www.fda.gov/FoodLabelingGuide, which is available on the FDA website.

IV. References

We have placed the following reference on display in the Division of Dockets Management, Food and Drug Administration, 5630 Fishers Lane, rm. 1061, Rockville, MD 20852. You may see it at that location between 9 a.m. and 4 p.m., Monday through Friday.

1. Foods Analysis and Residue Evaluation Program (FARE), Version 8.50, Consumption Analysis: Distribution and Means Analysis based on NHANES 2005-2006.

CH 12

Contains Nonbinding Recommendations
Draft-Not for Implementation
August 2016 (Replaces draft guidance issued July 2011)

Guidance for Industry[1]
Dietary Supplements: New Dietary Ingredient Notifications and Related Issues

I. Introduction

Under section 413(a)(2) of the Federal Food, Drug, and Cosmetic Act (FD&C Act) (21 U.S.C. 350b(a)(2)), the manufacturer or distributor of a new dietary ingredient (NDI) that has not been present in the food supply as an article used for food, or a dietary supplement containing such an NDI, must submit a premarket safety notification to FDA at least 75 days before introducing the product into interstate commerce. This guidance is intended to help manufacturers and distributors of dietary ingredients and dietary supplements ("you") decide whether to submit a premarket safety notification to FDA ("we" or "us") for a product that is or contains an NDI. These premarket safety notifications are commonly referred to as NDI notifications. The guidance is also intended to help you to prepare NDI notifications that we will be able to review more efficiently and respond to more quickly.

The guidance answers frequently asked questions about NDI notifications and related issues. The major topics it addresses are:

- What qualifies as an NDI;

- When an NDI notification is required;

- What are the procedures for submitting an NDI notification;

- What types of data and information FDA recommends you consider when you evaluate the safety of NDIs and dietary supplements containing an NDI; and

---

1   This guidance has been prepared by the Office of Dietary Supplement Programs in the Center for Food Safety and Applied Nutrition at the U.S. Food and Drug Administration. This guidance is available on the FDA website at https://www.fda.gov/Food/GuidanceRegulation/GuidanceDocumentsRegulatoryInformation/ucm257563.htm

• What FDA recommends you include in an NDI notification.

In addition, the guidance contains questions and answers about parts of the definition of "dietary supplement"[2] that can affect whether a particular substance may be marketed as a dietary ingredient in a dietary supplement. We encourage you to consult this guidance during your safety review of dietary supplements that contain an NDI and when you prepare NDI notifications.

The guidance focuses on interpreting the FD&C Act's requirements relating to NDIs and dietary supplements that contain an NDI. It does not discuss other parts of the FD&C Act that may affect the regulatory status of a particular ingredient or product, such as provisions of the FDA Food Safety Modernization Act (FSMA)[3] that may apply to dietary ingredients and/or dietary supplements.

FDA's guidance documents, including this guidance, do not establish legally enforceable responsibilities. Instead, guidances describe our current thinking on a topic and should be viewed only as recommendations, unless specific regulatory or statutory requirements are cited. The use of the word *should* in FDA guidances means that something is suggested or recommended, but not required.

II. Background

On October 25, 1994, the Dietary Supplement Health and Education Act of 1994 (DSHEA) (Pub. L. 103-417) was signed into law. DSHEA amended the FD&C Act by adding, among other provisions, (1) section 201(ff) (21 U.S.C. 321(ff)), which defines the term "dietary supplement"; and (2) section 413 (21 U.S.C. 350b), which defines the term "new dietary ingredient" and requires the manufacturer or distributor of an NDI, or of the dietary supplement that contains the NDI, to submit a premarket notification to FDA at least 75 days before introducing the product into interstate commerce or delivering it for introduction into interstate commerce, unless the NDI and any other dietary ingredients in the dietary supplement "have been present in the food supply as an article used for food in a form in which the food has not been chemically altered" (21 U.S.C. 350b(a)(1)).

The notification must contain the information, including any citation to published articles, which provides the basis on which the manufacturer or distributor of the NDI or dietary supplement (the notifier) has concluded that the dietary supplement containing the NDI will reasonably be expected to be safe (21 U.S.C. 350b(a)(2)). If the required premarket notification is not submitted to FDA, section 413(a) of the FD&C Act (21 U.S.C. 350b(a)) provides that the dietary supplement containing the NDI is deemed to be adulterated under section 402(f) of the FD&C Act (21 U.S.C. 342(f)). Even if the notification is submitted as required, the dietary supplement containing the NDI is adulterated under section 402(f) unless there is a history of use or other evidence of safety establishing that the NDI, when used under the conditions recommended or suggested in the labeling of the dietary supplement, will reasonably be expected to be safe.

---

2   "Dietary supplement" is defined in 21 U.S.C. 321(ff). Available at: https://www.gpo.gov/fdsys/pkg/USCODE-2014-title21/pdf/USCODE-2014-title21-chap9-subchapII-sec321.pdf
3   Pub. L. No. 111-353, 124 Stat. 3886 (2011).

To help industry comply with DSHEA, we issued a regulation in 21 CFR 190.6 (§ 190.6 or the NDI regulation) to implement the FD&C Act's premarket notification requirements for dietary supplements that contain an NDI (62 FR 49886; September 23, 1997). The NDI regulation specifies the information the manufacturer or distributor must include in its premarket NDI notification (21 CFR 190.6(b)):[4]

- The name and complete address of the manufacturer or distributor that is submitting the notification.

- The name of the NDI that is the subject of the premarket notification. For botanicals, the Latin binomial name must be given, including the author citation (the name of the scientist who gave the botanical its Latin binomial name).

- A description of the dietary supplement that contains the NDI, including:

  - the level of the NDI in the dietary supplement, and

  - the conditions of use recommended or suggested in the labeling of the dietary supplement, or if no conditions of use are recommended or suggested in the supplement's labeling, the ordinary conditions of use of the supplement.

- The history of use or other evidence of safety establishing that the dietary ingredient, when used under the conditions recommended in the labeling of the dietary supplement, will reasonably be expected to be safe.

- The signature of a person authorized by the manufacturer or distributor to sign the notification on its behalf.

In addition to the requirements for the content of NDI notifications, the NDI regulation establishes the administrative procedures for these notifications. Section 190.6(c) defines the filing date of a notification as the date we receive it and, consistent with section 413(a)(2) of the FD&C Act, prohibits the manufacturer or distributor of the dietary supplement that contains the NDI from introducing the product into interstate commerce, or delivering it for introduction into interstate commerce, for 75 days after the filing date (21 CFR 190.6(c)). If the manufacturer or distributor submits additional substantive information in support of the original NDI notification, § 190.6(d) provides that the date of this supplemental submission to FDA becomes the new notification filing date, and the 75-day period restarts. Consistent with section 413(a) of the FD&C Act, § 190.6(e) provides that FDA will not disclose the existence of, or the information contained in, an NDI notification for 90 days after the filing date of the notification. Section 190.6(e) further provides that after the 90th day, the entire notification, except trade secrets and confidential commercial information, will be placed on public display, as prescribed in section 413(a) of the FD&C Act. Finally, § 190.6(f) states that FDA's failure to respond to an NDI notification does not constitute a finding by the agency that the NDI or the dietary supplement containing the NDI is safe or is not adulterated under section 402 of the FD&C Act (21 U.S.C. 342).

On January 4, 2011, the President signed into law the FDA Food Safety Modernization Act (FSMA) (Pub. L. 111-353). Section 113(b) of FSMA requires FDA to publish, not later than 180 days after

CH 13

---

4   Please see question V.A.2 for a recommended template for the format and content of an NDI notification, and section VI.A for detailed recommendations on what to include in the identity section of an NDI notification.

the date of enactment, guidance that clarifies when a dietary supplement ingredient is an NDI, when the manufacturer or distributor of a dietary ingredient or dietary supplement should submit an NDI notification to FDA under section 413(a)(2) of the FD&C Act, the evidence needed to document the safety of an NDI, and appropriate methods for establishing the identity of an NDI. In July 2011, we published a draft guidance to comply with section 113(b) of FSMA (see 76 FR 39111; July 5, 2011). This revised draft guidance replaces the July 2011 draft guidance.

III. Goals and Public Health Importance of the Guidance

One key goal of this guidance is to improve the rate of compliance with the NDI notification requirement. In 2012, FDA estimated that the number of dietary supplements on the market was 55,600 and that 5,560 new dietary supplement products come on the market each year.[5] This is in contrast to the approximately 4,000 products that were on the market in 1994, when DSHEA was enacted.[6] As of December 2014, we had received and completed our evaluation of just over 750 NDI notifications since the first notification was received in 1995.[7] These figures, coupled with recent concern about the presence of undeclared active ingredients in products marketed as dietary supplements, highlight the importance of submitting NDI notifications as a preventive control to ensure that consumers are not exposed to unnecessary public health risks in the form of new ingredients with unknown safety profiles.[8] To improve public understanding of the NDI notification requirement, this guidance includes an in-depth discussion of the scope of the requirement, along with detailed examples of situations in which a notification would or would not be required.

A second goal of the guidance is to improve the quality of NDI notifications. Our aim in issuing the NDI regulation in 1997 was to ensure that NDI notifications contain the information that is necessary for FDA to evaluate whether a dietary supplement containing an NDI is reasonably expected to be safe, and that aim remains the same today. After many years of experience with reviewing NDI notifications and answering questions from industry, we have concluded that a guidance on NDI issues is needed to help the dietary supplement industry understand and comply with section 413 of the FD&C Act and the NDI regulation. We hope that the additional explanation in this guidance will help you decide when an NDI notification is required and what that notification should contain.

DSHEA does not specify the type or amount of evidence that must be included in an NDI notification. Accordingly, this guidance explains how to submit a premarket notification and makes detailed recommendations on the type and amount of evidence to include. As set forth in more detail in the rest of this guidance, we recommend including in your NDI notification the following:

---

5   Dietary Supplement Labeling Requirements and Recommendations Under the Dietary Supplement and Nonprescription Drug Consumer Protection Act, 77 FR 35687 (June 14, 2012).

6   Dietary Supplement Health and Education Act of 1994, Pub. L. 103-417, § 2(12)(C), 108 Stat. 4326. Available at: http://www.fda.gov/regulatoryinformation/legislation/significantamendmentstothefdcact/ucm148003.htm

7   Memorandum to File from Fred A. Hines, Consumer Safety Officer, FDA (December 17, 2014).

8   See, e.g., NDI Notification Response -E. coli Nissle strain (Oct. 28, 2011) Available at: https://www.regulations.gov/document?D=FDA-2012-S-1178-0014; NDI Notification Response -Human placenta extract (Apr. 6, 2011). Available at: https://www.regulations.gov/document?D=FDA-2011-S-0933-0133

- A full description of the identity and composition of the NDI and the dietary supplement in which the NDI will be marketed;

- A discussion of the basis for your conclusion that the substance is an NDI;

- A description of the conditions of use recommended or suggested in the labeling of the dietary supplement, or if no conditions of use are recommended or suggested in the labeling, the ordinary conditions of use of the supplement; and

- An explanation of how the history of use or other evidence of safety in the notification justifies your conclusion that the dietary supplement containing the NDI will reasonably be expected to be safe.

IV. Determining Whether a New Dietary Ingredient (NDI) Notification Is Required

A. What Is a New Dietary Ingredient?

1. What do the terms "dietary ingredient" and "new dietary ingredient" mean?

As defined in section 201(ff)(1) of the FD&C Act (21 U.S.C. 321(ff)(1)), a "dietary ingredient" is any one of the following:

(A) A vitamin;

(B) A mineral;

(C) An herb or other botanical;

(D) An amino acid;

(E) A dietary substance for use by man to supplement the diet by increasing the total dietary intake; or

(F) A concentrate, metabolite, constituent, extract, or combination of any ingredient described in (A), (B), (C), (D), or (E).

An NDI is defined as a dietary ingredient that was not marketed in the U.S. before October 15, 1994 (21 U.S.C. 350b(d)). Thus, to be an NDI, a substance must be a dietary ingredient.

2. Can a substance that is not a dietary ingredient be an NDI?

No. Because "new dietary ingredient" is defined to mean a dietary ingredient that was not marketed in the U.S. before October 15, 1994, a substance cannot be a new dietary ingredient unless it is also a dietary ingredient.

3. Must I submit an NDI notification for a dietary ingredient marketed in the U.S. prior to October 15, 1994?

No. Dietary ingredients marketed prior to October 15, 1994 ("pre-DSHEA dietary ingredients") are not NDIs and, therefore, do not require an NDI notification. See

CH
13

questions IV.A.4, IV.A.7 and IV.A.10 for more on how FDA interprets the terms "marketed" and "dietary ingredient" in the definition of an NDI (21 U.S.C. 350b(d)).

4. Is an ingredient that was used to make a conventional food marketed before October 15, 1994, an NDI?

It depends. The use of an ingredient in a conventional food before October 15, 1994, does not determine whether the ingredient is an NDI. What matters is whether the ingredient was marketed ***as a dietary ingredient*** — meaning that it was marketed in or as a dietary supplement, or for use in a dietary supplement —in the U.S. before October 15, 1994. Therefore, an ingredient that was used to make a conventional food before October 15, 1994, is still an NDI unless the ingredient was also marketed as a dietary ingredient in the U.S. before October 15, 1994. For example, an ingredient used to color a conventional food before October 15, 1994, would be an NDI unless it was also marketed before October 15, 1994, in or as a dietary supplement, or as a dietary ingredient for use in a dietary supplement.

We recognize that the present definitions of "dietary supplement" and "dietary ingredient" were not added to the FD&C Act until after October 15, 1994, and that many products now marketed as dietary ingredients for use in dietary supplements were marketed under other product categories, such as foods for special dietary use or food additives. Therefore, we interpret "dietary ingredient" to refer to ingredients that (1) if marketed today, would qualify as "dietary ingredients" under 21 U.S.C. 321(ff)(1); and (2) when marketed before October 15, 1994, were intended for use as or in a product that would now be a "dietary supplement" as defined in 21 U.S.C. 321(ff) and that would not also meet the definition of a drug. See questions IV.A.7 and IV.A.10 for more about FDA's views on the meaning of "marketing" and "dietary ingredient" in the NDI definition.

a. Is an NDI notification required for a dietary supplement containing an NDI if the supplement contains only dietary ingredients that have been present in the food supply as articles used for food in a form in which the food has not been chemically altered?

No, an NDI notification would not be required in this situation because of the exception to the notification requirement for dietary supplements that contain only dietary ingredients that have been present in the food supply as articles used for food in a form in which the food has not been chemically altered (21 U.S.C. 350b(a)(1)). See questions IV.B.4 and IV.B.5 for FDA's view on what "chemically altered" means. Example: Ingredient X is a food additive that was approved for use to sweeten baked goods in 1993 and was marketed for that use before October 15, 1994, but was not marketed for use as a dietary ingredient in dietary supplements before that date. ABC Company wants to market a supplement that contains Ingredient X, and it plans to use the same form of Ingredient X used as a sweetener in baked goods. Ingredient X will be the only dietary ingredient in the supplement, which will be called "X-cellent." Although Ingredient X is an NDI because it was not marketed as a dietary ingredient before October 15, 1994, ABC Company is not required to submit an NDI notification for X-cellent because Ingredient X has been present in the food supply as an article used for food in a form in which the food has not been chemically altered, and it is the only dietary ingredient in the supplement.

b. Does the adulteration standard in 21 U.S.C. 342(f)(1)(B)[9] apply to a dietary supplement containing an NDI even when an NDI notification is not required?

Yes. The adulteration standard in 21 U.S.C. 342(f)(1)(B) applies to all dietary supplements that contain an NDI, even in situations when no notification is required because the supplement contains only dietary ingredients that have been present in the food supply as articles used for food in a form in which the food has not been chemically altered. See section IV.B for more information about chemical alteration and the exception to the NDI notification requirement for certain NDIs that have been present in the food supply as conventional foods.

5. Is a substance that was a component of a conventional food marketed before October 15, 1994, an NDI if the component was not a dietary ingredient marketed in the U.S. before October 15, 1994?

Yes, assuming the component meets the definition of a dietary ingredient. The mere presence of a substance as a component of a conventional food that was marketed before October 15, 1994, does not establish that the substance was marketed as a dietary ingredient before that date. Similarly, the fact that a minor component may have been isolated as part of an analytical chemical procedure to examine the composition of the previously marketed food before October 15, 1994, is not sufficient to establish that the component is a pre-DSHEA dietary ingredient or even that it is a dietary ingredient at all. If it is not a dietary ingredient, it is ineligible to be an NDI. If the food component fits into one of the dietary ingredient categories (for example, if it is a metabolite or extract of another dietary ingredient) but was not marketed as a dietary ingredient before October 15, 1994, it would be an NDI. On the other hand, if the substance was marketed as a dietary ingredient before that date (in addition to its marketing for conventional food use), then it is not an NDI. (See questions IV.A.4, IV.A.7, and IV.A.10 for FDA's views on the meaning of "marketing" and "dietary ingredient" in the NDI definition.)

6. Is a substance that was an ingredient in a dietary supplement marketed before October 15, 1994, an NDI?

The answer depends on whether the substance was used as a dietary ingredient or for some other purpose (e.g., excipient or processing aid) in the pre-DSHEA dietary supplement. If the substance was added to the supplement as a dietary ingredient, it is not an NDI and may be used in dietary supplements without submitting an NDI notification to FDA.

---

9   Under 21 U.S.C. 342(f)(1)(B), a dietary supplement containing an NDI is adulterated unless there is adequate information to provide reasonable assurance that the NDI does not present a significant or unreasonable risk of illness or injury.

If the substance was not added to the pre-DSHEA dietary supplement as a dietary ingredient, however, the analysis becomes more complicated. If the substance was directly added to the pre-DSHEA dietary supplement, intended to become a component of the finished dietary supplement and have a technical effect in it, and was GRAS or approved as a food additive for that use, the substance would be an NDI. However, because most secondary direct food additives,[10] indirect food additives,[11] food contact substances,[12] and other indirectly added substances are not intended to have a technical effect in or become components of the finished food (see question IV.D.4), you would first have to consider whether such a substance fits into one of the dietary ingredient categories in section 201(ff)(1) of the FD&C Act (21 U.S.C. 321(ff)(1)) to determine whether it is an NDI. If the substance does not fit into any of the dietary ingredient categories, it would not be either an NDI or a pre-DSHEA dietary ingredient. Rather, it could not be used as a dietary ingredient in a dietary supplement at all.

7. What does "marketing" a dietary ingredient mean?

FDA considers "marketing" a dietary ingredient to mean selling or offering the dietary ingredient for sale (1) as or in a dietary supplement, (2) in bulk as a dietary ingredient for use in dietary supplements, or (3) as an ingredient in a blend or formulation of dietary ingredients for use in dietary supplements. A dietary ingredient may be "marketed" by offering the article for sale online or at a retail establishment, listing it for sale in a catalog or price list, or through advertising or other promotion, if the promotion makes clear that the article is available for purchase. "Coming soon" advertisements would not qualify. If a dietary supplement containing an NDI is sold before the manufacturer or distributor submits a required NDI notification or less than 75 days after the notification is submitted, the sale of the product is not evidence that the dietary supplement or NDI was lawfully marketed.

8. Is a dietary ingredient marketed outside the U.S. prior to October 15, 1994, considered to be an NDI if it was not marketed in the U.S. before that date?

Yes. Submitting documentation that the ingredient was marketed in any other country before this date does not establish that the ingredient is not an NDI. The only kind of marketing that is relevant to whether a dietary ingredient is an NDI is marketing in the

10   Secondary direct food additives are added during the manufacturing of a food to achieve a technical effect, but they have no technical effect in the finished food. See FDA, Food Ingredients and Packaging Terms.Available at: http://www.fda.gov/Food/IngredientsPackagingLabeling/Definitions/default.htm(accessedApril 22, 2015).
11   11 Indirect food additives come into contact with food as part of packaging, holding, or processing, but they are not intended to be added directly to, become a component of, or have a technical effect in or on the food. Before the FDA Modernization Act of 1997, indirect food additives were approved by regulation. Now, new indirect food additives are authorized through the food contact substance notification program. In addition, indirect food additives may be authorized through the threshold of regulation exemption process in 21 CFR 170.39. See FDA, Food Ingredients andPackaging Terms.Available at: http://www.fda.gov/Food/IngredientsPackagingLabeling/Definitions/default.htm (accessedApril 22, 2015).
12   A food contact substance is a substance intended for use as a component of materials used in manufacturing, packing, packaging, transporting, or holding food if that use is not intended to have any technical effect in the food. 21 U.S.C. 348(h)(6).

U.S. before October 15, 1994.[13]

9. What documentation does FDA recommend to showthat a dietary ingredient was marketed prior to October 15, 1994?

Documentation to show that a dietary ingredient is not an NDI should consist of written business records, promotional materials, or press` reports with a contemporaneous date prior to October 15, 1994. Examples include sales records, bills of lading, sales contracts, manufacturing records, commercial invoices, magazine advertisements, mail order catalogs, or sales brochures.

Documentation should include adequate information to establish that marketing took place in the U.S.: the identity (e.g., chemical or botanical name) of the marketed ingredient, including its form (e.g., ground herb, water extract, oil), and whether the ingredient was marketed as a dietary ingredient or for some other purpose. For example, advertising in body building magazines could be adequate evidence of marketing as a dietary ingredient. On the other hand, advertising or other references in gardening or landscaping magazines would not likely serve as adequate evidence of the marketing of a botanical or herb as a dietary ingredient.

We would also consider GRAS and food additive regulations in the *Code of Federal Regulations* as documentation that an ingredient was marketed as a dietary ingredient before October 15, 1994, if the regulation covers use of the substance as a nutrient supplement, became effective before October 15, 1994, and contains identity specifications that the ingredient meets. Although references published before October 15, 1994, such as the 1992 edition of *Herbs of Commerce*,[14] may be supportive, we are unlikely to regard a listing in *Herbs of Commerce* as being solely determinative of whether a dietary ingredient was marketed as such before October 15, 1994 because this listing may not specify necessary information such as the plant part and/or extract type. If you rely on *Herbs of Commerce* as evidence that your dietary ingredient is not an NDI, we recommend that you maintain additional documentation showing that the botanical was marketed as a dietary ingredient before October 15, 1994. The documentation should specify the plant part from which the botanical dietary ingredient was derived, and for botanical extracts it should also specify the extract type.

Affidavits attesting to recollection of when a dietary ingredient was first marketed generally would not be adequate to show that an ingredient was marketed prior to October 15, 1994, unless supported by contemporaneous written records. Because memory can be unreliable, especially when the event in question took place more than thirty years ago, we are not likely to regard such an affidavit alone, without any sort of objective, verifiable documentation from the time of marketing, as an adequate basis to establish pre-DSHEA marketing of a substance as a dietary ingredient for use in or as a dietary supplement.

CH

13

---

13 For evidence of marketing in another country as evidence of safety, especially when considering the differences in dietary consumption betweencountries, see question VI.B.3.

14 Moley, Timothy, Steven Foster, and Dennis Awang. *Herbs of Commerce*. Austin, TX: American Herbal Products Association, 1992.

10. Is marketing an ingredient for any use prior to October 15, 1994, sufficient to conclude that it is not an NDI?

No. FDA does not consider the marketing of an ingredient as a conventional food, as a drug, or for any other non-food use, to be evidence that an ingredient is not an NDI. Unless the ingredient was marketed as a dietary ingredient for use in or as a dietary supplement prior to October 15, 1994, it is an NDI.

11. Is there an authoritative list of dietary ingredients that were marketed prior to October 15, 1994 (a so-called "grandfathered list" or "old dietary ingredient list")?

Not currently. Some trade associations and other industry groups have compiled lists of "old dietary ingredients,"[15] though FDA is unable to verify the accuracy of these lists because we have not seen documentation showing that the ingredients on such lists were marketed as dietary ingredients prior to October 15, 1994. The lists contain ingredients FDA believes are unlikely to have been marketed as dietary ingredients, like acetaminophen or pharmaceutical glaze, and mixtures that are only vaguely described, like "sterol complete premix." Moreover, the introduction to one trade association list[16] states that the association did not independently verify that the substances on the list were in use before October 15, 1994. The cover page of the list specifically states, "This list is compiled solely for reference purposes and does not constitute verification that any specific dietary ingredient was or was not marketed as a dietary supplement before October 15, 1994." The trade association's introduction to the list also states, "There is no definitive list of 'grandfathered' dietary ingredients. The best policy is for any company to maintain its own records confirming long-term use of an ingredient." Because of the uncertainty about the existence of supporting evidence, FDA does not accept the inclusion of an ingredient on an industry list of pre-DSHEA dietary ingredients as proof that the ingredient is not an NDI. However, in response to comments, we are prepared to develop an authoritative list of pre-DSHEA ingredients, based on independent and verifiable data. Because FDA does not generally have access to marketing records for dietary ingredients and dietary supplements, the documentation of pre-DSHEA marketing would have to be supplied by industry.

FDA's current thinking is that the two main factors for placing an ingredient on an authoritative list of pre-DSHEA ingredients would be: (1) adequate documentation of marketing for use as or in a dietary supplement in the U.S. before October 15, 1994; and (2) a precise description of the identity of the ingredient marketed. Records offered to support an item's inclusion on the list should specify the date of marketing in the U.S. and clearly identify the ingredient marketed on that date. Documentation of an

---

15   See, e.g., National Nutritional Foods Association, NNFA List of Dietary Supplement Ingredients In Use Before October 15, 1994 (April 26, 1996). Docket No. FDA-2005-P-0259 [Document ID: FDA-2005-P-0259-0012]. Available at: https://www.pharmamedtechbi.com/~/media/Supporting%20Documents/The%20Tan%20Sheet/19/50/111212_UNPA_ODI_List.pdf
16   Council for Responsible Nutrition, CRN List of Dietary Ingredients "Grandfathered" Under DSHEA (September 1998). Docket No. FDA-2005-P-0259 [Document ID: FDA-2005-P-0259-0010]. Available at: http://www.fda.gov/ohrms/dockets/dockets/05p0305/05p-0305-cr00001-04-Council-For-Responsible-Nutrition-vol1.pdf

ingredient's identity should be sufficiently precise to uniquely identify the ingredient. See question IV.A.9 for the kinds of documentation FDA recommends to show that a dietary ingredient was marketed prior to October 15, 1994.

Including an ingredient on FDA's list of pre-DSHEA dietary ingredients would represent our view that the evidence is adequate to conclude that the dietary ingredient in question is not "new" and, therefore, not subject to the NDI notification requirement. The mere fact that an ingredient is not on the list would not, however, establish that the ingredient is an NDI or that dietary supplements containing that dietary ingredient are adulterated for failure to notify. Rather, the omission of an ingredient from the list would be regarded as neutral and would not affect the ingredient's regulatory status. Whether FDA would investigate dietary ingredients not on the list to determine whether an NDI notification should have been submitted would typically depend on factors relating to public health, such as potential for risk, extent of public exposure to the ingredient, and association with adverse events.

Although only one instance of marketing as a dietary ingredient before October 15, 1994 (pre-DSHEA marketing) need be shown to establish that an ingredient is not an NDI, each dietary supplement manufacturer and distributor is responsible for determining whether each dietary ingredient in each of its dietary supplements is an NDI and ensuring that the firm complies with the NDI notification requirements, if applicable. For ingredients that are not on FDA's list of pre-DSHEA dietary ingredients, a firm could either maintain its own records of the pre-DSHEA marketing of a dietary ingredient or rely on another firm or organization's records, with that entity's permission.

12. If I change the manufacturing process for a dietary ingredient that was marketed in the U.S. prior to October 15, 1994, does that make the ingredient an NDI?

The answer depends on the extent to which the manufacturing process change affects the resulting ingredient. As discussed in a separate FDA guidance on manufacturing changes,[17] such changes may affect the identity of the food substance or its safety and suitability for certain conditions of use. Manufacturing changes may also affect the purity of a food substance, such as the amounts of impurities and contaminants in the food substance.

Any changes in your manufacturing process that alter the identity of the ingredient will convert a previously marketed dietary ingredient into an NDI. Manufacturing changes that alter the physicochemical structure or properties, purity and impurities, or biological properties (such as bioavailability or toxicity) of the ingredient result in an NDI.[18] For example, using a solvent to prepare an extract from a pre-DSHEA dietary

CH
13

---

17   FDA, Guidance for Industry: Assessing the Effects of Significant Manufacturing Process Changes, Including Emerging Technologies, on the Safety and Regulatory Status of Food Ingredients and Food Contact Substances, Including Food Ingredients that are Color Additives;June 2014 Available at: http://www.fda.gov/food/guidanceregulation/guidancedocumentsregulatoryinformation/ucm300661.htm.

18   FDA, Guidance for Industry: Assessing the Effects of Significant Manufacturing Process Changes, Including Emerging Technologies, on the Safety and Regulatory Status of Food Ingredients and Food Contact Substances, Including Food Ingredients that are Color Additives; June 2014 Available at: http://www.fda.gov/food/

ingredient creates an NDI because the final extract contains only a fractionated subset of the constituent substances in the original dietary ingredient. A manufacturing change which changes the ingredient in a way that leads to alteration of the serving level or conditions of use of the product is another example of a significant change which is likely to create an NDI.

In addition, changes that alter the identity of the source material for an ingredient may create an NDI. For example, using a different part of a plant (e.g., using an extract of plant leaves where the root extract from the same plant is a pre-DSHEA dietary ingredient) would create an NDI. If the ingredient produced by the new manufacturing process is an NDI, an NDI notification is required unless the NDI has been present in the food supply as an article used for food in a form in which the food has not been chemically altered (see Section IV.B). On the other hand, if the manufacturing changes do not alter the identity of the ingredient (e.g., there are no changes in physicochemical structure or properties and no changes in purity, impurities or biological properties such as bioavailability or toxicity) then the regulatory status of the pre-DSHEA ingredient does not change and no NDI notification is needed.

Note that the question of whether a manufacturing change creates an NDI is different from the question of whether the manufacturing change constitutes chemical alteration, and different standards apply. The "chemically altered" standard in section 413(a)(1) of the FD&C Act (21 U.S.C. 350b(a)(1)) governs only the manufacturing of dietary ingredients that have been "present in the food supply" as articles "used for food" (i.e., conventional foods and their ingredients)[19] and is applied to determine whether an NDI notification is required for a conventional food ingredient that was not marketed as a dietary ingredient before October 15, 1994. In general, a broader range of manufacturing changes would create an NDI by changing the identity of a dietary ingredient than would "chemically alter" an article of food present in the food supply. For example, solution in water or tincture may change the composition of a pre-DSHEA dietary ingredient enough to make it an NDI for which a notification is required. However, solution in water or tincture would not constitute a "chemical alteration" of a conventional food ingredient (see questions IV.B.4 and IV.B.5), and therefore, no NDI notification would be needed when a tincture or solution in water made with a conventional food ingredient is used as a dietary ingredient.

It should also be noted that some manufacturing changes may alter the identity of the ingredient to the point that it no longer meets the definition of a dietary ingredient (see question IV.D.5). Firms planning a manufacturing change are encouraged to consult with FDA on any questions as to whether such a change would create an NDI or an ingredient that does not meet the definition of a dietary ingredient.[20]

---

guidanceregulation/guidancedocumentsregulatoryinformation/ucm300661.htm.

19   See question IV.B.1.

20   Contact information for the Office of Dietary Supplement Programs can be found on the title page.

13. Should I submit a new NDI notification if I change the manufacturing process for an NDI that is the subject of a notification for which I have received an acknowledgment without objection from FDA?

That depends on the nature of the change to the manufacturing process. If the manufacturing change does not alter the chemical or molecular composition or structure of the dietary ingredient or the specifications needed to describe the ingredient, it is not necessary to submit a second NDI notification. On the other hand, a manufacturing process change intended to produce an ingredient with particles in the 1 nm to 100 nm (approximate) nanoscale range may alter the chemical or molecular composition or structure of the NDI. In that case, the previously submitted notification for a related substance manufactured without using nanotechnology would not cover the ingredient made with the new manufacturing process, and a separate NDI notification with safety information taking into account the smaller particle size of the resulting new ingredient would then be required.

If you are planning a manufacturing change, we encourage you to consult with FDA on whether such a change would create a different NDI or a substance that is no longer a dietary ingredient.[21] (See questions IV.A.12 for additional discussion on manufacturing changes that affect the identity of an ingredient.)

B. Exception to Notification Requirement for Certain NDIs with a History of Use in Conventional Food

1. When is a notification not required for an NDI?

A notification is not required when the NDI and all other dietary ingredients in the dietary supplement have been present in the food supply as articles used for food in a form in which the food has not been chemically altered. See questions IV.B.4 and IV.B.5 for FDA's current thinking on when a dietary ingredient has been "chemically altered" from the form in which it is used in the food supply.

FDA interprets the phrase "present in the food supply" to refer to the conventional food supply. Accordingly, we interpret a dietary ingredient that has been "present in the food supply as an article used for food" to mean a conventional food or conventional food ingredient. We do not consider prior use in dietary supplements to constitute presence in the food supply. Interpreting "food supply" to include dietary supplements for purposes of this exemption from the NDI notification requirement would expand the exception to the point that it would risk swallowing the rule, as prior use in even one dietary supplement manufactured in small quantities and distributed over a small area would exempt all dietary supplements containing the NDI from the notification requirement, even if the intake level and conditions of use were much different. Moreover, such an interpretation would not make sense in light of the purpose of the NDI notification requirement, which is to ensure that dietary ingredients that have not been widely consumed receive a safety evaluation before reaching the marketplace.

---

21   Contact information for the Office of Dietary Supplement Programs can be found on the title page.

Because dietary supplements are generally consumed by a narrower segment of the population than conventional foods and typically have a shorter history of use than conventional food ingredients, prior use in a supplement or supplements typically provides less information about a substance's safety than prior use in conventional food. In addition, substances added to conventional foods must meet the safety standards for conventional food ingredients, which are more demanding than those that apply to dietary ingredients used in dietary supplements.

2. **Am I required to submit an NDI notification for a dietary ingredient that is an NDI, but has been (a) listed or affirmed by FDA as generally recognized as safe (GRAS) for direct addition to food or (b) approved as a direct food additive in the U.S.?**

No, as long as the following conditions are met. The direct food additive or GRAS substance (1) has been used in the food supply (i.e., in conventional foods) and (2) is to be used as a dietary ingredient without chemical alteration. (See questions IV.B.4 and IV.B.5 for further discussion on chemical alteration.)

If the NDI has been legally marketed in the U.S. as an ingredient for use in conventional food and has been introduced into the food supply as a result of such marketing, it would be exempt from the notification requirement under section 413(a)(1) of the FD&C Act (21 U.S.C. 350b(a)(1)) because it has been present in the food supply as an article used for food in a form in which the food is not chemically altered. Similarly, ingredients marketed in conventional foods outside the U.S. are exempt from the NDI notification requirement if they are not chemically altered. However, as discussed in the following question, the NDI adulteration standard still applies, and voluntary NDI notification may be advisable.

3. **Does the adulteration standard in 21 U.S.C. 342(f)(1)(B) apply to an NDI that has been listed or affirmed by FDA as GRAS for direct addition to food or approved as a direct food additive in the U.S.?**

Yes. The adulteration standard in section 402(f)(1)(B) of the FD&C Act (21 U.S.C. 342(f)(1)(B)) applies to all NDIs, including NDIs for which a notification is not required. In other words, if an ingredient was not marketed as a dietary ingredient in the U.S. before October 15, 1994 (see questions IV.A.4, IV.A.7 and IV.A.10), it is an NDI and the adulteration standard for NDIs applies. That standard provides that a dietary supplement containing the NDI is adulterated unless there is adequate information to provide reasonable assurance that the ingredient does not present a significant or unreasonable risk of illness or injury.

If the intake level of the NDI resulting from its use under the conditions recommended or suggested in the labeling of the dietary supplement is the same as or lower than the intake level approved in a food additive regulation or specified in a GRAS regulation and overall cumulative intake of the NDI from dietary sources is the same as or lower than the acceptable daily intake (see question VI.C.8), FDA is likely to conclude that there is adequate information to provide reasonable assurance of safety, assuming that other conditions of use remain unchanged. However, the same is not necessarily true if the intake level of the NDI in the dietary supplement is higher than that resulting from conventional food use of the NDI. For example, if an ingredient generally used in microgram quantities to flavor food is placed in a capsule with a serving level of hundreds of milligrams, a safety analysis would be necessary to determine the safety of the much higher intake level in the dietary supplement. In the absence of adequate information to provide reasonable assurance that the higher intake level of the NDI in the dietary supplement is safe, the dietary supplement would be adulterated.

Although an NDI notification is not required for a dietary supplement that contains an NDI that has been present in the food supply as an article used for food without chemical alteration, even if the dietary supplement contains more of the NDI than is used in conventional foods, FDA recommends that you consult with us about your basis for concluding that there is adequate information to provide reasonable assurance that the use of the NDI in the dietary supplement will not present a significant or unreasonable risk of illness or injury.[22] As with any new dietary supplement you intend to market, you should assure yourself that the product is safe under its labeled conditions of use before distributing it. To that end, it may be advisable to submit a NDI notification voluntarily when a dietary supplement contains a significantly higher level of an NDI than is used in conventional foods. FDA has reviewed and intends to continue reviewing voluntarily submitted notifications for NDIs that are exempt from the notification requirement under 21 U.S.C. 350b(a)(1) because they have been present in the food supply as articles used for food in a form in which the food has not been chemically altered.

Like higher daily intake levels, combining an NDI with other dietary ingredients could also present safety risks, as discussed in question IV.C.2 below.

4. **What are examples of processes that chemically alter an article of food present in the food supply?**

Below are some examples of processes that FDA would likely consider to involve chemical alteration. These processes would also be likely to affect the safety profile of a dietary ingredient. The examples below are intended only for the purpose of illustration and are not a comprehensive list of processes that result in chemical alteration. See question IV.B.5 for further discussion on chemical alteration.

CH 13

- A process that makes or breaks chemical bonds, unless the bonds created by the process are reversed when the ingredient is dissolved in water (e.g., creation of a soluble salt) or during ingestion. Example: hydrolysis.

- Removal of some components of a tincture or solution in water, which changes the chemical or molecular composition or structure of the mixture. Examples: chromatography, distillation, and filtration.

- Use of solvents other than water or aqueous ethanol to make an extract or tincture. The official legislative history of DSHEA specifies that "solution in water" and

---

22   Contact information for the Office of Dietary Supplement Programs can be found on the title page.

"tincture" (solution in aqueous ethanol) are not processes that chemically alter a food.[23] However, other solvents typically alter the composition of the extract in significantly different ways, usually by extracting different types of constituents than are extracted using water and aqueous ethanol.

- High temperature baking or cooking of an ingredient that has not previously been baked or cooked, unless the process causes only minor loss of volatile components with no other changes to the chemical or molecular composition or structure of the ingredient.

- Changing the manufacturing method for an ingredient such that the chemical or molecular composition or structure is significantly different. Examples: changes that alter the composition of materials used to make the ingredient, use of a different solvent, or use of a chromatographic matrix instead of a passive filter.

- Application of nanotechnology that results in new or altered chemical properties of the ingredient.

- Changing agricultural or fermentation conditions to alter the chemical or molecular composition or structure of the ingredient. Examples: sprouting garlic or fermenting yeast using a medium containing large amounts of sodium selenite to create large amounts of organic selenium compounds.

- Fermentation using a fermentation medium different from the one used to make conventional foods in the food supply. Example: use of a defined commercial growth medium to produce a microorganism previously made by fermenting milk into dairy products like yogurt or cheese.

- Use of a botanical ingredient that is at a different life stage than the life stage of the botanical ingredient used as a conventional food. Examples: making an extract from unripe instead of ripe apples or using the mycelium instead of the fruiting body of a fungus.

5. What processes for manufacturing a dietary ingredient from an article of food present in the food supply do not result in chemical alteration?

As set forth in the Congressional Statement of Agreement between the House and Senate sponsors of DSHEA, "[T]he term ''chemically altered' does not include the following physical modifications: minor loss of volatile components, dehydration, lyoph[i]lization, milling, tincture or solution in water, slurry, a powder, or solid in suspension."[24] FDA considers this list to represent examples of manufacturing processes that do not involve chemical alteration, but not necessarily a complete list of such processes.

FDA views "chemical alteration" specifically within the context of section 413(a)(1) of the FD&C Act, which creates an exemption from the NDI notification requirement for

---

23 Statement of Agreement, 140 Cong. Rec. S14801 (daily ed. Oct. 7, 1994).
24 Statement of Agreement, 140 Cong. Rec. S14801 (daily ed. Oct. 7, 1994).

NDIs that have been "present in the food supply" as "article[s] used for food in a form in which the food has not been chemically altered." Because this exemption is for articles that are used for food and present in the food supply (conventional foods and their ingredients), it applies to ingredients that meet the safety standards for conventional foods and have a history of safe use as food. These safeguards provide some confidence that such ingredients are likely to be safe when used in dietary supplements at comparable levels, as long as they are not chemically altered from their form in conventional food.

A process that chemically alters an ingredient found in the food supply can introduce contaminants, solvents, or impurities whose safety is unknown.[25] Such a process may result in an ingredient that not only differs from the source ingredient but also has an unknown safety profile. See question IV.B.4 for further discussion on chemical alteration. A well-characterized starting material may result in no change to the identity of the material after processing, in which case an NDI notification would not be required. However, dietary supplements and dietary ingredients that are complex mixtures introduce more variability into the processing. Therefore, their identity is more likely to change during processing.

In general, FDA considers a process that does not result in chemical alteration to mean a process that: (1) involves an ingredient composed of one single raw material, or derived from a single raw material using a manufacturing process that involves only physical steps (e.g., water extraction and condensation); and (2) does not involve attempts to selectively increase the concentration of particular active ingredients or cause a chemical reaction (other than esterification) that would modify the covalent bonds of any substance in the original material. This type of process is unlikely to affect the safety profile of the ingredient in question or of dietary supplements containing the ingredient.

Some of the processes characterized as "physical modifications" in the Congressional Statement of Agreement (milling, slurry, powder, or solid in suspension) do not alter the chemical or molecular composition or structure of the ingredient. FDA views such changes as unlikely to create a change in the safety profile of an ingredient being used in conventional food. Dehydration, lyophilization, or making a tincture, solution in water, or slurry can be said to change the composition of the ingredient, but only by changing the amount of water (or ethanol, in the case of a tincture). FDA regards such a minor change in composition as extremely unlikely to change the safety profile of an ingredient used in conventional food. Similarly, a minor loss of volatile components during processing is unlikely to change the safety profile of an ingredient used in conventional food. In a typical extraction, however, the first step is solution in water or another solvent, followed by filtration to remove undissolved material.

CH 13

---

25   FDA, Guidance for Industry: Assessing the Effects of Significant Manufacturing Process Changes, Including Emerging Technologies, on the Safety and Regulatory Status of Food Ingredients and Food Contact Substances, Including Food Ingredients that are Color Additives;June 2014. Available at: http://www.fda.gov/food/guidanceregulation/guidancedocumentsregulatoryinformation/ucm300661.htm

This is a much larger change in the composition of the ingredient. FDA generally regards extraction that includes a filtration step or that involves the use of a solvent other than water or alcohol (aqueous ethanol) as a process that chemically alters the source ingredient and therefore triggers the NDI notification requirement for the resulting dietary ingredient.

As industry develops new technologies and processes other than those described as physical modifications in the Congressional Statement of Agreement, we encourage you to consult with us when considering whether a notification is needed in a particular situation, as well as before submitting an NDI notification.[26] We intend to evaluate any new technology or process based on our guidance on chemical alteration as set forth in this document. We also intend to consider whether or not the technology or process would affect the safety profile of the dietary ingredient and the dietary supplement in which it is used.

We are willing to consider arguments supported by science demonstrating that particular manufacturing processes do not actually result in a chemical alteration or have any effect on the safety profile of the ingredient. In such cases, we encourage manufacturers and distributors to arrange a pre-notification meeting with FDA to discuss their basis for this belief.

C. Other Questions About When an NDI Notification Is Necessary

1. May I submit a single NDI notification that contains safety data for a range of conditions of use and covers multiple products?

Yes. We accept notifications that cover multiple dietary supplements and include safety data for a range of doses, daily intake levels, and/or other variations in conditions of use (e.g., serving size, duration of use, frequency of intake, target population, dosage form, or different formulations of pre-DSHEA ingredients in combination with the NDI). We recommend you submit safety data up to and including the highest dose and daily intake level, but indicate any lower daily intake levels at which the NDI may be marketed and include research that evaluates statistically relevant data points, such as a range of daily intake levels, to strengthen the safety analysis. FDA has received a number of notifications that cover a range of doses and daily intake levels. These notifications are publicly available in the NDI notification docket on *www.regulations.gov*. Contact FDA's Office of Dietary Supplement Programs for more information.[27]

You may also submit a confidential "NDI master file" to FDA which contains the manufacturing, specifications and other identity information needed to completely describe the ingredient. You may incorporate by reference the contents of the master file into an NDI notification. You may also authorize other firms to reference the contents of the master file in notifications describing the ingredient they obtain from you. FDA expects that most submitters will identify the contents of NDI master files and ingredient

---

26 Contact information for the Office of Dietary Supplement Programs can be found on the title page.
27 Contact information for the Office of Dietary Supplement Programs can be found on the title page.

specifications as trade secrets (see question V.A.16) and will only discuss them with the firm which submitted them.

If you are a dietary supplement manufacturer or distributor and either you or the manufacturer or distributor of the NDI have submitted an NDI notification that covers the conditions under which the NDI will be used in your supplement, you need not submit a new notification for the use of the NDI in that supplement. However, if you are planning to market a product that exceeds the highest daily intake level or single-serving dose for which safety information was submitted in the previous NDI notification, you should submit a new notification because the previous NDI notification does not cover the higher single-serving or daily intake level. Similarly, if the NDI is not identical to the NDI evaluated in the previous NDI notification, the dietary ingredients to be combined with the NDI in your product differ from those in the product that was the subject of the previous notification, or any other conditions under which the NDI will be used in the new product were not evaluated in the original notification, a new notification should be submitted. See questions IV.C.2 and IV.C.3.

2. If I submit an NDI notification for a dietary supplement that I manufacture or distribute and then decide to manufacture or distribute a different supplement that contains the same NDI, should I submit another NDI notification?

The answer depends on what was covered in your previous NDI notification, on how FDA responded, and on the extent to which the NDI's proposed conditions of use in your new dietary supplement differ from those evaluated in the notification. If you have already submitted an NDI notification for a dietary supplement containing an NDI, you need not submit a separate notification for a different dietary supplement containing the same NDI if the following criteria are met:

- The single-serving dose and daily intake level of the NDI specified in the labeling of the new supplement are less than or equal to the highest single-serving dose and daily intake level evaluated in your original NDI notification;

- The new supplement does not combine the NDI with other dietary ingredients that were not included in your original NDI notification;

- The target populations for the new supplement are the same as, or a subset of, the target populations specified in your original notification;

- All other conditions of use are the same as or more restrictive (e.g., lower dose and daily intake, shorter duration of use) than the conditions of use described in your prior NDI notification; and

- FDA did not express safety or other regulatory concerns in response to your prior NDI notification.

As discussed in question IV.C.1, you may submit a NDI notification that contains safety information about a range of daily intake levels and/or other conditions of use for dietary supplements containing the NDI. Once you have submitted a notification for an NDI that covers multiple conditions of use, you may market as many dietary

CH 13

supplements containing that NDI as you wish without submitting another notification, as long as the bulleted criteria above are met. Put another way, if the conditions of use for the dietary supplement you plan to market are within the conditions of use evaluated in your original notification and FDA did not object to that notification, you may market the supplement without submitting another notification.

However, if any of the bulleted criteria above are not met, you should submit another NDI notification. For example, suppose you want to market a dietary supplement with a higher daily intake level of the NDI than the level evaluated in your original notification. In general, the risk from a substance is likely to increase as intake increases above levels safely consumed in the past. A higher intake level of some substances could present toxicity risks to consumers. If you have not evaluated safety information for the higher daily intake level, you do not have an adequate basis on which to conclude that a dietary supplement containing the NDI at that higher level will reasonably be expected to be safe.

The same principle applies for other changes in conditions of use, such as combining the NDI with dietary ingredients other than those that were in the dietary supplement evaluated in the original NDI notification. When dietary ingredients are combined, they can interact. In some cases, these interactions can present risks to consumers. For example, adverse effects—such as low blood pressure, low heart rate, gastrointestinal distress, and in severe cases, irregular heartbeat—may occur when a new dietary ingredient with cholinesterase-inhibiting properties (such as huperzine A or galantamine) is combined with another dietary ingredient that is a cholinergic agonist (e.g., yohimbe bark extract). To have a basis to conclude that a dietary supplement that combines an NDI with one or more pre-DSHEA dietary ingredients will reasonably be expected to be safe, it is necessary to consider whether the addition of the other dietary ingredients will affect the safety of the NDI or the resulting dietary supplement.

The same analysis applies to other conditions of use that are outside the scope of the original notification. If the information in your original notification is insufficient to provide a basis to conclude that your new dietary supplement will reasonably be expected to be safe, then the statutory requirement for the "manufacturer or distributor of the dietary ingredient or dietary supplement" to provide FDA with "information . . . which is the basis on which the manufacturer or distributor has concluded that a dietary supplement containing such dietary ingredient will reasonably be expected to be safe" (21 U.S.C. 350b(a)(2)) has not been met. It is your responsibility to meet it by conducting a safety evaluation and submitting a notification with data about the safety of the NDI under the conditions of use in your proposed dietary supplement.

3. If a dietary supplement manufacturer or distributor has submitted an NDI notification prior to marketing a dietary supplement with the NDI, and I intend to market a dietary supplement containing the same NDI, should I also submit an NDI notification?

Yes. Section 413(a)(2) of the FD&C Act (21 U.S.C. 350b(a)(2)) states that a dietary supplement that contains an NDI is deemed adulterated unless, among other things, the manufacturer or distributor of the dietary ingredient or the dietary supplement submits an NDI notification at least 75 days before introducing it into interstate commerce. Note that, in situations where the NDI manufacturer or distributor has not submitted a notification, the statute deems a dietary supplement that contains the NDI to be adulterated unless the manufacturer or distributor of "the" dietary supplement (that particular dietary supplement), not "a" dietary supplement (some other dietary supplement containing the NDI) has submitted a notification. Accordingly, if the NDI manufacturer or distributor has not submitted a notification covering the conditions of the NDI's use, each manufacturer or distributor of a supplement containing the NDI must submit an NDI notification with "information, including any citation to published articles, which is the basis on which the manufacturer or distributor has concluded that a dietary supplement containing such dietary ingredient will reasonably be expected to be safe" (21 U.S.C. 350b(a)(2)). The supplement manufacturer or distributor may meet the requirement to provide safety information either by conducting its own safety evaluation or relying on a safety evaluation conducted by another entity, such as a previously submitted NDI notification (see question IV.C.4). Once the manufacturer or distributor of the supplement has submitted an NDI notification to FDA, that firm need not submit further notifications for other supplements containing the same NDI if the conditions of use of the other supplements are within the conditions of use evaluated in the firm's original notification (see question IV.C.2).

4. When I submit an NDI notification, may I rely on data from another NDI notification or master file?

Yes, if one of the following applies:

- you submitted the previous notification or master file,

- the previous notification (or portion of a previous notification) on which you wish to rely is public, or

- the person who submitted the previous notification or master file gives you written permission to rely on non-public information from that notification. If you are relying on non-public information from another firm's NDI master file or from another notification, you should provide FDA with documentation (such as a signed letter from the other notifier) showing that you are authorized to use the information, and the duration of that authorization. If the authorization does not extend to the entire master file or notification, the authorization from the previous notifier should specify the part(s) of the notification you are authorized to use.

CH 13

Manufacturing processes and specifications needed to establish the identity of an NDI are usually trade secrets that are not available in the NDI docket. It should be noted that the original notifier is under no obligation to share with other manufacturers and distributors any trade secrets or confidential commercial information that were part of the basis for a safety conclusion for the original notifier's product. A written authorization to reference a notification or master file in NDI notifications does not include the right to see or copy the notification or master file unless the submitter otherwise specifies. Note that while one firm may authorize another to reference confidential safety information in a subsequent notification, that subsequent notification must demonstrate that the submitting firm understands enough about that safety information to have a basis to conclude that consumption of the NDI in the new product will reasonably be expected to be safe under the conditions of use described in its notification.

5. **Can FDA provide examples with an explanation to help distinguish situations in which separate notifications are required for dietary supplements containing the same NDI from situations in which the same NDI notification covers multiple dietary supplements?**

Two important factors you should consider when deciding whether to submit a notification for a dietary supplement containing an NDI that was the subject of a previous notification are:

1) Are the NDI's conditions of use in the second product within the conditions of use evaluated in the previous notification? If not, you should submit a separate notification for the second product because the safety evaluation in the previous notification did not include any consideration of the new conditions of use in the second dietary supplement and therefore cannot provide a basis to conclude that the NDI will reasonably be expected to be safe under those conditions of use.

2) Who was the previous notifier and what is that entity's relationship (e.g., same firm, supplier, or competitor) to the manufacturer or distributor who intends to market the second product? See questions IV.C.2 and IV.C.3 and the examples below for more about how the answer to this question affects whether an NDI notification for the second product is necessary.

In each of the scenarios below, assume that FDA has acknowledged the filing of the first NDI notification and has not raised any safety or regulatory concerns in response to that notification.

Scenario 1: Ingredient Supplier A submits a notification for NDI-A1 and a master file describing its manufacturing process. Supplement Manufacturer X intends to market a single-ingredient dietary supplement containing a dietary ingredient (NDI-B1) that purports to be the same as NDI-A1, but is made by a different dietary ingredient manufacturer, Ingredient Supplier B.

Analysis: Manufacturer X should submit an NDI notification for the use of NDI-B1 in its single-ingredient dietary supplement because Supplier B has submitted no NDI notification for NDI-B1 (see question IV.C.3). However, if Manufacturer X can establish that NDI-B1 is the same as NDI-A1 and Supplier A's prior notification covers the conditions of use of NDI-A1 in Manufacturer X's single-ingredient dietary supplement, then the NDI notification for the new supplement made with NDI-B1 could simply consist of data showing that NDI-B1 is identical to NDI-A1, a reference to the safety evaluation in Supplier A's notification, and a signed authorization from Supplier A for Manufacturer

X to use any non-public safety data from A's notification and the manufacturing master file. On the other hand, if Manufacturer X cannot establish that NDI-B1 is the same as NDI-A1, X's notification will have to contain safety information specific to NDI-B1 because a different NDI requires its own safety evaluation.[28]

Scenario 2: Ingredient Supplier A submits a notification for NDI-A2. Supplier A's notification includes safety information for a dietary supplement tablet containing NDI-A2 as the sole dietary ingredient in a formulation with several non-dietary ingredients used as binders and fillers. Supplement Manufacturer X wants to use the same level of NDI-A2 in a dietary supplement tablet with NDI-A2 as the sole dietary ingredient, but in a formulation with different non-dietary ingredients used as binders and fillers.

Analysis: Manufacturer X does not need to submit an NDI notification because the only difference between Manufacturer X's product and the formulation described in Supplier A's notification is a change in non-dietary ingredients (i.e., inactive ingredients). However, Manufacturer X should evaluate whether the change affects the safety of the dietary supplement and document the basis for its conclusion before marketing the product.

Scenario 3: Ingredient Supplier A submits a notification for NDI-A3 that includes safety information for single-ingredient dietary supplement formulations containing up to 500 mg/day of the NDI. Supplement Manufacturer X is using NDI-A3 in a single-ingredient dietary supplement at a level of 250 mg/day but wants to increase the amount of NDI-A3 to 500 mg/day.

Analysis: Because Supplier A's initial notification included safety information for NDI-A3 up to 500 mg/day, Manufacturer X does not need to submit a notification for either the 250 mg/day or 500 mg/day formulation, assuming all other conditions of use are the same as those evaluated in Supplier A's notification.

Scenario 4: Ingredient Supplier A submits a notification for NDI-A4. Supplier A's notification includes safety information for a dietary supplement containing NDI-A4 in combination with vitamin A, vitamin C, sodium, calcium, and iron. Supplement Manufacturer X intends to use NDI-A4 in a dietary supplement at recommended doses and daily intake levels that do not exceed the high end of the range evaluated in Supplier A's notification. Manufacturer X's supplement will also contain some, but not all, of the vitamins and minerals included in Supplier A's notification. All other conditions of use will be the same as those evaluated in A's notification.

Analysis: Manufacturer X does not need to submit another notification because Supplier A's notification covers all the conditions of NDI-A4's use in Manufacturer X's new product.

Scenario 5: Company Q wants to market a supercritical fluid extract of *Convallaria majalis L*. The plant is on an industry list of pre-DSHEA dietary ingredients.

---

28   See 21 U.S.C. 350b(a)(2).

Analysis: Company Q must submit an NDI notification. Even though this botanical appears on an industry list of old dietary ingredients, it has historically been used only as an herbal drug, so a history of use in food has not been established. In addition, supercritical fluid extraction was not commonly used prior to 1994, and there is no evidence of extracts like this having being marketed as food prior to 1994.

Scenario 6: Company Q received an acknowledgment letter without objection in response to its NDI notification for the *Convallaria majalis L.* supplement described in Scenario 5. Now Company Q wants to market the ingredient in combination with another dietary ingredient, an extract from *Nerium oleander L.*, which has been the subject of an NDI notification from one of Company Q's competitors, Company Y. Company Y received an acknowledgment letter without objection in response to its notification. Both notifications discussed the safety of the extracts in depth and described manufacturing procedures and specifications for cardiac glycosides. The notifications also included results from clinical testing or testing in a non-rodent species appropriate for the evaluation of cardiac risk.

Analysis: Company Q must submit a new notification for the combination. A combination of two NDIs is itself an NDI. Although the notifications included in-depth discussions of the safety of the extracts, each of the plants is known to contain glycosides with potent cardiotoxic activity and it is difficult to predict the toxicity of the combination. The new notification should include a discussion of the safety of the combination, which is likely to be an in-depth discussion because both ingredients affect the same organ system. Given the overlapping toxicological endpoint and the severity of the potential toxicity, we would recommend that the new notification include results from safety testing of the combination. However, in a notification for a combination of two NDIs with no specific safety problems where each of the NDIs had been the subject of a prior notification to FDA that was acknowledged without objection, the section of the new notification discussing the safety of the combination could be brief.

6. Should I notify FDA about a microbial ingredient in my dietary supplement?

Yes, if it is an NDI that has not been present in the food supply as an article used for food in a form in which the food has not been chemically altered (21 U.S.C. 350b(a)(1)).

However, not all bacterial microorganisms are dietary ingredients, and a microorganism that is not a dietary ingredient cannot be an NDI. For example, pathogenic species of bacteria, such as *Salmonella* species or *Escherichia coli*, are not dietary ingredients even though they may have been inadvertently present in foods as contaminants. Bacteria that have never been consumed as food are unlikely to be dietary ingredients.

A bacterial microorganism is a dietary ingredient if it is a dietary substance (an intentional constituent of food) or otherwise falls within one of the dietary ingredient categories listed in 21 U.S.C. 321(ff)(1). For example, bacteria that are used to produce fermented foods that are eaten without a cooking or pasteurization step (e.g., lactic acid bacteria used to produce cheese or yogurt) could be "dietary substances for use by man to supplement the diet by increasing the total dietary intake," which are defined as dietary ingredients in section 201(ff)(1)(E) of the FD&C Act (21 U.S.C. 321(ff)(1)(E)). FDA does not have a separate regulatory category or definition for dietary ingredients consisting of live or viable microorganisms.

7. If I want to market a dietary supplement containing several pre-DSHEA ingredients that haven't previously been marketed together, do I have to submit an NDI notification?

No. The NDI notification requirement applies only to dietary supplements that contain at least one NDI. If each of the dietary ingredients in a dietary supplement was marketed in the United States before October 15, 1994, marketing these ingredients together for the first time in the same dietary supplement does not create an NDI or trigger the NDI notification requirement.

8. Can FDA provide visual aids to help me decide whether I should submit an NDI notification?

Yes. The following table illustrates when an NDI notification is required and when the NDI adulteration standard applies. In addition, Section VIII. Appendix: Decision Tree for NDI Notification has a decision tree to walk you through the steps of deciding whether to submit an NDI notification.

Table 1: Definition of New Dietary Ingredient (NDI), Requirement for NDI Notification and Applicability of NDI Adulteration Standard[29]

	New Dietary Ingredient (NDI)	NDI notification required?	NDI adulteration standard applies?
A dietary ingredient that was marketed in the U.S. before October 15, 1994	No	No	No
A dietary ingredient that was NOT marketed in the U.S. before October 15, 1994, AND was present in the food supply as an article used for food which has	Yes	See a) or b)	Yes
a) not been chemically altered	Yes	No	Yes
b) been chemically altered	Yes	Yes	Yes
A dietary ingredient that was NOT marketed in the U.S. before October 15, 1994, AND was NOT present in the food supply as an article used for food.	Yes	Yes	Yes

CH 13

29   The NDI adulteration standard in 21 U.S.C. 342(f)(1)(B) provides that a dietary supplement containing an NDI is adulterated unless there is adequate information to provide reasonable assurance that the NDI does not present a significant or unreasonable risk of illness or injury.

D. Additional Issues to Consider Before Submitting an NDI Notification

1. What is a dietary ingredient?

The definition of "dietary supplement" describes a "dietary ingredient" in 21 U.S.C. 321(ff)(1) as:

(A) A vitamin;

(B) A mineral;

(C) An herb or other botanical;

(D) An amino acid;

(E) A dietary substance for use by man to supplement the diet by increasing the total dietary intake; or

(F) A concentrate, metabolite, constituent, extract, or combination of any ingredient described in (A), (B), (C), (D), or (E).

2. May a contaminant that is found in the food supply be a dietary ingredient?

No. Although most constituents of conventional foods in the food supply would be "dietary substances" that could be used as dietary ingredients under section 201(ff)(1) (E) of the FD&C Act (21 U.S.C. 321(ff)(1)(E)), contaminants are different from other food constituents. A contaminant of food (like *Salmonella* or lead) is not a dietary substance that qualifies for use as a dietary ingredient in a dietary supplement product even if it is not harmful to health (e.g., sterilized *Salmonella*) because contaminants are not intended for ingestion, nor are they considered to be food or part of the food supply. Contaminants are consumed unintentionally and are not "dietary substance[s] for use by man to supplement the diet by increasing the total dietary intake" (21 U.S.C. 321(ff)(1) (E)).

3. Under what circumstances does FDA consider synthetically produced substances to be dietary ingredients under the FD&C Act?

Whether a synthetically produced substance qualifies as a dietary ingredient depends on whether the substance fits into one of the categories of dietary ingredients that are defined in section 201(ff)(1) of the FD&C Act (21 U.S.C. 321(ff)(1)). In some cases, description of the category in the FD&C Act encompasses synthetically produced substances; in others, it does not. The six dietary ingredient categories are discussed in the bullets below.

- Vitamins, Minerals, and Amino Acids (21 U.S.C. 321(ff)(1)(A), (B), (D))

  Synthetic vitamins, minerals, and amino acids qualify as dietary ingredients because vitamins, minerals, and amino acids, regardless of source, are specifically designated as dietary ingredients under sections 201(ff)(1)(A), 201(ff)(1)(B), and 201(ff)(1) (D) of the FD&C Act, respectively. Synthetic vitamins, minerals, and amino acids are recognized as dietary ingredients because a vitamin, mineral, or amino acid is defined by its nutritional function (its ability to provide nutrients to the human body), not by its state of matter like a botanical.

- Herb or other botanical (21 U.S.C. 321(ff)(1)(C))

Under a plain reading of the FD&C Act, a synthetic copy of an herb or other botanical does not qualify as a dietary ingredient under section 201(ff)(1)(C) of the FD&C Act. As defined in the glossary, an herb or botanical includes only plants, algae, fungi, their exudates (secretions, such as sap or resin), and their physical parts. A substance that has been synthesized in a laboratory or factory has never been part of an herb or other botanical and, therefore, is not a dietary ingredient under section 201(ff)(1)(C) of the FD&C Act.[30]

- Dietary substance for use by man to supplement the diet by increasing the total dietary intake (21 U.S.C. 321(ff)(1)(E))

For purposes of section 201(ff)(1)(E) of the FD&C Act, we interpret "dietary substance" in accordance with its common, usual meaning because the term is not defined in the FD&C Act or by regulation. According to *Webster's II New Riverside University Dictionary* (1994), "dietary" means "of or relating to diet" and "diet" means "an organism's usual food and drink." In conjunction with "for use by man," we interpret "dietary substance," as used in section 201(ff)(1)(E), to mean a substance commonly used as human food or drink. The rest of the definition, which specifies that the substance be for use "to supplement the diet by *increasing* the *total* dietary intake,"[31] is further evidence that "dietary substance" is intended to mean foods and food components that humans eat as part of their usual diet. One cannot increase the "total dietary intake" of something that is not part of the human diet in the first place.

Because the "dietary substance" category is defined in part by history of use, a synthetic copy of a botanical ingredient may qualify as a dietary ingredient under section 201(ff)(1)(E) if the synthetic copy has been used as a lawfully marketed ingredient in the conventional food supply. For example, a synthetic copy of a botanical ingredient would be a dietary ingredient under section 201(ff)(1)(E) if the synthetic copy has been used as an ingredient in the conventional food supply. Two common examples are vanillin and cinnamic acid, botanical constituents that, for economic reasons, are usually produced synthetically for use as flavorings in food.

- Concentrate, metabolite, constituent, extract, or combination of another dietary ingredient described in clause (A), (B), (C), (D), or (E) (21 U.S.C. 321(ff)(1)(F))

A "constituent" is an article that is a physical part of a whole and can be isolated from the whole. A synthetic copy of a constituent of a botanical was never part of

CH 13

---

30   Note, however, that if the synthetic copy has itself been used as a lawfully marketed ingredient in the conventional food supply, it may be a "dietary substance[s] for use by man to supplement the diet by increasing the total dietary intake" and therefore qualify as a dietary ingredient under 21 U.S.C. 321(ff)(1)(E) (see next bullet in text), even though it is not an herbal or botanical dietary ingredient under 21 U.S.C. 321(ff)(1)(C).
31   21 U.S.C. 321(ff)(1)(E) (emphasis added).

the botanical. Therefore, the synthetic copy is not a "constituent" of the botanical and does not qualify as a dietary ingredient under section 201(ff)(1)(F) of the FD&C Act (21 U.S.C. 321(ff)(1)(F)), even if the synthetic copy is chemically identical to a constituent of a plant.[32]

By the same principle, an extract made from a synthetic copy of one or more constituents of a botanical is not an "extract" of the botanical under section 201(ff)(1)(F) of the FD&C Act because the constituents were never part of the botanical and therefore could not be extracted from the botanical. Similarly, a synthetic copy of a botanical concentrate is not a concentrate of a botanical because, by definition, a "concentrate" is an article that has been reduced in volume or bulk by removal of liquid. To make a concentrate of a botanical, one must start by extracting the desired constituents from the botanical with a solvent and then concentrate the constituents by reducing the amount of solvent (e.g., by boiling the extract). If synthetic material that was never actually in the botanical is used as the starting point for a concentrate, the final product will be a concentrate of the synthetic material, not a concentrate of the botanical.

For more than a decade, FDA has consistently interpreted section 201(ff)(1)(F) of the FD&C Act as not including synthetic copies of botanical constituents, extracts, or concentrates.[33] Such a substance may in some cases, however, qualify as a dietary ingredient under another provision of section 201(ff)(1). For example, there are synthetically produced substances in the food supply that are dietary ingredients under section 201(ff)(1)(E) because they are "dietary substance[s] for use by man to supplement the diet by increasing the total dietary intake" (see discussion in preceding bullet). A synthetic copy of a botanical constituent (e.g., vanillin synthesized from lignins) or an extract made from a synthetic copy of a botanical constituent (e.g., artificial vanilla extract) would qualify as a dietary ingredient under section 201(ff)(1)(E) if used as a food ingredient.

A metabolite that has been synthesized from another dietary ingredient would be a dietary ingredient under section 201(ff)(1)(F) and could be used as a dietary ingredient in a dietary supplement. Although the definition of a metabolite[34]

---

32   See, e.g., Final Rule Declaring Dietary Supplements Containing Ephedrine Alkaloids Adulterated Because They Present an Unreasonable Risk, 69 FR 6788, 6793 (Feb. 11, 2004).

33   This interpretation dates back to at least 2001, and the dietary supplement industry has been aware of it since that time. See Letter from Dennis E. Baker, Associate Director for Regulatory Affairs, FDA, to Laura M. Nagel, Deputy Assistant Administrator, Office of Diversion Control, DEA (June 21, 2001) Available at: http://odspracticum.od.nih.gov/2011/readinglists/dea_ephedrine_letter.pdf; Final Rule Declaring Dietary Supplements Containing Ephedrine Alkaloids Adulterated, supra note 32; Natural Products Insider, Consumer Group Asks FDA to Seize Synthetic Ephedrine 'Supplements' (Feb. 1, 2002) Available at: http://www.naturalproductsinsider.com/news/2002/02/consumer-group-asks-fda-to-seize-synthetic-ephedri.aspx; Citizen Petition 2004P-0169 from Coalition to Preserve DSHEA (Apr. 8, 2004), Docket No. 2004P-0169 (asking FDA to reconsider position that botanical dietary ingredient category excludes synthetic equivalents) Available at: http://www.fda.gov/ohrms/dockets/dailys/04/apr04/040804/04p-0169-cp00001-vol1.pdf; Letter from Michael M. Landa, Acting Director, Center for Food Safety and Applied Nutrition, FDA, to Marc Ullman, Ullman, Shapiro & Ullman, LLP, responding to Citizen Petition FDA-2009-P-0298 from OVOS Natural Health Inc. (Feb. 23, 2011) Available at: https://www.regulations.gov/document?D=FDA-2009-P-0298-0008.

34   See section VII, "Metabolite."

requires human ingestion of the dietary ingredient to increase the production or flux of the metabolite in the human body, it does not require the metabolism to actually take place in a human being during the manufacture of a dietary ingredient. A metabolite may be synthetically produced, provided that the starting material is a dietary ingredient and the production process mimics the metabolic process in the body following ingestion.

4. Are food contact substances and other indirect food additives dietary ingredients? What about secondary direct food additives?

These substances generally do not qualify as dietary ingredients by virtue of their use as food additives. Although food contact substances[35] and other indirect food additives[36] may be present in the food supply because they migrate into certain foods from packaging or other articles that contact the food, their presence in these foods is merely incidental. A substance that migrates into a food during manufacturing or storage is not a "dietary substance for use by man to supplement the diet by increasing the total dietary intake" (21 U.S.C. 321(ff)(1)(E)) because it is not consumed as a component of the diet, but merely as a byproduct of its use in articles that contact food. However, if such a substance falls under one of the other dietary ingredient categories listed in section 201(ff)(1) of the FD&C Act, it could be a dietary ingredient.

For similar reasons, secondary direct food additives generally do not qualify as dietary ingredients through their use in food manufacturing. Secondary direct food additives are added during the manufacturing of a food to achieve a technical effect (e.g., controlling the growth of microbes), but they have no technical effect in the finished food. Generally, secondary direct food additives are used as processing aids, and often they also meet the definition of a food contact substance.[37] Although they may remain in the food after processing, they are generally present in the finished food only at trace levels, if at all. Like indirect additives, secondary direct food additives are not consumed as components of the diet, but are only incidentally present, if at all, in the finished food as byproducts of processing. Accordingly, they are not "dietary substances for use by man to supplement the diet by increasing the total dietary intake." However, as with indirect additives, a secondary direct food additive could be a dietary ingredient if it belongs to one of the other dietary ingredient categories listed in section 201(ff)(1) of the FD&C Act.

CH
13

---

35   A food contact substance is a substance intended for use as a component of materials used in manufacturing, packing, packaging, transporting, or holding food if that use is not intended to have any technical effect in the food. 21 U.S.C. 348(h)(6).

36   Indirect food additives come into contact with food as part of packaging, holding, or processing, but they are not intended to be added directly to, become a component of, or have a technical effect in or on the food. Before the FDA Modernization Act of 1997, indirect food additives were approved by regulation. Now, additional indirect food additives are authorized through the food contact substance notification program. In addition, indirect food additives may be authorized through the threshold of regulation exemption process in 21 CFR 170.39. See FDA, Food Ingredients and Packaging Terms. Available at: http://www.fda.gov/Food/IngredientsPackagingLabeling/Definitions/default.htm(accessedApril 22, 2015).

37   See FDA, Food Ingredients and Packaging Terms. Available at: http://www.fda.gov/Food/IngredientsPackagingLabeling/Definitions/default.htm(accessedApril 22, 2015).

5. If I alter the chemical structure of a dietary ingredient, is the new substance still a dietary ingredient?

It depends. Altering the chemical structure of a dietary ingredient (e.g., creation of new stereoisomers, addition of new chemical groups as in esterification) creates a new substance that is different from the original dietary ingredient. The new substance is not considered to be a dietary ingredient merely because it has been altered from a substance that is a dietary ingredient and, therefore, is in some way related to the dietary ingredient.

In some cases, however, the new substance may independently qualify for one of the dietary ingredient categories listed in section 201(ff)(1) of the FD&C Act. For example, taurine is the end product of the metabolism of the amino acid cysteine. It is thus a metabolite of an amino acid and fits one of the definitions of a dietary ingredient (see 21 U.S.C. 321(ff)(1)(D), (F)). The enzymatic or synthetic processing of cysteine or any other dietary ingredient would be an appropriate method for the manufacture of a metabolite of a dietary ingredient like taurine for use in a dietary supplement. See questions IV.B.4 and IV.B.5 for additional discussion on chemical alteration.

6. In what forms may a dietary supplement containing my NDI be sold?

The FD&C Act specifically provides for dietary supplements to be in tablet, capsule, powder, softgel, gelcap, or liquid form (21 U.S.C. 321(ff)(2)(A)(i), 350(c)(1)(B)(i)).

In addition, the statute permits dietary supplements in other forms as long as the product is intended for ingestion, is not represented as conventional food, and is not represented for use as a sole item of a meal or of the diet (21 U.S.C. 321(ff)(2), 350(c)(1)(B)(ii)).

7. When FDA reviews an NDI notification, does the agency consider whether the prohibition in section 301(ll) of the FD&C Act applies to the use of the NDI in a dietary supplement?

No. Section 301(ll) of the FD&C Act (21 U.S.C. 331(ll)) prohibits the introduction or delivery for introduction into interstate commerce of any food that contains a drug approved under 21 U.S.C. 355, a biological product licensed under 42 U.S.C. 262, or a drug or a biological product for which substantial clinical investigations have been instituted and their existence made public, unless one of the exemptions in section 301(ll)(1)-(4) applies. When reviewing NDI notifications, FDA's current practice is not to consider whether section 301(ll) or any of its exemptions apply to the NDI. Accordingly, a "no objection" response to an NDI notification should not be construed to be a statement that a dietary supplement containing the NDI, if introduced or delivered for introduction into interstate commerce, would not violate section 301(ll) of the FD&C Act.

8. May an ingredient that has not been marketed as a food or as a dietary supplement, but has been approved as a new drug or licensed as a biologic, be used as an NDI in a dietary supplement?

No, unless FDA issues a regulation, after notice and comment, finding that the ingredient, when used as or in a dietary supplement, would be lawful under the FD&C Act. A regulation of this type may be requested by filing a citizen petition under 21 CFR 10.30, but none has been issued to date. Absent such a regulation, an ingredient that has been approved as a new drug or licensed as a biologic can be a dietary ingredient for use in a dietary supplement if, and only if, prior to such approval or licensing, the ingredient was marketed as a dietary supplement or as a food.

9. May I use an ingredient in a dietary supplement if it has been clinically tested as a drug but has not been approved as a drug in the U.S.?

It depends on whether the ingredient was authorized for investigation in clinical trials under an investigational new drug application (IND), whether the date the IND went into effect was before or after the date the ingredient was first marketed as a food or as a dietary supplement, whether the clinical trials were "substantial clinical investigations," and whether their existence was made public. The general rule is that an article that was authorized for investigation as a new drug or as a biologic before being marketed as a food or as a dietary supplement cannot be marketed as a dietary supplement if substantial clinical investigations of the article have begun and the existence of such investigations has been made public.

FDA can create an exception to this prohibition by regulation, but only if the agency finds that the use of the article in dietary supplements would be lawful. To date, no such regulations have been issued. The appropriate mechanism to request such a regulation is to file a citizen petition under 21 CFR 10.30.

10. How do I determine whether a dietary ingredient is an article that is approved or authorized for investigation as a new drug?

Either an entire product or a component of the product, such as an active ingredient, may be "an article that is approved as a new drug" or an article "authorized for investigation as a new drug" within the meaning of section 201(ff)(3)(B) of the FD&C Act (21 U.S.C. 321(ff)(3)(B)).[38] For example, assume that Substance A, which is a constituent of a plant and has never been marketed as an article of food or as a dietary supplement, is a botanical dietary ingredient under section 201(ff)(1)(C) of the FD&C Act. A drug company is studying a salt of Substance A, "Substance A hydrochloride," as an investigational new drug under an IND. In this situation, the relevant article for purposes of whether Substance A can be used in a dietary supplement is not Substance A hydrochloride, but Substance A itself, because Substance A is the ***active moiety***[39] that is being studied for its possible therapeutic action. Any compound that delivers Substance A is excluded from being used in a dietary supplement.[40]

CH 13

---

38   Pharmanex v. Shalala, 221 F.3d 1151, 1154-1160 (10th Cir. 2000).

39   Under 21 CFR 316.3(b)(2), "active moiety" means "the molecule or ion, excluding those appended portions of the molecule that cause the drug to be an ester, salt (including a salt with hydrogen or coordination bonds), or other noncovalent derivative (such as a complex, chelate, or clathrate) of the molecule, responsible for the physiological or pharmacological action of the drug substance." See also 21 CFR 314.108(a).

40   Letter from Michael A. Chappell, Acting Associate Commissioner of Regulatory Affairs, FDA, to Kathleen M.

11. May a dietary ingredient that was authorized for investigation as a new drug in the past be used as an NDI in a dietary supplement if the IND was withdrawn or the ingredient is no longer being investigated as a new drug?

It depends on the facts of the particular situation (see answer to IV.D.9 above), but withdrawal of the IND and cessation of clinical trials of the ingredient's use as a new drug make no difference in whether the ingredient may be used in a dietary supplement. The dietary supplement category does not include an article authorized for investigation as a new drug or biologic for which substantial clinical investigations have been instituted and for which the existence of such investigations has been made public, which was not before such authorization marketed as a dietary supplement or as a food, unless FDA has issued a regulation finding that the article would be lawful under the FD&C Act (21 U.S.C. 321(ff)((3)(B)(ii)). "Authorized for investigation" means that the article is the subject of an IND that has gone into effect (see 21 CFR 312.40).

12. May I manufacture and sell a dietary supplement containing a dietary ingredient that was marketed as a food or dietary supplement before it was approved as a drug, licensed as a biologic, or authorized for investigation under an IND?

Yes, in this situation the dietary ingredient may be used in dietary supplements. In considering whether a substance has been "marketed as a dietary supplement or as a food," FDA looks for evidence of one of the following:

1. Evidence that the substance itself was sold or offered for sale in the U.S. as a dietary supplement, dietary ingredient for use in dietary supplements, or conventional food. For example, a catalog listing a product identified as a "Substance A supplement" would establish the marketing of Substance A as a dietary supplement. Similarly, business records documenting that a substance was sold or offered for wholesale or retail sale for use as an ingredient in a conventional food would establish the marketing of the substance as a food.

2. Evidence that the substance was a component of a food or dietary supplement that was sold or offered for sale in the U.S., and that a manufacturer or distributor of the food or dietary supplement marketed it for the content of the substance by, for example, making claims about the substance or otherwise highlighting its presence in the product.[41] For example, in *Pharmanex v. Shalala*, the firm marketed lovastatin, a component of its red yeast rice product Cholestin, by promoting the lovastatin content of Cholestin.[42] Merely showing that the substance was present as a component in a marketed food would not be enough to show that the substance was "marketed," however.

Sanzo, Morgan, Lewis & Bockius LLP, responding to Citizen Petition 2005P-0259 from Biostratum, Inc (Jan. 12, 2009). Docket No. FDA-2005-P-0259 [Document ID: FDA-2005-P-0259-0004].

41   See *Pharmanex v. Shalala*, 2001 WL 741419, at *4 & n.5 (D. Utah March 30, 2001).

42   Id. at *3.

V. NDI Notification Procedures and Timeframes

A. Procedure for Submitting an NDI notification

1. Who is required to submit an NDI notification?

Either the manufacturer or distributor of a dietary supplement that contains an NDI, or the manufacturer or distributor of the NDI, must notify FDA at least 75 days before marketing the article in the U.S., unless the NDI has been present in the food supply as an article used for food in a form in which the food has not been chemically altered (21 U.S.C. 350b(a); 21 CFR 190.6(a)). Although FDA does review notifications from manufacturers and distributors of NDIs, notifications from ingredient manufacturers do not eliminate the requirement for a notification from the manufacturer or distributor of the dietary supplement in which the NDI will be used unless the prior notification for the NDI: (1) included a description of the ***dietary supplement*** with the information required by 21 CFR 190.6(b); and (2) provided the history of use or other evidence of safety on the basis of which the notifier concluded that the ***dietary supplement*** would reasonably be expected to be safe under its labeled conditions of use. See questions IV.C.1 and IV.C.5 for more information.

2. What should be included in an NDI notification and how should it be presented?

The required elements of an NDI notification are listed in 21 CFR 190.6(b). FDA's recommendations for additional information to include are provided in the template below.

The NDI notification should be well organized to facilitate an efficient and timely FDA review. We recommend that the notification be organized by sections, with continuous and consecutive pagination throughout the notification. Each subject area should begin with a new page to facilitate division of the notification among reviewers. The page number should appear in the same general location on every page.

CH
13

Recommended Template for Organizing an NDI Notification

I. Cover Letter

Consumer Safety Officer
Office of Dietary Supplement Programs (HFS-810)
Center for Food Safety and Applied Nutrition
Food and Drug Administration
Department of Health and Human Services
5001 Campus Drive
College Park, MD 20740

DEAR SIR OR MADAM:

The undersigned, _____, *(Name of the primary contact person designated by the manufacturer or distributor that is submitting the notification)* submits this NDI notification under section 413(a)(2) of the Federal Food, Drug, and Cosmetic Act with respect to _____ _____*(Name of the dietary supplement containing the NDI)*, which contains the following new dietary ingredient: _____. *[For herbs and other botanicals, the name must include the Latin binomial name, including the author citation (21 CFR 190.6(b)(2)).]*

Additional information necessary to uniquely characterize the new dietary ingredient: _____
_____

- *If the NDI is a botanical or is derived from a botanical, the notification should specify the part of the botanical that is the source of the new dietary ingredient (e.g., leaf, bark, root).*
- *Examples of information sufficient to uniquely characterize an NDI that is a single molecular entity could include the common or usual name of the molecular entity, the chemical identity, the chemical structural formula as noted in ChemIDPlus Advanced, PubChem, or International Union of Pure and Applied Chemistry (IUPAC), and the Chemical Abstracts Service (CAS) registry number (if available).*
- *NDIs consisting of more than one molecule should be described in a way that accurately communicates the basic nature of the ingredient and its characterizing ingredients or components. Examples:*
  - *Bacteria should be described by Latin binomial name and strain designation.*
  - *Unusual forms of botanicals should be identified (e.g., immature apples or malted barley.)*
  - *If a botanical is grown or cultured to incorporate an unusual constituent (e.g., selenium yeast), that fact should be disclosed.*
- *If the NDI was the subject of a previous NDI notification submitted by you or by the manufacturer or distributor from which you obtain the NDI, please include the docket report number, which you can find in FDA's letter responding to the notification.*

_____

(Signature of the contact person designated by the manufacturer or distributor) [This signature is required by 21 CFR 190.6(b)(5) and should be the primary contact, i.e., the person who represents the notifier in any discussions with FDA and who designates any additional contact persons in the notification or in subsequent correspondence.]

Primary Contact: *(Typed or printed name, title, address, telephone number and, if available, email address and facsimile number of the primary contact person.)*

CH 13

Additional Contacts: *(Typed or printed name, title, address, telephone number and, if available, email address and facsimile number of each additional contact person.) Contact persons can be agents, employees, officers, consultants, or attorneys.*

II. Table of Contents

The table of contents should consist of a listing of the sections of the notification in the order in which they appear, along with the beginning page number of each section. Each section of the notification should begin on a new page.

III. Body of the Notification

A. Administrative

1. Description of the NDI, the dietary supplement containing the NDI, and the conditions of use of the dietary supplement (see questions V.A.3, V.A.4, and VI.A.19).

2. Identification of information believed to be trade secret or confidential commercial information, including the basis for identifying the information as such (see question V.A.16)

3. Safety narrative for the dietary supplement (see question VI.C.3)

B. Attachments used to establish identity

[Provide only the information that identifies your NDI and dietary supplement. Do not provide efficacy data unless it is included in references that also provide identity information.]

1. Detailed description of the identity of the new dietary ingredient and the dietary supplement.

2. Manufacturing methods and practices to establish identity and safety

3. Specifications to identify dietary ingredients, other ingredients, and contaminants, including the analytical methods used to establish each.

4. Identity References

This subsection should contain reprints or photocopies of the full text of all published and unpublished identity references that have not already been included in other subsections of the Identity section.

C. Safety and Toxicology Attachments

[Provide only the information that formed the basis for your conclusion that the dietary supplement containing the new dietary ingredient is reasonably expected to be safe. Do not provide efficacy data unless it is included in studies that also provide safety information.]

1. Comprehensive Safety Profile for the NDI (see question VI.C.2).

2. Toxicology Studies

3. Human Studies

4. Other Studies

5. History of Use

6. Other Evidence of Safety

7. Other Safety and Toxicology References

This subsection should contain reprints or photocopies of the full text of all published and unpublished safety and toxicology references that have not already been included in other subsections of the Safety and Toxicology section.

IV. Complete List of References

CH 13

3. How should the notification describe the NDI?

Your notification should:

(1) specify which of the dietary ingredient categories in section 201(ff)(1) of the FD&C Act the NDI belongs to and explain the basis for your conclusion;

(2) describe the manufacturing process used to make the NDI, including process controls;

(3) describe the physical properties and chemical or molecular composition and structure of the NDI; and

(4) include a specification sheet (preferably in table form) that describes the critical identity and safety attributes of the NDI, including the purity and strength of the NDI and the levels and identities of any impurities and contaminants. See section VI.A for further information.

4. How should the notification describe the dietary supplement in which the NDI will be used?

The notification should contain a description of the dietary supplement in which the NDI will be used, including:

(1) the level of the NDI in the dietary supplement;

(2) the identity and level of any other dietary ingredients and non-dietary ingredients (e.g., binders and fillers) in the dietary supplement;

(3) a description of the manufacturing process of the dietary supplement, including process controls;

(4) a specification sheet for the dietary supplement that describes its critical safety attributes; and

(5) the conditions of use recommended or suggested in the labeling of the dietary supplement, or if no conditions of use are recommended or suggested in the labeling of the dietary supplement, a discussion of the ordinary conditions of use of the dietary supplement. The conditions of use should include the serving form (e.g., tablet, capsule, powder, etc.), serving size (e.g., weight or volumetric measure per serving), frequency of use (e.g., number of servings per day and interval between servings), duration of use, instructions for use, target population, excluded populations (if any), and any other restrictions on use. For purposes of FDA's review, daily lifetime use by all age groups and other populations at the highest described serving size and number of servings will be assumed, unless the notification specifies otherwise.

5. What information should not be in the NDI notification?

The notification should only contain data or information, as described in the safety narrative or comprehensive safety profile, that helps provide a basis for the safety of the NDI or the dietary supplement containing the NDI. It should not contain general or extraneous information. For example, data or information that is used primarily to substantiate a claim about the efficacy of the ingredient or supplement is not useful unless it also contains information that pertains to safety. In addition, the requirement to notify FDA within 30 days after marketing a supplement with a labeling claim described in section 403(r)(6) of the FD&C Act (21 U.S.C. 343(r)(6)) cannot be met by submitting the required information in a premarket NDI notification.[43] An NDI notification should not include published review articles about other products, or publications and websites that promote other products, unless the information in the articles or websites can be specifically linked to the NDI or dietary supplement that is the subject of the notification.

6. Should I explain how the information in the notification provides a basis to conclude that the dietary supplement in which the NDI will be used will reasonably be expected to be safe?

Yes. Your notification should include a dietary supplement safety narrative containing your objective evaluation of the history of use or other evidence of safety cited in the notification, along with an explanation of how the evidence of safety provides a basis to conclude that the dietary supplement containing the new dietary ingredient, when used under the conditions described in the notification, will reasonably be expected to be safe. See question VI.C.3 for further information.

7. Does FDA accept NDI notifications electronically?

Yes, you may submit an NDI notification electronically through FDA's electronic submissions gateway at https://www.access.fda.gov. You also have the option of continuing to submit paper NDI notifications for us to review.

8. When must an NDI notification be submitted?

If you are the manufacturer or distributor of a dietary supplement containing an NDI for which a notification is required (i.e., an NDI that has not been present in the food supply as an article used for food in a form in which the food has not been chemically altered), you must submit your NDI notification at least 75 days before you introduce the dietary supplement into interstate commerce or deliver it for introduction into interstate commerce (21 U.S.C. 350b(a); 21 CFR 190.6(a)). If you are the manufacturer or distributor of the NDI, you must submit your NDI notification at least 75 days before you introduce the NDI into interstate commerce or deliver it for introduction into interstate commerce (21 U.S.C. 350b(a); 21 CFR 190.6(a)).

CH
13

9. How many copies of an NDI notification should be submitted?

You should submit an original and one copy of the NDI notification. If the NDI notification is a paper submission, the original should be a paper document. For

---

43   The regulation governing these notifications is 21 CFR 101.93. Please refer to this regulation for instructions on where and how to submit a notification of a dietary supplement labeling claim under 21 U.S.C. 343(r)(6). Notifications for labeling claims are not reviewed by the same staff who review NDI notifications.

the copy, FDA accepts either paper or an exact copy of the original scanned into an electronic file in PDF format on a CD-ROM disk.

10. Where should an NDI notification be submitted?

Submit your NDI notification to: Consumer Safety Officer, Office of Dietary Supplement Programs (HFS-810), Center for Food Safety and Applied Nutrition, Food and Drug Administration, 5001 Campus Drive, College Park, MD 20740. You may also submit an NDI notification electronically through FDA's electronic submissions gateway at https://www.access.fda.gov.

11. How should published literature and other scientific information cited in the notification be listed?

Publications and other scientific references cited in the notification should be listed in a reference section at the end of the notification (see suggested notification format in question V.A.2). The reference section should include the reference number or short descriptor used to cite each study or publication in the body of the notification. The list of references should include unpublished work as well as publications.

12. How should unpublished scientific work be described?

The more complete the description of the data and methods in an unpublished study report, the more easily FDA reviewers will be able to evaluate whether the data support the safe use of the dietary supplement containing the NDI. Abstracts or cursory summaries of data (e.g., "a 90-day study in 5 rats failed to show any toxicity") do not provide enough detail to be useful as a basis for a safety determination.

13. Do I have to provide copies of publications cited in the notification to FDA?

Yes. All references to published information offered in support of the notification must be accompanied by reprints or photocopies of such references (21 CFR 190.6(b)(4)). You should not submit only the abstract or bibliographic citation of any publication or other material with your notification; instead, submit a photocopy or reprint of the full text. Do not submit abstracts that are the only published report of a scholarly or scientific work. Because abstracts do not contain sufficient information to judge the reliability of the scientific conclusions drawn in the study and generally do not undergo the rigorous review and editing used to evaluate other publications, they do not provide data that are useful in evaluating the safety of an NDI.

14.May I use material published in languages other than English to support the safe use of my NDI?

Yes, material written in a foreign language may be used as part of the basis for a conclusion that the NDI will reasonably be expected to be safe under the conditions of its intended use in the dietary supplement; however, the material must be accompanied by an accurate and complete English translation (21 CFR 190.6(b)(4)).

15. Should raw data be provided?

The level of detail that should be provided (raw data vs. summary) depends on how important the data in question are to the conclusion of safety and also whether the data suggest a safety problem. The more critical the data are to the overall evaluation, the more detail is needed. Data summaries (e.g., a table containing the average value and range or standard deviation for each parameter measured in a safety study or the peaks in a spectrum or chromatogram) are usually sufficient unless the data suggest that some values are outside of the acceptable range, in which case the individual values (raw data) should be provided. During review of the notification, FDA may request submission of raw data or other additional information. If the additional information is a substantive amendment, FDA will reset the filing date and start a new 75-day review period (see 21 CFR 190.6(d)).

16. How should I identify information that I believe is trade secret or confidential commercial information?

As provided in 21 U.S.C. 350b(a)(2) and 21 CFR 190.6(e), after the 90th day after the filing date of the notification, all information in the notification will be placed on public display, except for any information that is trade secret or confidential commercial information (CCI).

We recommend that you clearly identify any information in the notification that you believe is trade secret or CCI—either by marking the information where it appears in the notification or by identifying this information in a separate document that accompanies the notification—and that you explain the basis for this belief. Likewise, if you believe there is no trade secret or CCI contained in the notification, we request that you state this in your notification.

Trade secret information may consist of any commercially valuable plan, formula, process, or device that is used for the making, preparing, compounding, or processing of trade commodities and that can be said to be the end product of either innovation or substantial effort (21 CFR 20.61(a)). There must be a direct relationship between the trade secret and the productive process; for example, information relating to the manufacturing process (see 21 CFR 20.61(a)). Examples of trade secret information might include manufacturing methods and product composition (if different from what is declared on the label), product specifications needed to protect proprietary composition information (including proprietary analytical methods used to evaluate the product), and certificates of analysis.

CCI covers information that is related to a business or trade and is "confidential" (21 CFR 20.61(b)). In the case of information that FDA requires to be submitted, such as an NDI notification, the information is "confidential" if its disclosure is likely to cause substantial harm to the competitive position of the submitter.[44] Examples of CCI might include sales statistics, dollar volume, amount or source of income (e.g., a company's list of

CH 13

---

44   National Parks & Conservation Ass'n v. Morton, 498 F.2d 765 (D.C. Cir. 1974).

customers), profits or losses, expenditures (of any person, firm, partnership, corporation, or association), names of suppliers or subcontractors, or brand of equipment.

FDA believes that the following data and information contained in a notification are generally not trade secrets or CCI and, therefore, would be available for public disclosure after the 90th day after receipt of the notification by FDA:

(1) Information about history of use or other safety information related to the NDI or the dietary supplement, including both published and unpublished studies.

(2) All correspondence and written summaries of oral discussions relating to the notification, except specific information that is exempt from disclosure under 21 CFR 20.61.

17. What signature and contact information should I provide?

The signature of the person designated by the notifier is required by 21 CFR 190.6(b)(5). This person should be the primary contact, who represents the notifier in any discussions with FDA and who designates any additional contact persons in the notification or in subsequent correspondence. The typed or printed name, title, address, telephone number and, if available, email address and facsimile number of the primary contact person should be listed at the end of the cover letter that accompanies the notification (see suggested notification format in question V.A.2) so that FDA can reach him or her when necessary. The typed or printed names, titles, addresses, telephone numbers and, if available, email addresses and facsimile numbers of additional contact persons for the notification should be listed after the contact information for the primary contact. Contact persons can be agents, employees, officers, consultants, or attorneys for the notifier.

B. What Happens After an NDI Notification Is Submitted?

1. When is an NDI notification considered to be filed?

The date when FDA receives a complete notification is the date of filing. A complete notification is a notification that contains all the information required by 21 CFR 190.6. The date of filing is the start of the 75-day premarket review period during which the manufacturer or distributor of a dietary supplement containing an NDI may not market the dietary supplement (21 U.S.C. 350b(a)(2); 21 CFR 190.6(c)). If the notification does not meet the requirements of 21 CFR 190.6, a member of FDA's Office of Dietary Supplement Programs will contact the notifier to determine how long it will take for the notifier to provide the missing information. If the notifier can provide the information within 14 days, FDA will file the notification upon receipt of the missing information. If the notifier cannot provide the missing information within 14 days, FDA will consider the notification incomplete and will mail a letter so informing the notifier. Upon request, members of the New Dietary Ingredient Review Team will provide advice on how to prepare a notification that meets the requirements of 21 CFR 190.6.

2. What are examples of omissions that cause a notification to be incomplete?

An incomplete notification does not satisfy the notification requirement found in section 413(a)(2) of the FD&C Act (21 U.S.C. 350b(a)(2)); therefore, if the dietary supplement containing the NDI is marketed, it is deemed to be adulterated under section 402(f) of the FD&C Act (21 U.S.C. 342(f)) unless the notifier has amended the notification to supply the missing information at least 75 days before the dietary supplement is introduced or delivered for introduction into interstate commerce (21 U.S.C. 350b(a)). FDA does not evaluate safety or identity information in incomplete NDI notifications.

The following are examples of omissions that make a notification incomplete:

- Material in a language other than English that is either not translated or is translated inaccurately.
- Citations to published literature for which a full copy of the publication is not provided.
- A notification that is not signed, or contact information that is inaccurate and does not permit FDA to establish contact with the notifier.
- Submitting a copy of the notification that is not the same as the original.

3. What type of response may I expect to receive from FDA, and when?

Within 75 days after FDA files your notification, you may expect a letter acknowledging receipt of the notification and stating the date on which the notification was filed. Examples of the types of response letters FDA commonly sends include:

- Letter of acknowledgment without objection;
- Letter listing deficiencies that make the notification incomplete under 21 CFR 190.6;
- Objection letter raising safety concerns based on information in the notification or identifying gaps in the history of use or other evidence of safety; and
- Letter raising other regulatory issues with the NDI or dietary supplement (e.g., the NDI is not a dietary ingredient under 21 U.S.C. 321(ff)(1), or the product is excluded from the definition of "dietary supplement" under 21 U.S.C. 321(ff)(2) because it is not intended for ingestion).

The letter may contain information about our review of your notification, and it may ask you to submit additional information if your notification is incomplete or raises safety or identity questions. The letter also contains a report number that identifies the notification in the FDA docket. If you provide FDA with an email address in your notification, FDA will send the response letter to that email address on the day the response letter is mailed.

CH
13

VI. What to Include in an NDI Notification

A. Identity Information About the NDI and the Dietary Supplement

1. What is the purpose of including information about the identity of the NDI and the dietary supplement containing the NDI in my notification?

The purpose of including identity information in an NDI notification is to establish what the NDI is, including the category of dietary ingredient in section 201(ff)(1) of the FD&C Act (21 U.S.C. 321(ff)(1)) to which it belongs; to identify the other ingredients and components of the dietary supplement; and to provide the basis for FDA to evaluate the qualitative and quantitative relationship between the NDI and the substances that are the subject of the history of use or other evidence of safety in your notification (see questions VI.A.5 and VI.C.2). Without complete and accurate identity information, FDA cannot evaluate whether there is a history of use or other evidence establishing that the dietary supplement containing the NDI will reasonably be expected to be safe under your proposed conditions of use.

2. What types of identity information should I include in my NDI notification?

We recommend including the following in the identity section of your NDI notification:

- The name of the NDI, as given in the cover letter (see question V.A.2), its trade name (if different), and any other names by which the NDI is known;

- A description of the physical properties of the NDI, a description of the chemical or molecular composition or structure of the NDI, or both;

- Controls and/or acceptable ranges for batch-to-batch variability, where applicable;

- The identity and level of any impurities and contaminants that may be in the NDI or dietary supplement;

- Additional information specific to the type of dietary ingredient, as recommended in question VI.A.6 (vitamins, minerals, amino acids, constituents, metabolites, and other discrete chemical entities), VI.A.7 (salts), VI.A.8 (enzymes), VI.A.9 (covalently modified derivatives of a dietary ingredient), VI.A.11(mixtures), VI.A.12 and VI.A.13 (botanicals), VI.A.15 (extracts and concentrates), VI.A.16 (ingredients produced using fermentation), and VI.A.17 (live microbial dietary ingredients); and

- A description of the identity of the other dietary ingredients and the other ingredients in the dietary supplement product.

FDA recommends that you establish identity specifications for the NDI and for those components of the NDI and dietary supplement that are relevant to establishing the basis for the safety of the dietary supplement. Your notification should provide a detailed description of the identity specifications in table form, as recommended in question VI.A.5.

In addition, for a manufactured NDI, you should describe the manufacturing process and provide detailed information about the aspects of the manufacturing process that are relevant to safety and identity, as recommended in question VI.A.3 below.

3. How much detail should my description of the manufacturing process contain?

The description should have sufficient detail to enable FDA to understand the overall process used to make the NDI and the dietary supplement. You should identify any points in the process that you know to be relevant to the safety of the dietary supplement. Detailed descriptions of manufacturing can be limited to those portions relevant to safety and identity, if they can be identified. For example, you might establish a specification to limit mold contamination of a component used to make your NDI (e.g., aflatoxin in corn). You might also use a specification for the temperature of a key extraction step to prevent formation of a toxic byproduct and/or a specification for that byproduct in an analysis of an interim material or of the final product. You may describe the entire process and all specifications or select only those that are relevant to the identity and safety information that provides the basis for the safety of your NDI.

4. What is a specification?

A specification is a set of standards developed by the manufacturer or distributor of a material (e.g., an NDI or a dietary supplement). The specification includes standards for each of the components of the material and for the material as a whole. For the purpose of an NDI notification, the specifications should include critical safety attributes and may omit attributes not relevant to safety or identity. The specification sheet should provide a list of tests, the acceptance criteria for each test, and analytical methods used to support the acceptance criteria. Acceptance criteria are numerical limits, ranges, or other criteria for the tests described. They are used to determine whether to accept or reject the ingredient or product being analyzed. Acceptance criteria should be specific, rather than vague.

The description of the analytical methods should include a detailed set of directions that must be followed exactly for the results to be accepted for the stated purpose. The directions should cover all steps, from preparing the test sample to reporting the results of the analysis. The description of the method should be complete, whether it is proprietary or included as a publication. Details of the method, such as a description of the chromatographic column, solvent elution conditions, and the source and authenticity of any reference standards, are integral to understanding how a method is used to identify the analyte.

A vague acceptance criterion is rarely useful. For example, it is not informative to say that a chromatogram or a spectrum "matches the reference sample" unless every peak matches (both height and location) or there is a description of which peak or peaks match and how they match (e.g., description of the acceptable variation in peak retention time and peak height or area under curve). The use of "fingerprint" analysis of complex spectra or chromatography of mixtures containing many ingredients does

CH 13

not require knowledge of the identity of all or even any of the peaks, but does require matching sufficient numbers of peaks across the entire spectrum or chromatogram to ensure the validity of the test result. Components that are known to be toxic can be identified by a single acceptance criterion (e.g., "less than"), but acceptance criteria for other components should be expressed as a range. The source and authenticity of analytical standards should also be documented.

5. What specifications for my process and ingredients should I include in the notification?

Manufacturers and distributors of dietary supplements must establish specifications for the components of their products (see 21 CFR 111.70(b)). The required types of component specifications include:

- An identity specification for each component;

- Component specifications necessary to ensure that specifications for the purity, strength, and composition of dietary supplements manufactured using the components are met; and

- Limits on the types of contamination that may adulterate or may lead to adulteration of the finished product.

Your notification should list and explain the role of those specifications that are relevant to the identity of the NDI and to the safe consumption of the dietary supplement containing the NDI, including how you arrived at the criteria for acceptance or rejection based on the results of each test in the specification. This might include specifications for starting materials used to make your NDI, process controls during manufacturing, and/or interim or final product specifications for the NDI or the dietary supplement. For ease of reference, we recommend listing the specifications in table form (see example in Table 2). You should describe the controls in place to maintain the strength, composition, and purity of the NDI throughout the shelf life of the product.

If you rely on history of use or other evidence of safety for materials other than your NDI, you should explain, based on the manufacturing method and specifications of your NDI, the qualitative and quantitative relationship between your NDI and the materials used to demonstrate safety. For example, if your NDI is a mixture of polyphenolic compounds extracted from grapes, you might use information such as quantitative high performance liquid chromatography (HPLC) analysis to relate the quantity of those compounds in a serving of your ingredient to the quantity in a serving of unprocessed grapes or grape juice.

Table 2. An Example of a Specification Sheet or Table for a Dietary Ingredient

Test	Acceptance Criteria	Analytical Method (Referenced Method or In-House Method Name)
Appearance: Color/physical state	White to off white/powder	Visual, R-01545[1]
Dietary ingredient identity	Matches reference standard	HPLC, R-02030[1]
Dietary ingredient assay	a ± b mg/capsule	HPLC, R-02030[1]
Related substances: Total related substances	No more than (NMT) 0.5% of total peak area of the dietary ingredient	HPLC, R-02030[1]
Microbial limits, if applicable: Total Aerobic Microbial Count Staphylococcus aureus Pseudomonas aeruginosa	NMT 100 CFU/g Absent Absent	USP <61>
Apparent pH, 25 °C (if applicable)	4.5 to 5.5	USP <791> or in house method
Residual solvent, e.g., ethanol, acetone, hexane[2]	NMT specified limit in ppm	GC, R-01901[1]
Heavy metals	NMT 20 ppm	USP 30<231> Method II

1 In-house analytical methods, which should be described in sufficient detail in the NDI notification for FDA to evaluate them. Use of a method published by an authoritative source (such as AOAC International or the United States Pharmacopeia (USP)) or described in a peer-reviewed journal (such as Journal of Chromatography) is also appropriate, as long as a reprint or copy of the publication is provided.

2 Solvents that were used in the manufacturing process.

6. What additional information should I submit if my NDI is a discrete chemical entity (e.g., a vitamin, mineral, amino acid, or a constituent or a metabolite of another dietary ingredient)?

You should provide sufficient information to uniquely characterize your NDI as a discrete molecular entity (or mixture of discrete molecular entities). Information that uniquely characterizes a single molecular entity should include the common or usual name of the molecular entity, the molecular formula and formula weight, the structural formula (as noted, for example, in ChemIDPlusAdvanced, PubChem, or International Union of Pure and Applied Chemistry (IUPAC)) and, if available, the Chemical Abstracts Service (CAS) registry number. For example, if the substance exists as a configurational isomer (stereoisomer), such as an enantiomer or a geometric isomer, the isomer in question should be specified and characterized. For an enantiomer, the notification should include the correct stereoisomeric structure and the correct chemical name with the appropriate R or S designations.

Other systems of nomenclature (such as D or L for amino acids) are also appropriate as long as the name unambiguously identifies which isomer(s) are present. For a

CH
13

geometric isomer, the correct cis (Z) or trans (E) stereoisomeric structure and the correct chemical name should be provided. In addition, if the notification asserts that the NDI is a metabolite, you should document the basis for this assertion. For example, the notification should cite evidence showing that the level of the NDI in the human body increases with intake of a precursor constituent of food. (See definition of "metabolite" in section VII.)

Other relevant information might include:

- Specifications for your raw materials (e.g., food grade), and evidence that your raw materials conform to the specifications.
- A detailed description of each step of the production process, including:
  - Reaction conditions in the synthesis and purification process.
  - The process and quality controls used in the manufacturing process; for example, temperature, time, pH, shielding gas, etc.
  - Flow diagrams of the manufacturing process.
  - Composition: Provide the identity and quantity (including units and any ranges) for each component.
  - A description of how undesirable byproducts of manufacturing are removed. Examples of undesirable byproducts include unreacted chemical reagents, reaction byproducts, and solvents like methanol or hexane.

7. What additional chemistry information should I submit if my NDI is a salt?

You should describe the extent to which the salt will dissociate following ingestion, particularly if the history of use or other evidence of safety describes forms of the ingredient other than the salt that is the subject of the notification. Specific discussion of whether different salt forms have different toxic properties also should be included.

8. What additional chemistry information should I submit if my NDI is an enzyme?

If your NDI is an enzyme, you should describe the following in the specifications portion of the identity section of your notification:

- The analytical method used to determine enzyme activity;
- The specifications for enzyme activity in the NDI; and
- The acceptance criteria for enzyme activity and for the number of units of activity per serving of the NDI in the dietary supplement.

9. What additional chemistry information should I submit if my NDI is a covalently modified derivative of a dietary ingredient?

Covalent modification chemically alters the ingredient and changes its identity. Examples include covalent bonding of one dietary ingredient to another or exchanging a functional group (e.g., an alcohol) for another (e.g., an acid or an ester). The chemical structure of the new ingredient should be described explicitly and clearly. Before submitting an NDI notification for the new ingredient, you should consider whether it qualifies as a dietary ingredient under one of the categories in section 201(ff)(1)(A)-(F) of the FD&C Act (21 U.S.C. 321(ff)(1)(A)-(F)) (see question IV.D.5). If not, the new ingredient cannot be an NDI because it is not a dietary ingredient.

10. What information should I submit if my notification relies on history of use or other evidence of safety for a substance or product that is similar to, but not exactly the same as, my NDI or dietary supplement?

You should use chemical, microbiological, and botanical characterizations, as appropriate, to explain how the substance or product is similar to your NDI or dietary supplement and to provide a rationale for how the safety information that is presented for the similar substance or product is relevant to the safety of your NDI or dietary supplement. Note that developing such a rationale requires knowledge of the identity (e.g., composition and strength) of the related substances that were studied or that have a history of safe use. The discussion in the notification should include the scientific rationale that supports extrapolating conclusions from a safety evaluation of the related substance or product to your NDI or dietary supplement. Otherwise, such evidence of safety may not provide a basis to conclude that your NDI or product will reasonably be expected to be safe.

11. What additional identity information should I submit if my product contains a mixture of ingredients?

You should state the identity and level of each ingredient in the dietary supplement, including both dietary ingredients and other ingredients, such as those used for a technical or functional effect in the product (e.g., binders, fillers, and color additives). You should also describe how the ingredient combination in the mixture relates to the history of safe use or other evidence of safety of the dietary supplement in which the NDI will be used. The dietary supplement safety narrative should address bioavailability of the ingredients as formulated, including use of any binders or fillers that affect bioavailability of any of the dietary ingredients in the dietary supplement.

12. What additional identity information should I submit if my NDI is a botanical or is derived from a botanical?

You must provide the Latin binomial name, including the author citation, for any ingredient that is a botanical or derived from a botanical (21 CFR 190.6(b)(2); see also 21 CFR 101.4(h)). We recommend that you also specify the part of the plant from which the ingredient is derived. You may, in addition, provide a common or usual name for your botanical ingredient. The Latin binomial name should be in accordance with internationally accepted rules on nomenclature, such as those found in the International Code of Nomenclature for algae, fungi, and plants (ICN) (formerly known as the International Code of Botanical Nomenclature). FDA recommends using the most

CH 13

recent edition of ICN.[45] We also recommend providing the following to help us evaluate whether your botanical ingredient is the same as or similar to botanical ingredients described in the history of use or other safety evidence in your notification:

- Description of specific tests or examinations you use to ensure correct taxonomic identity, including identification of any authenticated botanical reference materials or authoritative botanical descriptions used;

- Conditions of propagation, if they involve deliberate manipulation of propagation in a manner that is significantly different than common plant propagation and breeding practices;

- Conditions of cultivation (e.g., wild harvest, field, or greenhouse) and geographical origin of plant material, if necessary to accurately identify the NDI or relevant to your conclusion that the ingredient is reasonably expected to be safe;

- Periods during which the botanical is cultivated and harvested (season or month(s) and year, age of plant, or both) and the stage of maturity of the harvested plant part;

- The part of the plant from which the ingredient is derived;

- Whether the botanical is used in a fresh or dehydrated state;

- The form in which the botanical is used (e.g., whole, chopped, cut-and-sifted, or powdered);

- A properly prepared and curated voucher of the botanical source material; and

- The full Latin binomial name (with author) of any known adulterant species that must be excluded from use in production of the NDI, and a description of how its use is excluded.

13. Should I describe the production methods for my botanical NDI?

Yes. You should describe the production methods for your botanical NDI to the extent necessary to demonstrate that the NDI is the same as or similar to the botanical materials described in information submitted as evidence of the safety of the NDI. Thus, cultivation of plants, algae, or fungi in wild or standard conditions might not require extensive explanation. However, unusual production conditions should be explained. For instance, if you culture *Saccharomyces cerevisiae* in a medium with unusually large amounts of selenium, you should describe the fermentation process, as well as the levels and types of selenium compounds in your final product. If you use traditional or molecular methods to produce a variety with novel properties, you should describe the variety in sufficient detail to demonstrate that the ingredient you derive from it is reasonably likely to be safe under the conditions of use of the dietary supplement to which the NDI will be added.

---

45   McNeill, J.; Barrie, F.R.; Buck, W.R. et al., editors. International Code of Nomenclature for algae, fungi, and plants (Melbourne Code) 2012 (electronic ed.). Available at:http://www.iapt-taxon.org/nomen/main.php

14. How should the identity section of my NDI notification deal with toxins in related plants or microorganisms?

You should identify the toxins or classes of toxins or other deleterious constituents or properties (e.g., antibiotic resistance genes in microorganisms or toxigenic properties for which the toxin is unidentified) known to be present in the same species or in a family or genus that is phylogenetically related to the NDI. You should also document the absence (or the amount, if present) of those toxins or other deleterious constituents or properties in the NDI, as well as in the substances that are the subject of the history of use or other evidence of safety presented in the notification. Identification below the species level (e.g., plant variety or strain designation) can be relevant to the safety determination when some varieties or strains of a species are known to contain toxins.

15. How should I describe an extract or concentrate of a botanical or a dietary substance?

You should include the following in the description of your extract or concentrate:

- Overview of the manufacturing process, including a general description of each step (e.g., a flowchart), followed by a description of the method of manufacturing in sufficient detail to make clear the identity of the final product (the finished extract or concentrate) and how it is similar to and different from the starting material.

- Description and amount, expressed as a percentage or range of percentages, of all added ingredients, including all solvents used, along with specifications for residual solvents other than water in the finished NDI or dietary supplement.

- Concentration or dilution ratio, or range of concentration or dilution ratios, of the finished extract or concentrate relative to the original starting material. If the concentration or dilution ratio is based on the weight of fresh herb, rather than dried, this fact should be disclosed.

- Content, minimum content, or range of content of any marker substances, expressed as a percentage of the finished extract or concentrate, accompanied by (1) a description of whether the marker is a marker of effectiveness, toxicity, or a surrogate marker, and (2) a calculation or estimate of the relative level of each marker in the NDI compared to the original starting material.

- The names and specifications for any marker substances deemed relevant to the identity of the NDI (e.g., markers whose presence or absence is relevant to the identity of the botanical or that must occur in a particular ratio to each other to confirm identity).

- How the extract or concentrate is standardized from batch to batch.

- Measures taken to remove adulterants (e.g., nonfood solvents) that may be present due to production methods or to reduce such adulterants to within acceptable limits.

- Measures taken to control adulterants (e.g., pesticides, heavy metals, and filth) that may be present in raw materials from which the NDI is derived.

CH 13

- Quantitative limits on contaminants that must be controlled to ensure the NDI's safety, if any are present in the source material or may result from the manufacturing process.

- If reagents used during processing are likely to make covalent changes to components in the mixture during processing, you should determine whether the new material is still a dietary ingredient. For example, use of a large amount of an oxidizing acid like sulfuric acid to process a botanical mixture may create a new "semi-synthetic" mixture that is no longer a mixture of components that were present in the original plant. Therefore, the mixture would no longer be a dietary ingredient.

16. What additional information should I include if my NDI is produced using fermentation?

The notification should include information about the organism(s) and fermentation process used to culture the microorganism that produces the NDI. The safety of the fermenting organism for use in food production should be discussed. Poorly defined microbiological mixtures are acceptable if there is a long history of use in production of food (e.g., mixtures used to make dairy products like kefir or cheese) and the fermentation substrate is consistent with that history of use. The notification should describe the history of use of the fermenting organism(s) to produce food or, in the absence of such history, should thoroughly explain how the manufacturing process excludes toxins and other undesirable byproducts of fermentation from the finished NDI.

The information about the fermentation process should describe the complete media formulation, the fermentation vessel(s), the fermentation conditions, the methods used to harvest the NDI from the fermentation mixture, and any specifications for the production organism in the finished NDI, particularly if the production organism is not inactivated or removed.

You should also address methods used to ensure the integrity of the production organism, such as how you guard against contamination and genetic change. FDA is particularly concerned about contamination when fermentation occurs outside of a sterile production vessel (e.g., production of algae in ponds).

Note that the use of a major food allergen in the fermentation medium may require a separate notification or petition to the FDA if the presence of the allergen is not declared on the product label. See section 403(w) of the FD&C Act (21 U.S.C. 343(w)).

If your ingredient is an enzyme, the specifications portion of the identity section of your notification should describe the analytical method used to determine enzyme activity, the specifications for enzyme activity in the NDI, and the acceptance criteria for enzyme activity and for the number of units of activity per serving of the NDI in the dietary supplement. Post-fermentation harvest and processing should be described, including filtration, washing, and preservation methods.

17. What additional information should I include if my NDI is a live microbial dietary ingredient?

You should include a complete description of the organism, including:

- The strain;
- Methods used to establish the identity of the strain, such as identification by internationally recognized third-party repositories (e.g., the American Type Culture Collection); and
- The relationship of the strain to the strain(s) of the same species used to establish the history of use or other evidence of safety for the NDI.

The use of scientific names (Latin binomial name with author citation) is required for botanical ingredients (21 CFR 190.6(b)(2)) and is recommended for bacteria. For bacteria, FDA recommends using the Bacteriological Code (1990 Revision),[46] validated lists of names in the International Journal of Systematic and Evolutionary Microbiology, and public lists of prokaryotic nomenclature (e.g., Prokaryotic Nomenclature Up-to-Date[47] or the List of Prokaryotic Names with Standing in Nomenclature[48]). FDA will pay particularly close attention to the proper identification of organisms from genera or species that do not have a long history of food use and to those from genera, like *Bacillus* and *Streptococcus*, which contain both species with long histories of food use and species known to contain human pathogens.

FDA regards all members of a species that contains human pathogens as potentially harmful to human health and, therefore, inappropriate for use as dietary ingredients, because of the absence of a consensus that there are valid scientific ways to distinguish between pathogenic and non-pathogenic members of a single species or to prevent horizontal transfer of genes for pathogenic traits between members of the same bacterial species. Examples of species that should not be used in dietary supplements include *Escherichia coli*, *Enterococcus faecalis*, and *Enterococcus faecium*.

FDA considers each strain of a bacterial or yeast species to be a separate ingredient. You should explain how your strain was obtained and how it varies from other members of the same species. If your strain was genetically modified using either random mutagenesis or bioengineering, you should describe the process used and how you characterized the properties of the new strain.

FDA also considers the manufacturing process, including the fermentation, as an

CH
13

---

46 Lapage, S. P.; Sneath, P. H. A.; Lessel, E. F.; Skerman, V. B. D.; Seeliger, H. P. R.; Clark, W. A., editors. International Code of Nomenclature of Bacteria (Bacteriological Code), 1990 Revision. Washington (DC): American Society for Microbiology Press; 1992.

47 Leibniz Institute DSMZ-German Collection of Microorganisms and Cell Cultures, ProkaryoticNomenclature Up-to-Date. Available at:http://www.dsmz.de/bacterial-diversity/prokaryotic-nomenclature-up-to-date/prokariotic-nomenclature-up-to-date.html[Note that content on this website is updated frequently. Use the search function in the embedded link to retrieve the current validated name of a bacterial organism.]

48 Parte, A.C., editor. List of Prokaryotic Names with Standing in Nomenclature (LPSN) Database. Available at: http://www.bacterio.net/. [Note that content on this website is updated frequently. Use the search function in the embedded link to retrieve the current validated name of a bacterial organism.]

intrinsic part of the identity of an ingredient that is viable at the time of ingestion. We recommend that the fermentation and other parts of the manufacturing process relevant to safety and identity be described in detail in your notification, as recommended in questions VI.A.3 and VI.A.16. FDA will pay particular attention to the viability of microorganisms in the NDI. The per-serving level of a viable microorganism depends on both the mass (in grams) and the viability (e.g., number of colony-forming units) of the organism in the final product. The composition of the growth medium and the fermentation conditions of the organism are also relevant to the safety of the product, particularly when they alter the form of the organism (e.g., spore vs. vegetative) or the composition of the ingredient (e.g., when the ingredient includes both the organism and the growth medium). The notification should explain the relevance of safety information presented about other strains from the same species.

18. What information should I provide in my notification if the labeling of the NDI or dietary supplement containing the NDI will include an expiration date or "use by" date?

The expiration or "use by" date should be based on appropriate supportive stability data showing that (1) no new degradants will form during the labeled shelf life of the product under the conditions of storage specified in the notification, if any, or under normal storage conditions; and (2) the NDI or dietary supplement will continue to meet the critical safety attributes of identity, strength, and purity through its labeled expiration or "use by" date. You should provide these supportive data in the notification.

19. What information should I submit to describe the conditions of use that I intend to recommend or suggest in the labeling of my dietary supplement?

Your notification must describe the conditions of use that will be recommended or suggested in the labeling of your dietary supplement or, if no conditions of use will be recommended or suggested in the supplement labeling, the ordinary conditions of use of the supplement (21 CFR 190.6(b)(2)(ii)). Conditions of use include the dose (serving size), serving form (e.g., capsule or powder)), frequency of use (e.g., number of servings per day and interval between servings), duration of use, instructions for use, target population, other dietary ingredients in the dietary supplement, and any restrictions on use, such as excluded populations.

For purposes of review, daily lifetime use by all age groups and other populations at the highest recommended serving size will be assumed unless the notification specifies that the labeling will contain restrictions on conditions of use (e.g., excluded populations or frequency and duration of intake). Population restrictions could include exclusion of children, pregnant or lactating women, or sensitive individuals who should not consume the product. Allergen warnings are an example of a population restriction on conditions of use. The conditions of use to be recommended or suggested in the labeling of the dietary supplement(s) containing the NDI should be described prominently in the administrative section near the beginning of the notification (see question V.A.2).

B. History of Use or Other Evidence of Safety

1. What safety information is required to support an NDI notification?

You must provide the information that forms the basis on which you have concluded that a dietary supplement containing the NDI will reasonably be expected to be safe under the supplement's labeled conditions of use (21 U.S.C. 350b(a)(2)). In general, this information should include an adequate history of safe use, safety studies, or both.

For dietary supplements that contain dietary ingredients or other components in addition to the NDI, the notification should include safety information for the finished product as well as for the NDI because it is not possible to conclude that the dietary supplement containing the NDI will reasonably be expected to be safe without considering the safety of these other components. As discussed in section VI.C, FDA recommends including a comprehensive safety profile for the NDI and a safety narrative for the dietary supplement in NDI notifications (see questions VI.C.1 through VI.C.3).

2. Should I submit both a history of safe use and safety testing data for the NDI?

It depends. A notification should provide evidence of a history of safe use; other evidence of safety, including clinical testing, animal testing, or both; or some combination of history of use and other evidence of safety. The submitted data should provide the basis for a conclusion that there is a reasonable expectation of safety under the proposed conditions of use of the dietary supplement containing the NDI.

FDA expects that when history of use evidence alone is adequate to support the safety of the NDI in the supplement, notifiers will prefer to use that route. Compared to the cost and time needed to conduct clinical or animal toxicology studies, it is generally less expensive and faster to gather historical information and to conduct chemistry studies to establish the identity of the historically used materials.

Submitting clinical studies, animal studies, or both, in addition to history of use data, would be appropriate when the history of use evidence contains gaps or when the proposed conditions of use for the NDI differ from the historical conditions of use.

3. What data and information should I submit to substantiate an NDI's history of safe use?

A history of safe use can be substantiated by providing evidence that the substance was safely consumed as a food or dietary supplement or as a component of a more complex mixture (e.g., calcium in milk or beta-glucan in oatmeal) at levels equal to or higher than those that would be consumed by someone taking the NDI-containing supplement under the proposed conditions of use. This history of use could be from the United States or another country, as long as the substance was consumed as a food, dietary supplement, or, in the case of foreign history of use, category of product comparable to a dietary supplement in the U.S.

Elements that FDA recommends to substantiate that an NDI has a history of safe use include: (1) a characterization and comparison of the identity of the NDI and the historically consumed article; and (2) an explanation of how the compositions of the two are related. That is, the composition and other identifying characteristics of the NDI and the historically consumed article should be characterized in sufficient detail to demonstrate that safe use of the historically consumed article is relevant to the safety of the NDI and provides a basis to conclude that the supplement in which the NDI will be marketed will reasonably be expected to be safe under the proposed conditions of use. If the NDI's history of use was as a component of a more complex mixture, you should demonstrate how the NDI is qualitatively and quantitatively related to the historically consumed component. If the NDI is itself a mixture of dietary ingredients, you should demonstrate how the component dietary ingredients in the NDI are related to historically consumed ingredients or components.

In addition, (a) the dose (per-serving intake) and total daily intake; (b) duration of use; (c) frequency of intake; and (d) any additional information that describes the conditions of use of the historically consumed material should be provided. For example, if consumption is not uniform within the population, you should provide information about the mean and high (e.g., 90th percentile) exposure levels. Finally, the size and relevant characteristics of the consuming population (e.g., everyone vs. limitations based on age, gender, or health status) should be discussed.

For these data to demonstrate a history of safe use, the intake level for the historically consumed article should be the same as or higher than the anticipated intake level of the NDI in the dietary supplement, based on the conditions of use described in the NDI notification. For example, information showing that a steroid hormone is present in nanogram amounts in a serving of milk or beef—foods that have a long history of safe use—would not support the safety of a highly concentrated bovine extract that contains the steroid hormone in milligram amounts. In contrast, consumption of cow's milk could be used to support the safety of a specific protein purified from milk at a serving level equal to or lower than the amount of the protein found in an 8 ounce serving of milk. As another example, if your NDI is an oil made from a plant or fish and you can show that the oil consists only of a mixture of fatty acids, each of which you can identify and demonstrate to be widely consumed at higher levels in conventional foods, you may be able to conclude that the dietary supplement containing the NDI will reasonably be expected to be safe based on compositional information alone.

The safety assessment should describe and discuss situations in which the conditions of use and composition of the NDI differ from the documented conditions of use and composition of the historically consumed substance (e.g., when the NDI is derived from a plant variety bred to produce an additional constituent or to remove a toxic constituent). When the historical usage differs substantially from the proposed use of the NDI, additional supportive data may be needed. Examples of differences in an NDI's proposed use that might necessitate further supportive data include:

- Higher dosage;
- Different route of administration (e.g., an article that has a history of safe use in sublingual form and is now intended for ingestion as an NDI);
- Longer duration of use;
- Other changes that increase exposure to potential toxic effects; and
- Any other difference that raises new safety issues, such as a change in target population (see definition in section VII).

4. What documentation of an NDI's history of use should I submit?

Documentation of an NDI's history of safe use in food could include published data and information, such as peer-reviewed scientific literature, reports from authoritative bodies, survey data on food or nutrient composition and consumption, advertisements or other published promotional material describing the composition of products, published agricultural or food production data, or cookbooks or other published recipes documenting the use of an ingredient to prepare conventional foods. Documentation of history of use could also include trade secret or confidential commercial information, such as proprietary survey or consumption data, product sales data, and compositional analyses.

5. Am I required to submit a comprehensive survey of every historical use of the NDI?

No, only the data and information on which your reasonable expectation of safety is based are required. For example, if you have documentation that soybeans have a history of safe use in a large population in Asia, data describing lower historical consumption in the U.S. or Europe is not necessary to support the safety of an NDI that is a constituent of soybeans.

6. How do I determine whether historical use was "daily chronic" or "intermittent"?

Daily chronic use of the historically consumed material refers to ingestion at least once a day, every day, for at least three months in a row. Daily chronic use includes long-term use. Intermittent use, for purposes of this guidance, means less than daily chronic use and can be either daily and finite in duration or non-daily and lifetime in duration. An example of intermittent use is the use of seasonal fruit for less than 90 days.

7. Should I estimate the intake of historically consumed materials related to my NDI if I am relying on those related materials to establish a history of safe use, and should this estimate be included in my NDI notification?

Yes to both questions. If your conclusion that the dietary supplement containing your NDI will reasonably be expected to be safe is based on a history of safe use of materials other than the NDI itself, you should estimate the historical intake of the materials that you determine to be relevant (see question VI.A.10) and include this information in your NDI notification. In developing these estimates, you should take into account the

CH 13

complete pattern of intake, including dose, duration, and frequency of intake, as well as the size of the population known to have consumed the substance. The distribution of intake within the population (e.g., the mean and 90th percentile amounts consumed) is also important.

8. Where may I find information on how to estimate consumer intake?

For references and information on methods of estimating consumer intake of food ingredients, including dietary ingredients in dietary supplements, refer to "Estimating Dietary Intake of Substances in Food"[49]; section III.G, "Intake Estimate," in "Recommendations for Submission of Chemical and Technological Data for Direct Food Additive Petitions"[50]; and "Principles and Methods for the Risk Assessment of Chemicals in Food."[51] FDA is also aware of the existence of extensive analyses of consumption of specific conventional foods, especially in the U.S., in proprietary databases. Because these proprietary databases contain food categories much narrower than those described in public databases, they may be helpful in estimating consumer intake of a food constituent that becomes an NDI for use in a dietary supplement.

9. How is the reliability of history of use data evaluated?

One important component of reliability is the length of an ingredient's history of use. A description of the population consuming the ingredient and the ways in which they use it is also important. Finally, the number of consumers who used the ingredient and the frequency of consumption are at least as important as the number of years over which the ingredient has been used. FDA considers 25 years of widespread use to be the minimum to establish a history of safe use.[52] Because there is little scientific literature addressing this topic, we cannot make more specific recommendations at this time.

10. Should I cite the history of use of an NDI in traditional medicine?

It depends on how much information is available about the use of the NDI in traditional medicine and how similar the traditional medicine use is to the proposed use in a dietary supplement. The history of use of an NDI in traditional medicine can help to establish

49 FDA, Center for Food Safety and Applied Nutrition, Office of Food Additive Safety. Guidance for Industry: Estimating Dietary Intake of Substances in Food; August 2006. Available at: http://www.fda.gov/Food/GuidanceRegulation/GuidanceDocumentsRegulatoryInformation/IngredientsAdditivesGRASPackaging/ucm074725.htm
50 FDA, Center for Food Safety and Applied Nutrition, Office of Food Additive Safety. Guidance for Industry: Recommendations for Submission of Chemical and Technological Data for Direct Food Additive Petitions; March 2006; revised March 2009. Available at: http://www.fda.gov/Food/GuidanceRegulation/GuidanceDocumentsRegulatoryInformation/IngredientsAdditivesGRASPackaging/ucm124917.htm
51 Principles and Methods for the Risk Assessment of Chemicals in Food. Environmental Health Criteria 240. A joint publication of the Food and Agriculture Organization of the UnitedNations and the World Health Organization. 2009. Available at: http://whqlibdoc.who.int/ehc/WHO_EHC_240_4_eng_Chapter1.pdf
52 See, e.g., the definition proposed in the European Union: "'[H]istory of safe food use in a third country'means that the safety of the food in question is confirmed with compositional data and from experience of use and continued use for at least 25 years in the customary diet of a large part of the population of a country." Official Journal of the European Union C 122 E (May 11, 2010); p. 38-57.

a reasonable expectation of safety for the NDI's use in a dietary supplement. However, because differences in composition, conditions of use, and target population often limit the relevance of a safe history of use in traditional medicine to the safety of an NDI in a dietary supplement, additional safety information is almost always needed.

As previously described, it is important to document the size and characteristics of the population that consumed the NDI in or as a traditional medicine, as well as conditions of use, such as dose, duration, and frequency (see questions VI.B.3 and VI.B.7). In addition, if the medicinal product was consumed under the supervision of a trained practitioner of traditional medicine, it is important to document safety-related restrictions on use within the written or oral tradition. Often, traditional medicinal products are chemically and compositionally very different from the NDI that is the subject of the NDI notification. Therefore, it is important to document and explain how any information about a substance's history of safe use in traditional medicine is qualitatively and quantitatively related to the NDI that is the subject of the notification and its proposed conditions of use.

11. Does FDA recommend submitting additional animal and human studies to supplement evidence of a history of safe use by humans?

It depends on the situation. Data on history of use in humans should be the first evidence considered in evaluating the safety of an NDI.

When the NDI has been previously consumed by humans, additional animal or human safety data are seldom needed if (1) the proposed use level is similar to or less than the levels safely consumed by humans in the past; and (2) the population expected to consume the NDI is the same as, or a subset of, the population that safely consumed the substance in the past. In many cases, no additional animal or human safety data are needed because the NDI is reasonably expected to be safe based on a large margin of safety between the level shown to cause no observed adverse effects in humans and the intake level that would result from the proposed use of the NDI in the dietary supplement, or based on longstanding and widespread use of the ingredient as a constituent of conventional food at or below the intake level that would result from the proposed use of the NDI in the dietary supplement.

When the historical use differs significantly from the proposed use of the NDI in a dietary supplement, however, additional supportive data are usually needed. Examples of differences in proposed use that would ordinarily necessitate further supportive data include higher dosage than the historical use, different route of administration, longer duration of use, other changes that increase exposure to potential toxic effects, and any other differences that raise new safety concerns (e.g., a different target population). These examples are based on the general principle that the risk of a substance is likely to increase as intake increases above levels safely consumed in the past. When historical use of an NDI differs significantly from the proposed dietary supplement use, FDA encourages you to submit additional animal studies, human studies, or both. Such studies should be designed to address gaps in the history of use evidence.

CH
13

12. What factors are helpful in evaluating whether to submit animal or human safety studies in addition to history of use data?

Generally, the best way to determine whether history of use data provides a basis for a reasonable expectation that a dietary supplement containing an NDI will be safe is to compare the conditions of use proposed in the NDI notification with the documented historical conditions of safe use. The following are examples of situations where FDA would typically recommend that history of use data be supplemented with additional animal or human safety studies:

- Higher proposed per-serving intake level or total daily intake level.

- Longer proposed duration of consumption than historically reported (e.g., notification states that NDI will be marketed with labeling that recommends or implies continuous daily use for improved digestive function, but the history of safe use involves only infrequent, short-term use for indigestion).

- Different proposed route of administration (e.g., data about historical use of a substance as a poultice or by injection ordinarily would not be sufficient to support the safety of an NDI for use in a dietary supplement, which by definition is intended for ingestion).

- A change from historical use that might increase potential toxic effects (e.g., the NDI will be sold as capsules of a ground leaf, but the form historically used was a tea made from the plant's roots).

- A change in the target population (e.g., history of safe use has been established in adults, but NDI will be used in a dietary supplement marketed for use by young children).

13. Should I use toxicology or clinical studies published by others, or unpublished studies I have performed, if those studies used test articles that are similar but not identical to the NDI or the dietary supplement containing the NDI?

FDA generally recommends that the test article used in safety studies be identical to the NDI or the dietary supplement that is the subject of your notification. However, in the absence of safety data on the NDI or supplement itself, it may be useful to provide data on the safety of a related substance or product.

For example, if the NDI is a component of another substance for which safety studies are available, it may be helpful to submit data from those studies, accompanied by an explanation of why the data on the related substance support the safety of your NDI. Data from a study involving the oral administration of the dried ground root of a plant could be relevant to the safety of an NDI that is an isopropanol extract of the same root if you document that the components of the isopropanol extract were present at the same or lower levels in the ground root fed to the study subjects. The safety of an ester ingredient can be inferred if you can provide data to demonstrate that the ingredient is rapidly hydrolyzed in the stomach or intestine into an acid and an alcohol, and that the acid and the alcohol each have a long history of safe use in food.

The more different the composition of the test article in a study is from that of the NDI, however, the more difficult it will be to argue that the study is relevant.

14. Are there scenarios in which FDA considers additional safety data unnecessary if the proposed use of the NDI leads to intake levels that are the same as or less than the levels consumed historically?

Yes. When the proposed use of the NDI leads to intake levels that are the same as or less than the levels for which there is a documented history of safe use, additional safety data are not needed if the dietary supplement containing the NDI is intended for (1) daily chronic use, and the documented historical use data support safe daily chronic use in the same population or a broader population; (2) intermittent use, and the documented historical use data support safe intermittent use in the same population or a broader population; or (3) intermittent use, and the documented historical use data support safe daily chronic use in the same population or a broader population. In other circumstances, we recommend submitting additional safety data as shown in Table 3 and discussed in the following six questions. (See Table 3: *Safety Testing Recommendations Matrix*.)

15. What types of data does FDA recommend to assess safety if the dietary supplement containing the NDI is intended for daily chronic use, the NDI has a documented history of safe intermittent use, and the proposed use of the NDI leads to intake levels that are the same as or less than the levels consumed historically?

(1) A three-study genetic toxicity (genetox) battery (bacterial mutagenesis, in vitro cytogenetics, and in vivo mammalian test) that includes a test for gene mutations in bacteria, either an in vitro mouse lymphoma thymidine kinase+/- gene mutation assay (preferred) or another suitable in vitro test with cytogenetic evaluation of chromosomal damage using mammalian cells, and an in vivo test for chromosomal damage using mammalian hematopoietic cells;

(2) A 14-day range-finding oral study to establish a maximum tolerated dose (MTD) in an appropriate animal model;

(3) A 90-day subchronic oral study (see questions VI.B.6 and VI.B.28-30) in the same species as the range-finding study to establish an MTD and a No Observed Adverse Effect Level (NOAEL) for use in calculating the margin of safety;

(4) A multi-generation rodent reproductive study (minimum of two generations) (see note at end of list); and

(5) A teratology study (rodent or non-rodent) (see note at end of list).

Note: The rodent reproductive study and the teratology study are not needed if the product is labeled as not for use by women of childbearing age, pregnant or lactating women, or children 13 and younger. (See Table 3: *Safety Testing Recommendations Matrix*.)

CH 13

16. What types of data does FDA recommend to assess safety if the dietary supplement containing the NDI is intended for daily chronic use, the NDI has a documented history of safe daily chronic use, and the proposed use of the NDI leads to intake levels that are greater than the levels consumed historically?

(1) A two-study genetox battery (bacterial mutagenesis and in vitro cytogenetics) that includes a test for gene mutations in bacteria, either an in vitro mouse lymphoma thymidine kinase+/- gene mutation assay (preferred) or another suitable in vitro test with cytogenetic evaluation of chromosomal damage using mammalian cells;

(2) A 14-day range-finding oral study to establish an MTD in an appropriate animal model;

(3) A 90-day subchronic oral study (same species as the range-finding study) to establish an MTD and a NOAEL for use in calculating the margin of safety;

(4) A repeat-dose tolerability study in humans (30-90 day duration);

(5) A one-year chronic toxicity study in an appropriate animal model or a two-year carcinogenesis study in rodents;

(6) A one-generation rodent reproductive study (see note at end of list); and

(7) A teratology study (rodent or non-rodent) (see note at end of list).

Note: The rodent reproductive study and the teratology study are not needed if the product is labeled as not for use by women of childbearing age, pregnant or lactating women, or children 13 and younger. (See Table 3: *Safety Testing Recommendations Matrix*.)

17. What types of data does FDA recommend to assess safety if the dietary supplement containing the NDI is intended for daily chronic use, the NDI has a documented history of safe intermittent use, and the proposed use of the NDI leads to intake levels that are greater than the levels consumed historically?

(1) A three-study genetox battery as described in question VI.B.15;

(2) 14-day range-finding oral studies to establish an MTD in at least two appropriate species, at least one of which is non-rodent;

(3) Two 90-day subchronic oral studies (one for each species for which there is a range-finding study) to establish an MTD and a NOAEL for use in calculating the margin of safety; (4) A one-year chronic toxicity study in an appropriate animal model or a two-year carcinogenesis study in rodents;

(5) A repeat-dose tolerability study in humans (30-90 day duration);

(6) A multi-generation rodent reproductive study (minimum of two generations) (see note at end of list); and

(7) A teratology study (rodent or non-rodent) (see note at end of list). Note: The rodent reproductive study and the teratology study are generally not needed if the product

is labeled as not for use by women of childbearing age, pregnant or lactating women, or children 13 and younger. (See Table 3: *Safety Testing Recommendations Matrix*.)

18. **What types of data does FDA recommend to assess safety if the dietary supplement containing the NDI is intended for intermittent use, the NDI has a documented history of safe intermittent use, and the proposed use of the NDI leads to intake levels that are greater than the levels consumed historically?**

(1) A two-study genetox battery (bacterial mutagenesis and in vitro cytogenetics) as described in question VI.B.16;

(2) A 14-day range-finding oral study to establish an MTD in an appropriate animal model

(3) A 90-day subchronic oral study (same species as the range-finding study) to establish an MTD and a NOAEL for use in calculating the margin of safety

(4) A single-dose or repeat-dose tolerability study in humans and/or an absorption, distribution, metabolism, and excretion (ADME) study in animals, humans, or both; (5) A one-generation rodent reproductive study (see note at end of list);

(6) A teratology study (rodent or non-rodent) (see note at end of list).

Note: The rodent reproductive study and the teratology study are not needed if the product is labeled as not for use by women of childbearing age, pregnant or lactating women, or children 13 and younger. (See Table 3: *Safety Testing Recommendations Matrix*.)

19.**What types of data does FDA recommend to assess safety if the dietary supplement containing the NDI is intended for intermittent use, the NDI has a documented history of safe daily chronic use, and the proposed use of the NDI leads to intake levels that are greater than the levels consumed historically?**

(1) A two-study genetox battery as described in question VI.B.16;

(2) A 14-day range-finding oral study to establish an MTD in an appropriate animal model; (3) A 90-day subchronic oral study (same species as the range-finding study) to establish an MTD and a NOAEL for use in calculating the margin of safety;

(4) A single-dose or repeat-dose tolerability study in humans and/or an ADME study in animals, humans, or both; and

(5) A teratology study (rodent or non-rodent) (see note at end of list). Note: The teratology study is not needed if the product is labeled as not for use by women of childbearing age, pregnant or lactating women, or children 13 and younger. (See Table 3: *Safety Testing Recommendations Matrix*.)

CH 13

20. What types of data does FDA recommend to assess safety if there is no history of use of the NDI that can be relied on to provide evidence of safe use in dietary supplements?

(1) A three-study genetox battery as described in question VI.B.15;

(2) 14-day range-finding oral studies to establish an MTD in at least two appropriate species, at least one of which is non-rodent;

(3) Two 90-day subchronic oral studies (one for each species for which there is a range-finding study) to establish an MTD and a NOAEL for use in calculating the margin of safety (see footnote "‡" in Table 3: *Safety Testing Recommendations Matrix*);

(4) A repeat-dose tolerability study in humans and/or an ADME study in animals, humans, or both (30-90 day duration);

(5) A one-year chronic toxicity study or a two-year carcinogenesis study in at least two animal species, if the proposed use is either intermittent or daily chronic;

(6) A multi-generation rodent reproductive study (minimum of two generations) (see note at end of list); and

(7) A teratology study (rodent or non-rodent) (see note at end of list).

Note: The rodent reproductive study and the teratology study are not needed if the product is labeled as not for use by women of childbearing age, pregnant or lactating women, or children 13 and younger.

Based on the nature of the NDI and the results of other testing, special studies (e.g., carcinogenicity, ADME) may be needed to provide a reasonable expectation of safety. Other nonclinical studies to assess immunotoxicity and neurotoxicity should be conducted on a case-by-case basis, as appropriate. (See Table 3: *Safety Testing Recommendations Matrix*.)

21. Am I required to use only FDA-published safety test protocols?

No. You should use your own judgment in selecting among FDA's protocols and other internationally recognized safety testing protocols and testing batteries developed for other types of products when you choose safety testing protocols for your NDI or the dietary supplement to which your NDI will be added. Regardless of the protocols used, you should cite the source for each protocol and why the protocol or the battery of protocols you chose is appropriate for the safety endpoints that are being investigated.

The NDI safety standard is different than the standard for food additives, drugs, and other FDA-regulated products. Recommendations in guidance documents that are tailored to the safety assessment needs of other FDA-regulated products may not always be appropriate for dietary ingredients or dietary supplements. You should compile scientific evidence that provides a basis to conclude that the NDI that is the subject of your notification will reasonably be expected to be safe when used under the conditions recommended or suggested in the labeling of the dietary supplement described in the notification.

CH
13

Table 3: Safety Testing Recommendations Matrix

Documented Historical Use	Proposed Use of the NDI	Two-Study Genetic Toxicity Battery[1]	Three-Study Genetic Toxicity Battery[1]	14-Day Range-Finding Oral Study In Animals	90-Day Subchronic Oral Study in Animals[3]	One-Generation Rodent Reproductive Study [2]	Multi-Generation Rodent Reproductive Study[2]	Teratology Study in Animals[2]	One-Year Chronic Toxicity or Two-Year Carcinogenesis Study in Animals*	Single-Dose Tolerability and/or ADME Study in Animals and/or Humans*	Repeat-Dose Tolerability and/or ADME Study in Animals and/or Humans*
Daily Chronic	Intermittent: Less Than Historical Use (see question VI.B.14)	Documented history of use should be sufficient as evidence of safety.									
Daily Chronic	Intermittent: Greater Than Historical Use (see question VI.B.19)	X		X	X			X		X	
Daily Chronic	Daily Chronic: Less Than Historical Use (see question VI.B.14)	Documented history of use should be sufficient as evidence of safety.									
Daily Chronic	Daily Chronic: Greater Than Historical Use (see question VI.B.16)	X		X	X	X		X	X	X	X
Intermittent	Intermittent: Less Than Historical Use (see question VI.B.14)	Documented history of use should be sufficient as evidence of safety.									
Intermittent	Intermittent: Greater Than Historical Use (see question VI.B.18)	X		X	X	X		X		X	
Intermittent	Daily Chronic: Less Than Historical Use (see questionVI.B.15)		X	X	X		X	X			
Intermittent	Daily Chronic: Greater Than Historical Use (see question VI.B.17)		X	X	X [3]		X	X	X [3]		X
No History	Daily Chronic (see question VI.B.20)		X	X	X [3]	x	X	X	X [3]		X
No History	Intermittent (see question VI.B.20)		X	X	X [3]	x	X	X	X [3]		X

CH
13

> **Table 3: Safety Testing Recommendations Matrix (Table notes)**
>
> 1 Genetic toxicity batteries are described in questions VI.B.15 and VI.B.16.
>
> 2 Reproductive and teratology testing is not needed if the product is labeled as not for use by women of childbearing age, pregnant or lactating women, and children 13 and younger.
>
> 3 In general, if there is no history of use, two species should be used for 90-day subchronic studies. In addition, the one-year chronic toxicity study or two-year carcinogenesis study should be done in two species. However, the one-year chronic toxicity study, two-year carcinogenesis study, or second subchronic study may not be necessary in some cases based on the amount and type of historical use data or the duration of use of the NDI, if significantly shorter than lifetime daily use. For example, if the proposed use of the NDI is for 30 days or less, then a 28-day animal study might be sufficient under certain circumstances (e.g., live microbial NDI).
>
> *Special studies (such as one-year chronic toxicity studies in animals; two-year carcinogenicity studies in animals; and ADME, bioavailability, and tolerability studies in animals, humans, or both) should be conducted on a case-by-case basis, as appropriate, if the toxicology data or the identity of the NDI raises a special safety concern.

22. What are some sources of safety testing protocols that can be used in testing NDIs and dietary supplements?

Useful guidelines for safety testing include:

- OECD Guidelines for the Testing of Chemicals, Section 4: Health Effects, published by the Organization for Economic Co-operation and Development[53];

- Harmonized Test Guidelines, published by the Office of Chemical Safety and Pollution Prevention of the U.S. Environmental Protection Agency (EPA)[54]; and

- Principles and Methods for the Risk Assessment of Chemicals in Food, published jointly by the Food and Agriculture Organization of the United Nations and the World Health Organization.[55]

23. What is the appropriate highest dose of an NDI to use in animal and human safety studies?

To maximize the chance that toxicity associated with the test article can be detected, the highest dose (commonly referred to as the "top dose") in animal studies should be the maximum tolerated dose (MTD) (see definition in section VII). Lower doses are used to establish the dose-response relationship and the no-effect dose (see question VI.C.4 for information on the latter). Shorter-term studies are needed to estimate the MTD for longer studies; for example, the results of a 14-day study must be known before the dose for a 90-day study can be determined.

CH
13

---

53   Organisation for Economic Co-operation and Development (OECD). OECD Guidelines for the Testing of Chemicals, Section 4: Health Effects. Available at:http://www.oecd.org/chemicalsafety/testing/oecdguidelinesforthetestingofchemicals.htm.

54   U.S. Environmental Protection Agency (EPA), Office of Chemical Safety and Pollution Prevention (OCSPP). OCSPP Harmonized Test Guidelines; September 2015.Available at: https://www.epa.gov/test-guidelines-pesticides-and-toxic-substances.

55   Principles and Methods for the Risk Assessment of Chemicals in Food. Environmental Health Criteria 240. A joint publication of the Food and Agriculture Organization of the United Nations and the World Health Organization. 2009.Available at: http://whqlibdoc.who.int/ehc/WHO_EHC_240_4_eng_Chapter1.pdf.

Considering a broad range of biological information is essential to pick the correct top dose or MTD. For example, data concerning changes in body and organ weight and clinically significant alterations in hematological, urinary, neurological, and clinical chemistry parameters, in combination with more definitive toxic, gross, or histopathologic endpoints, can be used to estimate the MTD. FDA intends to consider whether the test article was tested at the MTD as a major factor in evaluating the adequacy of studies submitted in an NDI notification. The studies should include a description of the process used to select the MTD for the study, if it is not readily apparent.

Please note that it is not scientifically valid to select doses for tests based on information unrelated to the toxicity of the test article. For example, the highest dose should not be selected so as to provide a pre-determined margin of safety over the maximum expected human consumption of the test article, assuming that the results of testing at that dose will be negative.

FDA recognizes that there may be limitations on using a top dose. For example, limits on top doses can be based on animal handling considerations, such as the amount that can be safely administered by gavage or the amount in feed that still permits proper nutrition. The top dose in clinical studies should be governed by safety considerations, as determined by an Institutional Review Board. However, within the limits of safety, the top dose in clinical studies should be as high as feasible. At a minimum, the top dose or total daily intake level in a clinical trial of an NDI should be as high as the top dose or total daily intake level of the NDI under the conditions of use proposed in the notification. Preferably, the highest total daily intake level in the trial should be higher than the highest total daily intake level of the NDI proposed in the notification.

24. What should I do to justify the use of a particular protocol?

You should cite an authoritative source for the protocol and explain how information generated by the study using the protocol supports the safety of the dietary supplement in which the NDI will be used. If you decide to deviate from a standard or published protocol, you should explain why you altered the protocol and how the alteration affects the relevance of the study results to the safety of your product.

25. How will I identify a potential hazard using a standard genetic toxicity test, and what should I do after identifying a potential genetic toxicity hazard?

A positive finding in one or more of the standard genetic toxicity tests constitutes a clear but non-quantitative identification of a potential hazard. Positive results in genetic toxicity tests may necessitate additional safety testing, such as an evaluation of carcinogenicity from two-year or lifetime chronic toxicity assays. General guidance on following up positive results in genetic toxicity testing can be found in the scientific literature on this topic.[56]

---

56   Dearfield KL, Thybaud V, Cimino MC, Custer L, Czich A, Harvey JS, *et al*. Follow-up actions from positive results of in vitro genetic toxicity testing. Environ Mol Mutagen. 2011 Apr; 52(3):177-204.

26. Should the NDI notification discuss the history of use or other evidence of safety that forms the basis for my conclusion that a genotoxic dietary ingredient can reasonably be expected to be safe?

Yes, your NDI notification should discuss this history of use or other evidence of safety. You should conduct a risk assessment to determine whether the genetic toxicity of the NDI prevents the dietary supplement from being reasonably expected to be safe under the proposed conditions of use.

27. Where can I find good examples of genotoxicity protocols that can be used in conducting animal and human studies on NDIs?

The sources cited in the answer to question VI.B.22 contain test guidelines and testing batteries for evaluating genetic toxicity.

28. What is the purpose of a subchronic oral toxicity study?

When properly conducted (e.g., with doses selected based on shorter term repeat-dose studies), subchronic oral toxicity studies are used to identify the maximum tolerated dose (MTD) of a substance, as well as the substance's No Observed Adverse Effect Level (NOAEL). Toxicity data and the NOAEL identified by the subchronic oral study are used (1) to predict the organ toxicity or other types of toxicity that are likely to be associated with human or animal consumption of unsafe quantities of the test article; (2) to determine the need for and design of additional animal studies, such as specialized toxicity studies and chronic toxicity studies; and (3) to assess the safety of short-term repeat-dose exposure to the test article, either for consumers or for participants in clinical trials.

29. What is the appropriate duration for a subchronic oral toxicity study?

Subchronic oral toxicity studies are generally conducted for 90 days (3 months). Protocols described as lasting 12 or 13 weeks are considered equivalent. Subchronic toxicity studies provide information on the possible health hazards likely to arise from repeated exposure to a substance over a three-month period.

30. Where can I find more information and examples of a subchronic oral toxicity study?

We recommend referring to the OECD Guidelines for the Testing of Chemicals. Protocols for rodent studies are in OECD Guideline 408, "Repeated Dose 90-day Oral Toxicity Study in Rodents."[57] Protocols for non-rodent studies are in OECD Guideline 409, "Repeated Dose 90-Day Oral Toxicity Study in Non-Rodents."[58] The appropriate animal species and

---

57   Organisation for Economic Co-operation and Development. OECD Guidelines for the Testing of Chemicals, Guideline 408: Repeated Dose 90-day Oral Toxicity Study in Rodents. Paris: OECD Publishing; May 1981; revised September 1998. Available at: http://www.oecd-ilibrary.org/environment/test-no-408-repeated-dose-90-day-oral-toxicity-study-in-rodents_9789264070707-en.

58   Organisation for Economic Co-operation and Development. OECD Guidelines for the Testing of Chemicals, Guideline 409: Repeated Dose 90-day Oral Toxicity Study in Non-Rodents. Paris: OECD Publishing; May 1981; revised September 1998. Available at: http://www.oecd-ilibrary.org/environment/test-no-409-repeated-dose-90-

study design may vary depending on the safety questions associated with the NDI being studied.

31. What is the purpose of reproductive toxicity and teratology studies?

The purpose of reproductive toxicity studies is to provide information regarding the effects of a dietary ingredient on all aspects of reproduction, including sexual behavior, spermatogenic and estrus cycles, gonadal function, fertility, parturition (giving birth), lactation, and prenatal development. The purpose of teratology studies is to provide information on whether the test article causes congenital malformations in the offspring of a test animal. The purpose of multi-generation reproductive studies is to provide growth and reproductive function data regarding the effects of the test article on male and female offspring of test animals and on the growth and reproductive function of their offspring in the subsequent generation(s).

32. Should I include a discussion of the reproductive and teratology studies in my NDI notification?

Yes. FDA recommends that you provide a summary and a detailed discussion of the results of each reproductive and teratology study in the comprehensive safety profile for the NDI (see question VI.C.2).

33. Should I identify the "No Observed Adverse Effect Level" (NOAEL) for all test substance-related changes in both reproductive and teratology test endpoints?

Yes. You should identify the NOAEL for parental animals and their offspring in each generation in reproductive studies, including teratology studies. In addition to information about reproductive success, data from the study should also be used to provide information on development (i.e., growth and function of the offspring) and teratogenesis (i.e., birth defects, both structural and functional).

34. Where can I find sample protocols for reproductive and teratology studies?

We recommend that you refer to the OECD Guidelines for the Testing of Chemicals, Guidelines 415 ("One-Generation Reproduction Toxicity Study"),[59] 416 ("Two-Generation Reproduction Toxicity Study"),[60] 421 ("Reproduction/Developmental Toxicity Screening Test"),[61] and 422 ("Combined Repeated Dose Toxicity Study with the Reproduction/

---

day-oral-toxicity-study-in-non-rodents_9789264070721-en.

59   Organisation for Economic Co-operation and Development. OECD Guidelines for the Testing of Chemicals, Guideline 415: One-Generation Reproduction Toxicity Study. Paris: OECD Publishing; May 1983. Available at: http://www.oecd.org/chemicalsafety/risk-assessment/1948458.pdf

60   Organisation for Economic Co-operation and Development. OECD Guidelines for the Testing of Chemicals, Guideline 416: Two-Generation Reproduction Toxicity Study. Paris: OECD Publishing; May 1983; revised January 2001. Available at: http://www.oecd.org/chemicalsafety/risk-assessment/1948466.pdf

61   Organisation for Economic Co-operation and Development. OECD Guidelines for the Testing of Chemicals, Guideline 421: Reproduction/Developmental Toxicity Screening Test. Paris: OECD Publishing; July 2015. Available at: http://www.oecd-ilibrary.org/environment/test-no-421-reproduction-developmental-toxicity-screening-test_9789264242692-en

Developmental Toxicity Screening Test")[62] to find protocols for conducting reproductive toxicity and teratology studies. You may also wish to consider how data from these studies are assembled and used for other regulatory programs (e.g., for pesticides, see EPA's "Harmonized Test Guidelines,"[63] and for medicinal products, see ICH's "Safety Guidelines"[64]). In particular, "Detection of Toxicity to Reproduction for Medicinal Products & Toxicity to Male Fertility"[65] contains useful guidelines for detecting reproductive toxicity.

35. What is the purpose of repeat-dose toxicity testing?

In general, the purpose of repeat-dose toxicity testing is to define toxic effects on body systems and target organs based on repeated and/or cumulative exposure to the test substance or to constituents and/or metabolites of the test substance. Repeat-dose testing defines the nature of the tissue or organ damage, particularly in relation to dose and duration of exposure. Repeat-dose testing is also used to identify dosages associated with toxic and biological responses and to define a NOAEL.

The route of administration in repeat-dose testing for a dietary supplement containing an NDI should always be oral, and the study should include a range of doses at and above the proposed dose of the NDI in the dietary supplement. An "oral study," as described in this guidance, can include administration in feed or drinking water (with the feed or water consumption measured to confirm actual intake) or via gavage, which involves introduction of the test article through a tube passed through the mouth into the stomach. Ideally, the test article used in these studies should have the same composition and form as the dietary supplement described in the notification since the other ingredients can affect the safety of the NDI as used in the product.

36. Am I required to conduct human clinical studies to assess the safety of my NDI or the dietary supplement containing my NDI?

The FD&C Act contains no explicit requirement for a manufacturer or distributor to conduct human clinical studies before submitting an NDI notification. However, there may be circumstances in which you find it necessary to perform such studies because

---

62   Organisation for Economic Co-operation and Development. OECD Guidelines for the Testing of Chemicals, Guideline 422: Combined Repeated Dose Toxicity Study with the Reproduction/Developmental Toxicity Screening Test. Paris: OECD Publishing; March 1996. Available at:http://www.oecd-ilibrary.org/environment/test-no-422-combined-repeated-dose-toxicity-study-with-the-reproduction-developmental-toxicity-screening-test_9789264070981-en

63   U.S. Environmental Protection Agency (EPA), Office of Chemical Safety and Pollution Prevention (OCSPP). OCSPP Harmonized Test Guidelines; September 2015.Available at:https://www.epa.gov/test-guidelines-pesticides-and-toxic-substances.

64   International Conference on Harmonisation of Technical Requirements for Registration of Pharmaceuticals for Human Use (ICH). Safety Guidelines. Available at:http://www.ich.org/products/guidelines/safety/article/safety-guidelines.htmlAccessed August 28, 2015.

65   International Conference on Harmonisation of Technical Requirements for Registration of Pharmaceuticals for Human Use (ICH). Detection of Toxicity to Reproduction for Medicinal Products & Toxicity to Male Fertility S5(R2); June 1993; addendum dated November 2000 incorporated November 2005.Available at: http://www.ich.org/fileadmin/Public_Web_Site/ICH_Products/Guidelines/Safety/S5/Step4/S5_R2_Guideline.pdf.

---

the existing history of use data, safety data, and data on population exposure do not provide a sufficient basis for you to conclude that the dietary supplement containing the NDI will reasonably be expected to be safe under its proposed conditions of use.[66]

37. What kinds of human clinical studies are useful to assess the safety of an NDI or dietary supplement containing an NDI?

The most useful studies are usually short-term tolerability studies and absorption, distribution, metabolism, and excretion (ADME) studies. The test article used in these studies should have the same identity and composition (including ingredients used in combination with the NDI) and forms as described in the dietary supplement composition section of your notification. When human ADME studies are done in conjunction with ADME studies conducted in the animal species used for toxicological testing, the relevance of the animal data to humans can be demonstrated and the safety factors used to calculate the margin of safety can be reduced (see question VI.C.5).

Tolerability studies identify acute toxicity, such as that associated with toxins or with indigestible nutrients at very high serving levels of ingredients like fats and oils. Human repeat-dose studies are more rarely used to directly demonstrate the safety of the test article in humans. They can be used to allay specific safety concerns raised by animal studies or history of use information, or to establish a margin of safety for an NDI when the proposed conditions of use would result in doses that cannot be humanely administered to animals.

38. What is the purpose of "repeat-dose" human studies, and how are such studies classified?

Human studies can be used alone or in conjunction with animal studies. If animal toxicity studies or history of use data do not document an adequate margin of safety between the NOAEL for your NDI and the expected intake of the NDI from its proposed dietary supplement use, we recommend a human clinical trial consisting of a repeat-dose study. Clinical trials should include male and female subjects, as well as an adequate sample size and duration. Sample size is a very important consideration, as the study should be sufficiently powered to show differences in your data. If a clinical trial is not powered by a large enough sample size, results showing no adverse effects cannot be relied on as evidence of safety because the absence of adverse effects from intake of the NDI could be due to chance. Duration of the clinical trial is also an important factor in your study design and depends on the proposed conditions of use.

Clinical trials may be grouped by their purpose and objective. Phase I trials are the first stage of testing in humans. They are designed to assess absorption, distribution,

CH
13

---

66   Human clinical studies must comply with FDA's regulations for the protection of human subjects (21 CFR Parts 50 and 56). A clinical study intended to evaluate the safety of a dietary ingredient or dietary supplement generally does not require an investigational new drug application (IND), but if the study also evaluates the use of the productto treat or mitigate a disease (i.e., a use of the product as a drug), it would require an IND. See FDA, Guidance for Clinical Investigators, Sponsors, and IRBs: Investigational New Drug Applications (INDs) – Determining Whether Human Research Studies Can Be Conducted Without an IND; September 2013. Available at: http://www.fda.gov/downloads/Drugs/Guidances/UCM229175.pdf.

metabolism, and excretion (ADME), safety, tolerability, pharmacokinetics, and pharmacodynamics. Phase I studies are generally single-dose studies, followed by dose-range or dose escalation studies, and finally short-term repeat-dose studies to evaluate pharmacokinetic parameters and tolerance (see Table 3: Safety Testing Recommendations Matrix). Single-dose and repeat-dose studies are elements of Phase I studies to assess human pharmacology. Phase II studies (designed to assess dosing requirements and efficacy) and Phase III studies (randomized, controlled multicenter studies involving large sample sizes to evaluate effectiveness of a treatment) focus on efficacy and are generally not useful to establish the safety of a dietary supplement. A clinical trial of less than 90 days is considered subchronic and cannot, by itself, support safety of chronic use. The endpoints of any clinical study should be clearly defined.

39. Where can I find more information and examples of clinical protocols that can be used in conducting human studies for NDIs and dietary supplements?

FDA recommends consulting "Principles and Methods for the Risk Assessment of Chemicals in Food"[67] for a good general discussion of this topic. This reference, which recognizes the value of the experience gained from pharmaceutical safety studies in designing food safety studies, also includes a discussion of the similarities and differences between clinical studies conducted for foods and those for pharmaceuticals. "Guidance for Industry—M3 (R2) Nonclinical Safety Studies for the Conduct of Human Clinical Trials and Marketing Authorization for Pharmaceuticals"[68] contains a useful discussion of selecting an appropriate dose for subchronic oral studies in animals and clinical trials in human volunteers (pp. 1-5).

40. What information should I submit to demonstrate the safety of an NDI produced by fermentation using microorganisms like bacteria or yeast?

You should identify the microorganism using scientifically valid nomenclature for the genus, species, and the name of the strain. You should also discuss the history of use of the organism or related organisms as food or to produce food. In addition, you should identify any human pathogens that are phylogenetically related to the fermentation microorganism at the species or genus level. You should also identify any toxins, classes of toxins, or other deleterious substances known to be present in the same species as the microorganism or in a genus or species that is phylogenetically related to the microorganism. Finally, you should document the absence (or the amount, if present) of such toxins or other deleterious substances in the microorganism. The absence of unsafe levels of such deleterious substances should be demonstrated by an appropriate combination of specifications for the NDI, safety testing in humans, and/or safety testing in an appropriate animal model.

---

67   Principles and Methods for the Risk Assessment of Chemicals in Food. Environmental Health Criteria 240. A joint publication of the Food and Agriculture Organization of the United Nations and the World Health Organization. 2009.Available at: http://whqlibdoc.who.int/ehc/WHO_EHC_240_4_eng_Chapter1.pdf

68   FDA, Center for Drug Evaluation and Research and Center for Biologics Evaluation and Research. Guidance for Industry: M3 (R2) Nonclinical Safety Studies for the Conduct of Human Clinical Trials and Marketing Authorization for Pharmaceuticals, Revision 1; January 2010. Available at: http://www.fda.gov/downloads/Drugs/GuidanceComplianceRegulatoryInformation/Guidances/ucm073246.pdf

41. What information should I submit to demonstrate the safety of a microbial NDI (live or killed)?

You should identify any human pathogens that are phylogenetically related to the microbial NDI at the species or genus level. You should identify any toxins, classes of toxins, or other deleterious substances known to be present in the same species or in a phylogenetically related family or genus. You should also document the absence (or the amount, if present) of such toxins or other deleterious substances in the NDI. You should document resistance to any clinically relevant antibiotics, and if applicable, the genetic nature of the resistance. If the microbial NDI is resistant to any clinically relevant antibiotics, it is also recommended that you perform an assessment of the ability of the antibiotic resistance genes to mobilize and transfer to human pathogens under the conditions of use of the dietary supplement.

If your notification cites the history of use of a live microorganism as evidence of safety, FDA recommends a careful assessment of the relative level of historical exposure compared to the proposed conditions of use of the NDI, including a discussion of how the form of the dietary supplement and any non-dietary ingredients (e.g., binders and fillers) used in it affect delivery of the NDI to various points in the human gastrointestinal tract.

If history of use data are inadequate to support the safety of the microbial NDI, you should include safety studies in humans or appropriate animal models in your notification. FDA considers pigs to be the most appropriate animal model for the human digestive tract. Human or animal safety studies should include measurements of the persistence of the organism in the body after administration, the ability of the organism to translocate outside of the gastrointestinal tract, and tolerance of the ingredient using the proposed serving form. Because this is a rapidly evolving scientific discipline, FDA recommends that notifiers be familiar with the state of the recent scientific literature at the time the notification is submitted.

42. What should I do to demonstrate the safety of an NDI that contains nanomaterials or otherwise involves the application of nanotechnology?

Because there is little scientific literature discussing the safety of nanomaterials in dietary supplements, FDA recommends that notifiers contact FDA[69] prior to submitting an NDI notification for an NDI that contains nanomaterials or otherwise involves the application of nanotechnology.[70]

---

69 Contact information for the Office of Dietary Supplement Programs can be found on the title page.

70 FDA, Guidance for Industry: Assessing the Effects of Significant Manufacturing Process Changes, Including Emerging Technologies, on the Safety and Regulatory Status of Food Ingredients and Food Contact Substances, Including Food Ingredients that are Color Additives. June 2014. Available at: http://www.fda.gov/food/ guidanceregulation/guidancedocumentsregulatoryinformation/ucm300661.htm. See also FDA, Guidance for Industry: Considering Whether an FDA-Regulated Product Involves the Application of Nanotechnology; June 2014. Available at: http://www.fda.gov/RegulatoryInformation/Guidances/ucm257698.htm.

C. Summary of the Basis for Your Conclusion of Safety

1. Should my notification include separate safety profiles for the NDI and the dietary supplement in which the NDI will be used?

Yes. FDA recommends that the discussion of history of use and other evidence of safety in your notification should include two separate safety profiles: first, a comprehensive safety profile evaluating the safety of the NDI, and second, a dietary supplement safety narrative explaining why the information in the notification provides a basis to conclude that the dietary supplement that contains the NDI will reasonably be expected to be safe when used under the conditions recommended or suggested in the dietary supplement's labeling. Each piece of data or information in the notification should be cited in the comprehensive safety profile, the safety narrative, or both, so that it is clear how each piece of data or information is used to form the basis for the safety of the dietary supplement containing the NDI.

When a notification describes a dietary supplement containing more than one NDI, FDA recommends including a comprehensive safety profile for each NDI, with the safety of the combination of NDIs addressed in the safety narrative. However, when there is history of use or other evidence of safety for the combination of NDIs used in the dietary supplement, it may be appropriate to have a comprehensive safety profile for that combination in addition to a separate profile for each NDI (or instead of separate profiles for the individual NDIs when most or all of the safety information is for the combination).

2. What should I include in my comprehensive safety profile for the NDI?

The NDI comprehensive safety profile should provide objective summaries of all available human and animal toxicological information (including both published and unpublished safety studies) and any other information relevant to the safety assessment of the NDI.

The information in the NDI comprehensive safety profile should substantiate the safe use of the NDI in humans under the proposed conditions of use described in the notification. A history of use discussion in the NDI comprehensive safety profile should document the identity and historical uses of the NDI, including the intake level, frequency, and duration of the historical uses, as well as a description of the size and characteristics of the population that consumed the NDI. To the extent that test articles or materials described in the history of use and other evidence of safety are not identical to the NDI, the similarities and differences should be described, and the applicability of the study to the safety evaluation of the NDI should be explained.

If the NDI notification relies on safety studies, the NDI comprehensive safety profile should qualitatively and quantitatively compare the ingredients tested in each of the studies cited with the NDI. If you cite a study on the feeding of a whole herb to a test animal and the NDI is an extract of that herb, the NDI comprehensive safety profile should qualitatively and quantitatively compare the dose and total daily intake of the herb in the study to the proposed dose and total daily intake of the NDI. Whenever possible, the notification should identify the effect and no-effect doses in each human and animal study, and the relationships between observed adverse effects and other related observed effects should be described.

The NDI comprehensive safety profile should identify the NOAEL (see question VI.C.4) and describe the toxicity data or adverse events that were the basis for determining it. The comprehensive safety profile should also describe the acceptable daily intake (ADI) for the NDI and explain how it was calculated (see question VI.C.5). Finally, the comprehensive safety profile should state the basis for the margin of safety for the NDI and how the margin of safety was calculated. The NDI comprehensive safety profile may need to rely heavily on trade secrets or confidential commercial information. Any information in the NDI comprehensive safety profile that you believe to be a trade secret or confidential commercial information should be identified as such (see question V.A.16).

3. What should I include in my dietary supplement safety narrative?

The dietary supplement safety narrative should include a concise summary of the scientific basis for your conclusion that the dietary supplement containing the NDI will reasonably be expected to be safe when used under the conditions recommended or suggested in the supplement's labeling. The purpose of the dietary supplement safety narrative is to explain how the various pieces of data and information fit together to form the basis for your conclusions about the safety of the dietary supplement.

The dietary supplement safety narrative should be based on the identity information, safety information, and analyses in other sections of the NDI notification, including the NDI comprehensive safety profile. The dietary supplement safety narrative should include a summary of the more detailed discussion in the comprehensive safety profile of how you concluded that the NDI in the dietary supplement will reasonably be expected to be safe based on the margin of safety between the NDI intake level that shows no adverse effects (the NOAEL) and the proposed intake level and other conditions of use of the NDI in the dietary supplement.

If the supplement contains dietary ingredients other than the NDI, the dietary supplement safety narrative should identify the NOAEL and ADI for each ingredient (see questions VI.C.4 and VI.C.5), describe the toxicity data or adverse events that were the basis for determining the NOAEL, state the basis for the margin of safety for each ingredient, and discuss whether there is any possible synergy or interaction among any or all ingredients that could affect the safety of the dietary supplement. For each dietary ingredient other than the NDI, the dietary supplement safety narrative should concisely evaluate known safety concerns and describe how the notifier concluded that the combination of ingredients will reasonably be expected to be safe. If the formulation of the product, including other ingredients, affects the bioavailability of dietary ingredients, then the safety narrative should include a discussion of the effective per-serving intake level of the dietary ingredient(s) in the products compared to per-serving intake levels or

CH 13

dosages described in the history of use or other evidence of safety.

The safety narrative should also describe the function of each food additive, color additive, and GRAS substance (i.e., each non-dietary ingredient), including the technical effect and the quantity needed to achieve that technical effect. References to the applicable food additive regulation, color additive regulation, GRAS regulation, or GRAS notification are also recommended.

The dietary supplement safety narrative should estimate the total daily human intake of the dietary supplement containing the NDI and describe any potential toxicity or health concerns associated with human consumption of the dietary supplement, particularly if concerns that may result from the proposed use of the dietary supplement by a vulnerable population have been identified. The description of toxicity and health concerns should include the effects of binders, fillers, formulation aids, and other non-dietary ingredients present in the dietary supplement, particularly if they alter the safety profile of one or more ingredients, such as by increasing uptake into the body after ingestion. If any ingredient in the dietary supplement is present at a level close to the ADI, the presence of that ingredient from other sources in the diet should also be addressed.

Because of the central importance of the dietary supplement safety narrative to the overall conclusion of safety, the dietary supplement safety narrative should be written in such a way that it will be comprehensible after FDA has redacted any trade secrets and confidential commercial information and placed the notification in the public docket. As with the comprehensive safety profile, any information in the dietary supplement safety narrative that you believe to be a trade secret or confidential commercial information should be identified as such (see question V.A.16).

4. What is the difference between a NOEL and a NOAEL, and which should I use?

The No-Observed-Adverse-Effect Level (NOAEL) is a number signifying the highest dose or total daily intake level that did not elicit an adverse effect in a properly designed and executed toxicological study.[71] The No-Observable-Effect Level (NOEL) is the highest dose at which no effects of any kind were observed, including beneficial and neutral effects as well as adverse effects. Therefore, the NOAEL, which is the threshold for adverse effects, is the appropriate level to use in calculating the margin of safety for an NDI.

FDA expects that many dietary ingredients, because they are intended to have beneficial nutritional effects or other effects on the structure or function of the body, will cause changes in parameters that are measured in animal and clinical safety studies. FDA also expects that, as dose and total intake increase, effects that are neutral or beneficial at lower exposures may become adverse effects or be supplanted by adverse effects. Thus, it is important that the notification contain a discussion of the nature of the effects that are observed in safety studies. This discussion should distinguish between adverse effects and other effects (neutral or beneficial effects).

---

71   Adapted from Hayes, A. Wallace, editor. Principles and Methods of Toxicology. 5th ed. New York: Informa Healthcare USA, Inc; 2008.

The purpose of the NOAEL, which is typically higher than the NOEL, is to identify a safe level of a substance (that is, the level at which no adverse effects are observed); therefore, the NOAEL should be used to calculate the margin of safety in the NDI notification. A comparative discussion of the effects observed at different doses of an NDI should appear in the comprehensive safety profile for the NDI. FDA also recommends that this discussion be summarized in the dietary supplement safety narrative because it is central to the overall safety evaluation.

5. What safety factors should be used if only animal toxicity studies are available?

It is important for the notifier to determine the ADI, in addition to the NOAEL, to conduct an adequate risk assessment of the NDI. The NOAEL, expressed on a body weight basis (e.g., mg/kg/day), is divided by a safety factor (also referred to as an uncertainty factor) to derive the ADI. Safety factors account for the uncertainty in extrapolating from experimental data to predict the safety of a substance in humans.

If the NOAEL is derived from a chronic toxicity study (one-year duration or longer) in animals, the combined safety factor is usually 100. This number is calculated using a factor of 10 to account for interspecies variation between animals and humans and another factor of 10 to account for the variation in sensitivity within the human population.

Extrapolation from subchronic toxicity studies to chronic use of an NDI or dietary supplement necessitates an additional safety factor. In this situation, FDA recommends using at least two subchronic toxicity studies, at least one of which was conducted in a non-rodent species and the other in a rodent species, and introducing another safety factor of 10 for a combined safety factor of 1,000. In the absence of supporting history of use data, using only a single rodent subchronic toxicity study as a basis to conclude that chronic use of an NDI in humans will be safe is strongly discouraged, but may be acceptable if a safety factor of 2,000 is used and there is no toxicity to the rodents at the maximum tolerated dose (MTD). The additional safety factor of 2 is used in this situation because a complete animal toxicology assessment includes two subchronic (90-day) animal studies.

The safety factors in these examples are approximate values, which can vary with the specific data that are available. For example, a higher value may be appropriate if toxicity is particularly severe or the variation in human sensitivity is expected to be great. On the other hand, a lower value may be appropriate if subchronic studies in both rodent and non-rodent species showed no adverse effects. If human data from chronic toxicity or ADME (absorption, distribution, metabolism, and excretion) studies (typically one year in duration) are available, a safety factor lower than 100 may be appropriate. While FDA does not consider the ADI to be a sharp dividing line between safe and unsafe levels, the ADI does provide a useful benchmark for protecting the consumer.

In summary, safety factors are uncertainty factors used multiplicatively to arrive at the combined safety factor that is applied to a particular dataset provided in a notification. This combined safety factor is used to calculate the ADI.

CH 13

$$ADI = NOAEL/\text{combined safety factor} = NOAEL/ (Uf_{intra} \times Uf_{extrap} \times Uf_{inter})$$

- **Uf_{intra}**: An uncertainty factor to account for *intraspecies* variation is introduced to protect sensitive members of the population when clinical trials include only healthy subjects, since dietary supplements may be consumed by anyone—the young, the aged, the healthy, and the infirm. A value of 10 is usually used. The size of the intraspecies uncertainty factor should be smaller when there is a long history of food use by a large, diverse population. The size of the intraspecies uncertainty factor should be larger when toxicity is severe or when a notification relies on studies with limited duration or small populations.

- **Uf_{inter}**: Extrapolation from animal to human requires an uncertainty factor for *interspecies* variation. A factor of 10 is usually used to capture the uncertainty associated with using chronic animal studies to predict the safety of chronic human exposure. A factor of 10 can also be used to account for the uncertainty of using subchronic animal studies to predict the safety of subchronic (including intermittent) human exposure.

- **Uf_{extrap}**: Extrapolating from a set of two subchronic toxicity studies in different animal species to chronic exposure in humans is not recommended, but the associated uncertainty may be approximated by an additional safety factor of 10 to account for the use of subchronic data to predict chronic use. If subchronic toxicity data are available in only a single animal species, an additional safety factor should be used. Usually, this additional safety factor should be approximately 2.

6. Does FDA recommend including margin of safety discussions in NDI notifications?

Yes. To conclude that a dietary supplement containing an NDI is reasonably expected to be safe based on animal or human safety studies, it is necessary to determine the margin of safety between the level of the NDI shown to cause no observed adverse effects (the NOAEL) in each animal and/or human study and the intake level that would result from the proposed conditions of use of the NDI in the dietary supplement.

The margin of safety is calculated by dividing the NOAEL (not the NOEL) in animal or human studies by the estimated daily intake (EDI) of the NDI. If you are calculating a margin of safety for a combination of ingredients or for the finished dietary supplement, the same principles apply.

Appropriate safety factors and margin of safety should be discussed for each particular study or safety endpoint and should also be summarized in the dietary supplement safety narrative because of its importance to the overall safety evaluation.

7. What is the difference between a safety factor and a margin of safety?

Safety factors are used to account for uncertainty about the extent to which data gathered in one context can be used to predict the safety of a substance in other contexts. For example, safety factors attempt to account for differences between animals and humans and differences in sensitivity among humans. The use of safety factors is based on the observation that toxic substances usually have thresholds below which toxic effects cannot be detected. Safety factors are used in calculating an acceptable daily intake (ADI) for various FDA-regulated products, including color additives, food additives, and new animal drugs. Safety factors can be combined multiplicatively to predict toxicity in the human population.

- ADI = NOAEL/combined safety factors
- Margin of safety = NOAEL/EDI

In contrast, the margin of safety is a calculation derived from the NOAEL in a single study and the highest total daily intake level determined from the conditions of use in the NDI notification, the EDI. A margin of safety is a measure of how close the EDI is to the level that has been shown to have no adverse effect in animal or human studies (the NOAEL). When reviewing notifications, FDA intends to calculate the EDI based on the highest daily intake level that is possible under the conditions of use proposed in the notification as well as cumulative exposure from all dietary sources.

The margin of safety for a dietary ingredient is calculated by dividing the NOAEL in animal or human studies by the EDI of the dietary ingredient. So a margin of safety of 100-fold means the doses shown to be without adverse effects in animals or humans are 100 times greater than the levels that would be consumed from the use of the dietary supplement. Discussions of how ADIs and EDIs are calculated and used in safety evaluations for a variety of products can be found in the following references:

- Frankos, V.H., and J.V. Rodricks. *Food additives and nutrition supplements. Regulatory Toxicology*, 2nd Ed., S.C. Gad, ed. London: Taylor and Francis, 2001.
- World Health Organization. Principles for the Safety Assessment of Food Additives and Contaminants in Food. Environmental Health Criteria 70. Geneva, Switzerland: 1987. Available at: http://www.inchem.org/documents/ehc/ehc/ehc70.htm.
- Food and Nutrition Board, Institute of Medicine. *Dietary Reference Intakes: A Risk Assessment Model for Establishing Upper Intake Levels for Nutrients*. Washington, DC: National Academy Press, 1998.

Example: The only safety evidence available is a single subchronic rat study during which no adverse effects were noted at the highest dose, which was the maximum tolerated dose of 3,000 mg/kg body weight. The top dose was limited by the fact that larger volumes could not be humanely administered to the animals.

CH 13

If the proposed conditions of use for the ingredient are 1 mg/person per day in adults daily, the EDI is (1 mg/person)/70 kg average adult = 0.014 mg/kg. The margin of safety is $3,000/0.014 = 2.1 \times 10^5$. The safety factors chosen are $Uf_{intra} \times Uf_{extrap} \times Uf_{inter} = 10 \times 20 \times 10 = 2,000$. The ADI is $3,000/2,000 = 1.5$ mg/kg. The EDI/ADI ratio is $0.014/1.5 = 0.01$. This value is much less than 1, which suggests that, if these safety factors are appropriate, the test article may reasonably be expected to be safe at the proposed daily intake level. An intake level of 1 g per day (1,000 times greater) would result in an EDI/ADI ratio of close to 10. More studies would be needed to justify the higher serving level.

8. When is the ratio of the EDI to the ADI adequate to support the conclusion that a dietary supplement containing an NDI will reasonably be expected to be safe?

The ratio of the EDI to the ADI should be less than or equal to 1 to support a conclusion that the proposed use of the NDI in the dietary supplement will reasonably be expected to be safe under the conditions recommended or suggested in the supplement's labeling. The size of the EDI/ADI ratio will vary in accordance with the nature and extent of data available and the circumstances of use of the NDI. For example, a ratio of 1, where the proposed dose (EDI) is equal to the safe dose (ADI), could be adequate if the levels of historical chronic safe use of the ingredient are the same as the levels proposed in the dietary supplement. Stated another way, the EDI of the NDI or dietary supplement must be less than or equal to the ADI of the NDI or dietary supplement.

The EDI for the NDI or for the dietary supplement is the highest total daily intake level under the proposed conditions of use described in the notification. The ADI is calculated as the ratio of the NOAEL to the combined safety factor, which is calculated by multiplying the individual safety factors for each study. If the ratio of the EDI to the ADI is greater than unity (EDI/ADI > 1), then the study does not support a reasonable expectation of safety for the NDI under the proposed conditions of use.

9. What is an example of a common error about margin of safety in NDI notifications that have been submitted to FDA for review?

Many manufacturers or distributors assume that if the NDI has a history of safe use in humans, no further safety discussion is warranted. That is incorrect. A margin of safety for NDI intake should be calculated, and the method of calculation explained and justified in the notification, even if a history of safe use is the basis of the safety evaluation. When the notification relies on a history of safe use, the margin of safety should be calculated based upon the historical levels of the NDI that were safely consumed and the NDI intake levels that would result from the conditions of use proposed in the notification. A margin of safety less than or equal to 1 corresponds to the argument that a history of safe use alone is sufficient to demonstrate the safety of the proposed use based on conditions of use that are the same or lower than the conditions of historical use (see question VI.B.14).

10. Are the recommendations in section VI requirements for safety information to include in an NDI notification?

No. The answers to the questions in section VI.A, VI.B, and VI.C are guidance on how to approach the task of describing the basis for the safety of the dietary supplement containing an NDI. These answers are recommendations and not requirements. In many cases FDA has tried to provide detailed recommendations to illustrate specific examples of situations which might arise. These details are specific to the situation described. The amount of information needed to identify an ingredient and provide a basis for a reasonable expectation of safety will vary enormously from notification to notification based on factors such as the complexity of the ingredient, history of use, and the presence or absence of specific safety concerns.

VII. Definitions

The following definitions represent FDA's current thinking on the meaning of the terms below in the context of the new dietary ingredient provisions of the FD&C Act and regulations. The definitions are intended for use only in that context and may not be appropriate in other contexts.[72]

Acceptable daily intake (ADI): The daily intake of a substance that, during the human lifetime, appears to be without appreciable risk on the basis of all known facts at the time.[73] In the context of an NDI notification, the ADI of an NDI or dietary supplement is calculated as the ratio of the NOAEL to the total safety factor (determined from the studies submitted in the notification).

Amino acid: An alpha-amino carboxylic acid used as a constituent of proteins or peptides.[74]

Botanical or herbal: A plant, alga, or fungus; a part of a plant, alga, or fungus (e.g., bark, leaves, stems, roots, flowers, fruits, seeds, berries, or parts thereof); or an exudate (secretion) of a plant, alga, or fungus.

Botanical raw material: Whole or physically processed (e.g., cleaned, frozen, dried, or sliced) parts of a single species of plant or a fresh or processed alga or fungus.

Chemically altered: See questions IV.B.4 and IV.B.5.

Chronic: Chronic exposure is exposure for more than 3 months. Periods of daily use interspersed with periods of non-use would be considered chronic exposure. In the context of toxicology studies, the term "chronic" generally refers to studies with at least 1 year of repeated dosing. Repeated exposure is divided into 3 categories: subacute, subchronic, and chronic. Subacute exposure refers to repeated exposure to a substance for 1 month or less, subchronic for 1 to 3 months, and chronic for longer than subchronic.[75]

Component: A substance that is part of a mixture. Includes substances that cannot be isolated from the whole, as well as those that can. Once isolated, a component of a mixture is also a constituent (see definition below).

CH 13

---

72 For example, FDA recognizes that "amino acid" can be defined differently in non-nutritional contexts than in the definition in this section.

73 Hayes, A. Wallace, editor. *Principles and Methods of Toxicology.* 5th ed. New York: Informa Healthcare USA, Inc; 2008.

74 Letter from Michael M. Landa, Acting Director, Center for Food Safety and Applied Nutrition, FDA, to Marc Ullman, Ullman, Shapiro& Ullman, LLP, responding to Citizen Petition FDA-2009-P-0298 from OVOS Natural Health Inc. (Feb. 23, 2011). Docket No. FDA-2009-P-0298 [Document ID: FDA-2009-P-0298-0008]. Available at: http://www.regulations.gov/#!documentDetail;D=FDA-2009-P-0298-0008

75 Curtis D. Klaassen, ed. *Casarett and Doull's Toxicology: The Basic Science of Poisons.* 8thEdition. Chapter 2: General Principles of Toxicology. McGraw-Hill Education, 2013.

Concentrate: An article in which constituents are more concentrated than in the original. An herbal concentrate is an extract from which all or most of the solvent has been removed, reducing the product to a solid, semi-solid, or syrupy form. The solvent and the process by which the concentrate is made are part of the definition of the concentrate.

Configurational isomer: See Stereoisomers.

Constituent: An article that is a physical part of the whole and can be isolated from the whole.

Dietary ingredient: A dietary ingredient is (A) a vitamin, (B) a mineral, (C) an herb or other botanical, (D) an amino acid, (E) a dietary substance for use by man to supplement the diet by increasing the total dietary intake, or (F) a concentrate, metabolite, constituent, extract, or combination of any ingredient described in (A) through (E).[76]

Dietary substance: A substance that is commonly used as human food or drink.

Dietary supplement: See definition in 21 U.S.C. 321(ff).

Enantiomers: Mirror-image isomers (optical isomers) that generally have similar chemical and physical properties, but different biological properties in a chiral environment.

Estimated daily intake (EDI): For purposes of an NDI notification, the EDI is the highest possible total daily intake level (in mg/day or mg/kg/day) of an NDI, as determined from the proposed conditions of use in the notification and any background exposure from other dietary sources. It is the maximum amount that would be consumed based on the conditions of use proposed in the notification, taking into account cumulative exposure from other dietary sources. The EDI should not be higher than the ADI.

Extract: A product consisting of a solvent (menstruum) combined with a dietary substance or botanical biomass by a process that physically separates constituents from the dietary substance or botanical and dissolves them into the solvent. The extract can be further concentrated through drying to a dry powder or semi-solid form.

Formulation: A formula that (1) lists the identity and quantity of each dietary ingredient and other ingredients (formulation aids) of a dietary supplement, and (2) describes the administered form (e.g., powder, liquid, capsule, etc.).

Geometric isomers: Compounds that have the same molecular formula, but differ from each other in the way that the atoms are oriented in space, and therefore have different chemical, physical, and biological properties (unless interconverted in the gut).

Ingestion: Taking an article, such as a dietary supplement or other food, into the stomach and gastrointestinal tract by swallowing.

---

76   21 U.S.C. 321(ff)(1).

Live microbial dietary ingredient: A single-celled prokaryotic or eukaryotic microorganism that is intended to be viable at the point of ingestion.

Margin of safety: A measure of how close the estimated daily intake (EDI) is to the level that has been shown to have no adverse effect in animal or human studies (the NOAEL). It is calculated as the ratio of the NOAEL to the highest total daily intake level (EDI) of the NDI or dietary supplement, as determined from the proposed conditions of use in the NDI notification, and is usually expressed in terms of fold change (e.g., a ten-fold margin of safety).

Marketed: *See* question IV.A.7.

Master File: In the dietary supplement context, a master file is a file containing manufacturing or other identity information submitted to FDA for use in an NDI notification by the submitter of the master file or by a person designated by the submitter. The submitter may rely on information from the master file in an NDI notification by incorporating it by reference, or may grant written authorization to other parties to incorporate information from the master file by reference in notifications covering the use of the NDI in their own products. A written authorization granting a right of reference to a master file in NDI notifications does not include the right to see or copy the master file unless the submitter of the master file otherwise specifies.

Maximum tolerated dose (MTD): The highest dose that causes no more than a 10 percent reduction in body weight and does not produce mortality, clinical signs of toxicity, or pathologic lesions that would be predicted to shorten the natural life span of an experimental animal for any reason other than the induction of neoplasms.[77]

Metabolite: A metabolite is a product of metabolism. In the dietary supplement context, a metabolite of a dietary ingredient is a molecular intermediate that incorporates structural elements of the ingested dietary ingredient and whose flux or net production in the human body increases on ingestion of the dietary ingredient. A metabolite can be part of (or an intermediate of) the catabolic or metabolic pathway of a dietary ingredient. FDA considers X to be a metabolite of Y if ingestion of Y by humans results in net production of/increased flux of X, incorporating structural elements of Y.[78]

Mineral: A substance of defined chemical composition which provides a form or source of inorganic elements to the diet. An element is one of a class of substances that cannot be separated into simpler substances by chemical means. Examples: calcium, iodine, and zinc.

Nanomaterial, nanotechnology: FDA has not established regulatory definitions of "nanotechnology," "nanomaterial," "nanoscale," or other related terms. In the absence of

---

77   Hayes, A. Wallace, editor. *Principles and Methods of Toxicology.* 5th ed. New York: Informa Healthcare USA, Inc; 2008.

78   See Hardy, Constance J. (Executive Secretary, Dietary Supplements Subcommittee of the FDA Food Advisory Committee). Summary Minutes of March 25, 2003 Meeting of the Dietary Supplements Subcommittee; College Park, MD; dated June 3, 2003. Available at: http://www.fda.gov/ohrms/dockets/ac/03/minutes/3942m1.pdf.

a formal definition, when considering whether an FDA-regulated product, including dietary ingredients, contains nanomaterials or otherwise involves the application of nanotechnology, FDA intends to ask: (1) Whether a material or end product is engineered to have at least one external dimension, or an internal or surface structure, in the nanoscale range (approximately 1 nm to 100 nm); and (2) Whether a material or end product is engineered to exhibit properties or phenomena, including physical or chemical properties or biological effects, that are attributable to its dimension(s), even if these dimensions fall outside the nanoscale range, up to 1 micrometer (1,000 nm).[79]

New dietary ingredient: A dietary ingredient that was not marketed in the U.S. before October 15, 1994.[80]

No-Observable-Effect Level (NOEL): The highest dose or total daily intake level at which no effects (beneficial, neutral, or adverse) are observed in a properly designed and executed toxicological study.

No-Observed-Adverse-Effect Level (NOAEL): The highest dose or total daily intake level that did not elicit an adverse effect in a properly designed and executed toxicological study.[81]

Pre-DSHEA dietary ingredient: A dietary ingredient that was marketed in the U.S. before October 15, 1994.

Safety factor or uncertainty factor: A multiplier used to account for uncertainty about the extent to which data gathered in one context can be used to predict the safety of a substance in other contexts. For example, safety factors attempt to account for differences between animals and humans (uncertainty factor of interspecies variation), differences in sensitivity among humans (uncertainty factor of intraspecies variation), and extrapolation of subchronic to chronic data (uncertainty factor of extrapolated data from subchronic to chronic). Safety factors can be combined multiplicatively to account for multiple sources of uncertainty. Safety factors are used in calculating an acceptable daily intake (ADI) for various FDA-regulated products, including color additives, food additives, and new animal drugs. See questions VI.C.5 and VI.C.7.

Salt of a dietary ingredient: Salts are composed of cations (positively charged ions) bound to anions (negatively charged ions). The salt of a dietary ingredient is a neutral compound that is formed by the union of an acid or a base with a counter ion and that dissociates to the starting ingredients after ingestion.

Stereoisomers: Stereoisomers are molecules that are identical in atomic composition and bonding, but differ in the three-dimensional arrangement of the atoms.

CH
13

---

79   See FDA, Office of the Commissioner. Guidance for Industry: Considering Whether an FDA-Regulated Product Involves the Application of Nanotechnology; June 2014.Available at: www.fda.gov/downloads/ regulatoryinformation/guidances/ucm401695.pdf

80   21 U.S.C. 350b(d).

81   Adapted from Hayes, A. Wallace, editor. *Principles and Methods of Toxicology.* 5th ed. New York: Informa Healthcare USA, Inc; 2008.

Subchronic: Refers to toxicological studies that are 1 to 3 months in duration.

Target Population: The target population for a dietary supplement means the population group or groups (defined by gender, age, and/or health status) that a manufacturer or distributor identifies (e.g., in product labeling, promotional materials, or in an NDI notification) as those for whom the product is appropriate or recommended. Examples of target populations include adults, children 14 and over, and women going through menopause.

Tincture: An aqueous alcoholic solution (e.g., an aqueous alcoholic extract of leaves or other plant material). A tincture is characterized by the ratio of the weight of the dried botanical to the volume or weight of the finished product. A 1:5 ratio is 1 part botanical to 5 parts solution.

Uncertainty factor: See Safety factor.

Vitamin: An organic substance that is a minor component of foods, is essential for normal physiological functions (e.g., maintenance, growth, or development), is normally not produced endogenously (within the body) in amounts adequate to meet normal physiologic needs, and which causes, by its absence or underutilization, a clinically defined deficiency syndrome

CH 13

VIII. Appendix: Decision Tree for NDI Notification

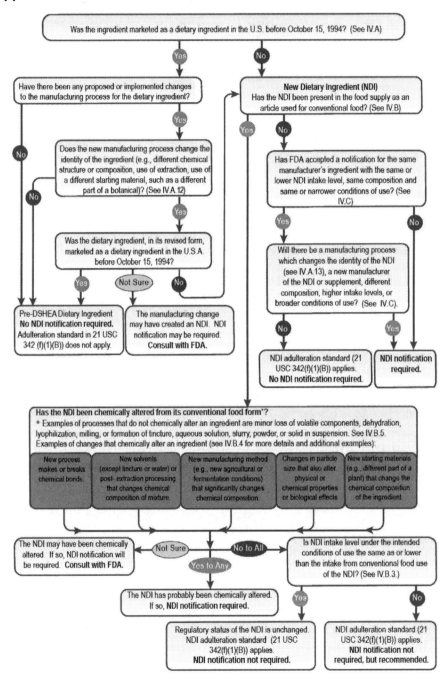

CH
13

VIII. Appendix: Decision Tree for NDI Notification

Text description of the Decision Tree for NDI Notification to Determine When a Dietary Ingredient Requires a New Dietary Ingredient Notification Before Marketing

1. Was the dietary ingredient marketed in the U.S. before October 15, 1994? (See IV.A). If yes, go to 2. If no, go to 7.

2. Have there been any proposed or implemented changes to the manufacturing process for the dietary ingredient? If yes, go to 3. If no, go to 5.

3. Does the new manufacturing process change the identity of the ingredient (e.g., different chemical structure or composition, use of extraction, use of a different starting material, such as a different part of a botanical)? (See IV.A.12) If yes, go to 4. If no, go to 5.

4. Was the dietary ingredient, in its revised form, marketed as a dietary ingredient in the U.S.A. before October 15, 1994? If yes, go to 5. If not sure, go to 6. If no, go to 7.

5. Pre-DSHEA Dietary Ingredient. No NDI notification required. Adulteration standard in 21 USC 342 (f)(1)(B) does not apply.

6. The manufacturing change may have created an NDI. NDI notification may be required. Consult with FDA.

7. New Dietary Ingredient (NDI). Has the NDI been present in the food supply as an article used for food? (See IV.B) If yes, go to 11. If no, go to 8.

8. Has FDA accepted a notification for the same manufacturer's ingredient with the same or lower NDI intake level, same composition, and same or narrower conditions of use? (See IV.C) If yes, go to 9. If no, go to 17.

9. Will there be a manufacturing process which changes the identity of the NDI (see IV.A.13), a new manufacturer of the NDI or supplement, different composition, higher intake levels, or broader conditions of use? (See IV.C) If yes, go to 17. If no, go to 10.

10. NDI adulteration standard (21 USC 342(f)(1)(B)) applies. No NDI notification required.

11. Has the NDI been chemically altered from its conventional food form*? *Examples of processes that do not chemically alter an ingredient are minor loss of volatile components, dehydration, lyophilization, milling, or formation of tincture, aqueous solution, slurry, powder, or solid in suspension. See IV.B.5. Examples of changes that chemically alter an ingredient (see IV.B.4 for more details and additional examples):

    11. A. New process makes or breaks chemical bonds. If yes to 11 A, B, C, D or E, go to 12. If not sure to 11 A, B, C, D and E, go to 13. If no to 11 A, B, C, D and E, go to 14.

    11. B. New solvents (except tincture or water) or post-extraction processing that changes chemical composition of mixture. If yes to 11 A, B, C, D or E, go to 12. If not sure to 11 A, B, C, D and E, go to 13. If no to 11 A, B, C, D and E, go to 14.

    11. C. New manufacturing method (e.g., new agricultural or fermentation conditions) that significantly changes chemical composition. If yes to 11 A, B, C, D or E, go to 12.

CH 13

If not sure to 11 A, B, C, D and E, go to 13. If no to 11 A, B, C, D and E, go to 14.

11. D. Changes in particle size that also alter physical and chemical properties or biological effects. If yes to 11 A, B, C, D or E, go to 12. If not sure to 11 A, B,C, D and E, go to 13. If no to 11 A, B, C, D and E, go to 14.

11. E. New starting materials (e.g., different part of a plant) that change the chemical composition of the ingredient. If yes to 11 A, B, C, D or E, go to 12. If not sure to 11 A, B, C, D and E, go to 13. If no to 11 A, B, C, D and E, go to 14.

12. The NDI has probably been chemically altered. If so, NDI notification required.

13. The NDI may have been chemically altered. If so, NDI notification will be required. Consult with FDA.

14. Is NDI the intake level under the intended conditions of use, the same as, or lower than the intake from conventional food use of the NDI? (See IV.B.3) If yes, go to 15. If no, go to 16.

15. Regulatory status of the NDI is unchanged. NDI adulteration standard (21 USC 342(f)(1)(B)) applies. NDI notification not required.

16. NDI adulteration standard (21 USC 342(f)(1)(B)) applies. NDI notification not required, but recommended.

17. NDI notification required.

Chapter 14

Claims
Guidance

Contains Nonbinding Recommendations
January 2009

Guidance for Industry[1]:
Evidence-Based Review System for the Scientific Evaluation of Health Claims

I. Introduction

This guidance document is for industry. It represents the agency's current thinking on 1) the process for evaluating the scientific evidence for a health claim, 2) the meaning of the significant scientific agreement (SSA) standard in section 403(r)(3) of the Federal Food, Drug, and Cosmetic Act (the Act) (21 U.S.C. 343(r)(3)) and 21 CFR 101.14(c), and 3) credible scientific evidence to support a qualified health claim.

This guidance document describes the evidence-based review system that FDA intends to use to evaluate the publicly available scientific evidence for SSA health claims or qualified health claims on the relationship between a substance and a disease or health-related condition.[2] This guidance document explains the agency's current thinking on the scientific review approach FDA should use and is intended to provide guidance to health claim petitioners.[3]

---

1   This guidance has been prepared by the Office of Nutrition, Labeling, and Dietary Supplements in the Center for Food Safety and Applied Nutrition at the U.S. Food and Drug Administration. This guidance is available on the FDA website at https://www.fda.gov/Food/GuidanceRegulation/GuidanceDocumentsRegulatoryInformation/ucm073332.htm

2   For brevity, "disease" will be used as shorthand for "disease or health-related condition". "Disease or health-related condition" is defined as damage to an organ, part, structure, or system of the body such that it does not function properly (e.g., cardiovascular disease), or a state of health leading to such dysfunctioning (e.g., hypertension). 21 CFR 101.14(a)(5).

3   (3) This new guidance document replaces FDA's guidance entitled "Guidance for Industry and FDA: Interim Evidence-based Ranking System for Scientific Data," which addressed the scientific review of qualified health claims. Although the interim evidence-based ranking system guidance included a section on ranking the strength of the scientific evidence, this new guidance document does not include such a section because studies are being conducted on the consumer's understanding of various possible ranking systems that could be used to describe the strength of the evidence for a health claim. FDA intends to reexamine its ranking systems and issue appropriate guidance once these studies are completed. In addition, this guidance document replaces FDA's guidance entitled

The specific topics addressed in this guidance document are: (1) identifying studies that evaluate the substance/disease relationship, (2) identifying surrogate endpoints for disease risk, (3) evaluating the human studies to determine whether scientific conclusions can be drawn from them about the substance/disease relationship, (4) assessing the methodological quality of each human study from which scientific conclusions about the substance/disease relationship can be drawn, (5) evaluating the totality of scientific evidence, (6) assessing significant scientific agreement, (7) specificity of claim language for qualified health claims, and (8) reevaluation of existing SSA or qualified health claims.

FDA's guidance documents, including this guidance, do not establish legally enforceable responsibilities. Instead, guidances describe the Agency's current thinking on a topic and should be viewed only as recommendations, unless specific regulatory or statutory requirements are cited. The use of the word *should* in Agency's guidances means that something is suggested or recommended, but not required.

II. Background

The Nutrition Labeling and Education Act of 1990 (NLEA) (Pub. L. 101-553) was designed to give consumers more scientifically valid information about foods they eat. Among other provisions, the NLEA directed FDA to issue regulations providing for the use of statements that describe the relationship between a substance and a disease ("health claims") in the labeling of foods, including dietary supplements, after such statements have been reviewed and authorized by FDA.[4] For these health claims, that is, statements about substance/disease relationships, FDA has defined the term "substance" by regulation as a specific food or food component (21 CFR 101.14(a)(2)). An authorized health claim may be used on both conventional foods and dietary supplements, provided that the substance in the product and the product itself meet the appropriate standards in the authorizing regulation. Health claims are directed to the general population or designated subgroups (e.g., the elderly) and are intended to assist the consumer in maintaining healthful dietary practices.

In evaluating a petition for an authorized health claim, FDA considers whether the evidence supporting the relationship that is the subject of the claim meets the SSA standard. This standard derives from 21 U.S.C. 343 (r)(3)(B)(i), which provides that FDA shall authorize a health claim to be used on conventional foods if the agency "determines based on the totality of the publicly available evidence (including evidence from well-designed studies conducted in a manner which is consistent with generally recognized scientific procedures and principles), that there is significant scientific agreement among experts qualified by scientific training and experience to evaluate such claims, that the claim is supported by such evidence." This scientific standard was prescribed by statute for conventional food health claims; by regulation, FDA adopted the same standard for dietary supplement health claims. See 21 CFR 101.14(c).

"Guidance for Industry: Significant Scientific Agreement in the Review of Health Claims for Conventional Foods and Dietary Supplements."

4   In 1997, Congress enacted the Food and Drug Administration Modernization Act, which established an alternative authorization procedure for health claims based on authoritative statements of certain federal scientific bodies or the National Academy of Sciences. This guidance document does not address that alternative procedure.

The genesis of qualified health claims was the court of appeals decision in *Pearson v. Shalala* (*Pearson*). In that case, the plaintiffs challenged FDA's decision not to authorize health claims for four specific substance-disease relationships in the labeling of dietary supplements. Although the district court ruled for FDA (14 F. Supp. 2d 10 (D.D.C. 1998), the U.S. Court of Appeals for the D.C. Circuit reversed the lower court's decision (164 F.3d 650 (D.C. Cir.1999)). The appeals court held that the First Amendment does not permit FDA to reject health claims that the agency determines to be potentially misleading unless the agency also reasonably determines that a disclaimer would not eliminate the potential deception. The appeals court also held that the Administrative Procedure Act (APA) required FDA to clarify the "significant scientific agreement" (SSA) standard for authorizing health claims.

On December 22, 1999, FDA announced the issuance of its *Guidance for Industry: Significant Scientific Agreement in the Review of Health Claims for Conventional Foods and Dietary Supplements* (64 Fed. Reg.17494). This guidance document was issued to clarify FDA's interpretation of the SSA standard in response to the court of appeals' second holding in Pearson.

On December 20, 2002, the agency announced its intention to extend its approach to implementing the *Pearson* decision to include health claims for conventional foods (67 Fed. Reg. 78002). Recognizing the need for a scientific framework for qualified health claims, the Task Force on "Consumer Health Information for Better Nutrition" was formed. The Task Force recognized that there could be significant public health benefits when consumers have access to, and use, more and better information in conventional food as well as dietary supplement labeling to aid them in their purchases, information that goes beyond just price, convenience, and taste, but extends to include science-based health factors. Armed with more scientifically based information about the likely health benefits of the foods and dietary supplements they purchase, consumers can make a tangible difference in their own long-term health by lowering their risk of numerous chronic diseases.

To maximize the public health benefit of FDA's claims review process, the Task Force's Final Report[5] provides a procedure to prioritize on a case-by-case basis all complete petitions according to several factors, including whether the food or dietary supplement that is the subject of the petition is likely to have a significant impact on a serious or life-threatening illness; the strength of the evidence; whether consumer research has been provided to show the claim is not misleading; whether the substance that is the subject of the claim has undergone an FDA safety review (i.e., is an authorized food additive, has been Generally Recognized as Safe (GRAS) affirmed, listed, or has received a letter of "no objection" to a GRAS notification); whether the substance that is the subject of the claim has been adequately characterized so that the relevance of available studies can be evaluated; whether the disease is defined and evaluated in accordance with generally accepted criteria established by a recognized body of qualified experts; and whether there has been prior review of the evidence or the claim by a recognized body of qualified experts.

As part of the Task Force's final report, FDA developed an interim evidence-based review system that the agency intended to use to evaluate the substance/disease relationships that are subjects

CH
14

---

5   See guidance (Attachment A) entitled "Guidance for Industry and FDA: Interim Procedures for Qualified Health Claims in the Labeling of Conventional Human Food and Human Dietary Supplements," July 10, 2003 (http://www.cfsan.fda.gov/~dms/hclmgui3.html)

of qualified health claims. In reviewing the December 22, 1999 SSA guidance document and the 2003 Task Force report, it became apparent to the agency that the components of the scientific review process for an SSA health claim and qualified health claim are very similar. Because of the similarity between the scientific reviews for SSA and qualified health claims, FDA intends to use the approach set out in this guidance for evaluating the scientific evidence in petitions that are submitted for an SSA health claim or qualified health claim. The evidence-based review system set out in this guidance will assist the agency in determining whether the scientific evidence meets the SSA standard or, if not, whether the evidence supports a qualified health claim. In addition to a science review, health claims undergo a regulatory review. Health claims that meet the SSA standard are authorized by publication of a final rule or an interim final rule in the Federal Register. For qualified health claims supported by credible evidence, FDA issues a letter regarding its intent to consider enforcement discretion.

Although this guidance replaces the *Guidance for Industry: Significant Scientific Agreement in the Review of Health Claims for Conventional Foods and Dietary Supplements* (64 Fed. Reg. 17494), issued to clarify FDA's interpretation of the SSA standard in response to the court of appeals' second holding in *Pearson*, FDA believes this guidance continues to be consistent with the court's holding. The basic principles of SSA articulated in the 1999 guidance have not changed. A finding of SSA still requires the agency's best judgment as to whether qualified experts would likely agree that the scientific evidence supports the substance/disease relationship that is the subject of a proposed health claim. In fact, many of the explanations of SSA in this guidance are taken verbatim from the 1999 guidance. This guidance represents further scientific developments in the agency's approach to the review of scientific evidence rather than a change in its understanding of what constitutes SSA.

III. Evidence-Based Review System for the Scientific Evaluation of Health Claims

A. What is an Evidence-Based Review System?

An evidence-based review system is a systematic science-based evaluation of the strength of the evidence to support a statement. In the case of health claims, it evaluates the strength of the scientific evidence to support a proposed claim about a substance/disease relationship. The evaluation process involves a series of steps to assess scientific studies and other data, eliminate those from which no conclusions about the substance/disease relationship can be drawn, rate the remaining studies for methodological quality and evaluate the strength of the totality of scientific evidence by considering study types, methodological quality, quantity of evidence for and against the claim (taking into account the numbers of various types of studies and study sample sizes), relevance to the U.S. population or target subgroup, replication of study results supporting the proposed claim, and overall consistency of the evidence. After assessing the totality of the scientific evidence, FDA determines whether there is SSA to support an authorized health claim, or credible evidence to support a qualified health claim.

B. Identifying Studies That Evaluate the Substance/Disease Relationship

The agency considers the publicly available data and written information pertaining to the relationship between a substance and disease. FDA reviews studies that must be submitted in petitions seeking health claims (21 CFR 101.70). Through a literature search, the agency identifies additional studies that are relevant to the proposed health claim. Before the strength of the evidence for a substance/disease relationship can be assessed, FDA separates individual relevant articles on human studies from other types of data and information. FDA intends to focus its review primarily on articles reporting human intervention and observational studies because only such studies can provide evidence from which scientific conclusions can be drawn about the substance/disease relationship in humans. Next, the agency considers a number of threshold questions in the review of the scientific evidence:

• *Have the studies specified and measured the substance that is the subject of the claim?* Studies should identify a substance that is measurable. A "substance" is defined as a specific food or component of food regardless of whether the food is in conventional food form or a dietary supplement. 21 CFR 101.14(a) (2). A food component can be, for example, a nutrient or dietary ingredient.[6] If the substance is to be consumed as a component of conventional food at decreased dietary levels, the substance must be a nutrient that is required to be included in the Nutrition Facts label (21 CFR 101.14(b)(2)). If the substance is to be consumed at other than decreased dietary levels, the substance must contribute taste, aroma, nutritive value,[7] or a technical effect listed in 21 CFR 170.3(o) to the food, and must be safe and lawful for use at the levels necessary to justify a claim (21 CFR 101.14(b)(3)).

• *Have the studies appropriately specified and measured the specific disease or health-related condition that is the subject of the claim?* "Disease or health-related condition" is defined as damage to an organ, part, structure, or system of the body such that it does not function properly (e.g., cardiovascular disease), or a state of health leading to such dysfunctioning (e.g., hypertension). 21 CFR 101.14(a) (5). Studies should identify a specific measurable disease or health-related condition by either measuring incidence, associated mortality, or validated surrogate endpoints that predict risk of a specific disease.

For example, cancer is a constellation of more than 100 different diseases, each characterized by the uncontrolled growth and spread of abnormal cells (American Cancer Society, 2004). Cancer is categorized into different types of diseases based on the organ and tissue sites (National Cancer Institute). Cancers at different organ sites have different risk factors, treatment modalities, and mortality risk (American Cancer Society, 2004). Both genetic and environmental (including diet) risk factors may affect the risk of different types of cancers. Risk factors may include a family history of a specific type of cancer, cigarette smoking, alcohol consumption, overweight and obesity, exposure to ultraviolet or ionizing radiation, exposure to cancer-causing chemicals, and dietary factors. The etiology, risk factors,

CH
14

---

6   See 21 U.S.C. 321(ff)(1).
7   "Nutritive value" is defined in 21 CFR 101.14(a)(3) as value in sustaining human existence by such processes as promoting growth, replacing loss of essential nutrients, or providing energy.

diagnosis, and treatment for each type of cancer are unique (Hord et al., 2007; Milner et al., 2006). Since each form of cancer is a unique disease based on organ site, risk factors, treatment options, and mortality risk, FDA's current approach is to evaluate each form of cancer individually in a health claim or qualified health claim petition to determine whether the scientific evidence supports the potential substance-disease relationship for that type of cancer, which would constitute a disease under 21 CFR 101.14(a)(5). The agency has used this approach in several letters of enforcement discretion including green tea and cancer dated June 30, 2005, tomatoes/lycopene and various cancers dated November 8, 2005, calcium and various cancers dated October 12, 2005 as well as the Federal Register notice entitled "Health Claims and Qualified Health Claims; Dietary Lipids and Cancer, Soy Protein and Coronary Heart Disease, Antioxidant Vitamins and Certain Cancers, and Selenium and Certain Cancers; Reevaluation" (72 Fed. Reg. 72738, December 21, 2007)

After considering these threshold issues, FDA categorizes the studies by type.

Intervention Studies

In an intervention study, subjects are provided the substance (food or food component) of interest (intervention group), typically either in the form of a conventional food or dietary supplement. The quality and quantity of the substance should be controlled for. In randomized controlled trials, subjects are assigned to an intervention group by chance. Individual subjects may not be similar to each other, but the intervention and control groups should be similar after randomization. Randomized controlled trials offer the best assessment of a causal relationship between a substance and a disease because they control for known confounders of results (i.e., other factors that could affect risk of disease). Through random assignment of subjects to the intervention and control groups, these studies avoid selection bias — that is, the possibility that those subjects most likely to have a favorable outcome, independent of an intervention, are preferentially selected to receive the intervention. Potential bias is also reduced by "blinding" the study so that the subjects do not know whether they are receiving the intervention, or "double blinding," in which neither the subjects nor the researcher who assesses the outcome knows who is in the intervention group and who is in the control group. By controlling the test environment, including the amount and composition of substance consumed and all other dietary factors, these studies also can minimize the effects of variables or confounders on the results.[8] Therefore, randomized, controlled intervention studies provide the strongest evidence of whether or not there is a relationship between a substance and a disease (Greer et al., 2000).

Furthermore, such studies can provide convincing evidence of a cause and effect relationship between an intervention and an outcome (Kraemer et al., 2005 at 113). Randomization, however, may result in unequal distribution of the characteristics of the subjects between the control and treatment groups (e.g., baseline age or blood [serum or plasma] LDL cholesterol levels are significantly different). If the baseline values are significantly different, then it is difficult to determine if differences at the end of the study were due to the

CH
14

---

8   Confounders are factors that are associated with both the disease in question and the intervention, and that if not controlled for, prevent an investigator from being able to conclude that an outcome was caused by an intervention.

---

intervention or to differences at the beginning of the study. When the substance is provided as a supplement, a placebo should be provided to the control group. When the substance is a food, it may not be possible to provide a placebo and therefore subjects in such a study may not be blinded. Although the study may not be blinded in this case, a control group is still needed to draw conclusions from the study.

Randomized controlled trials typically have either a parallel or cross-over design. Parallel design studies involve two groups of subjects, the test group and the control group, which simultaneously receive the substance or serve as the control, respectively. Cross-over design involves all subjects crossing over from the intervention group to the control group, and vice versa, after a defined time period.

Although intervention studies are the most reliable category of studies for determining a cause-and effect relationship, generalizing from the studies conducted on selected populations to different populations may not be scientifically valid. For example, if the evidence consists of studies showing an association between intake of a substance and reduced risk of juvenile diabetes, then such studies should not be extrapolated to the risk of diabetes in adults.

Observational Studies

Observational studies measure associations between the substance and disease. Observational studies lack the controlled setting of intervention studies. Observational studies are most reflective of free-living[9] populationsand may be able to establish an association between the substance and the disease. In contrast to intervention studies, observational studies cannot determine whether an observed relationship represents a relationship in which the substance caused a reduction in disease risk or is a coincidence (Sempos et al., 1999). Because the subjects are not randomized based on various disease risk factors at the beginning of the study, known confounders of disease risk need to be collected and adjusted for to minimize bias. For example, information on each subject's risk factors, such as age, race, body weight and smoking, should be collected and used to adjust the data so that the substance/disease relationship is accurately measured. Risk factors that need to be adjusted for are determined for each disease being studied. For example, the risk of cardiovascular disease increases with age; therefore, an adjustment for age is needed in order to eliminate potential confounding.

In determining whether the substance that is the subject of the claim has been measured appropriately, it is important to critically evaluate the method of assessment of dietary intake. Many observational studies rely on self-reports of diet (e.g., diet records, 24-hour recalls, diet histories, and food frequency questionnaires), which are estimates of food intake (National Research Council, 1989). Diet records are based on the premise that food weights provide an accurate estimation of food intake. Subjects weigh the foods they consume and record those values. The 24-hour recall method requires that subjects describe which foods and how much of each food they consumed during the prior 24-hour period. Diet histories

CH
14

---

9   Free-living populations represent those who consume diets and have lifestyles (e.g., smoking, drinking, and exercise) of their own choice.

use questionnaires or interviewers to estimate the typical diet of subjects over a certain period of time. A food frequency questionnaire is the most common dietary assessment tool used in large observational studies of diet and health. Validated food frequency questionnaires are more reliable in estimating "usual" intake of foods than diet records or 24-hour recall methods (Subar et al., 2001). The questionnaire asks participants to report the frequency of consumption and portion size from a list of foods over a defined period of time. One problem with the dietary intake assessment methods described above is that there may be bias in the self-reporting of certain foods. For example, individuals who are overweight tend to under-report their portion sizes (Flegal et al., 1999) and therefore the actual amount of substances consumed is often underestimated. If there are reliable biomarkers of intake[10] of a substance, these biomarkers are often measured rather than using self-reported intakes.

Observational studies may be prospective or retrospective. These types of studies are subject to different forms of bias (information and selection).[11] In prospective studies, investigators recruit subjects and observe them prior to the occurrence of the disease outcome. Prospective observational studies compare the incidence of a disease with exposure to the substance. In retrospective studies, investigators review the medical records of subjects and/ or interview subjects after the disease has occurred. Retrospective studies are particularly vulnerable to measurement error and recall bias because they rely on subjects' recollections of what they consumed in the past. Because of the limited ability of observational studies to control for variables, they are often susceptible to confounders, such as complex substance/disease interactions.

Well-designed observational studies can provide useful information for identifying possible associations to be tested by intervention studies (Kraemer et al., 2005 at 107). In contrast to intervention studies, even the best-designed observational studies cannot establish cause and effect between an intervention and an outcome (Kraemer et al., 2005 at 114). However, as discussed above, intervention studies can test whether there is evidence to show a cause and effect between a substance and a reduced risk of a disease. Observational studies from which scientific conclusions can be drawn, in some situations, can be support for a substance/disease relationship for an SSA or qualified health claim. Each observational study design has its strength and weaknesses as discussed below (Sempos et al., 1999).

Cohort studies are prospective studies that compare the incidence of a disease in subjects who receive a specific exposure of the substance that is the subject of the claim with the incidence of the disease in subjects who do not receive that exposure. Because the intake of the substance precedes disease development, this study design ensures that the subjects are not consuming the substance in response to having the disease. Cohort studies can yield relative estimates of risk (Szklo and Nieto, 2000).[12] Cohort studies are considered to be the most reliable observational study design (Greer et al., 2000).

---

10   Biomarkers of intake are measurements of the substance itself or a metabolite of the substance in biological samples (e.g., serum selenium) that have been validated to confirm that they reflect the intake of that substance.
11   Bias is the systematic error that may result in flaws from subject selection (selection bias) or exposure and disease outcome measurements (information bias) (Szklo and Nieto, 2000).
12   Relative risk is expressed as the ratio of the risk (disease incidence) in exposed individuals to that in unexposed individuals. It is calculated in prospective cohorts by measuring exposure of the substance in subjects with and without disease. An adjusted relative risk controls for potential confounders.

In *case-control studies*, subjects with a disease (cases) are compared to subjects who do not have the disease (controls).[13] Prior intake of the substance is estimated from dietary assessment methods for both cases and control. These retrospective studies often ask about food consumption at least 1 year prior to diagnosis of the disease, making it difficult to obtain an accurate estimate of intake. Furthermore, a key assumption is that food consumption has not been altered by the disease process or by knowledge of having the disease. Thus, the case-control study design does not control for changes in intake caused by or in response to the disease. Case-control studies can yield an odds ratio, which is an estimate of the relative risk of getting the disease (Szklo and Nieto, 2000).[14] Case-control studies are considered to be less reliable than cohort studies (Greer et al., 2000).

A *nested-case control* or *case-cohort study* uses subjects from a pre-defined cohort, such as the population of an ongoing cohort study. Cases are subjects diagnosed with the disease (e.g., lung cancer) in the cohort. In a nested-case control study, controls are subjects selected from individuals at risk each time a case (e.g., lung cancer) is diagnosed. In a case-cohort study, controls are selected randomly from the baseline cohort (Szklo and Nieto, 2000). Either a relative risk or odds ratio may be calculated in these types of studies. Nested-case control or case-cohort studies are considered less reliable than cohort studies but more reliable than case-control studies.

Cross-sectional studies usually involve collecting information on food consumption at a single point in time in individuals with and without a specific disease.[15] These studies can be useful for identifying possible correlates (i.e., by determining the correlation coefficient[16] between dietary intake of a substance and prevalence of a disease) and for providing baseline information for subsequent prospective studies (Kraemer et al., 2005 at 99-100). However, because dietary intake and disease status are measured at the same time, it is not possible to determine whether dietary intake of the substance is a factor affecting the risk of the disease or a result of having the disease. Cross-sectional studies calculate the prevalence of a disease based on exposure and this may be a measure of survival of the disease rather than the risk of developing the disease (Szklo and Nieto, 2000). Further, cross-sectional studies are considered to be a "relatively weak method of studying diet-disease associations" because they can be subject to significant potential measurement error regarding dietary intake due to inaccuracy of survey methods used and limited ability to control for dietary intake variations (Sempos et al., 1999). For these reasons, cross-sectional study results "have the

---

13   An example of a case-control study is a study design that assesses parameters related to the frequency and distribution of disease in a population, such as leading cause of death.

14   An odds ratio is the odds of developing the disease in exposed compared to unexposed individuals. It is calculated in case control studies by measuring disease development in subjects based on exposure to the substance. Adjusted odds ratio controls for potential confounders.

15   A few cross-sectional studies are time-series studies that compare outcomes during different time periods (e.g., whether the rate of occurrence of a particular outcome during one five-year period changed during a subsequent five-year period).

16   The correlation coefficient (r) is a measure of the interdependence of two variables, such as intake of a substance and prevalence of a disease. It is expressed as a point on a scale of -1 and 1, where -1 indicates a perfect negative correlation, 0 indicates an absence of correlation, and +1 indicates a perfect positive correlation at +1. See Webster's II New Riverside University Dictionary (Riverside Publishing Co., 1984).] Thus, the closer the correlation coefficient is to either of the endpoints on the scale, the stronger the relationship between the two variables.

CH 14

potential to mislead as errors of interpretation are very common" (Kraemer et al., 1005 at 103). Cross-sectional studies are considered to be less reliable than cohort and case-control studies (Greer et al., 2000).

Ecological studies compare disease incidence across different populations. Case reports describe observations of a single subject or a small number of subjects. Ecological studies and case reports are the least reliable types of observational studies.

Research Synthesis Studies

Reports that discuss a number of different studies, such as review articles,[17] do not provide sufficient information on the individual studies reviewed for FDA to determine critical elements such as the study population characteristics and the composition of the products used. Similarly, the lack of detailed information on studies summarized in review articles prevents FDA from determining whether the studies are flawed in critical elements such as design, conduct of studies, and data analysis. FDA must be able to review the critical elements of a study to determine whether any scientific conclusions can be drawn from it. Therefore, FDA intends to use review articles and similar publications[18] to identify reports of additional studies that may be useful to the health claim review and as background about the substance/disease relationship. If additional studies are identified, the agency intends to evaluate them individually. Most meta-analyses,[19] because they lack detailed information on the studies summarized, will only be used to identify reports of additional studies that may be useful to the health claim review and as background about the substance-disease relationship. FDA, however, intends to consider as part of its health claim review process a meta-analysis that reviews all the publicly available studies on the substance/disease relationship. The reviewed studies should be consistent with the critical elements, quality and other factors set out in this guidance and the statistical analyses adequately conducted.

Animal and in vitro Studies

FDA intends to use animal and *in vitro* studies as background information regarding mechanisms that might be involved in any relationship between the substance and disease. The physiology of animals is different than that of humans. *In vitro* studies are conducted in an artificial environment and cannot account for a multitude of normal physiological processes such as digestion, absorption, distribution, and metabolism that affect how humans respond to the consumption of foods and dietary substances (IOM, 2005). Animal and *in vitro* studies can be used to generate hypotheses, investigate biological plausibility of hypotheses, or to explore a mechanism of action of a specific food component through controlled animal diets; however, these studies do not provide information from which scientific conclusions can be drawn regarding a relationship between the substance and disease in humans.

---

17   Review articles summarize the findings of individual studies on a given topic.
18   Other examples include book chapters, abstracts, letters, and committee reports.
19   A meta-analysis is the process of systematically combining and evaluating the results of clinical trials that have been completed or terminated (Spilker, 1991).

C. Identifying Surrogate Endpoints of Disease Risk

Surrogate endpoints are risk biomarkers[20] that have been shown to be valid predictors of disease risk and therefore may be used in place of clinical measurements of the onset of the disease in a clinical trial (Spilker, 1991). Because a number of diseases develop over a long period of time, it may not be possible to carry out the study for a long enough period to see a statistically meaningful difference in the incidence of disease among study subjects in the treatment and control groups.

These are examples of surrogate endpoints of disease risk accepted by the National Institutes of Health and/or FDA's Center for Drug Evaluation and Research: (1) serum low-density lipoprotein (LDL) cholesterol concentration, total serum cholesterol concentration, and blood pressure for cardiovascular disease; (2) bone mineral density for osteoporosis; (3) adenomatous colon polyps for colon cancer; and (4) elevated blood sugar concentrations and insulin resistance for type 2 diabetes.

There can be multiple pathways to a specific disease, such as cardiovascular disease. Therefore, the accepted surrogate endpoints that are involved in a single pathway may not be applicable to certain substances that are involved in a different pathway. For example, the long chain omega-3 fatty acids generally have no effect on serum LDL cholesterol levels, and studies suggest that these fatty acids alter cardiovascular risk through a different pathway. Therefore, LDL cholesterol levels cannot be used in evaluating the relationship between the long chain omega-3 fatty acids and risk of cardiovascular disease.

D. Evaluating Human Studies

Under the evidence-based review approach set out in this guidance, FDA intends to evaluate each individual human study to determine whether any scientific conclusions about the substance/disease relationship can be drawn from the study. Certain critical elements of a study, such as design, data collection, and data analysis, may be so seriously flawed that they make it impossible to draw scientific conclusions from the study. FDA does not intend to use studies from which it cannot draw any scientific conclusions about the substance/disease relationship, and plans to eliminate such studies from further review. Below are examples of questions that the agency intends to consider whether scientific conclusions can be drawn from an intervention or observational study about the substance/disease relationship.

Intervention Studies

• *Were the study subjects healthy or did they have the disease that is the subject of the health claim?* Health claims involve reducing the risk of a disease in people who do not have the disease that is the subject of the claim. FDA considers evidence from studies with subjects who have the disease that is the subject of the claim only if it is scientifically appropriate to extrapolate to individuals who do not have the disease. That is, the available scientific evidence demonstrates that (1) the mechanism(s) for the mitigation or treatment

CH 14

---

20   Risk biomarkers are biological indicators that signal a changed physiological state that is associated with the risk of a disease.

effects measured in the diseased populations are the same as the mechanism(s) for risk reduction effects in non-diseased populations and (2) the substance affects these mechanisms in the same way in both diseased and healthy people. If such evidence is not available, the agency cannot draw any scientific conclusions from studies that used subjects that have the disease that is the subject of the health claim to evaluate the substance/disease relationship and, therefore, the agency does not intend to use these studies to evaluate the substance/disease relationship. On the other hand, if, for example, FDA was reviewing a health claim on reduction of risk of coronary heart disease, it would consider studies that include individuals who have an unrelated disease (e.g., osteoporosis) or are at risk (e.g., elevated LDL cholesterol levels) of getting the disease that is the subject of the claim.

• *Was the disease that is subject of the claim measured as a "primary" endpoint?* Intervention studies screen for prevalent cases of the disease at the beginning of the study to minimize bias. For example, intervention studies evaluating the recurrence of colorectal polyps prescreen the subjects to ensure there are no existing colorectal polyps at the onset of the intervention study. Intervention studies may evaluate the outcomes of other diseases as secondary endpoints, but do not screen for these diseases at the onset of the study. For example, a study evaluating the recurrence of colorectal polyps may also evaluate the incidence of prostate cancer; however, because the prostate cancer endpoint is not the primary endpoint, the study would not screen the subjects to ensure that they are free of prostate cancer before enrolling them. Consequently, the results with respect to prostate cancer may be biased due to an uneven distribution of cases of prostate cancer between the treatment and placebo groups at the beginning of the study. Uneven distribution of important patient or disease characteristics between groups may lead to mistaken interpretation (Spilker, 1991); therefore, scientific conclusions about a disease endpoint cannot be drawn from a study unless the study evaluates that outcome as a primary endpoint.

• *Did the study include an appropriate control group?* An appropriate control group represents study subjects who did not receive the substance. If an appropriate control group is not included, then it is not possible to ascertain whether changes in the endpoint of interest were due to the substance or due to unrelated and uncontrolled extraneous factors (Spilker, 1991; Federal Judicial Center, 2000). Without an appropriate control group, scientific conclusions cannot be drawn about a substance/disease relationship and, therefore, the agency does not intend to use these studies to evaluate the substance/disease relationship.

When the intervention study involves providing a whole food rather than a food component, the experimental and control diets should be similar enough that the relationship between the substance and disease can be evaluated. For example, if the substance is a specific type of fatty acid, then the composition of the experimental and control diets should be similar for all food components, except that particular fatty acid. Scientific conclusions cannot be drawn about the relationship between a substance and a disease when the amounts of other substances that are known to affect the risk of the disease that is subject of the claim are different between the control and experimental diets.

- *Was the study designed to measure the independent role of the substance in reducing the risk of a disease?* When the substance is a food component, it may not be possible to accurately determine its independent effects when whole foods or multi-nutrient supplements are provided to the intervention group. For example, if the claim is about a relationship between lutein and age-related macular degeneration (AMD), then scientific conclusions cannot be drawn from a study in which the intervention group received spinach or multi-nutrient supplements that contain other substances (e.g., vitamin C, vitamin E, and zinc) that have been suggested to have a role in protecting against AMD. As another example, if the substance is a fatty acid that has been shown to alter blood cholesterol levels, but the levels of other food components (e.g., cholesterol) known to affect cholesterol levels markedly vary between the intervention and control diets, then it is not possible to determine the independent effect of the fatty acid.

- *Were the relevant baseline data (e.g., on the surrogate endpoint) significantly different between the control and intervention group?* If the baseline values for the endpoint being measured are significantly different, then it is difficult to interpret the findings of the intervention. For example, in a study of the effects of a low-sodium diet on the risk of cardiovascular disease, having baseline blood pressure levels higher in the intervention group than in the control group would lead to uncertainty as to whether any observed effect resulted from the difference in the sodium intake between the two groups. Providing a "lead-in"[21] diet or a "wash-out" period[22] for studies with a cross-over design for an adequate duration prior to randomization can help reduce the likelihood of different baseline values.

- *How were the results from the intervention and control groups statistically analyzed?* Statistical analysis of the study data is a critical factor because it provides the comparison between subjects consuming the substance and those not consuming the substance, to determine whether there is a reduction in risk of the disease. Furthermore, when conducting statistical analyses among more than two groups, the data should be analyzed by a test designed for multiple comparisons (e.g., Bonferroni, Duncan). Thus when statistical analyses are not performed between the control and intervention group or are conducted inappropriately, scientific conclusions cannot be drawn about the role of the substance in reducing the risk of the disease and, therefore, the agency does not intend to use such studies to evaluate the substance/disease relationship.

- *What type of biomarker of disease risk was measured?* As discussed above, when the study does not measure disease incidence or associated mortality, then surrogate endpoints are essential for measuring risk. Scientific conclusions cannot be drawn about the relationship between the substance and risk of the disease if the risk biomarker is not a surrogate endpoint (see discussion above in Section III.C). The agency does not intend to use such studies from which scientific conclusions cannot be drawn in its evaluation of the substance/disease relationship.

CH
14

---

21   A diet that is provided to all study groups prior to randomization.
22   Time period within a cross-over design study during which subjects do not receive an intervention.

- *How long was the study conducted?* Studies that use a surrogate endpoint should be conducted long enough to ensure that any change in the endpoint is in response to the dietary intervention. If the study is run for a short time period such that the effects of the substance cannot be evaluated, then scientific conclusions cannot be drawn about the relationship between the substance and the disease and, therefore, the agency does not intend to use such a study to evaluate the substance/disease relationship. For example, FDA has considered 3 weeks to be the minimum duration for evaluating the effect of an intervention with various saturated fats on serum LDL cholesterol concentration (Kris-Etherton and Dietschy, 1997)

- *If the intervention involved dietary advice, was there proper follow-up to ascertain whether the advice resulted in altered intake of the substance?* When the dietary intervention involves dietary advice rather than a prescribed diet administered under a controlled condition, there should be some type of assessment of the changes in intake of the substance (e.g., dietary assessment or measurement of a biomarker of intake in response to dietary advice). Without some type of assessment of whether the dietary advice resulted in a change in intake of the substance, scientific conclusions cannot be drawn about the substance/disease relationship and, therefore, the agency does not intend to use studies that lack such an assessment to evaluate the substance/disease relationship.

- *Where were the studies conducted?* It is important that the study population is relevant to the general U.S. population or the population subgroup identified in the proposed claim. Thus, FDA evaluates each study to determine if the study population lives in an area where malnutrition or inadequate intakes of the specific substance is common, and/or where the prevalence or etiology of the disease that is the subject of the claim is not similar to that in the United States. For certain countries, there may be risk factors of a specific disease that are not relevant to disease risk in the United States (e.g., risk factors for gastric cancer in certain Asian countries). Differences in nutrition, diet, and disease risk factors between the United States and the country where a study was done may mean that the study results cannot be extrapolated to the U.S population or population subgroup. For example, scientific conclusions about the comparatively well-nourished U.S. population cannot be drawn from studies in subjects that are malnourished. Nutrient status and metabolism can be severely altered when an individual is malnourished, and therefore the effect of the substance on a particular surrogate endpoint may be very different between a malnourished and well-nourished individual (Shils et al., 2006). Scientific conclusions cannot be drawn from studies conducted in countries or regions where inadequate intake of the substance is common since a response to the intake of the substance may be due to the correction of a nutrient deficiency for which health claims are not intended.

Furthermore, conclusions cannot be drawn from studies conducted in countries or regions where the etiology of the disease is very different than in the United States. For example, major risk factors for gastric cancer in Japan (high salt intake and Helicobacter pylori (H. pylori) infection) are significantly more prevalent than in the United States. Therefore, it is not appropriate to extrapolate from data on a Japanese population concerning the relationship between a substance and gastric cancer to reach conclusions about potential effects on the U.S. population.

Observational Studies

- *What type of information was collected?* Biological samples (e.g., blood, urine, tissue, or hair) should be used to establish intake of a substance only if a dose-response relationship has been demonstrated between intake of the substance and the level of the substance (or a metabolite of the substance) in the biological sample. There should be evidence to demonstrate a strong correlation[23] between the intake level of the substance and the level of the substance or a metabolite in the biological sample (e.g., selenium intake and serum selenium concentration). If the correlation is weak for a specific biological sample, then scientific conclusions cannot be drawn from studies that used that biological sample as a biomarker of intake. Biological samples in case-control studies should not be used to establish intake of the substance since the metabolism or concentration of the substance may be altered in subjects as a result of the disease.

- *Were scientifically acceptable and validated dietary assessment methods used to estimate intake of the substance?* A single 24-hour diet recall or diet record is generally regarded as an inadequate method for assessing an individual's usual intake of a substance, although it may be useful for assessing mean intake of a group. A diet history involves extensive interviews with the study subjects. However, diet histories are also usually inadequate for assessing intake of a substance since respondents are asked to make judgments about intakes of usual foods and the amounts eaten. A food frequency questionnaire contains a limited number of food items and is inadequate for assessing intake of a substance if the major sources of the substance are not included in the questionnaire. Food frequency questionnaires also do not always account for different varieties of a particular food or different cooking methods. Because of these limitations, validation of the food frequency questionnaire method to assess food intake is essential in order to be able to draw conclusions from the scientific data, as the failure to validate may lead to false associations between dietary factors and diseases or disease-related markers.[24]

- *Did the observational study evaluate the relationship between a disease and a food or a food component?* Because observational studies estimate intake of a whole food based on recorded dietary intake methods such as food frequency questionnaires, diet recalls, or diet records, a common weakness of observational studies is the limited ability to ascertain the actual intake of the substance for the population studied. Furthermore, if the substance is a food component rather than a whole food, there is an additional estimation of the amount of the food component that is present in the individual foods. The content of foods' components can vary based on factors such as soil composition, food

---

23   Correlation is evaluated using correlation coefficients (r). Correlation coefficients range from -1 (negative correlation) through +1 (positive correlation). The closer to 1, the stronger the correlation; the closer to zero, the weaker the correlation.

24   "Validation of the food frequency questionnaire method is essential, as incorrect information may lead to false associations between dietary factors and disease or disease-related markers." Cade, J., Thompson, R., Burley, V., and Warm D. Development, Validation and Utilization of Food-Frequency Questionnaires-A Review. *Public Health Nutrition*, 5: page 573, 2002. See, also, Subar, A., et al., Comparative validation of the Block, Willett, and National Cancer Institute Food Frequency Questionnaires, *American Journal of Epidemiology*, 154: 1089-1099, 2001.

processing/cooking procedures, or storage (duration, temperature). Thus, it is difficult to ascertain an accurate amount of the food component consumed based on reports of dietary intake of whole foods.

In addition, the whole food and products that include several food components, e.g., multi-nutrient dietary supplements, contain not only the food component that is the subject of the claim, but also other food components that may be associated with the metabolism of the food component of interest or the pathogenesis of the disease or health-related condition. Because whole foods and products such as multi-nutrient dietary supplements consist of many food components, it is difficult to study the food components in isolation (Sempos et al., 1999). For studies based on recorded dietary intake of whole foods or multiple food components, it is not possible to accurately determine whether any observed effects of the food component that is the subject of the claim on disease risk were due to: (1) that food component alone; (2) interactions with other food components; (3) other food components acting alone or together; or (4) decreased consumption of other substances contained in foods displaced from the diet by the increased intake of foods rich in the food component of interest (See Sempos et al. (1999), Willett (1990) and Willett (1998) regarding the complexity of identifying the relationship between a specific food component within a food and a disease).

In fact, evidence demonstrates that in a number of instances, observational studies based on the recorded dietary intake of conventional foods may indicate a benefit for a particular nutrient with respect to a disease, but it is subsequently demonstrated in an intervention study that the nutrient-containing dietary supplement does not confer a benefit or actually *increases* risk of the disease (Lichtenstein and Russell, 2005). For example, previous observational studies reported an association between fruits and vegetables high in beta-carotene and a reduced risk of lung cancer (Peto et al., 1981). However, subsequent intervention studies, the Alpha-Tocopherol and Beta Carotene Prevention Study (ATBC) and the Carotene and Retinol Efficiency Trial (CARET), demonstrated that beta-carotene supplements increase the risk of lung cancer in smokers and asbestos-exposed workers, respectively (The Alpha-Tocopherol and Beta Carotene Cancer Prevention Study Group, 1994; Omenn et al., 1996). These studies illustrate that the effect of a nutrient provided as a dietary supplement exhibits different health effects compared to when it is consumed among many other food components. Furthermore, these studies demonstrate the potential public health risk of relying on results from epidemiological studies, in which the effect of a nutrient is based on recorded dietary intake of conventional foods as the sole source for concluding that a relationship exists between a specific nutrient and disease risk; the effect could actually be harmful. For the above reasons, scientific conclusions from observational studies cannot be drawn about a relationship between a food component and a disease. Observational studies, however, can be used to measure associations between a whole food and a disease.[25]

CH
14

---

25   In *Pearson v. Shalala,* the D.C. Circuit noted that FDA had "logically determined" that the consumption of antioxidant vitamins in dietary supplement form could not be scientifically proven to reduce the risk of cancer where the existing research had examined only foods containing antioxidant vitamins, as the effect of those foods on reducing the risk of cancer may have resulted from other substances in those foods. 164 F.3d 650, 568 (D.C. Cir.

E. Assessing the Methodological Quality of Studies

For the studies that are not eliminated during the earlier evaluation, FDA intends to independently rate each such study for methodological quality. Studies can receive a high, moderate, or low quality rating. FDA intends to base this quality rating on several factors related to study design, data collection, the quality of the statistical analysis, the type of outcome measured, and study population characteristics other than relevance to the U.S. population (e.g., selection bias and the provision of important subject information [e.g., age, smokers]). If the scientific study adequately addressed all or most of the above factors, FDA plans to give it a high methodological quality rating. FDA plans to give moderate or low quality ratings based on the extent of the deficiencies or uncertainties in the quality factors. Studies that are so deficient in quality that they receive a low quality rating are studies from which scientific conclusions cannot be drawn about the substance/disease relationship and are eliminated from further review.

Examples of factors FDA intends to consider in assessing the methodological quality of individual studies remaining at this point in the scientific evaluation approach set out in this guidance include the following:

Intervention Studies

- *Were the studies randomized and blinded and was a placebo provided?* Appropriate randomization eliminates intrinsic and/or extrinsic factors, other than the substance, that could have an influence on the outcome of the study. Blinding is especially important when the endpoint can be influenced by a subject's awareness that he or she is receiving something that may be beneficial. Blinding would be critical when the outcome measure is cognitive performance, mental status (e.g. memory, depression), or behavior. Including a placebo in a supplementation trial prevents the subject from knowing whether he or she is receiving the substance or not.

1999). The D.C.Circuit, however, concluded that FDA's concern with granting antioxidant vitamins a qualified health claim could be accommodated by simply adding a prominent disclaimer noting that the evidence for such a claim was inconclusive, given that the studies supporting the claim were based on foods containing other substances that might actually be responsible for reducing the risk of cancer. Id. The court noted that FDA did not assert that the dietary supplements at issue would "threaten consumer's health and safety." Id. at 656. There is, however, a more fundamental problem with allowing qualified health claims for individual nutrients based on studies of foods containing those nutrients than the problem the D.C. Circuit held could be cured with a disclaimer. Even if the effect of the specific component of the food could be determined with certainty, recent scientific findings on the complex nature of nutrient-food interactions and on the relationships among diet, biological parameters, and disease indicate that nutrients found to have health benefits when consumed in one food or group of foods may not necessarily have the same beneficial effect when they are consumed in dietary supplement form or in other foods. See Lichtenstein and Russell (2005). For example, not only have studies on dietary supplements established that the benefits associated with the dietary intake of certain nutrients do not materialize when the nutrients are taken as a supplement, but some of these studies have actually indicated an increased risk for the very disease the nutrients were predicted to prevent. Id. Thus, a study based on intake of a specific food or foods provides no information from which scientific conclusions may be drawn for the nutrient itself. Further, even if the nutrients are consumed in other foods rather than in a dietary supplement, the physiological effects may be different because the food matrix can affect the bioavailability and bioactivity of the nutrients. Id.

CH 14

- *Were inclusion/exclusion criteria and key information on the characteristics of the study population provided?* For instance, were healthy or high-risk subjects allowed to take medications that can affect the disease that is subject of the claim during the study? If so, was the proportion of subjects taking medications similar between the control and intervention groups?

- *Was subject attrition (subjects leaving the study before the study is completed) assessed, explained in the article reporting the study, and reasonable?* If there were a marked number of drop-outs, then it would be important to know why subjects dropped out and how the drop-outs affected the number and composition of the intervention and placebo group.

- *How was compliance with the study protocol verified?* Intervention studies should include a mechanism for verifying that the subjects followed the study protocol. For example, a supplementation trial should have a mechanism for determining how frequently the subjects took their supplements. It would be important to know 1) if the subjects took all of the supplements provided by the study or only a portion and 2) what proportion of the subjects for each group took less than the directed amount.

- *Was statistical analysis conducted on baseline data for the all subjects initially enrolled in the study or only those who completed the study?* If there were a marked number of drop-outs which, in turn, affected the composition of the intervention groups differently from the placebo groups, then it would be important to determine if statistical analysis on baseline data was conducted for all subjects initially enrolled in the study or only for those who completed the study.

- *Did the study measure disease incidence or a surrogate endpoint of disease risk?* While surrogate endpoints of disease risk have been validated, they are not as accurate as measuring the actual onset of a disease. This quality issue would also apply to observational studies.

- *How was the onset of a disease determined?* When disease incidence is the endpoint being measured, it is important that the disease that is subject of the claim is confirmed either through medical records and/or pathology reports. Relying on less specific records, such as death certificates, is not sufficient. This quality issue would also apply to observational studies.

Observational Studies

- *Was there an adequate adjustment for confounders of disease risk?* Several aspects of a substance/disease relationship may give rise to confounders. Therefore, it is important to adjust for confounders of the disease of interest so that observed effects on risk of disease that may be due to confounders are not incorrectly attributed to the substance of interest. For example, there can be multiple non-dietary risk factors for a disease (e.g., smoking, body mass index, and age for hypertension). Therefore, when evaluating the relationship between sodium and blood pressure, an adjustment of the risk analysis should be made based on age, smoking, body mass index and age.

• *What type of dietary assessment method was used to estimate dietary intake?* Validated food frequency questionnaires are more reliable in estimating "usual" intake of foods compared to diet records or 24-hour recall methods. See Section III.B.

F. Evaluating the Totality of Scientific Evidence

Under the approach set out in this guidance, at this point, FDA intends to evaluate the results of the studies from which scientific conclusions can be drawn and rate the strength of the total body of publicly available evidence. The agency plans to conduct this evaluation by considering the study type (e.g., intervention, prospective cohort, case-control, cross-sectional), methodological quality rating previously assigned, number of the various types of studies and sample sizes, relevance of the body of scientific evidence to the U.S. population or target subgroup, whether study results supporting the proposed claim have been replicated[26], and the overall consistency[27,28] of the total body of evidence. Based on the totality of the scientific evidence, FDA determines whether such evidence meets the SSA standard or whether such evidence is credible to support a qualified health claim for the substance/disease relationship.

Within each study type, the studies are reviewed for:

• *Number* of studies and number of subjects per group

• *Methodological quality* (high, moderate, or low).

• *Outcome* (beneficial effect, no effect, adverse effect) of the studies within each study type. For the outcome of an intervention study to demonstrate an effect, the intervention group should be statistically significantly different from the control group ($P < 0.05$). For observational studies, confidence intervals (CI) for risk are significant when the value is less than or greater than "1". Many studies analyze for the statistical significance of the linear relationship (P for trend) between the substance and the disease. While this trend may be significant ($P<0.05$), the difference in risk between subjects at the various levels of intake (e.g., tertiles, quartiles or quintiles of intake)[29] may not be significant. In that case, the studies show no effect. Evaluation of the size of the effect (e.g., percent reduction in LDL cholesterol) may be useful for comparing effects within a study (e.g., relative effect of two forms of the substance or the relative effect of frequency of consumption).

26   Replication of scientific findings is important for evaluating the strength of scientific evidence (Wilson, E.B. An Introduction to Scientific Research. Dover Publications, 1990; pages 46-48).
27   In this guidance, "consistency" is used to mean the level of agreement among the studies from which scientific conclusions could be drawn about the substance/ disease relationship.
28   Consistency of findings among similar and different study designs is important for evaluating causation and the strength of scientific evidence (Hill A.B. The environment and disease: association or causation? *Proceedings of the Royal Society of Medicine.* 1965;58:295-300).; see also Agency for Healthcare Research and Quality, Systems to Rate the Scientific Evidence, which defines "consistency " as " the extent to which similar findings are reported using similar and different study designs." [http://www.ahrq.gov/clinic/epcsums/strengthsum.htm#Contents]
29   Tertile, quartile and quintile of intake is the result of dividing a study population into 3, 4 or 5 groups, respectively, such that the average intake level of the substance varies across the groups (e.g., lowest intake group represents the lowest tertile of intake and the highest intake group represents the highest tertile). The study population is divided such that each group has the same number of subjects.

- In general, the greater the *consistency* among the studies in showing a beneficial relationship, the greater the level of confidence that a substance/disease relationship exists. Conflicting results do not disprove an association (because the elements of the study design may account for the lack of an effect in negative studies) but tend to weaken confidence in the strength of the association. The greater the magnitude of the beneficial effect, the more likely the association may exist.

- *Relevance* to the general U.S. population. For example,

  To what extent did the studies that showed a benefit include populations that represent the general U.S. population or a population subgroup (e.g., elderly, women)?

  Did the studies only include subjects with unique lifestyles (e.g., smokers, vegetarians)?

  Do the studies suggest that the intake level of the substance that provides a benefit significantly exceeds usual intakes in the United States?

FDA evaluates whether the totality of the evidence supports a claim for the entire U.S. population or just a subgroup. If the evidence only supports a claim for a subgroup, that information would be set out in the claim. If the substance is one that must be used for risk reduction at much higher levels than the normal U.S. intake, that information would also be reflected in the claim.

In general, intervention studies provide the strongest evidence for the claimed effect, regardless of existing observational studies on the same relationship. Intervention studies are designed to avoid selection bias and avoid findings that are due to chance or other confounders of disease (Sempos et al., 1999). Although the evaluation of substance/disease relationships often involves both intervention and observational studies, observational studies generally cannot be used to rule out the findings from more reliable intervention studies (Sempos et al., 1999). One intervention study would not be sufficient to rule out consistent findings of observational studies. However, when several randomized, controlled intervention studies are consistent in showing or not showing a substance/disease relationship, they trump the findings of any number of observational studies (Barton, 2005). This is because intervention studies are designed and controlled to test whether there is evidence of a cause and effect relationship between the substance and the reduced risk of a disease, whereas observational studies are only able to identify possible associations. There are numerous examples — such as vitamin E and CVD and beta-carotene and lung cancer — where associations identified in observational studies have been publicized. However, when randomized, controlled intervention studies were later conducted to test these possible associations, the intervention studies found no evidence to support the relationships (Lichtenstein and Russell, 2005).

G. Assessing Significant Scientific Agreement

Significant scientific agreement refers to the extent of agreement among qualified experts in the field. On the continuum of scientific evidence that extends from very limited to inconclusive evidence, SSA lies closer to consensus. FDA's determination of SSA represents the agency's best judgment as to whether qualified experts would likely agree that the scientific evidence supports the substance/disease relationship that is the subject of a proposed health claim. The SSA standard is intended to be a strong standard that provides a high level of confidence in the validity of the substance/disease relationship. SSA means that the validity of the relationship is not likely to be reversed by new and evolving science, although the exact nature of the relationship may need to be refined. SSA does not require a consensus based on unanimous and incontrovertible scientific opinion. SSA occurs well after the stage of emerging science, where data and information permit an inference, but before the point of unanimous agreement within the relevant scientific community that the inference is valid.

For qualified experts to reach an informed opinion regarding the validity of a claim, the data and information that pertain to the claim must be available to the relevant scientific community. A finding of SSA then derives from the conclusion that there is a sufficient body of relevant, publicly available scientific evidence that shows consistency across different studies and among different researchers. The usual mechanism to show that the evidence is available to qualified experts is that the data and information are published in peer-reviewed scientific journals. The value of an expert's opinion will be limited if he or she did not have access to all the evidence.

In determining whether there is significant scientific agreement, FDA takes into account the viewpoints of qualified experts outside the agency, if evaluations by such experts have been conducted and are publicly available. For example, FDA intends to take into account:

- documentation of the opinion of an "expert panel" that is specifically convened for this purpose by a credible, independent body;

- the opinion or recommendation of a federal government scientific body such as the National Institutes of Health (NIH) or the Centers for Disease Control and Prevention (CDC); or the National Academy of Sciences (NAS);

- the opinion of an independent, expert body such as the Committee on Nutrition of the American Academy of Pediatrics (AAP), the American Heart Association (AHA), American Cancer Society (ACS), or task forces or other groups assembled by the National Institutes of Health (NIH);

- review publications that critically summarize data and information in the secondary scientific literature.

FDA accords the greatest weight to the conclusions of federal government scientific bodies, especially when the evidence for the validity of a substance/disease relationship has been judged by such a body to be sufficient to justify dietary recommendations to the public. When the validity of a substance/disease relationship is supported by the conclusions of federal government scientific bodies, FDA typically finds that significant scientific agreement exists. Conclusions of other expert bodies may also be relevant to support a determination of SSA. Although reviews by individual outside experts are considered in assessing SSA, evidence from such reviews alone would not necessarily support a conclusion that the standard has been met, especially if the conclusions of such reviews were not supported by available assessments of the same body of evidence from federal scientific bodies, expert

CH
14

panels, or independent expert bodies. Reviews by outside experts or expert panels are most useful when there is a reasonable basis to conclude that they represent the larger group of qualified experts in the field. Most importantly, the relevance of an outside expert review depends on whether the evidence examined applies to the claim in terms of considerations such as specification and measurement of the substance and the disease.

When conclusions from qualified experts are not available (for instance, if the data supporting a proposed health claim are relatively new and have not yet been reviewed by an independent expert panel or body), a compelling and relevant body of evidence may nonetheless cause the agency to conclude that significant scientific agreement exists. Because each situation may differ with the nature of the claimed substance/disease relationship, it is necessary to consider both the extent of agreement and the nature of the disagreement on a case-by-case basis. If scientific agreement were to be assessed under arbitrary quantitative or rigidly defined criteria, the resulting inflexibility could cause some valid claims to be disallowed where the disagreement, while present, is not persuasive.

Application of the significant scientific agreement standard is intended to be objective, in relying upon a body of sound and relevant scientific data; flexible, in recognizing the variability in the amount and type of data needed to support the validity of different substance/disease relationships; and responsive, in recognizing the need to re-evaluate data over time as research questions and experimental approaches are refined.

H. Specificity of the Claim Language for Qualified Health Claims

When the evidence for a substance-disease relationship is credible but does not meet the SSA standard, then the proposed claim for the relationship should include qualifying language that identifies limits to the level of scientific evidence to support the relationship.

The health claim language should reflect the level of scientific evidence with specificity and accuracy. However, gaps in the scientific evidence may sometimes limit the information that can be included in the claims. For example, when the scientific evidence is limited but credible, it may not be possible for the qualified health claim to identify an amount of the substance that is associated with a reduced risk of the disease.

Under FDA's health claim regulations, a health claim must specify the daily dietary intake of the substance necessary to achieve the claimed effect when there is no regulation defining what constitutes a "high" level of the substance in food (21 CFR 101.14(d)(2)(vii)). FDA has defined "high" in its nutrient content claim regulations as meaning that the food contains 20% or more of the Daily Value of the substance (21 CFR 101.54(b)). Therefore, when no Daily Value for the substance has been established, the agency cannot establish a definition for a "high" level of the substance. When the substance that is the subject of the claim has no Daily Value, FDA determines the daily dietary intake necessary to achieve the claimed effect whenever the available evidence is sufficient to make such a determination possible. See, e.g., 21 CFR 101.83(c)(2)(G) (health claim regulation for plant sterol/stanol esters and reduced risk of coronary heart disease). However, there are times when the credible evidence for the risk reduction effect is not specific enough for FDA to identify even a possible level of intake for the general U.S. population. See FDA's September 8, 2004, letter of enforcement discretion for qualified health claim about omega-3 fatty acids and reduced risk of coronary heart disease (Martek petition)

When there is credible evidence available to suggest a relationship between the substance and disease, it is important to determine whether the substance has an independent role in the relationship or whether its role is based on the inclusion or replacement (i.e., substitution) of other substances. An example of where the evaluation of the independent role of a substance can be challenging is when the substance is a conventional food or macronutrient (e.g., fat or carbohydrate). In studies evaluating the possible health effects of a conventional food or macronutrient, the inclusion of either in the diet usually requires the removal of other conventional foods or macronutrients (i.e., substitution to yield isocaloric diets). If it is determined that the substance does not play an independent role and/or requires the reduction or inclusion of another substance to show a beneficial effect, the claim language will reflect this finding.

I. Reevaluation of Existing SSA or Qualified Health Claims

FDA may reevaluate a health claim in response to a petitioner or on its own initiative, and when it does so it intends to use the scientific evaluation process described above. To maximize the public health benefit of its health claims review, FDA intends to evaluate new information that becomes available to determine whether it necessitates a change to an existing SSA or qualified health claim. For example, scientific evidence may become available that will (1) support the revision of claim language for an SSA or qualified health claim, (2) support change of an SSA claim to a QHC or support change of a QHC to an SSA claim, or (3) raise safety concerns about the substance that is the subject of a health claim or otherwise no longer support a health claim (SSA or QHC).

IV. References

American Cancer Society, Cancer Facts and Figures, 2004.

The Alpha-Tocopherol, Beta Carotene Cancer Prevention Study Group. The effect of vitamin E and beta carotene on the incidence of lung cancer and other cancers in male smokers. *New England Journal of Medicine* 1994; 330:1029-1035.

Barton S. Which clinical studies provide the best evidence? The best RCT still trumps the best observational study. *British Medical Journal* 2000; 321:255-256.

Cade J, Thompson R, Burley V, Warm D. Development, validation and utilization of food-frequency questionnaires – a review. *Public Health Nutrition* 2002; 5:567-587.

Federal Judicial Center, Reference Manual on Scientific Evidence, Second Edition, 2000.

Flegal KM. Evaluating epidemiological evidence of the effects of food and nutrient expo-sures. *American Journal of Clinical Nutrition* 1999; 69:1339S-1344S.

Greer N, Mosser G, Logan G, Halaas GW. A practical approach to evidence grading. Joint Commission Journal on Quality Improvements 2000; 26:700-712.

Hill AB. The environment and disease: association or causation? *Proceedings of the Royal Society of Medicine* 1965; 58:295-300

CH
14

Hord NG, Fenton JI. Context is everything: mining the normal and preneoplastic microenvironment for insights into the diet and cancer risk conundrum. *Molecular Nutrition and Food Research* 2007; 51:100-106.

IOM, Institute of Medicine. Dietary Supplements: A Framework for Evaluating Safety. National Academies Press, Washington, DC. 2005.

Kraemer HC, Lowe KK, Kupfer DJ. To Your Health: How to Understand What Research Tell Us About Risk. Oxford University Press, 2005.

Kris-Etherton PM, Dietschy J. Design criteria for studies examining individual fatty acid effects on cardiovascular disease risk factors: human and animal studies. *American Journal of Clinical Nutrition* 1997; 65:1590S-1596S.

Lichtenstein AH, Russell RM. Essential Nutrients: Food or Supplements? *Journal of American Medical Association* 2005; 294:351-358.

Milner JA. Diet and Cancer: Facts and Controversies. *Nutrition and Cancer* 2006; 56: 216-224.

National Cancer Institute, Dictionary of Cancer Terms, http://www.cancer.gov/dictionary

National Research Council. Diet and Health: Implications for Reducing Chronic Disease Risk. National Academy Press, Washington, DC, 1989.

Omenn, GS, Goodman GE, Thornquist MD, Balmes J, Cullen MR, Glass A, Keogh JP, Meyskens FL, Valanis B, Williams JH, Barnhart S, Hammer S. Effects of a combination of beta carotene and vitamin A on lung cancer and cardiovascular disease. *New England Journal of Medicine* 1996; 334:1150-1155.

Peto R, Doll R, Buckley JD, Sporn MB. Can dietary beta-carotene materially reduce human cancer rates? Nature 1981; 290:201-208.

Sempos CT, Liu K, Earnst ND. Food and nutrient exposures: what to consider when evaluating epidemiologic data. *American Journal of Clinical Nutrition* 1999; 69:1330S-1338S.

Torun B. Protein-energy malnutrition. In: Modern Nutrition in Health and Disease. Williams and Williams, New York, 2006.

Spilker B. Guide to Clinical Studies. Raven Press, New York, 1991.

Subar AF, Thompson FE, Kipnis V, Midthune D, Hurwitz P, McNutt S, McIntosh A, Rosenfeld S. Comparative validation of the Block, Willett, and National Cancer Institute Food Frequency Questionnaires, *American Journal of Epidemiology* 2001; 154: 1089-1099.

Szklo M., Nieto FJ. Epidemiology Beyond the Basics, Aspen Publishing, 2000.

Willett W.C. Overview of nutritional epidemiology. Nutritional Epidemiology, Oxford University Press, Oxford. 1990.

Willett W.C. Issues in analysis and presentation of dietary data. In: Nutritional Epidemiology, Second Edition, Oxford University Press, Oxford, 1998.

Wilson E.B. An Introduction to Scientific Research, General Publishing Company, Toronto, 1990.

CH
14

Contains Nonbinding Recommendations
December 2008
OMB Control No. 0910-0626
Expiration Date: 08/31/2011

Guidance for Industry:
Substantiation for Dietary Supplement Claims Made Under Section 403(r)(6) of the Federal Food, Drug, and Cosmetic Act[1]

I. Introduction

A. What Does This Guidance Document Address?

Section 403(r)(6) of the Federal Food, Drug, and Cosmetic Act (the Act) (21 U.S.C. 343(r)(6)) requires that a manufacturer of a dietary supplement making a nutritional deficiency, structure/function, or general well-being claim[2] have substantiation that the claim is truthful and not misleading.[3]

This guidance document is intended to describe the amount, type, and quality of evidence FDA recommends a manufacturer have to substantiate a claim under section 403(r)(6) of the Act. This guidance document is limited to issues pertaining to substantiation under section 403(r)(6) of the Act; it does not extend to substantiation issues that may exist in other sections of the Act.[4]

---

1 The Office of Nutrition, Labeling, and Dietary Supplements in FDA's Center for Food Safety and Applied Nutrition prepared this guidance document. This guidance is available on the FDA website at https://www.fda.gov/food/guidanceregulation/guidancedocumentsregulatoryinformation/ucm073200.htm

2 Under section 403(r)(6)(A) of the Act (21 U.S.C. 343(r)(6)(A)), such a statement is one that "claims a benefit related to a classical nutritional deficiency disease and discloses the prevalence of such disease in the United States, describes the role of a nutrient or dietary ingredient intended to affect the structure or function in humans, characterizes the documented mechanism by which a nutrient or dietary ingredient acts to maintain such structure or function, or describes general well-being from consumption for a nutrient or dietary ingredient...."

3 Comments to the Draft Guidance published November 9, 2004 (69 FR 64942), questioned the constitutionality, under the First Amendment, of the substantiation requirement in section 403(r)(6), as interpreted by the Draft Guidance. This Guidance offers FDA's non-binding interpretation of what constitutes substantiation and does not change the statutory or Constitutional requirement in any way. We believe the statutory substantiation requirement in section 403(r)(6) is constitutional under the Supreme Court's analysis governing commercial speech in Central Hudson Gas & Electric Corp. v. Public Service Commission of New York (447 U.S. 557 (1980)). Claims made under section 403(r)(6) are misleading when made without substantiation. The misleading nature of a claim made under section 403(r)(6) that is not substantiated cannot be cured by a disclaimer stating that the claim lacks support. For example, a product cannot claim "to promote the structure and function of the skeletal system" and then attempt to cure the misleading nature of the claim with a statement "no evidence exists that this product promotes the structure and function of the skeletal system." However, nothing in this Guidance addresses the circumstances under which a claim made under section 403(r)(6) that includes qualifying language may be substantiated.

4 This guidance does not discuss the criteria to determine whether a statement about a dietary supplement is

FDA's guidance documents, including this guidance, do not establish legally enforceable responsibilities. Instead, guidances describe the Agency's current thinking on a topic and should be viewed only as recommendations, unless specific regulatory or statutory requirements are cited. The use of the word should in Agency guidances means that something is suggested or recommended, but not required.

B. Why Is Guidance on Substantiation Helpful?

The Act, as amended by the Dietary Supplement Health and Education Act of 1994 (DSHEA) and the legislative history accompanying DSHEA do not define "substantiation." For this guidance, we drew upon our own expertise with respect to the regulations and case law regarding substantiation of various statements that may be made in the labeling of dietary supplements, conventional foods, and drug products (recognizing that conventional foods and drugs are regulated differently from dietary supplements), the Federal Trade Commission's (FTC) experience with its policy on substantiating claims made for dietary supplements in advertising, and recommendations from the Commission on Dietary Supplement Labels.

The Commission on Dietary Supplement Labels (the Commission), a seven-member body that was established under DSHEA to "provide recommendations for...the regulation of label claims and statements for dietary supplements, including the use of literature in connection with the sale of dietary supplements and procedures for the evaluation of such claims," held public meetings around the United States from 1996 through 1997. During these meetings, several manufacturers asked the Commission to provide guidance regarding the type of information that manufacturers should have in hand to substantiate a statement of nutritional support.[5]

Under the Act, FDA has exclusive jurisdiction over the safety, and primary jurisdiction over the labeling, of dietary supplements. The FTC has primary jurisdiction over advertisements for dietary supplements. Given these jurisdictional assignments, we and the FTC share an interest in providing guidance on what "substantiation" means. In April 2001, FTC issued a guidance document entitled, "Dietary Supplements: An Advertising Guide for Industry."[6] Our guidance document is modeled on, and complements, the FTC guidance document.

Dietary supplement manufacturers should be familiar with the requirements under both DSHEA and the Federal Trade Commission Act that they have substantiation that labeling and advertising claims are truthful and not misleading. Our approach provides manufacturers flexibility in the precise amount and type of evidence that constitutes adequate substantiation. Providing a standard for substantiation may also help to preserve consumer

a structure/function claim under section 403(r)(6) of the Act or a disease claim. Please see the Federal Register of January 6, 2000 (65 FR 1000, codified at 21 CFR 101.93) for the final rule defining structure/function claims for dietary supplements and the January 9, 2002 Small Entity Compliance Guide for structure/function claims (Updated web reference: Structure/Function Claims; Small Entity Compliance Guide).

5   See Report of the Commission on Dietary Supplement Labels, November 1997, at page 42. The Commission's recommendations on substantiation are at pages 42 through 45 of the report.

6   See Bureau of Consumer Protection, Federal Trade Commission, "Dietary Supplements: An Advertising Guide for Industry," April 2001 (hereinafter referred to as "FTC Advertising Guide"), available at www.ftc.gov.

confidence in these products. To ensure compliance with the Act, we recommend that dietary supplement manufacturers carefully draft their labeling claims and carefully review the support for each claim to make sure that the support relates to the specific product and claim, is scientifically sound, and is adequate in the context of the surrounding body of evidence.

The FTC has typically applied a substantiation standard of "competent and reliable scientific evidence" to claims about the benefits and safety of dietary supplements and other health-related products. FDA intends to apply a standard for the substantiation of dietary supplement claims that is consistent with the FTC approach. This guidance document, using examples of claims that might be made for a dietary supplement, describes criteria to be considered in evaluating the nature of the claim and the amount, type, and quality of evidence in support of the claim.

II. Discussion

A. What is the Substantiation Standard?

The FTC standard of competent and reliable scientific evidence has been defined in FTC case law as "tests, analyses, research, studies, or other evidence based on the expertise of professionals in the relevant area, that has been conducted and evaluated in an objective manner by persons qualified to do so, using procedures generally accepted in the profession to yield accurate and reliable results."[7]

Although there is no pre-established formula as to how many or what type of studies are needed to substantiate a claim, we, like the FTC, will consider what the accepted norms are in the relevant research fields and consult experts from various disciplines. If there is an existing standard for substantiation developed by a government agency or other authoritative body, we may accord some deference to that standard.

In determining whether the substantiation standard has been met with competent and reliable scientific evidence, we recommend that firms consider the following issues in their assessment:

1. The meaning of the claim(s) being made;

2. The relationship of the evidence to the claim;

3. The quality of the evidence; and

4. The totality of the evidence.

Each of these issues is discussed further in this guidance.

B. Identifying the Meaning of the Claim

The first step in determining what information is needed to substantiate a claim for a dietary supplement is to understand the meaning of the claim and to clearly identify each implied

CH 14

---

7   See, e.g. *Vital Basics, Inc.*, C-4107 (Consent April 26, 2004); *see also In Re Schering Corp.*, 118 F.T.C. 1030, 1123 (1994).

and express claim. When a claim may have more than one reasonable interpretation, we recommend that a firm have substantiation for each interpretation. Consumer testing may be useful to determine consumer understanding of each claim, in context. We recommend that firms not only focus on individual statements or phrases, but also on what expected effect or benefit are being promoted when all of the statements being made for the product are considered together. Although it is important that individual statements be substantiated, it is equally important to substantiate the overall "message" contained when the claims are considered together.

Example 1: The label of a dietary supplement containing "X" uses the following claims: "The amino acid 'X' is the chemical precursor to nitric oxide. Blood vessel cells contain enzymes that produce nitric oxide. Nitric oxide is important in maintaining blood vessel tone." Assuming this statement were supported by sound science so that each individual statement was substantiated, the "message" conveyed by the claims, when considered together, is that taking oral "X" will affect nitric oxide production and blood vessel tone. Therefore, we recommend in this case that the dietary supplement manufacturer have substantiation that taking the amount of "X" provided by the product affect nitric oxide production and blood vessel tone under the product's recommended conditions of use.

The firm's clear understanding of the meaning of the claim is useful in ensuring that the evidentiary basis for substantiation is appropriate for the claim. Understanding the claim's meaning will help identify the appropriate study hypotheses and measurable endpoints, which can be used to ensure that the firm has appropriate studies to substantiate the claim. For example, a firm making a claim that a dietary supplement "helps maintain blood vessel tone" or "supports healthy immune system" should have a clear understanding of the claim's meaning to develop endpoints that could be measured and replicated in studies used as a basis for substantiation.

Example 2: The labeling of a dietary supplement includes the statement "promotes weight loss." The dietary supplement contains various vitamins and minerals and a botanical extract. The manufacturer relies on a randomized controlled double blind clinical study showing that subjects who took the botanical extract had a small but significant increase in metabolism over subjects taking a placebo over a 24 hour period. The study did not examine the effect of the extract on subjects' weight and there is no research showing that a short term increase in metabolism will translate into any measurable weight loss. The weight loss claim would likely not be adequately substantiated.

Example 3: The labeling for a dietary supplement contains a statement saying, "Recommended by Scientists," in connection with the product's claim. The statement gives consumers the impression that there is a body of scientists, qualified experts, who believe that the claim being made is supported by evidence. Consumers might also reasonably interpret the statement as meaning that there is general scientific agreement or consensus regarding the claim. If the manufacturer does not possess evidence to demonstrate such a consensus, the claim may not be substantiated. The opinion of a single scientist or small group of scientists is probably not adequate substantiation for such a claim.

**CH
14**

Example 4: The labeling states, in connection with the product's claim, that the dietary supplement has been "studied for years" in a particular country or region and is the subject of clinical or "university" research. Here, the labeling conveys the impression that the product has been studied and also conveys the impression that there is a substantial body of competently conducted scientific research supporting the claim. We recommend that manufacturers possess evidence to substantiate both the express statements and their implied meaning.

C. The Relationship of the Evidence to the Claim

Whether studies or evidence have a relationship to the specific claim being made or to the dietary supplement product itself is an important consideration in determining if a claim is substantiated. The following are some threshold questions in determining this relationship:

□ *Have the studies specified and measured the dietary supplement that is the subject of the claim?* We recommend that the studies being used as substantiation for dietary supplement claims identify a specific dietary supplement or ingredient and serving size and that the conditions of use in the studies are similar to the labeling conditions of the dietary supplement product. Factors that would tend to indicate a stronger relationship between a substance that is the subject of a study and the substance that is the subject of the dietary supplement claim includes similarities in formulation, serving size, route of administration, total length of exposure, and frequency of exposure. Manufacturers should be aware that other substances involved in the study or included in the dietary supplement product itself might also affect the dietary supplement's performance or the study results.

Example 5: To illustrate this issue, assume that a firm has high quality studies that are also consistent with the totality of the scientific evidence. The firm would like to use these studies to substantiate a claim that its dietary supplement has a particular effect on the human body, but the studies involved the impact of a specific ingredient in foods on the human body, and did not involve the dietary supplement product itself. In this instance, although the studies might be of high quality, the results of these studies of conventional foods are not applicable to the specific dietary supplement product.[8]

---

8   For example, a study using a conventional food or a multi-nutrient supplement would not substantiate a single ingredient dietary supplement claim. When the substance studied contains many nutrients and substances, it is difficult to study the nutrient or food components in isolation (Sempos, et al., 1999). It is not possible to accurately determine whether any observed effects of the substance were due to: 1) the substance alone; 2) interactions between the substance and other nutrients; 3) other nutrients acting alone or together; or 4) decreased consumption of other nutrients or substances contained in foods displaced from the diet by the increased intake of foods rich in the substance at issue. Furthermore, although epidemiological studies based on the recorded dietary intake of conventional foods have indicated a benefit for a particular nutrient, it has been subsequently demonstrated in an intervention study that the single ingredient nutrient-containing dietary supplement did not confer a benefit or actually was harmful. See Lichtenstein and Russell, 2005. We note that the D.C. Circuit Court in *Pearson v. Shalala*, 164 F.3d 650, 658 (D.C. Cir. 1999) indicated that FDA had "logically determined" that the consumption of a dietary supplement containing antioxidants could not be scientifically proven to reduce the risk of cancer where the existing research had examined only foods containing antioxidants as the effect of those foods on reducing the risk of cancer may have resulted from other substances. The court, however, concluded that FDA's concern with granting antioxidant vitamins a qualified health claim could be accommodated by simply adding a

CH
14

    □ *Have the studies appropriately specified and measured the nutritional deficiency, structure/function, or general well-being that is the subject of the claim?* We recommend that the studies clearly identify the endpoints that are to be used to substantiate the claimed effect.

    □ *Were the studies based on a population that is similar to that which will be consuming the dietary supplement product?* For example, if the study involved young adults, but the product's claims involve conditions seen only in the elderly, the study might not be applicable to the claims.

    □ *Does the claim accurately convey to consumers the extent, nature, or permanence of the effect achieved in the relevant studies and the level of scientific certainty for that effect?*

A note on foreign research: Foreign research could be sufficient to substantiate a claim as long as the design and implementation of the foreign research are scientifically sound and the foreign research pertains to the dietary supplement at issue. In evaluating data from studies conducted in a foreign population, care should be taken in extending the results to what might be expected in consumers in the United States who will use the product. Differences between the two populations, such as differences in diets, general health, or patterns of use, could confound the results. Also, it is important to make sure that the study examined the same dietary ingredient about which the claim is being made since there may be instances where, due to provincial or regional differences in custom, language, or dialect, the same name is given to different substances or different names to the same substance.

Example 6: A firm claims that its dietary supplement contains an ingredient shown to promote claim Y. The firm conducts a literature search and finds several references for carefully conducted, well-controlled studies demonstrating that the substance appears to be helpful in persons with claim Y associated with aging when the substance is applied topically to the affected area. However, there is no information provided concerning the effect of the substance when taken orally. Although the evidence may demonstrate that the product is effective when used topically, this information would generally not be useful to substantiate a claim for a dietary supplement (by definition, a product that is intended for ingestion (section 201(ff)(2)(A) of the Act (21 U.S.C. 321(ff)(1)(A))).

---

prominent disclaimer noting that the evidence for such a claim was inconclusive given that the studies supporting the claim were based on foods containing other substances that might actually be responsible for reducing the risk of cancer. Id. The court noted that FDA did not assert that the dietary supplements at issue would "threaten consumer's health and safety." Id. at 656. As the agency has stated in the context of qualified health claims, that is, claims regarding the relationship between a substance and the reduced risk of a disease, there is a more fundamental problem with allowing qualified health claims for nutrients in dietary supplements based solely on studies of foods containing those nutrients than the problem the D.C. Circuit held could be cured with a disclaimer. As noted in endnote 3, even if the effect of the specific component of the food constituting the dietary supplement could be determined with certainty, recent scientific studies have shown that nutrients in food do not necessarily have the same beneficial effect when taken in the form of a dietary supplement. Such studies established either that there was no benefit when the nutrients are taken as a supplement and some studies even showed an increased risk for the very disease the nutrients were predicted to prevent. We would expect similar issues with structure/ functions claims made under § 403(r)(6). Thus, an observational study based on food does not provide competent and reliable scientific evidence for a dietary supplement and, and therefore, cannot substantiate a claim made under § 403(r)(6).

Example 7: A dietary supplement firm wants to promote an amino acid product to improve blood circulation and improve sexual performance. The firm conducts a literature search and finds many abstracts and articles about the amino acid's effect on biological mediators of circulation and a few animal and human studies designed to study the effect of the amino acid on blood flow. The firm intends to use this list of studies as substantiation for its claim.

Although the firm appears to have a significant amount of information for its claim, the list is likely not adequate because the firm has not demonstrated that the information is directly related to the claim being made. For example, in this situation we would recommend that the firm provide information to clarify the meaning of "improves blood circulation" and "improves sexual performance." We would also recommend that the firm determine whether the studies examined a dosage of product similar to the firm's product and whether any study measured outcomes (i.e., improved sexual performance) other than blood flow/blood circulation. Until the firm has reviewed the underlying studies, it should not assume that merely finding studies testing the same substance necessarily constitutes adequate substantiation.

Example 8: A firm wishes to market its mineral supplement by using a claim that "studies show that the mineral supplement promotes "Z." The firm has the results of a randomized, double blind, placebo-controlled study conducted in a foreign country showing that a similar product did, in fact, promote "Z," although the study indicates that the foreign study subjects had low blood levels of the mineral at the start of the study. The general U.S. population does not have such a mineral deficiency. Although this study is a high quality study, it may not be adequate to substantiate a claim about the product's use intended for consumers in the United States because it is confounded by the initial abnormal blood levels of the mineral. Since the study is not designed to answer the question of whether the effect would be expected to occur in subjects with normal blood levels of the mineral, the study may not be adequate evidence to substantiate the claim.

Example 9: A firm is marketing a product specifically to reduce nervousness during stressful everyday situations, such as public speaking. The firm has results from several small studies demonstrating that the product will raise blood levels of a chemical that is well known to relax people in stressful situations. The firm also has two small, randomized, placebo-controlled studies showing that its product positively affected measurable indices of anxiety in people placed in stressful situations, including public speaking. These studies may be adequate evidence to support the product claims. Although the studies may be small in terms of the numbers of subjects tested, they are well-designed studies that resulted in statistically significant positive results that are consistent with the larger body of scientific evidence related to stress anxiety in public situations.

Example 10: A firm has developed a product to improve memory and cognitive ability and intends to market the product to parents for their school-aged children. The firm has several high quality clinical studies that examined the ingredient's effect in elderly people with diagnosed, age-related memory problems. These studies alone would likely not be adequate substantiation for a claim about memory improvement in young children because the patient

CH

14

population (elderly people with memory problems) is completely different from the intended population (children) in the claim.

Example 11: A dietary supplement firm is marketing an iron dietary supplement with the claim that the dietary supplement is to correct iron-deficiency anemia in the 10% of menstruating women with menorrhagia. The firm has not studied the product in this population of women directly, but has assembled and carefully reviewed the scientific literature of studies that have investigated the oral dosage and intestinal absorption of the type of iron used in its product, both in the population in general, and in women that match the target consumer of the product. Using this information, the firm has formulated its product to provide the amount of bioavailable iron needed by this population of women. Even though the firm did not test its product directly, it has examined the existing scientific literature and has formulated the product in a manner to meet the standards of products shown effective in well-controlled studies. There is, therefore, a basis to conclude that the existing literature is applicable to the product in the target population in which it is intended. Thus, the firm's claim that the product will be useful in correcting iron-deficiency anemia would likely be adequately substantiated.

Example 12: A firm claims that its multi-vitamin, multi-mineral product "provides the vitamins and minerals needed to promote good health and wellness." In this case, the firm's claim is likely substantiated by the substantial scientific evidence showing that certain vitamins and minerals are essential nutrients that are needed to maintain good health, even though the firm does not have data from specific scientific studies to show that its product results in any measurable outcome. Scientific evidence studying the firm's particular product formulation probably would not be needed for this claim unless the firm were to make claims that its formulation is different or superior to other formulations or confers benefits above and beyond the benefits demonstrated to be associated with adequate intake of vitamins and minerals.

D. The Quality of the Evidence

In deciding whether studies substantiate a claim, an important consideration is the scientific quality of studies. Scientific quality is based on several criteria including study population, study design and conduct (e.g., presence of a placebo control), data collection (e.g., dietary assessment method), statistical analysis, and outcome measures. For example, if the scientific study adequately addressed all or most of the above criteria, it could be considered of high quality. Generally accepted scientific and statistical principles should be used to determine the quality of the studies used as evidence to substantiate a claim. The "gold" standard is randomized, double blind, placebo-controlled trial design. However, trials of this type may not always be possible, practical, or ethical. There are several systems available to rate scientific information.[9] Firms making claims are encouraged to refer to these systems when developing substantiation for claims or relying on existing information. The following provides some commonly accepted scientific principles in evaluating the quality of scientific evidence.

---

9   See "Systems to Rate the Strength of Scientific Evidence. Evidence Report/Technology Assessment Number 47, "Agency for Healthcare Research and Quality and Research (AHRQ), Publication No. 02-E016, April 2002.

What Are the Types of Evidence that May Substantiate a Claim?

As a general principle, one should think about the type of evidence that would be sufficient to substantiate a claim in terms of what experts in the relevant area of study would consider to be competent and reliable. Competent and reliable scientific evidence adequate to substantiate a claim would consist of information derived primarily from human studies.

Human studies can be divided into two types: intervention studies and observational studies.[10] Of these types of studies, intervention studies can provide causal evidence to substantiate the effect of a dietary supplement in humans because they can evaluate the product's direct effect in the human body. Observational studies have a more limited ability than intervention studies to distinguish relationships between a substance and the outcomes being evaluated and cannot provide causal evidence.

- Intervention studies

  In intervention studies, an investigator controls whether the subjects receive the treatment or intervention of interest in order to test whether the intervention or treatment supports a pre-determined hypothesis. Firms should determine the hypothesis that should be supported or tested prior to identifying supportive documentation or developing a study protocol. Randomized, double blind, parallel group, placebo-controlled trials offer the greatest assessment of a relationship between a dietary supplement and an outcome. Although intervention studies are the most reliable studies for determining a cause-and-effect relationship, generalizing from such evidence on selected populations to different populations may not be scientifically valid. For example, as described in Example 10 above, if there is evidence to demonstrate a relationship in a specific population (elderly patients with diagnosed age-related memory problems), then such evidence should not be extrapolated to a different population (children).

- Observational studies

  In observational studies, the investigator does not have control over the exposure to the treatment or intervention of interest. In prospective observational studies, investigators recruit subjects and observe them before a particular outcome occurs. In retrospective observational studies, investigators review the records of subjects and interview subjects after the outcome has occurred. Retrospective studies are usually considered to be more vulnerable to recall bias (error that occurs when subjects are asked to remember past behaviors) and measurement error, but are less likely to require large sample size, cost, or encounter the ethical problems that may occur in prospective studies. Types of observational studies include:

  - Case reports, which describe observations of a single subject or a small number of subjects.

  - Case-series studies, which are a descriptive account of a series of "outcomes" observed over time and reported for a group of subjects. No control group is described.

---

10   See Spilker, B. *Guide to Clinical Trials*. Raven Press, New York, 1991.

CH 14

- Case-control studies, which compare subjects with a condition (cases) to subjects who do not have the same condition (controls). Subjects are enrolled based on their outcome rather than based on their exposure.

- Cohort studies, which compare the outcome of subjects who have been exposed to the substance to the outcome of subjects who have not been exposed.

- Cross-sectional (prevalence) studies, which compare, at a single point in time, the number of individuals with a condition who have been exposed to a substance to the number of individuals without the condition who were not exposed to the substance.

- Time-series studies, which compare outcomes during different time periods, e.g., whether the rate of occurrence of a particular outcome during one five-year period changed during a subsequent five-year period.

- Epidemiological studies, which compare the rate of a condition across different populations.

What types of information are useful as background to support a claim?

The following additional types of information would generally be considered background information, but alone may not be adequate to substantiate a claim.

- Animal studies - Animal studies may provide useful background on the biological effects of a substance. However, they often have limited or unknown value in predicting the effect of the substance in humans. Care should be exercised in extrapolating results obtained in animal research directly to the human condition. The strongest animal evidence is based on data from studies in appropriate animal models, on data that have been reproduced in different laboratories, and on data that give a statistically significant dose-response relationship. Without any data from human studies, the results of animal studies alone are not sufficient to substantiate a claim.

- In vitro studies are studies that are done outside a living body. For example, such studies might examine a product's effect on isolated cells or tissues. These studies are of limited value in predicting the effect of a substance when consumed by humans. The strongest in vitro evidence would be based on data that have been reproduced in different laboratories, but this evidence alone would not substantiate a claim.

- Testimonials and other anecdotal evidence - This type of evidence includes descriptions of experiences of individuals using a dietary supplement product or ingredient. It might also include descriptions of the use of the product or ingredient by others, for example, by other cultures in the past or present. It might consist of an opinion or statement of an expert or someone who endorses the product. Anecdotal evidence generally would not be sufficient to substantiate claims regarding a dietary supplement's effect because each individual's experience might be attributable to factors other than the dietary supplement itself. For example, a person might have experienced a placebo or coincidental effect, rather than an effect attributable to the

CH 14

dietary supplement itself. Additionally, the "honest opinion" of a consumer testimonial or an expert endorsement would not be enough to substantiate a claim; rather, the endorsement should also be supported by competent and reliable scientific evidence.

- Meta-analysis is the process of systematically combining and evaluating the results of clinical trials that have been completed or terminated. Meta-analysis may identify relevant reports, which may provide substantiation for the claim.

- Review articles summarize the findings of primary reports. Review articles may identify relevant primary reports, which may provide substantiation for the claim. Review articles may also provide background information that is useful to understand the scientific issues about the relationship between the substance and the claimed effect.

- Comments and Letters to the Editor usually focus on a particular issue or issues from a study, presentation at a meeting etc. Comments generally do not present the results of a study. Comments and letters to the editor may identify relevant primary reports, which may provide substantiation for the claim. Comments and letters to the editor may also provide background information that is useful to understand the scientific issues about the relationship between the substance and the claimed effect.

- Product monographs are prepared by the manufacturer to convey specific information about a product such as its specifications. Product monographs may provide background information that is useful to understand the scientific issues about the relationship between the substance and the claimed effect.

Example 13: A dietary supplement claim states, "Data suggest that including Substance X in the diet may promote brain neuron health in healthy individuals." The firm cites a study in which rats were fed diets containing Substance X and the brains of all rats were examined for ischemia-induced brain damage. The study does not provide a basis that Substance X would have the same effect on brain health in otherwise healthy humans. This study alone likely would not provide adequate substantiation of the claim being made because it relies solely on animal data.

Example 14: A dietary supplement claim states, "Grain Y has been used effectively for centuries to promote gastrointestinal health." The firm has no clinical studies in humans, but has an industry monograph that relies only on historical descriptions of grain Y use by pre-modern civilizations. Although the monograph may be an accurate review of the historical use of grain Y, it would likely not constitute competent and reliable evidence to support the claim because it is not based on objective scientific evidence. Rather, it is largely anecdotal evidence that cannot be objectively evaluated to determine if it applies to the consumers who would use the product.

Example 15: A dietary supplement label claims that, in laboratory tests (i.e., in vitro tests), the enzymes in the supplement can digest up to 20 grams of protein and 15 grams of dietary fat, and the firm is promoting the supplement to assist in breaking down protein and fat that its users eat. The firm has not tested its product or the ingredients in the supplement in humans. Although this evidence may be accurate, it would generally not be adequate

CH
14

substantiation for the claimed effects on dietary components because it is insufficient for reaching a conclusion on whether the enzymes, when consumed, would behave equivalently in the human body. Corroborating evidence from some human studies would likely be needed to determine if the in vitro findings reflect the outcomes of the product when consumed by humans.

Example 16: A botanical product label uses the claim "improves vitality." The substantiation that the firm is relying upon consists of testimonial experience it has collected from consumers and descriptions of the botanical product's traditional use. Although the firm may have testimonial experience to back up the basic claim being made, the claimed benefit would likely not be adequately substantiated because neither source is based on scientific evidence. If the firm wants to make a claim of this type, we recommend that it have scientific evidence that some measurable outcome(s) associated with the general conditions cited in the claim is (are) significantly improved.

What Design Factors Affect the Quality of a Study?

Multiple factors should be considered in study design. These include, but are not limited to:

▫ Bias, confounders, and other limitations - Potential sources of bias include lack of appropriate randomization and blinding, the number of subjects called for in the protocol vs. the number of subjects who actually participated in the trial, demographics, adequacy of primary variables, compliance, control agent, drop-outs, statistical procedures, subgroup analysis, safety issues, and reproducibility of results. Confounders are factors that are associated with the outcome in question and the intervention and prevent the measured outcome from being attributed unequivocally to the intervention. Potential confounders include variability in the quantity of the dietary supplement being administered or the presence of other dietary ingredients that may have their own independent effects. These factors can limit the reliability of the study.

▫ Quality assessment criteria - Factors that contribute to higher quality studies include:

  ▪ Adequacy and clarity of the design

    ▪ The questions to be answered by the study are clearly described at the outset.

    ▪ The methodology used in the study is clearly described and appropriate for answering the questions posed by the study.

    ▪ The duration of the study intervention or follow-up period is sufficient to detect an effect on the outcome of interest.

    ▪ Potential confounding factors are identified, assessed, and/or controlled.

    ▪ Subject attrition (subjects leaving the study before the study is completed) is assessed, explained, and reasonable.

  ▪ Population studied

CH 14

- The sample size is large enough to provide sufficient statistical power to detect a significant effect. (If the study is underpowered, it may be impossible to conclude that the absence of an effect is not due to chance.)

- The study population is representative (with respect to factors such as age, gender distribution, race, socioeconomic status, geographic location, family history, health status, and motivation) of the population to which the claim will be targeted.

- The criteria for inclusion and exclusion of study subjects were clearly stated and appropriate.

- The study used recruitment procedures that minimized selection bias.

- For controlled interventions, the subjects were randomized. If matching was employed to assign the subjects to control and treatment groups, appropriate demographic characteristics and other variables were used for the matching. The randomization was successful in producing similar control and intervention groups.

□ Assessment of intervention or exposure and outcomes

- The analytical methodology and quality control procedures to assess dietary intake are adequate.

- The dietary supplement serving size is well defined and appropriately measured.

- The background diets to which the dietary supplement was added, or the control and interventional diets, are adequately described, measured, and suitable.

- In studies with cross-over designs, the "wash-out" period (the period during which subjects do not receive an intervention) between dietary supplement exposures is appropriate. Lack of a sufficient wash-out period between interventions may lead to confusion as to which intervention produced the health outcome.

- The form and setting of the intervention are representative of the way the product will be normally used.

- Other possible, concurrent changes in diet or health-related behavior (weight loss, exercise, alcohol intake, and smoking cessation) present during the study that could account for the outcome identified are assessed and/or controlled.

- The study's outcomes are well defined and appropriately measured

- Efforts were made to detect harmful as well as beneficial effects.

□ Data Analysis and Assessment

- Appropriate statistical analyses were applied to the data.

- "Statistical significance" was interpreted appropriately.

- Relative and absolute effects were distinguished.

CH
14

□ Peer Review - The nature and quality of the written report of the research are also important. Although studies or evidence used to substantiate a claim do not have to be published in a peer-reviewed journal or publication, such publications do give some level of assurance that qualified experts have reviewed the research and found it to be of sufficient quality and validity to merit publication. In contrast, an abstract or informal summary of an article is less reliable, because such documents usually do not give the reader enough insight into how the research was conducted or how the data were analyzed to objectively evaluate the quality of the research data and the conclusions drawn by the authors. Moreover, the mere fact that the study was published does not necessarily mean that the research is competent and reliable evidence adequate to substantiate a particular claim.

Example 17: A dietary supplement label claims, "Randomized, double blind, placebo-controlled studies demonstrate that herbal extract 'Z' is beneficial in relieving menopausal symptoms." The firm is relying on the results of more than one randomized, double blind, placebo-controlled intervention study using menopausal women as subjects, and the results of those studies are in general agreement. The claim would likely be substantiated because it relies on high quality studies in humans that directly addressed conditions described in the claim.

E. Consider the Totality of the Evidence

How Well Does the Totality of Evidence Support the Claims?

In determining whether there is adequate evidence to substantiate a claim, one should consider the strength of the entire body of evidence, including criteria such as quality, quantity (number of various types of studies and sample sizes), relevance of exposure, and consistency and replication of the findings.

To determine whether the available scientific evidence is adequate to substantiate a claim, it is important to consider all relevant research, both favorable and unfavorable. Ideally, the evidence used to substantiate a claim agrees with the surrounding body of evidence. Conflicting or inconsistent results raise serious questions as to whether a particular claim is substantiated. If conflicts or inconsistencies exist in the scientific evidence, one should determine whether there are plausible explanations for such conflicts or inconsistencies. For example, an inconsistency between two studies might be attributable to different concentrations of the dietary supplement, different test methodologies, different study populations,[11] or other factors.

There is no general rule for how many studies, or what combination of types of evidence, is sufficient to support a claim. However, the replication of research results in independently conducted studies makes it more likely that the totality of the evidence will support a claim.

CH 14

---

11   For example, with respect to human drug products, it is fairly well known that children and the elderly may experience different drug effects compared to those seen in the adult population. These differences may be due to physiological differences (such as hormonal differences, differences in kidney function, etc.) between children, adults, and the elderly.

Although the quality of individual pieces of evidence is important, each piece should be considered in the context of all available information; that is, the strength of the total body of scientific evidence is the critical factor in assessing whether a claim is substantiated.

Example 18: A firm intends to promote an herbal product "X" to "help maintain cognitive performance" of people who are fatigued. The firm has researched the scientific literature and found many studies that demonstrate that the botanical ingredient is effective. However, there are some studies that demonstrate no effect. Still other studies examined the botanical ingredient combined with other ingredients, typically caffeine, which demonstrated mixed positive and negative results. Many reports do not adequately describe the study participants and products examined. Consequently, it is not possible to explain the disparate results. However, the firm's review suggests that either the botanical and/or caffeine are the most likely dietary ingredients that act to maintain better cognition test results in fatigued study participants. As a result, the firm conducts a large, randomized, placebo-controlled study to compare the botanical ingredient against caffeine in the treatment of cognitive performance deficits associated with fatigue. The results demonstrate that caffeine improved cognition test results in all of the fatigued subjects that received caffeine, while test performance was unaffected in all subjects receiving the botanical ingredient. The study cannot explain the results reported in the earlier studies; however, it demonstrates that the botanical ingredient studied is most likely ineffective for improving or maintaining cognitive performance in fatigued people.

Example 19: A firm plans to promote its herbal product "to effectively relieve occasional, nocturnal leg cramps." The firm has one study demonstrating the product to be effective in ameliorating nocturnal leg cramps. The firm is also aware of several other randomized controlled trials that do not show a benefit. All these studies are of equal quality and used similar patient populations and test materials. When considered as a whole, even though some evidence to support the claim exists, the totality of the evidence does not support the proposed claim. If no plausible explanation can be found to explain the disparate results, the available evidence would probably not be considered adequate to substantiate the claim.

Example 20: An herbal product is promoted "to help you get to sleep when you have difficulty falling asleep." The firm has one randomized, placebo-controlled study in volunteers who had trouble falling asleep. The study showed that those who used the product decreased the amount of time needed time to fall asleep. There are several other high-quality studies, however, that found that the herbal ingredient used in the product did not consistently help people get to sleep. It is not clear whether the different results of the various studies are a consequence of differences in product formulation or dosage or some other factor. Even though the firm's single study is positive, it may not provide adequate substantiation because the totality of existing evidence suggests that the herbal ingredient does not decrease time to fall asleep in persons who have trouble falling asleep. Given the contrary evidence against the claim, it is unlikely that this sleep-related claim would be substantiated for this product.

CH 14

Example 21: A company plans to promote its product containing ingredient X to athletes "to improve endurance performance." There are some well-designed published studies demonstrating that other products containing ingredient X are effective, but other well-designed studies show no effect for certain products containing ingredient X. The firm sponsored a randomized, blinded, six-month study comparing its product to four other products containing ingredient X in a dose (serving size)-response fashion. The findings demonstrate that the firm's product and two other products that provided the highest amount of ingredient X per day produced substantial, statistically significant improvements in athletic endurance. When the firm compared the results of this study to prior studies, the firm concluded that the explanation for previous conflicting study results is that when the serving size of ingredient X is below a certain amount, there is no measurable benefit. Taken together, the positive results from their study, and the identification of a plausible explanation to explain why some studies showed no positive effects, would likely provide evidence to substantiate adequately the endurance performance claim for the dietary supplement.

F. Conclusion

Section 403(r)(6) of the Act requires dietary supplement manufacturers to have substantiation that structure/function, nutrient deficiency, and general well-being claims on a dietary supplement product's labeling are truthful and not misleading. To meet this statutory requirement, we recommend that manufacturers possess adequate substantiation for each reasonable interpretation of the claims. We intend to apply a standard that is consistent with the FTC standard of "competent and reliable scientific evidence" to substantiate a claim. We consider the following factors important to establish whether information would constitute "competent and reliable scientific evidence:"

- Does each study or piece of evidence bear a relationship to the specific claim(s)?
- What are the individual study's or evidence's strengths and weaknesses? Consider the type of study, the design of the study, analysis of the results, and peer review.
- If multiple studies exist, do the studies that have the most reliable methodologies suggest a particular outcome?
- If multiple studies exist, what do most studies suggest or find? Does the totality of the evidence agree with the claim(s)?

III. Paperwork Reduction Act of 1995

This guidance contains information collections that are subject to review by the Office of Management and Budget (OMB) under the Paperwork Reduction Act of 1995 (44 U.S.C. 3501-3520).

Contains Nonbinding Recommendations
January 9, 2002

Guidance for Industry:
Structure/Function Claims; Small Entity Compliance Guide[1]

The Food and Drug Administration has prepared this Small Entity Compliance Guide in accordance with section 212 of the Small Business Regulatory Enforcement Fairness Act (P.L. 104-121). This guidance document restates in plain language the legal requirements set forth in a regulation concerning labeling claims for dietary supplements. This is a Level 2 guidance document published for immediate implementation in accordance with FDA's good guidance practices (21 CFR 10.115). The regulations are binding and have the force and effect of law. However, this guidance document represents the agency's current thinking on this subject and does not, itself, create or confer any rights for or on any person and does not operate to bind FDA or the public. An alternative approach may be used if such approach satisfies the requirements of the applicable statute and regulations.

Summary

On January 6, 2000, the Food and Drug Administration (FDA) published a final rule in the **Federal Register** defining the types of statements that may be used on the label and in the labeling of dietary supplements without prior review by the agency (65 FR 1000) (http://www.cfsan.fda. gov/~lrd/fr000106.html). Called structure/function claims, these claims are statements that describe the effect a dietary supplement may have on the structure or function of the body. The regulation also provides criteria to assist you in determining when a statement about a dietary supplement is a disease claim, that is, a claim to diagnose, cure, mitigate, treat, or prevent disease. Disease claims require prior approval by FDA and may be made only for products that are approved drug products or for foods under separate legal provisions that apply to claims called "health claims."

This guidance discusses only the requirements that apply to determining whether a claim is a structure/function claim or a disease claim. It should be noted that other regulations also cover labeling and packaging requirements for dietary supplements. These requirements were published as final rules in the Federal Registers of September 23, 1997 (62 FR 49826) (http://www.cfsan.fda.gov/~lrd/fr97923a.html) , June 5, 1998 (63 FR 30615) (http://www. fda.gov/ohrms/dockets/98fr/060598b.pdf), and Jan 15, 1997 (62 FR 2218) (access via (http:// www.access.gpo.gov/su_docs/aces/aces140.html) (see Title 21 of the Code of Federal Regulations (21 CFR) Parts 101 and 111).

CH
14

---

1   This guidance is available on the FDA website https://www.fda.gov/Food/GuidanceRegulation/ GuidanceDocumentsRegulatoryInformation/ucm103340.htm

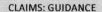

Questions & Answers

The regulation added §101.93(f) and (g) to Title 21 of the Code of Federal Regulations, Part 101. These two sections define what types of claims are structure/function claims and what types of claims are disease claims. In addition to these definitions, the regulation includes criteria that are intended to assist you in determining whether a particular statement is or is not a disease claim. Finally, the preamble to this rule clarifies several legal issues that are important to understand if you use structure/function claims on the labels or in the labeling of your products. They are restated below.

A. Basic Legal Requirements for Structure/Function Claims.

What are structure/function claims?

The Dietary Supplement Health and Education Act of 1994 (DSHEA) added section 403(r)(6) to the Federal Food, Drug, and Cosmetic Act (FD&C Act). This section of the law states that a dietary supplement may bear certain statements on its label or in its labeling if the claim meets certain requirements. Section 101.93(f) simply restates part of the definition of the types of claims that may be made under section 403(r)(6) of the FD&C Act. Section 101.93(f) reads:

> (f) *Permitted structure/function statements.* Dietary supplement labels or labeling may, subject to the requirements in paragraphs (a) through (e) of this section, bear statements that describe the role of a nutrient or dietary ingredient intended to affect the structure or function in humans or that characterize the documented mechanism by which a nutrient or dietary ingredient acts to maintain such structure or function, provided that such statements are not disease claims under paragraph (g) of this section. If the label or labeling of a product marketed as a dietary supplement bears a disease claim as defined in paragraph (g) of this section, the product will be subject to regulation as a drug unless the claim is an authorized health claim for which the product qualifies.

Are there other claims that can be made for dietary supplements under this section of the law?

Yes. Section 403(r)(6) also states that dietary supplements can use claims about nutrient deficiency diseases (for example, vitamin C and scurvy) or that describe the effect of the dietary supplement on general well-being.

What requirements must I meet to make any of these types of claims for my dietary supplement?

There are three requirements you must meet. First, the law says you can make these claims if you have substantiation that the claims are truthful and not misleading. You must have this substantiation before you make the claims. Second, you must notify FDA that you are using the claim within 30 days of first marketing your product. Third, the claim must include a mandatory disclaimer statement that is provided for in the law.

Where can I find information on the mandatory disclaimer and the notification I need to send in?

We have published regulations that describe exactly what the disclaimer must say and what you must include in your notification to us and where you must send it in the September 23, 1997 **Federal Register** (62 FR 49859 and 49883, respectively). These requirements can be found in 21 CFR 101.93(b) through (e) and 21 CFR 101.93(a), respectively.

B. When and What You Must Do To Comply With the New Regulation.

When does this rule become effective?

The rule became effective on February 7, 2000, for any products marketed for the first time after publication of the final rule or for any new claims made for an existing product after publication of the final rule (i.e., new claims made after January 6, 2000).

If I have existing inventory, do I need to re-label it now?

Large businesses had until January 7, 2001, to bring existing claims on products into compliance. FDA granted this period for firms to use up their label inventories. Small businesses had until July 7, 2001, to bring existing claims on products into compliance. Any existing inventory not used up after these dates would need to be relabeled.

C. How Do I Determine if a Claim is a Structure/Function Claim or a Disease Claim?

It may not be possible always to draw a bright line between structure/function and disease claims. You should look at the objective evidence in your labeling to assess whether a claim explicitly or implicitly is a disease claim. For example, a statement may not mention a disease but may refer to identifiable characteristic signs or symptoms of a disease such that the intended use of the product to treat or prevent the disease may be inferred. It is important that you keep in mind two things. First, the context of the statement, decided from information on the label and in other labeling, will determine if the statement is considered to be a disease claim. Second, dietary supplements may not bear disease claims, explicit or implied, unless the claim has undergone premarket review by FDA and has been authorized or approved under the rules for health claims or drugs, as appropriate. To assist you in deciding whether a claim is or isn't a disease claim, the new regulation contains a definition for disease, and then includes 10 criteria intended to help clarify the types of claims that may be made for dietary supplements without prior authorization or approval by FDA. We are providing that disease definition and an explanation of the 10 criteria below.

What is the definition of a disease?

Section 101.93(g) defines disease as:

> ...damage to an organ, part, structure, or system of the body such that it does not function properly (e.g., cardiovascular disease), or a state of health leading to such dysfunctioning (e.g., hypertension); except that diseases resulting from essential nutrient deficiencies (e.g., scurvy, pellagra) are not included in this definition.

What are the criteria for determining if a statement is a disease claim?

There are 10 criteria in the rule that are useful in determining if a statement is a disease claim.

CH
14

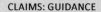

Criterion 1: Claims an effect on a disease or class of diseases (see section E, starting on page 1012 of the preamble to the rule).

A statement is a disease claim if it mentions a specific disease or class of diseases. For example, a claim that a product is "protective against the development of cancer" or "reduces the pain and stiffness associated with arthritis" would be a disease claim.

A statement also is a disease claim if it implies that it has an effect on a specific disease or class of diseases by using descriptions of the disease state. Examples of implied disease claims are "relieves crushing chest pain (angina)," "improves joint mobility and reduces inflammation (rheumatoid arthritis)," or "relief of bronchospasm (asthma)."

Criterion 2: Claims an effect on characteristic signs or symptoms of disease using scientific or lay terminology (see section F, starting on page 1015 of the preamble to the rule).

How can I tell if a particular claimed effect is a sign or symptom of a specific disease?

The test of whether claimed effects are characteristic signs or symptoms depends on 2 questions: (1) Is the condition, to which the signs and symptoms refer, related to a disease; and (2) are the signs and symptoms referred to in the labeling characteristic of the disease and permit the inference that the product is intended to affect that disease.

Does it matter if I don't use every sign or symptom of a condition or if I use layman's terms instead of technical language?

No. The standard focuses on whether the labeling suggests that the product will produce a change in a set of one or more signs or symptoms that are characteristic of the disease. You can meet this standard using technical or layman's language and it isn't necessary that every possible sign or symptom is used.

How can I determine if a claim is about a sign or symptom that is "characteristic" of a disease?

You can look to medical texts and other objective sources of information about disease to determine if a label statement implies treatment or prevention of a disease. Some claims imply disease treatment or prevention because they are so intimately tied to a disease. For example, "inhibits platelet aggregation" or "reduces cholesterol" are such characteristic signs or symptoms associated with stroke and cardiovascular disease and interventions to treat those diseases that any claim about them would be an implied disease claim.

Other signs or symptoms are associated with a wide range of disease and non-disease states and do not necessarily imply an effect on a specific disease. For example, although "improves absentmindedness" might imply treatment of Alzheimer's disease and "relieves stress and frustration" might imply treatment of anxiety disorders, both of these signs also are characteristic of non-disease states. So, if there is no context linking them to a disease, they would be appropriate structure/function claims.

CH 14

For the claims that always imply disease, is there context that can make them appropriate structure/function claims, since platelet function and blood cholesterol also may be considered to be normal conditions?

Yes. There are many conditions that are "normal," but under certain circumstances are also disease claims. The rule states that such claims (for example, maintaining normal cholesterol levels) may be appropriate structure/function claims and would not imply a disease if the claim made absolutely clear that the claim is referring to structure/function claims that are already normal. This context would remove the inference to an effect on a structure/function that was abnormal (for example, "maintain cholesterol levels that are already in the normal range").

What kinds of words can be used that would not constitute implied claims about signs or symptoms?

No specific adjectives constitute a disease claim. Therefore, words such as "restore," "support," "maintain," "raise," "lower," "promote," "regulate," or "stimulate" might create an implied disease claim if, in the context they are used, they imply an effect on disease. Similarly, words like "prevent," "mitigate," "diagnose," "cure," or "treat" would be disease claims if the context of their use implied an effect on a disease.

Criterion 3: Claims an effect on a condition associated with a natural state or process (see section G, starting on page 1019 of the preamble to the rule).

What is meant by "a natural state or process?"

Some natural states or processes such as aging, menopause, and the menstrual cycle are not themselves diseases, but can be associated with abnormal conditions that are diseases.

What is the determining characteristic when a claim to effect these states is a disease claim?

The conditions associated with these stages or processes can vary from common, relatively mild abnormalities, for which medical attention is not required, to serious conditions that can cause significant or permanent harm if not treated effectively. Two criteria determine if such a condition will be considered a disease: (1) if the condition is uncommon; or (2) if the condition can cause significant or permanent harm. For purposes of the rule, a condition is uncommon if it occurs in fewer than one-half of those experiencing that stage or process. A condition can cause significant or permanent harm if it must be treated effectively to prevent that harm and for which effective treatments are available.

Examples of acceptable structure/function claims are "mild memory loss associated with aging," "noncystic acne," or "mild mood changes, cramps, and edema associated with the menstrual cycle."

Examples of disease claims are "Alzheimer's disease or senile dementias in the elderly," "cystic acne," or "severe depression associated with the menstrual cycle."

CH 14

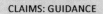
Criterion 4: It is an implied disease claim because of the product name, formulation, use of pictures, or other factors (see sections H through M, starting on page 1021 of the preamble to the rule).

1. Claims that are the name of the product.

Two principles form the basis for the distinction between product names that are structure/function claims and those that are disease claims. To be a structure/ function claim: (1) the name should not contain the name, or a recognizable portion of the name, of a disease; and (2) the name should not use terms such as "cure," "treat," "correct," "prevent," or other terms that suggest treatment or prevention of a disease. Additionally, context is very important here.

Names such as "CarpalHealth" or "CircuCure" are disease claims because they are implied disease claims for carpal tunnel syndrome and circulatory disorders, respectively. In some cases, whether a product name is a disease claim will depend on context. For example, "Soothing Sleep" could be considered a claim to treat insomnia, a disease, unless other context in the labeling makes clear that the claim relates to a non-disease condition, such as occasional sleeplessness.

2. Claims about product formulation.

Can I claim that my product contains an ingredient that is also used in some drug products?

If the ingredient has been regulated by FDA primarily as a drug (either over-the-counter or prescription) and is well known to consumers for its use or claimed use in preventing or treating a disease, you have made an implied disease claim when you list it in the ingredient list or make a claim that a product contains that ingredient. For example, aspirin, digoxin, and laetrile. Of course, an ingredient that is excluded from the definition of a dietary supplement under section 201(ff)(3) of the FD&C Act because it was approved as a drug before being marketed as a dietary supplement never can be used in a supplement.

3. Claims that use citations of publication titles.

Can I use citations of publications that relate to my product's intended use in labeling if the publication title or the journal name mentions a disease name?

Yes, but some limitations apply. If the citation implies treatment or prevention of a disease, it is a disease claim. Thus, if in the context of the labeling as a whole its presence implies treatment or prevention of disease (for example, by placement on the immediate product label or packaging, inappropriate prominence, or lack of relationship to the product's express claims), the citation is a disease claim.

If the citation is used in labeling, its context determines if it is a disease claim. A citation that is used in the bibliography section of labeling, is included in a balanced discussion of the scientific literature, is not excessively prominent relative to other citations, and provides legitimate support for a structure/function claim made for the product would not be a disease claim.

4. Claims that use the term "disease" or "diseased."

Can I make claims about health promotion and disease prevention?

Yes, you may make general statements about health promotion and disease prevention as long as the statement doesn't imply that your product can diagnose, cure, mitigate, treat, or prevent a disease. In general, if the statement identifies a specific disease or directly references the product or its ingredients, it would imply that the product itself has the effect and would be a disease claim.

An example of an acceptable claim is "a good diet promotes good health and prevents the onset of disease" or "better dietary and exercise patterns can contribute to disease prevention and better health."

An example of a disease claim is "Promotes good health and prevents the onset of disease" because the claim infers that the product itself will achieve the intended effect.

5. Use of pictures, vignettes, symbols, or other means.

Can I use pictures of organs or medical symbols on labels?

In general, any picture or vignette or other symbol can be used if it doesn't imply a disease. For example, pictures of healthy organs would constitute an appropriate structure/function claim while a picture of an abnormal tissue or organ would be an implied disease claim. As with other types of implied claims, it is the context of the total claim that is important.

Are there some symbols that are implied disease claims?

Yes. Some symbols, like the heart symbol, are so widely recognized as symbols for disease treatment and prevention that their use is ordinarily an implied disease claim. Symbols such as EKG tracings are also implied disease claims because they are strongly associated with heart disease and the average consumer cannot distinguish a healthy tracing from an unhealthy one to provide context to remove the implied disease treatment or prevention claim. It would be an unusual circumstance in which the use of these two symbols would not be implied disease claims.

Can the Rx symbol be used without implying that the product is intended to treat disease?

In general, the use of the prescription drug symbol "Rx" or the use of the word "prescription" should not be interpreted automatically as a disease claim because not all prescription drugs are intended for disease conditions (some are for conditions that would not be considered to be diseases). However, the use of these terms on dietary supplements may deceive consumers into thinking they are purchasing a prescription drug without a prescription. Thus, the use of these two terms is misleading and will misbrand the product if, in the context of the labeling as a whole, the terms imply that the product is a prescription drug.

CH
14

Criterion 5: Claims that a product belongs to a class of products that is intended to diagnose, mitigate, treat, cure, or prevent a disease (see section N, starting on page 1026 of the preamble to the rule).

Certain product class names are so strongly associated with treating and preventing diseases that claiming membership in the product class constitutes a disease claim. Examples of such product classes are analgesics, antibiotics, antidepressants, antimicrobials, antiseptics, antivirals, or vaccines.

However, some product classes may be associated both with diseases and with structure/function effects. In such cases, if it is clear from the context of the claim that the dietary supplement is represented as a member of the product class intended to affect structure/function and not disease, then the claim will not be a disease claim. That is, claiming to be a laxative, an anti-inflammatory, or a diuretic will not be a disease claim if there is context that makes clear that the intended effect of the product is on structure/function and not disease. For example, an appropriate product claim would be "diuretic that relieves temporary water-weight gain."

Criterion 6: Claims to be a substitute for a product that is a therapy for a disease (see section O, starting on page 1027 of the preamble to the rule).

A claim that a product is a substitute for a drug or other therapy for disease, or has fewer side effects than a therapy for disease, is an implied disease claim. Such claims carry with them the clear implication that the dietary supplement is intended for the same disease treatment or prevention purpose as the therapeutic product. However, if a dietary supplement claims to be a substitute for a drug that is not intended to treat or prevent disease (i.e., a drug intended to affect the structure or function of the body), the claim comparing the drug and the dietary supplement would not be a disease claim.

Criterion 7: Claims to augment a therapy or drug intended to diagnose, mitigate, treat, cure, or prevent a disease (see section P, starting on page 1028 of the preamble to the rule).

A claim that a dietary supplement will augment a particular therapy or drug action that is intended to diagnose, mitigate, treat, cure, or prevent disease is a disease claim. A dietary supplement may state that it is useful in providing nutritional support, as long as that claim doesn't imply disease. In general, mentioning the name of a specific therapy, drug, or drug action will associate the claim with the intended use of the therapy, drug, or drug action and be a disease claim.

Criterion 8: Has a role in the body's response to a disease or to a vector of disease (see section Q, starting on page 1028 of the preamble to the rule).

A claim that a dietary supplement fights disease or enhances disease-fighting functions of the body is a disease claim. Under this criterion, context and specificity are important. Claims such as "supports the body's ability to resist infection" and "supports the body's antiviral capabilities" are disease claims because the context of the claim is limited to the disease prevention and treatment capabilities. However, a claim that a product "supports the immune system" is not specific enough to imply prevention of disease because the immune system has both structure/function and disease fighting roles. A general claim of this type doesn't specifically focus the intended use of the product on the disease aspect of the system's function.

Criterion 9: Claims to treat, prevent, or mitigate adverse events associated with a therapy for a disease (see section R, starting on page 1029 of the preamble to the rule).

A claim that a product will affect adverse events associated with a therapy for disease is a disease claim if the adverse event is itself a disease. For example, "to maintain the intestinal flora in people on antibiotics" is a disease claim because the claim implies that the product will prevent pathogenic bacterial overgrowth (a disease condition) associated with antibiotic use. If the adverse event is not a disease, then this type of claim is acceptable. For example, a claim that a product is useful because it counterbalances the effect of a drug in depleting a nutrient or interfering with the metabolism of a nutrient would be an acceptable structure/function claim.

Criterion 10: Otherwise suggests an effect on a disease or diseases (see section S, starting on page 1029 of the preamble to the rule).

This provision of the regulation is intended to allow for implied disease claims that may not fit into the other nine criteria. This provision recognizes that a claim may be a disease claim based on its wording or on the context in which the claim appears on the product's label or labeling, even if not covered by the other nine criteria.

CH 14

Contains Nonbinding Recommendations
June 11, 1998
OMB Control No. 0910-0374
Expiration Date: 04/30/2018

Guidance for Industry[1]:
Notification of a Health Claim or Nutrient Content Claim Based on an Authoritative Statement of a Scientific Body[2]

Prior to the Food and Drug Administration Modernization Act of 1997 (FDAMA), companies could not use a health claim or nutrient content claim in food labeling unless the Food and Drug Administration (FDA) published a regulation authorizing such a claim. Two new provisions of FDAMA (specifically sections 303 and 304 which amend, respectively, sections 403(r)(3) and 403(r)(2) (21 U.S.C. 343(r)(3) and (2)) of the Food, Drug, and Cosmetic Act, known as the Act) will now permit distributors and manufacturers to use claims if such claims are based on current, published, authoritative statements from certain federal scientific bodies, as well as from the National Academy of Sciences. These provisions are intended to expedite the process by which the scientific basis for such claims is established.

Since the passage of FDAMA, FDA has been reviewing both the statute and the accompanying legislative history in order to determine the most appropriate approach for implementing these new provisions. Due to the speed with which the FDAMA provisions became effective, the agency has decided to issue this guidance document during the initial phase of implementing these new provisions.

Submission procedures and use of a public docket for claims

Notifications should be submitted in duplicate to Center for Food Safety and Applied Nutrition, 5100 Paint Branch Parkway, College Park, MD 20740 or by email at label.claims@cfsan.fda.gov. The notification should be clearly marked as "Notification for a Health Claim (or Nutrient Content Claim) Based on an Authoritative Statement." Whether notifications will be placed in a public docket upon receipt will be addressed in notice and comment rulemaking for an implementing regulation.

When a notification is received, FDA intends to review whether the notification includes the

**CH
14**

---

1   This guidance has been prepared by the Office of Food Labeling in the Center for Food Safety and Applied Nutrition at the Food and Drug Administration. This guidance represents the Agency's current thinking on the procedures for a firm to notify FDA of their intent to use a health claim or nutrient content claim based on an authoritative statement of a scientific body. It does not create or confer any rights for or on any person and does not operate to bind FDA or the public. An alternative approach may be used if such approach satisfies the requirement of the applicable statute, regulations, or both.
2   This guidance is available on the FDA website at https://www.fda.gov/Food/GuidanceRegulation/GuidanceDocumentsRegulatoryInformation/ucm056975.htm

information necessary for the claim to be authorized under sections 303 and 304 of FDAMA. This may include, for example, a review for the submission of all the required elements and the identification of an appropriate statement from an appropriate scientific body (as identified below). The agency intends to notify the submitter by letter as soon as possible within the 120 days after submission when the notification does not comply with sections 303 and 304. When a notification does not meet the requirements of sections 303 and 304, the use of the claim is not authorized under FDAMA. The submitter may choose to revise the notification and resubmit it, in which case a food could not be marketed with the claim until at least 120 days after resubmission. As provided by FDAMA, FDA also may act to prohibit or modify a claim by regulation or a United States district court may find that the requirements of section 303 or 304 of FDAMA have not been met.

Scientific body

FDAMA permits claims based on current, published authoritative statements from "a scientific body of the United States with official responsibility for public health protection or research directly related to human nutrition . . . or the National Academy of Sciences (NAS) or any of its subdivisions." The National Institutes of Health (NIH) and the Centers for Disease Control and Prevention (CDC) are federal government agencies specifically identified as scientific bodies by FDAMA.

FDA believes that other federal agencies may also qualify as appropriate sources for such authoritative statements. Along with NAS (or any of its subdivisions), the agency currently considers that the following federal scientific bodies may be sources of authoritative statements: the CDC, the NIH, and the Surgeon General within Department of Health and Human Services; and the Food and Nutrition Service, the Food Safety and Inspection Service, and the Agricultural Research Service within the Department of Agriculture.

Authoritative statement

FDA also believes it is necessary to clarify what constitutes an authoritative statement under FDAMA. FDAMA itself states that an authoritative statement: (1) is "about the relationship between a nutrient and a disease or health-related condition" for a health claim, or "identifies the nutrient level to which the claim refers" for a nutrient content claim, (2) is "published by the scientific body" (as identified above), (3) is "currently in effect," and (4) "shall not include a statement of an employee of the scientific body made in the individual capacity of the employee."

In addition, given the legislative history of sections 303 and 304 of FDAMA, FDA currently believes authoritative statements also should: (5) reflect a consensus within the identified scientific body if published by a subdivision of one of the Federal scientific bodies, and (6) be based on a deliberative review by the scientific body of the scientific evidence.

Not all pronouncements by the designated scientific bodies would meet these criteria. For example, authoritative statements by the Surgeon General would normally be found only in the Surgeon General Reports.

CH
14

FDA intends to consult, as appropriate, with the scientific body that is the source of a statement cited as the basis for a claim, as well as with the other federal scientific bodies that have public health responsibilities and expertise relative to the claim. The agency has already begun this liaison process.

Scientific standard with respect to health claims

FDAMA upholds the "significant scientific agreement" standard for health claims. This conclusion is based on FDAMA and its legislative history. FDAMA provides that FDA may issue a regulation under section 403(r)(3)(B)(i) of the Act to prohibit or modify a claim. Section 403(r)(3)(B)(i) permits FDA to promulgate regulations authorizing health claims only if FDA "determines, based on the totality of publicly available scientific evidence (including evidence from well-designed studies conducted in a manner which is consistent with generally recognized scientific procedures and principles), that there is significant scientific agreement among experts qualified by scientific training and experience to evaluate such claims, that the claim is supported by such evidence."

Consistent with this provision, FDA intends to determine whether the standard of significant scientific agreement is met by a health claim based on an authoritative statement. And consistent with earlier regulations, FDA does not believe this standard would allow for a claim based on, for example, findings characterized as preliminary results, statements that indicate research is inconclusive, or statements intended to guide future research.

Content of notification and other statutory requirements

FDAMA requires that a person must submit a notification of the claim at least 120 days before the first introduction into interstate commerce of the food with a label containing the claim. FDA notes that, as indicated by FDAMA, the notification is to include: (1) "the exact words used in the claim," (2) "a concise description of the basis upon which such person relied for determining that the requirements" for an authoritative statement "have been satisfied," (3) "a copy of the statement referred to . . . upon which such person relied in making the claim," and (4) for a health claim, "a balanced representation of the scientific literature relating to the relationship between a nutrient and a disease or health-related condition to which the claim refers," or, for a nutrient content claim, "a balanced representation of the scientific literature relating to the nutrient level to which the claim refers."

FDA expects that to provide a "balanced representation of the scientific literature," a bibliography of the scientific literature on the topic of the claim would be compiled. A brief, balanced account or analysis of how this literature either supports or fails to support the authoritative statement should be submitted.

FDAMA imposes several additional conditions on claims based on authoritative statements and the foods for which such claims are made. For example, FDAMA requires that such a claim be "stated in a manner so that the claim is an accurate representation of the authoritative statement referred to" and "so that the claim enables the public to comprehend the information provided in the claim and to understand the relative significance of such information in the context of a total daily diet."

FDAMA requires, with respect to health claims, that the food for which such a claim is made not exceed the disqualifying amounts of nutrients that may increase the risk of a disease or health-related condition in the general population. FDAMA also requires, for example, that nutrient content claims use the terms already defined in regulations by the agency, in, e.g., Title 21, Code of Federal Regulations (CFR) sections 101.13 and 101.54. Finally, FDAMA requires that a claim based on an authoritative statement, with the food for which the claim is made, not be false or misleading in any particular.

Under FDAMA, persons submitting notifications must include "the exact words used in the claim." Submitted health claims should use the word "may" to characterize the relationship between the nutrient and the disease or health related condition so as to indicate that the disease or health-related condition is caused by many factors. Likewise, a claim for a health effect attributed to a single brand name product would be misleading. Foods bearing health claims based on authoritative statements should comply with the provisions of 21 CFR 101.14. These include, for example, requirements that the substance that is the subject of a claim is safe and lawful and that its level is sufficiently high and in an appropriate form to justify the claim.

A nutrient content claim based on an authoritative statement that uses terms the agency has defined, such as "good source" or "high," must, under FDAMA, refer to a nutrient level (i.e., a daily value) that is identified by the authoritative statement. In addition, foods bearing such nutrient content claims should comply with 21 CFR 101.13.

To ensure that compliance with all relevant regulations can be assessed, the FDA believes that information on analytical methodology for the nutrient that is the subject of a claim should be submitted as part of the notification, consistent with 21 CFR 101.69 and 21 CFR 101.70.

Dietary Supplements

Finally, FDA believes that there is need for further consideration concerning dietary supplements. FDAMA does not provide for health claims based on authoritative statements for dietary supplements. This is because FDAMA amended the section of the Act that deals with procedures and standards for health claims for conventional foods, but did not amend the section that deals with procedures and standards for health claims for dietary supplements. That is, section 403(r)(3) of the Act specifies the procedure and standard by which health claims may be made for conventional foods. Section 403(r)(5)(D) specifies that health claims with respect to dietary supplements shall not be subject to section 403(r)(3), but rather to a procedure and standard established by regulation by FDA. Section 303 of FDAMA amended section 403(r)(3) of the Act to allow for health claims based on authoritative statements, but did not address section 403(r)(5)(D).

The FDA intends to propose that health claims based on authoritative statements be permitted for dietary supplements.

In contrast, with respect to nutrient content claims, FDAMA amended section 403(r)(2) of the Act, which applies to both conventional foods and dietary supplements. Thus, dietary supplements may make nutrient content claims based upon authoritative statements in accordance with FDAMA and the applicable regulations for nutrient content claims, and the contents of this guidance document would apply.

CH 14

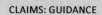

Paperwork Reduction Act of 1995

This guidance contains information collections that are subject to review by the Office of Management and Budget (OMB) under the Paperwork Reduction Act of 1995 (44 U.S.C. 3501-3520).

Federal Register Notice: June 11, 1998

Contains Nonbinding Recommendations
May 12, 2006

Guidance for Industry:
FDA's Implementation of "Qualified Health Claims": Questions and Answers; Final Guidance[1]

Background

1. Why is FDA providing for "qualified" health claims?

Through the Better Nutrition Information for Consumer Health Initiative (see Consumer Health Information for Better Nutrition Initiative, issued July 10, 2003), FDA acknowledged that consumers benefit from more information on food labels concerning diet and health. As part of this initiative, the agency established interim procedures whereby "qualified" health claims can be made not only for dietary supplements but for conventional foods as well (see Interim Procedures for Qualified Health Claims in the Labeling of Conventional Human Food and Human Dietary Supplements). Moreover, past court decisions have clarified the need to provide for health claims based on less science evidence rather than just on the standard of significant scientific agreement (SSA), as long as the claims do not mislead the consumers. FDA began considering qualified health claims under its interim procedures on September 1, 2003.

2. What are the similarities and differences between SSA health claims established under the 1993 regulations and the newer "qualified" health claims?

Both types of health claims characterize a relationship between a substance (specific food component or a specific food) and a disease (e.g., lung cancer or heart disease) or health-related condition (e.g., high blood pressure), and are supported by scientific evidence (see 21 CFR 101.14). Health claims generally undergo review by FDA through a petition process. All SSA health claims as provided for by Congress in 1990 (see Significant Scientific Agreement in the Review of Health Claims for Conventional Foods and Dietary Supplements) must meet the SSA standard. Past court decisions resulting in qualified health claims on dietary supplements focused on whether a manufacturer could make statements about diet/disease relationships when the science supporting the claim did not meet the significant scientific agreement standard, provided that the claim about the relationship was stated or "qualified" in such a way as to not mislead consumers. Thus, qualified health claims differ from SSA health claims in that they must be accompanied by a disclaimer or otherwise qualified.

CH
14

---

1   This guidance is available on the FDA website at https://www.fda.gov/Food/GuidanceRegulation/ GuidanceDocumentsRegulatoryInformation/ucm053843.htm

3. Why are the procedures for qualified health claims "interim"?

FDA believes that more information is needed before the agency can establish final procedures to provide for qualified health claims, and therefore issued an Advanced Notice of Proposed Rulemaking (ANPR) to solicit comments on the agency's options. FDA has and continues to conduct research in order to obtain information about appropriate qualifying language for use with the claims and the extent to which consumers can understand different levels of supporting science. The agency is also interested in knowing if there are better formats for presenting the supporting science than through the use of words alone.

The interim procedures for qualified health claims are available on the FDA website in the form of two documents: Interim Procedures for Qualified Health Claims in the Labeling of Conventional Human Food and Human Dietary Supplements (see Interim Procedures for Qualified Health Claims in the Labeling of Conventional Human Food and Human Dietary Supplements) and Interim Guidance for Evidence-based Ranking System for Scientific Data (see Interim Evidence-based Ranking System for Scientific Data).

4. Will rulemaking for qualified health claims take place?

FDA is currently considering various options regarding the development of proposed regulations related to qualified health claims. In the meantime, the agency plans to review qualified health claim petitions on a case-by-case basis to determine whether to issue a letter concerning the use of enforcement discretion for a qualified health claim or to deny the qualified health claim (Consumer Health Information for Better Nutrition Initiative).

5. What is a letter of enforcement discretion?

A letter of enforcement discretion is a letter issued by FDA to the petitioner specifying the nature of the qualified health claim for which FDA intends to consider the exercise of its enforcement discretion. If a letter of enforcement discretion has been issued, FDA does not intend to object to the use of the claim specified in the letter, provided that the products that bear the claim are consistent with the stated criteria.

All letters of enforcement discretion will be posted on the FDA website. Once the letter is posted on the website, all manufacturers will have notice about how the agency intends to exercise its enforcement discretion on the use of the qualified health claim.

6. How are health claims different from structure/function claims?

Both SSA and qualified health claims characterize the relationship between a substance and its ability to reduce the risk of a disease or health-related condition (see 21 CFR 101.14). Structure/function claims describe the effect that a substance has on the structure or function of the body and do not make reference to a disease. An example of a structure/function claim is "Calcium builds strong bones." Structure/function claims must be truthful and not misleading and are not pre-reviewed or authorized by FDA. [21 U.S.C. 343(r)(6); 21 CFR 101.93]

CH 14

7. How are health claims different from statements about dietary guidance?

Health claims characterize a relationship between a substance (specific food or food component) and a disease or health-related condition (see 21 CFR 101.14). Both elements of 1) a substance and 2) a disease are present in a health claim. Dietary guidance does not contain both elements (and therefore does not constitute a health claim (see 58 FR 2478 at 2487; January 6, 1993), but may contain one element or another. Typically, dietary guidance statements make reference to a category of foods (i.e., a grouping that is not readily characterized compositionally) and not to a specific substance. The following illustrations may be helpful:

Two examples of an authorized health claim, which by definition must contain the elements of a substance and a disease or health-related condition, are: "Diets low in sodium may reduce the risk of high blood pressure, a disease associated with many factors" and "Diets low in saturated fat and cholesterol that include 25 grams of soy protein a day may reduce the risk of heart disease".

An example of dietary guidance, which does not refer to a specific substance but rather refers to a broad class of foods without an expressed or implied connection to a specific substance that is present the class of foods is: "Diets rich in fruits and vegetables may reduce the risk of some types of cancer". One element is present, but not both. It is not a health claim because it cannot reasonably be understood to be about a specific substance.

A dietary guidance statement that refers to a specific food or food component but not a disease or health-related condition is: "Carrots are good for your health, " or "Calcium is good for you." Again, one element is present, but not both.

8. How is dietary guidance provided for on food labels?

Truthful, non-misleading dietary guidance statements may be used on food labels, and do not undergo pre-review by FDA. However, once the food is marketed with the statement, FDA can consider whether the statement meets the requirement to be truthful and not misleading (see 21 CFR 101.14).

FDA, as part of its recent Better Nutrition Information for Consumer Health Initiative, recognized that scientifically sound and non-misleading dietary guidance statements may be useful to consumers when placed on food labels.

Procedures for Qualified Health Claims

9. What are the regulatory procedures associated with qualified health claims?

All health claims, whether SSA or qualified, require that a petition be submitted to FDA. The requirements for health claim petitions are specified in 21 CFR 101.70, and the general requirements for health claims are in 21 CFR 101.14. Both types of health claims can be applicable to conventional foods and dietary supplements, must characterize the substance's ability to reduce the risk of disease, and cannot be about mitigating or treating disease.

CH
14

Qualified health claims have differences that relate to scientific support, wording of the claim, use of enforcement discretion, and timelines.

10. How is the science supporting a qualified health claim different from that for an SSA health claim?

SSA health claims require significant scientific agreement based on the totality of publicly available scientific evidence (see 21 CFR 101.14). Qualified health claims are still based on the totality of publicly available evidence but the scientific support does not have to be as strong as that for significant scientific agreement. Under its interim guidance (see Interim Evidence-based Ranking System for Scientific Data), FDA is tentatively providing for 3 levels of science below the Significant Scientific Agreement standard: good to moderate level of scientific agreement, low level of scientific agreement, and very low level of scientific agreement. The criteria for the scientific review are described in the interim guidance.

11. How the language for qualified health claims is different?

Qualified health claims language must be worded ("qualified") in such a way that consumers are not misled about the nature of the supporting science. As part of its interim guidance (see Interim Evidence-based Ranking System for Scientific Data), FDA has specified qualifying language for the 3 levels of scientific support below the Significant Scientific Agreement standard. FDA also notes that it may consider other qualifying language on a case-by-case basis.

12. How do the regulatory procedures for qualified health claims differ from SSA health claims?

Petitions requesting an SSA health claim are evaluated under the Significant Scientific Agreement standard (see Significant Scientific Agreement in the Review of Health Claims for Conventional Foods and Dietary Supplements). If FDA decides that standard is met, it authorizes the claim through notice-and-comment rulemaking.

Petitions requesting a qualified health claim are posted on the FDA web page for a 60-day public comment period. Qualified health claims meeting the interim procedures criteria are provided for by letters of enforcement discretion (as described above). The letter of enforcement discretion will be posted on the FDA web page. Petitions for a qualified health claim that have no credible scientific evidence for the claim may be denied. These letters will be posted on FDA's website.

13. What is the procedural timeline for qualified health claims?

- Within 15 days of receipt, FDA will acknowledge the petition.
- Within 45 days of receipt, FDA will file the petition and a docket number will be assigned. Note: Petitions that do not meet content requirements as specified in 21 CFR 101.70 will not be filed and will be returned to the petitioner.
- At the time of filing, FDA will post the petition on the FDA webpage for a 60-day public comment period. During this time, written comments may be submitted to the docket.

CH
14

□ On or before 270 days after receipt of the petition, a final decision will be sent to the petitioner in the form of a letter as to whether FDA intends to exercise enforcement discretion with respect to a qualified health claim or deny the petition. The letter will be posted on FDA's website.

□ Extensions beyond 270 days can be granted upon mutual agreement between the petitioner and the agency.

Submitting a Petition

14. How will FDA know that I wish to have my petition reviewed under the standards for a qualified health claim rather than those for an SSA health claim (i.e., under the Significant Scientific Agreement standard)?

The petitioner may indicate within the petition's cover letter that he/she is waiving the right to a review under the Significant Scientific Agreement standard and request that the petition be reviewed under the interim procedures for a qualified health claim. This request will result in FDA proceeding directly to the qualified health claim procedures and its 270-day timeline (see next question). In the absence of such a request, FDA contacts the petitioner to determine if they are petitioning for a SSA or qualified health claim.

15. What information is required to be included in the petition?

The requirements of 21 CFR 101.70 apply. A general summary of these requirements follows.

1. Preliminary Requirements (see 21 CFR 101.70(f)(A)) Explanation of how substance conforms to the requirements of CFR 101.14(b):

□ Relationship between substance and disease in U.S;

□ Substance contributes taste, aroma, nutritive value, or a technical effect listed in 21 CFR 170.3(o);

□ Substance is a food, food ingredient, or component that has been shown to be safe and lawful at levels necessary to justify a claim.

2. Summary of Scientific data (see 21 CFR 101.70(f)(B))

3. Analytical data to show amount of substance that is present in representative foods (see 21 CFR 101.70(f)(C))

4. Proposed model health claim(s) (see 21 CFR 101.70(f)(D))

5. Attachments (see 21 CFR 101.70(f)(E))

□ Scientific data supporting a claim:

□ Copies of computer literature searches;

□ Copy of all research articles relied upon for support of petition — English only;

□ Information concerning adverse consequences pertinent to any segment of the US population.

CH 14

6. A claim for categorical exclusion or an environmental assessment (see 21 CFR 101.70(f)(F))

> **NOTE**: FDA encourages petitioners to specify whether they are requesting that their petition be reviewed as a qualified health claim, and that they waive review under the Significant Scientific Agreement standard.

16. Where should I send the petition?

Mail the original and one copy of the petition (or a computer readable disk containing the petition) to the following address:

Food and Drug Administration
Office of Nutritional Products, Labeling and Dietary Supplements (HFS-800)
5001 Campus Drive
College Park, MD 20740

Electronic submissions may also be emailed to: label.claims@cfsan.fda.gov

Other

17. Are there circumstances when FDA will not file a petition?

Yes, if the petition is incomplete in that it does not provide the required information that is summarized above (#15).

Contains Nonbinding Recommendations
July 2003

Guidance for Industry:
Interim Procedures for Qualified Health Claims
in the Labeling of Conventional Human Food and Human Dietary Supplements[1]

I. Introduction

This guidance is intended to notify the public of interim procedures that the Food and Drug Administration (FDA) is implementing for petitioners who submit qualified health claim petitions to the agency. This guidance describes the procedures that FDA intends to use, on an interim basis, to respond to qualified health claim petitions until the agency can promulgate regulations under notice-and-comment rulemaking; it also provides a linkage between the ranking of scientific evidence and the wording of qualified health claims. In addition, this guidance updates the agency's approach outlined in December 2002 (Guidance for Industry: Qualified Health Claims in the Labeling of Conventional Foods and Dietary Supplements) and the agency's approach to implementing Pearson v. Shalala (164 F.3d 650 (D.C. Cir. 1999)) to include conventional foods. This guidance does not apply to unqualified health claims, which must meet the "Significant Scientific Agreement" (SSA) standard.[2]

FDA's guidance documents, including this guidance, do not establish legally enforceable responsibilities. Instead, guidances describe the Agency's current thinking on a topic and should be viewed only as recommendations, unless specific regulatory or statutory requirements are cited. The use of the word should in Agency guidances means that something is suggested or recommended, but not required.

II. Background

FDA is issuing this document as final guidance setting out interim procedures that the agency intends to use for qualified health claims in the labeling of conventional human food and dietary supplements until the agency can promulgate regulations under notice and comment rulemaking.

CH
14

---

1   This guidance has been prepared by the Center for Food Safety and Applied Nutrition (CFSAN) at the U.S. Food and Drug Administration. This guidance is available on the FDA website at https://www.fda.gov/Food/GuidanceRegulation/GuidanceDocumentsRegulatoryInformation/ucm053832.htm

2   FDA uses the term, "unqualified health claim," to refer to health claims that are or could be authorized under the Nutritional Labeling and Education Act of 1990 (NLEA) and regulations promulgated under that act, including 21 CFR 101.70.

III. Objective

FDA intends to use the following interim procedures to ensure that its premarket review is consistent with the spirit of the Nutrition Labeling and Education Act and the First Amendment. FDA will continue to evaluate unqualified health claims under its current regulatory process and standard for significant scientific agreement (21 CFR 101.14 and 101.70).

A. Criteria for Exercise of Enforcement Discretion

FDA plans to establish criteria for considering exercising enforcement discretion for qualified health claims based on the extent to which the totality of the publicly available evidence supports the claim (see Guidance for Industry and FDA: Interim Evidence-based Ranking System for Scientific Data). Different levels of evidence will result in different qualifying language as described in Table 1, which provides standardized language for the B, C, and D categories to be used as part of the qualifying language for qualified health claims until consumer research (3) is complete.

Table 1. Standardized Qualifying Language for Qualified Health Claims.		
*Scientific Ranking**	*FDA Category*	*Appropriate Qualifying Language***
Second Level	B	... "although there is scientific evidence supporting the claim, the evidence is not conclusive."
Third Level	C	"Some scientific evidence suggests ... however, FDA has determined that this evidence is limited and not conclusive."
Fourth Level	D	"Very limited and preliminary scientific research suggests... FDA concludes that there is little scientific evidence supporting this claim."

*From Guidance for Industry and FDA: Interim Evidence-based Ranking System for Scientific Data.

**The language reflects wording used in qualified health claims as to which the agency has previously exercised enforcement discretion for certain dietary supplements. During this interim period, the precise language as to which the agency considers exercising enforcement discretion may vary depending on the specific circumstances of each case.

B. Procedures

1. Filing Review

FDA plans to begin accepting petitions for qualified health claims on September 1, 2003. Within 45 days of receipt of a qualified health claim petition, FDA intends to determine whether the petition is complete (see Section C below). If the petition is incomplete, the agency plans to inform the petitioner of the deficiencies and what steps the petitioner should take to rectify these deficiencies. If FDA determines that the petition is complete, it intends to file the petition. The agency recognizes that it can evaluate petitions more efficiently and effectively if they are well-organized and contain all the relevant information. FDA encourages potential petitioners to meet with the agency prior to preparing a petition to discuss their plans.

2. Prioritization

FDA has only limited resources for reviewing health claims. Thus, to maximize the public health benefit of its claims review process, FDA intends to prioritize on a case-by-case basis all complete petitions according to several factors, including whether the food or dietary supplement that is the subject of the petition is likely to have a significant impact on a serious or life-threatening illness; the strength of the evidence; whether consumer research has been provided to show the claim is not misleading; whether the substance of the claim has undergone an FDA safety review (i.e., is an authorized food additive, has been GRAS (generally recognized as safe) affirmed, listed, or has received a letter of "no objection" to a GRAS notification); whether the substance that is the subject of the claim has been adequately characterized so that the relevance of available studies can be evaluated; whether the disease is defined and evaluated in accordance with generally accepted criteria established by a recognized body of qualified experts; and whether there is prior review of the evidence or the claim by a recognized body of qualified experts.

3. Opportunity for Public Comment

Upon filing of a petition, FDA intends to post the petition on its website and request public comment for 60 days. FDA plans to post comments submitted by the public on FDA's website or to make comments available for public review at the Division of Dockets Management, HFA-305.

4. Scientific Review

After the comment period closes, FDA may pursue any one of several options for scientific review of data submitted in a petition in support of the substance/disease relationship. For example, FDA may conduct the review internally, it may convene an advisory subcommittee, or it may use appropriate third-party reviewers under contract to FDA, e.g., the Agency for Healthcare Quality and Research (AHRQ). In the case of a petition forwarded to AHRQ, AHRQ plans to send the petition to an Evidence-Based Practice Center (EPC) with which it has a contract to review the scientific evidence in the petition and to rank the degree of scientific certainty of the validity of the substance/disease relationship. AHRQ also plans to ask the EPC to review those science-related public comments received by FDA that discuss or provide evidence. Within 120 days after the commencement of the third party review, FDA would expect to receive a report that includes a description of the evidence reviewed, an analysis of that evidence, a summary of and response to public comments that pertain to the evidence, and its assessment as to the degree of scientific certainty in support of the substance/disease relationship.

5. Consolidation of Like Petitions

If FDA receives more than one petition for a qualified health claim that describes the same relationship between a substance and a disease or health-related condition during its review, the agency plans to consolidate all of the related petitions received, if appropriate.

CH
14

6. Consultation with Other Federal Agencies

To fully inform FDA's review, FDA intends, as appropriate, on a case-by-case-basis, to consult with other scientific Federal agencies with official responsibility for public health protection or research related to human nutrition and dietary supplements.

7. Regulatory Decision

As mentioned above, FDA plans to either conduct its own review or use an appropriate third party to conduct a scientific review. In the case of third party review, after FDA receives, for example the EPC report, FDA intends, based on the totality of the publicly available evidence, public comment, and other relevant regulatory considerations, to determine whether to consider exercising enforcement discretion with respect to the proposed claim. If FDA decides to consider exercising enforcement discretion, the agency plans to determine what qualifying statement(s) and other information should accompany the claim to ensure that it is truthful and not misleading. In reaching its determination, FDA intends to review and evaluate the third party report, the totality of the publicly available evidence, and all of the public comments submitted within the comment period, as well as consider how the proposed qualified claim will affect consumers' dietary choices. FDA also intends to consider whether to exercise enforcement discretion with respect to other requirements in 21 CFR 101.14, and what other factors, in addition to qualifying language, are relevant to considering the exercise of enforcement discretion.

8. Notification to Petitioner

On or before day 270 after receipt of the filed petition, FDA plans to notify the petitioner in a letter of: a) the agency's determination; b) the basis for its determination; and c) if the agency decides to consider exercising enforcement discretion, the qualified claim for which the agency intends to consider exercising such discretion and the provisions of 21 CFR 101.14 for which the agency intends to consider exercising such discretion. FDA also plans to notify the petitioner of any other factors the agency intends to consider in deciding whether to exercise enforcement discretion when the claim appears in labeling of conventional human food or dietary supplements. FDA plans to post the letter and any third party report on the agency's website.

9. Extensions

If the agency determines that it is appropriate, upon good cause, FDA may, decide to extend by 30-60 days the time period to notify the petitioner.

10. Reconsideration

If a petitioner or other party disagrees with an FDA determination, that party may request reconsideration. FDA intends to reconsider its determination if the party presents significant new relevant evidence or provides a persuasive analysis that the agency's interpretation of the original evidence was incorrect. FDA intends to use the same process described above for reconsideration of the agency's determination. FDA may, on its own initiative, decide to reconsider a determination.

C. Content of Petitions

1. Requirements

Except as described in C.2. (below), the agency believes that the requirements of 21 CFR 101.70 continue to apply, including the requirement to demonstrate that the substance that is the subject of the claim is safe and lawful under 21 CFR 101.14(b)(3)(ii).

2. Summary of Scientific Information

FDA intends to exercise enforcement discretion with respect to the requirement in 21 CFR 101.70 that the summary establish that the proposed claim is supported by significant scientific agreement. Instead, the summary should explain how credible evidence supports the claim as worded in the petition and why the petitioner believes that the specific wording of the claim, including any explanatory information, disclaimer or other qualification, is accurate and not misleading. As required by 21 CFR 101.70, the summary should include an analysis of the potential effect of the claim on total intakes of the substance (i.e., current intakes plus increases due to the claim), including any adverse or beneficial changes in dietary practices. The agency encourages petitioners to include consumer research to document consumer understanding. FDA recommends that the consumer research address the research questions set out in Attachment D of the Task Force Report.[3]

This document supercedes
Qualified Health Claims in the Labeling of Conventional Foods and Dietary
Supplements (December 18, 2002)

**CH
14**

---

3   Attachment D of the Task Force Report (available at http://www.fda.gov/oc/mcclellan/chbn.html).

Summary of Qualified Health Claims Subject to Enforcement Discretion[1]

Qualified Health Claims About Atopic Dermatitis Risk

100% Whey-Protein Partially Hydrolyzed Infant Formula and Reduced Risk of Atopic Dermatitis

Docket No. FDA-2009-Q-0301
05/24/2011 enforcement discretion letter

Claim Statements for 100% Whey-Protein Partially Hydrolyzed Infant Formula and Reduced Risk of Atopic Dermatitis

1. "Very little scientific evidence suggests that, for healthy infants who are not exclusively breastfed and who have a family history of allergy, feeding a 100 % Whey-Protein Partially Hydrolyzed infant formula from birth up to 4 months of age instead of a formula containing intact cow's milk proteins may reduce the risk of developing atopic dermatitis throughout the 1st year of life and up to 3 years of age."

2. "Little scientific evidence suggests that, for healthy infants who are not exclusively breastfed and who have a family history of allergy, feeding a 100 % Whey-Protein Partially Hydrolyzed infant formula from birth up to 4 months of age instead of a formula containing intact cow's milk proteins may reduce the risk of developing atopic dermatitis throughout the 1st year of life."

3. "For healthy infants who are not exclusively breastfed and who have a family history of allergy, feeding a 100% Whey-Protein Partially Hydrolyzed infant formula from birth up to 4 months of age instead of a formula containing intact cow's milk proteins may reduce the risk of developing atopic dermatitis throughout the 1st year of life and up to 3 years of age. FDA has concluded that the relationship between 100% Whey-Protein Partially Hydrolyzed infant formulas and the reduced risk of atopic dermatitis is uncertain, because there is very little scientific evidence for the relationship."

4. "For healthy infants who are not exclusively breastfed and who have a family history of allergy, feeding a 100% Whey-Protein Partially Hydrolyzed infant formula from birth up to 4 months of age instead of a formula containing intact cow's milk proteins may reduce the risk of developing atopic dermatitis throughout the 1st year of life. FDA has concluded that the relationship between 100% Whey-Protein Partially Hydrolyzed infant formulas and the reduced risk of atopic dermatitis is uncertain, because there is little scientific evidence for the relationship."

---

1   https://www.fda.gov/Food/LabelingNutrition/ucm073992.htm

Eligible foods

- 100% Whey-Protein Partially Hydrolyzed Infant Formula

Factors

The following language is placed immediately adjacent to and directly beneath the claim:

"Partially hydrolyzed formulas should not be fed to infants who are allergic to milk or to infants with existing milk allergy symptoms. If you suspect your baby is already allergic to milk, or if your baby is on a special formula for the treatment of allergy, your baby's care and feeding choices should be under a doctor's supervision."

Qualified Claims About Cancer Risk

Calcium and Colon/Rectal Cancer & Calcium and Recurrent Colon/Rectal Polyps

Docket No. 2004Q-0097
10/12/2005 enforcement discretion letter

Claim Statement for Colon/Rectal Cancer

Some evidence suggests that calcium supplements may reduce the risk of colon/rectal cancer, however, FDA has determined that this evidence is limited and not conclusive.

Claim Statement for Recurrent Colon Polyps

Very limited and preliminary evidence suggests that calcium supplements may reduce the risk of colon/rectal polyps. FDA concludes that there is little scientific evidence to support this claim.

Eligible foods

- Dietary supplements containing calcium

Factors

The claim meets the general requirements for health claims in 21 CFR 101.14, except for the requirement that the evidence for the claim meet the significant scientific agreement standard and be made in accordance with an authorizing regulation (21 CFR 101.14(c)).

The dietary supplement meet or exceed the requirement for a "high" level of calcium as defined in 21 CFR 101.54(b) (i.e., 200 mg or more calcium per reference amount customarily consumed)

The calcium content of the dietary supplement must be assimilable (i.e., bioavailable) (21 CFR 101.72(c)(ii)(B), and meet the United States Pharmacopeia (U.S.P.) standards for disintegration and dissolution applicable to their component calcium salts. For dietary supplements for which no U.S.P. standards exist, the dietary supplement must exhibit appropriate assimilability under the conditions of use stated on the product label (21 CFR 101.72(c)(ii)(C).

CH
14

Green Tea & Cancer

Docket No. FDA-2004-Q-0427
02/24/2011 enforcement discretion letter
04/17/2012 letter

Claim Statement

Green tea may reduce the risk of breast or prostate cancer although the FDA has concluded that there is very little scientific evidence for this claim.

Green tea may reduce the risk of breast or prostate cancer. FDA has concluded that there is very little scientific evidence for this claim.

Eligible foods

- Green tea and conventional foods and dietary supplements that contain green tea

Factors

- Disqualifying Nutrient Levels

  □ Green tea does not exceed the disqualifying nutrient levels for total fat, saturated fat, cholesterol, and sodium specified in 21 CFR 101.14(a)(4).

  □ FDA intends to consider the exercise of its enforcement discretion for the qualified health claim for green tea and breast or prostate cancer to be used on the label or in the labeling of green tea-containing foods when the food does not exceed any of the disqualifying nutrient levels for fat, saturated fat, cholesterol, and sodium.

- 10% Minimum Nutrient Content Requirement

  □ FDA intends to consider the exercise of its enforcement discretion for green tea that does not meet the 10% minimum nutrient content requirement in 21 CFR 101.14(e)(6).

  □ FDA does not intend to consider the exercise of its enforcement discretion for green tea-containing foods that do not meet the requirements of § 101.14(e)(6).

Selenium & Cancer

Docket No. 02P-0457
02/21/2003 enforcement discretion letter, 04/28/2003 letter
Docket No. FDA-2008-Q-0323
06/19/2009 enforcement discretion letter
Summary of settlement in *Alliance for Natural Health v. Sebelius*

Claim Statements

1. Selenium may reduce the risk of certain cancers. Some scientific evidence suggests that consumption of selenium may reduce the risk of certain forms of cancer. However, FDA has determined that this evidence is limited and not conclusive. or,

CH 14

2. Selenium may produce anticarcinogenic effects in the body. Some scientific evidence suggests that consumption of selenium may produce anticarcinogenic effects in the body. However, FDA has determined that this evidence is limited and not conclusive.

3. One study suggests that selenium intake may reduce the risk of bladder cancer in women. However, one smaller study showed no reduction in risk. Based on these studies, FDA concludes that it is highly uncertain that selenium supplements reduce the risk of bladder cancer in women. or,

4. Two weak studies suggest that selenium intake may reduce the risk of prostate cancer. However, four stronger studies and three weak studies showed no reduction in risk. Based on these studies, FDA concludes that it is highly unlikely that selenium supplements reduce the risk of prostate cancer. or,

5. One weak, small study suggests that selenium intake may reduce the risk of thyroid cancer. Based on this study, FDA concludes that it is highly uncertain that selenium supplements reduce the risk of thyroid cancer.or,

6. Selenium may reduce the risk of colorectal cancer. Scientific evidence concerning this claim is inconclusive. Based on its review, FDA does not agree that selenium may reduce the risk of colorectal cancer.or,

7. Selenium may reduce the risk of colon and rectal cancer. Scientific evidence concerning this claim is inconclusive. Based on its review, FDA does not agree that selenium may reduce the risk of colon and rectal cancer. or,

8. Selenium may reduce the risk of colon cancer. Scientific evidence concerning this claim is inconclusive. Based on its review, FDA does not agree that selenium may reduce the risk of colon. or,

9. Selenium may reduce the risk of prostate cancer. Scientific evidence concerning this claim is inconclusive. Based on its review, FDA does not agree that selenium may reduce the risk of prostate cancer. or,

10. Selenium may reduce the risk of bladder, colon, prostate, rectal and thyroid cancers. Based on its review, FDA does not agree that selenium may reduce the risk of these cancers.

Eligible foods

- Dietary supplements containing selenium

Factors

The disclaimer (i.e., Some scientific evidence suggests...) is placed immediately adjacent to and directly beneath the claim (i.e., Selenium may reduce the risk), with no intervening material, in the same size, typeface, and contrast as the claim itself.

CH 14

The supplement does not recommend or suggest in its labeling, or under ordinary conditions of use, a daily intake exceeding the Tolerable Upper Intake Level established by the National Academy of Sciences/Institute of Medicine for selenium (400 micrograms per day).

The claim meets all general health claim requirements of 21 CFR 101.14, except for the requirement that the evidence for the claim meet the significant scientific agreement standard and be made in accordance with an authorizing regulation.

Paragraph 101.14(d)(2)(vii) requires that the dietary supplement bearing the claim meet the nutrient content claim definition for high (i.e., 20% or more of the daily value (DV) per RACC[1]). 20% DV for selenium is 14 micrograms.

Antioxidant Vitamins & Cancer

Docket No. 91N-0101
04/01/2003 enforcement discretion letter
Docket No. FDA-2008-Q-0299
06/19/2009 enforcement discretion letter
Summary of settlement in *Alliance for Natural Health v. Sebelius*

Claim Statements

1. Some scientific evidence suggests that consumption of antioxidant vitamins may reduce the risk of certain forms of cancer. However, FDA has determined that this evidence is limited and not conclusive. or,

2. Some scientific evidence suggests that consumption of antioxidant vitamins may reduce the risk of certain forms of cancer. However, FDA does not endorse this claim because this evidence is limited and not conclusive. or,

3. FDA has determined that although some scientific evidence suggests that consumption of antioxidant vitamins may reduce the risk of certain forms of cancer, this evidence is limited and not conclusive.

4. Vitamin C and Gastric (Stomach) Cancer, "One weak study and one study with inconsistent results suggest that vitamin C supplements may reduce the risk of gastric cancer. Based on these studies, FDA concludes that it is highly uncertain that vitamin C supplements reduce the risk of gastric cancer."

5. Vitamin E and Bladder Cancer, "One small study suggests that vitamin E supplements may reduce the risk of bladder cancer. However, two small studies showed no reduction of risk. Based on these studies, FDA concludes that it is highly unlikely that vitamin E supplements reduce the risk of bladder cancer."

---

1   Abbreviation: RACC - reference amount customarily consumed per eating occasion, as defined in 21 CFR 101.12

6. Vitamin E and Colorectal Cancer, "Two weak studies and one study with inconsistent results suggest that vitamin E supplements may reduce the risk of colorectal cancer. However, another limited study showed no reduction of risk. Based on these studies, FDA concludes that it is highly unlikely that vitamin E supplements reduce the risk of colorectal cancer."

7. Vitamin E and Renal Cancer, "One weak and limited study suggests that vitamin E supplements may reduce the risk of renal cell cancer. FDA concludes that it is highly uncertain that vitamin E supplements reduce the risk of renal cell cancer."

8. Vitamin C may reduce the risk of gastric cancer although the FDA has concluded that there is very little scientific evidence for this claim.

9. Vitamin C may reduce the risk of gastric cancer. FDA has concluded that there is very little scientific evidence for this claim.

10. Vitamin E may reduce the risk of bladder cancer although the FDA has concluded that there is very little scientific evidence for this claim.

11. Vitamin E may reduce the risk of bladder cancer. FDA has concluded that there is very little scientific evidence for this claim.

12. Vitamin E may reduce the risk of colorectal cancer although the FDA has concluded that there is very little scientific evidence for this claim.

13. Vitamin E may reduce the risk of colorectal cancer. FDA has concluded that there is very little scientific evidence for this claim.

14. Vitamin E may reduce the risk of renal cancer although the FDA has concluded that there is very little scientific evidence for this claim.

15. Vitamin E may reduce the risk of renal cancer. FDA has concluded that there is very little scientific evidence for this claim.

Eligible foods

- Dietary supplements containing vitamin E and/or vitamin C

Factors

The disclaimer (i.e., ...evidence is limited and not conclusive, or ...FDA concludes that it is highly...) is placed immediately adjacent to the claim, with no intervening material, in the same size, typeface, and contrast as the claim itself.

The supplement does not recommend or suggest in its labeling, or under ordinary conditions of use, a daily intake exceeding the Tolerable Upper Intake Levels established by the Institute of Medicine for vitamin C (2000 mg per day) or for vitamin E (1000 mg per day).

CH 14

The claim meets all 21 CFR 101.14 general health claim requirements, except for the requirements that the claim meet the significant scientific agreement standard and be made in accordance with an authorizing regulation.

Paragraph 101.14(d)(2)(vii) requires that the food bearing the claim meet the nutrient content claim definition for high (i.e., 20% or more of the daily value (DV) per RACC). 20% DV for vitamin C is 12 mg; 20% DV for vitamin E is 6 IU.

Qualified Claims About Cardiovascular Disease Risk

Omega-3 Fatty Acids & Coronary Heart Disease

Docket No. 2003Q-0401
09/08/2004 enforcement discretion letter

Claim Statement

Supportive but not conclusive research shows that consumption of EPA and DHA omega-3 fatty acids may reduce the risk of coronary heart disease. One serving of [Name of the food] provides [ ] gram of EPA and DHA omega-3 fatty acids. [See nutrition information for total fat, saturated fat, and cholesterol content.]

Note: Dietary supplements may declare the amount of EPA and DHA per serving in "Supplement Facts," instead of making the declaration in the claim.

Eligible foods

- Conventional foods and dietary supplements that contain EPA and DHA omega-3 fatty acids.

Factors

Dietary supplements should not recommend or suggest in their labeling a daily intake exceeding 2 grams of EPA and DHA

Total fat content

Dietary supplements that weigh 5 g or less per RACC (RACC for dietary supplement is labeled serving size) are exempted from the total fat disqualifying level, but if dietary supplements that weigh 5 g or less per RACC exceed the total fat disqualifying level (13.0 g per 50 g) the disclosure statement (i.e., "See nutrition information for total fat content") must be placed immediately adjacent to the health claim. Dietary supplements that weigh more than 5 g per RACC must not exceed the total fat disqualifying level (13.0 g per RACC and per 50 g if RACC is ≤ 30 g or ≤ 2 tbsp).

Fish (i.e., "products that are essentially all fish") may not exceed 16.0 g total fat per RACC. Fish with a total fat content greater than 13.0 g per RACC must include "See nutrition information for total fat content" with the health claim. The "products that are essentially all fish" include fish without any added ingredients and fish with a small amount of added fat or carbohydrate that meets the definition of an insignificant amount in 21 CFR 101.9(f)(1). Examples of these products are raw fish, boiled fish, and broiled fish.

Conventional foods other than fish may not exceed the total fat disqualifying levels. For individual foods, the total fat disqualifying level is 13.0 g per RACC and per 50 g if RACC is ≤ 30 g or ≤ 2 tbsp. The total fat disqualifying level is 26.0 g per label serving size for meal products and 19.5 g per label serving size for main dish products.

Saturated fat content

Dietary supplements must meet the criterion for low saturated fat with regard to the saturated fat content (≤ 1 g per RACC) but not with regard to the no more than 15 percent calories from saturated fat criterion.

Fish may not exceed the saturated fat disqualifying level of 4.0 g per RACC (or 4.0 g per 50 g if reference amount is ≤ 30 g or ≤ 2 tbsp).

Conventional foods other than fish must meet the criteria for low saturated fat (≤ 1 g per RACC and no more than 15 percent of calories from saturated fat for individual foods, ≤ 1 g per 100 g and less than 10 percent calories from saturated fat for meal products and main dish products). There is an error in the enforcement discretion letters in the section of "low saturated fat," stating that meal products and main dishes meet all criteria specified for the "low saturated fat" criteria (21 CFR 101.62(c)(2)). The CFR number should be (21 CFR 101.62(c)(3)).

Cholesterol content

Dietary supplements that weigh 5 g or less per RACC are exempt from the cholesterol disqualifying level (60 mg per 50 g), but those that exceed the cholesterol disqualifying level must include "See nutrition information for cholesterol content" with the health claim. Dietary supplements that weigh more than 5 g per RACC must meet the criterion for low cholesterol (≤ 20 mg per 50g).

Fish must meet the extra lean criterion with regard to cholesterol content (< 95 mg per RACC and per 100 g, whichever is greatest), but not with regard to saturated fat content. Fish with cholesterol content greater than 60 mg per RACC must include "See nutrition information for cholesterol content" with the health claim.

Conventional foods other than fish must meet the low cholesterol criterion (21 CFR 101.62(d)(2)). See 21 CFR 101.62(d)(2) for the low cholesterol criterion specific for individual foods, meal products, and main dish products.

Sodium All conventional foods and dietary supplements must meet the sodium disqualifying level (≤ 480 mg per RACC and per 50 g if RACC is ≤ 30 g or ≤ 2 tbsp for individual foods, ≤ 960 mg per label serving size for meal products, ≤ 720 mg per label serving size for main dish products). The 10 percent minimum nutrient requirement

All conventional foods must meet the 10 percent minimum nutrient requirement (Vitamin A 500 IU, Vitamin C 6 mg, Iron 1.8 mg, Calcium 100 mg, Protein 5 g, Fiber 2.5 g per RACC), prior to any nutrient addition.

The 10 percent minimum nutrient requirement does not apply to dietary supplements (21 CFR 101.14(e)(6)).

CH
14

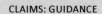

Qualified Claims About Cardiovascular Disease Risk

B Vitamins & Vascular Disease

Docket No. 99P-3029
05/15/2002 clarification letter
11/28/2000 enforcement discretion letter

Claim Statement

As part of a well-balanced diet that is low in saturated fat and cholesterol, Folic Acid, Vitamin B6 and Vitamin B12 may reduce the risk of vascular disease. FDA evaluated the above claim and found that, while it is known that diets low in saturated fat and cholesterol reduce the risk of heart disease and other vascular diseases, the evidence in support of the above claim is inconclusive.

Eligible foods

- Dietary supplements containing vitamin B6, B12, and/or folic acid

Factors

The disclaimer (i.e., FDA evaluated the above claim...) must be immediately adjacent to and directly beneath the first claim (i.e., As part of a well-balanced diet...) with no intervening material that separates the claim from the disclaimer, and the second sentence must be in the same size, type face and contrast as the first sentence.

Products that contain more than 100 percent of the Daily Value (DV) of folic acid (400 micrograms), when labeled for use by adults and children 4 or more years of age, must identify the safe upper limit of daily intake with respect to the DV. The folic acid safe upper limit of daily intake value of 1,000 micrograms (1 mg) may be included in parentheses.

The claim meets all 21 CFR 101.14 general health claim requirements, except for: (1) the requirement that the claim meet the significant scientific agreement standard and be made in accordance with an authorizing regulation, and (2) the requirement that the claim specify the daily dietary intake necessary to achieve the claimed effect. The claim may not suggest a level of vitamins B6, B12, and/or folic acid as being useful in achieving the claimed effect.

Dietary supplements containing folic acid must meet the United States Pharmacopeia (USP) standards for disintegration and dissolution, except that if there are no applicable USP standards, the folate in the dietary supplement shall be shown to be bioavailable under the conditions of use stated on the product label.

**CH
14**

Monounsaturated Fatty Acids From Olive Oil and Coronary Heart Disease

Docket No. 2003Q-0559
11/01/2004 enforcement discretion letter

Claim Statement

Limited and not conclusive scientific evidence suggests that eating about 2 tablespoons (23 grams) of olive oil daily may reduce the risk of coronary heart disease due to the monounsaturated fat in olive oil. To achieve this possible benefit, olive oil is to replace a similar amount of saturated fat and not increase the total number of calories you eat in a day. One serving of this product contains [x] grams of olive oil.

Note: The last sentence of the claim "One serving of this product contains [x] grams of olive oil." is optional when the claim is used on the label or in the labeling of olive oil.

Eligible foods

- All products that are essentially pure olive oil and labeled as such (see * for definitions)

- Dressings for salads (i.e. salad dressings) that contain 6 g or more olive oil per reference amount customarily consumed (RACC), are low in cholesterol (21 CFR 101.62(d)(2)), and do not contain more than 4 g of saturated fat per 50 g.

- Vegetable oil spreads that contain 6 g or more olive oil per RACC, are low in cholesterol (21 CFR 101.62(d)(2)) and do not contain more than 4 g of saturated fat per RACC.

- Olive oil-containing foods that contain 6 g or more olive oil per RACC, are low in cholesterol (21 CFR 101.62(d)(2)), contain at least 10% of either vitamin A, vitamin C, iron, calcium, protein or dietary fiber. If the RACC of the olive oil-containing food is greater than 30 g the food cannot contain more than 4 g of saturated fat per RACC and if the RACC of the olive oil-containing food is 30 g or less the food cannot contain more than 4 g of saturated fat per 50 g.

- Shortenings that contain 6 g or more olive oil per RACC and are low in cholesterol (21 CFR 101.62(d)(2)) and do not contain more than 4 g of saturated fat per RACC.

- Meal products (21 CFR 101.13(l)) or Main dish products (21 CFR 101.13(m)) are not eligible for the claim.

Factors

The claim meets the general requirements for health claims in 21 CFR 101.14, except for: (1) the requirement that the evidence for the claim meet the significant scientific agreement standard and be made in accordance with an authorizing regulation (21 CFR 101.14(c)); (2) the requirement that the food comply with the total fat disqualifying level (21 CFR 101.14(e)(3)); (3) for olive oil, vegetable oil spreads, and shortenings the requirement that the food comply with the 50 gram-criterion of the saturated fat disqualifying level (21 CFR 101.14(e)(3)); and (4) for olive oil, dressings for salads, and shortenings, the requirement that the food contain a minimum of 10 percent of the Daily

CH
14

Value per RACC of at one of the following: vitamin A, vitamin C, iron, calcium, protein, or dietary fiber per reference amount customarily consumed (21 CFR 101.14(e)(6)).

When the total fat disqualifying level is exceeded in vegetable oil spreads, dressings for salads, shortenings, or olive-oil containing foods the disclosure statement (i.e., See nutrition information for saturated fat content) must be placed immediately following the claim, with no intervening material, in the same size, typeface, and contrast as the claim itself.

When the food does not meet the definition of low saturated fat (21 CFR 101.62(c)(2)) the disclosure statement (i.e., See nutrition information for saturated fat content) must be placed immediately following the claim, with no intervening material, in the same size, typeface, and contrast as the claim itself.

If both of the above two conditions are met the disclosure statements for total fat and saturated fat can be combined (i.e., See nutrition information for total and saturated fat content)

*For the purposes of this qualified health claim:

1. Olive oil means virgin olive oil, or blends of virgin olive oil and refined olive oil; where virgin olive oil is the oil resulting from the first pressing of olives and is suitable for human consumption without further processing and refined olive oil is the oil obtained from subsequent pressings and which is suitable for human consumption by refining processes which neutralize the acidity or remove particulate matter.

2. Vegetable oil spread means margarine (21 CFR 166.110) and margarine-like products.

3. Olive oil-containing foods means foods, such as sauces or baked goods, excluding olive oil, vegetable oil spreads, dressings for salads, and shortenings.

Qualified Claims About Cognitive Function

Phosphatidylserine & Cognitive Dysfunction and Dementia

Docket No. 02P-0413
02/24/2003 enforcement discretion letter
05/13/2003 letter
11/24/2004 updated letter

Claim Statements

- Consumption of phosphatidylserine may reduce the risk of dementia in the elderly. Very limited and preliminary scientific research suggests that phosphatidylserine may reduce the risk of dementia in the elderly. FDA concludes that there is little scientific evidence supporting this claim. or,

- Consumption of phosphatidylserine may reduce the risk of cognitive dysfunction in the elderly. Very limited and preliminary scientific research suggests that phosphatidylserine may reduce the risk of cognitive dysfunction in the elderly. FDA concludes that there is little scientific evidence supporting this claim.

Eligible foods

- Dietary supplements containing soy-derived phosphatidylserine

Factors

The disclaimer (i.e., Very limited and preliminary scientific research...) is placed immediately adjacent to and directly beneath the claim (i.e., Phosphatidylserine may reduce...), with no intervening material, in the same size, typeface, and contrast as the claim itself.

The claim meets all 21 CFR 101.14 general health claim requirements, except for: (1) the requirement that the claim meet the significant scientific agreement standard and be made in accordance with an authorizing regulation, and (2) the claim specify the daily dietary intake necessary to achieve the claimed effect. The claim may not suggest a level of phosphatidylserine as being useful in achieving the claimed effect.

The soy-derived phosphatidylserine used is of very high purity.

Qualified Claims About Diabetes

Psyllium Husk & Diabetes

Docket No. FDA-2013-Q-0167
06/24/2014 enforcement discretion letter

Claim Statements

Psyllium husk may reduce the risk of type 2 diabetes, although the FDA has concluded that there is very little scientific evidence for this claim.

Psyllium husk may reduce the risk of type 2 diabetes. FDA has concluded that there is very little scientific evidence for this claim.

Eligible foods

- Conventional foods
- Dietary supplements

Factors

The claim statements meet all applicable statutory and regulatory requirements under the Federal Food, Drug, and Cosmetic Act. In particular, the claim statements must meet all general requirements of 21 CFR 101.14 except for the requirements that the claim meet the significant scientific agreement standard and that the claim be made in accordance with an authorizing regulation.

Other factors that FDA will consider in exercising enforcement discretion are the following:

- Psyllium husk must not be present in trivial amounts, although FDA is not specifying a minimum level of psyllium husk.
- Psyllium husk must be at least 95% pure to minimize potential allergenicity.

CH 14

- Foods containing dry or incompletely hydrated psyllium husk may need a label statement warning that the product should be taken with water or other liquids to avoid choking.

Chromium Picolinate & Diabetes

Docket No. 2004Q-0144
08/25/2005 enforcement discretion letter
Claim Statement

One small study suggests that chromium picolinate may reduce the risk of insulin resistance, and therefore possibly may reduce the risk of type 2 diabetes. FDA concludes, however, that the existence of such a relationship between chromium picolinate and either insulin resistance or type 2 diabetes is highly uncertain.

Eligible foods

- Dietary supplements

Factors

Dietary supplement containing chromium should meet or exceed the requirement for a "high" level of chromium as defined in 21 CFR 101.54(b) (i.e., 24 mg or more per reference amount customarily consumed under the current regulation) for FDA to exercise enforcement discretion.

The claim meets all applicable statutory and regulatory requirements under the Federal Food, Drug, and Cosmetic Act, with the exception of the requirement that a health claim meet the significant scientific agreement standard and the requirement that the claim be made in accordance with an authorizing regulation.

Qualified Claims About Hypertension

Calcium & Hypertension, Pregnancy-Induced Hypertension, and Preeclampsia

Docket No. 2004Q-0098
10/12/2005 enforcement discretion letter

Claim Statements

1. Some scientific evidence suggests that calcium supplements may reduce the risk of hypertension. However, FDA has determined that the evidence is inconsistent and not conclusive. or,

2. Four studies, including a large clinical trial, do not show that calcium supplements reduce the risk of pregnancy-induced hypertension during pregnancy. However, three other studies suggest that calcium supplements may reduce the risk. Based on these studies, FDA concludes that it is highly unlikely that calcium supplements reduce the risk of pregnancy-induced hypertension. or,

CH
14

3. Three studies, including a large clinical trial, do not show that calcium supplements reduce the risk of preeclampsia during pregnancy. However, two other studies suggest that calcium supplements may reduce the risk. Based on these studies, FDA concludes that it is highly unlikely that calcium supplements reduce the risk of preeclampsia.

Eligible foods

- Dietary supplements containing calcium

Factors

The claim meets the general requirements for health claims in 21 CFR 101.14, except for the requirement that the evidence for the claim meet the significant scientific agreement standard and be made in accordance with an authorizing regulation (21 CFR 101.14(c)).

The dietary supplement meet or exceed the requirement for a "high" level of calcium as defined in 21 CFR 101.54(b) (i.e., 200 mg or more calcium per reference amount customarily consumed)

The calcium content of the dietary supplement must be assimilable (i.e., bioavailable) (21 CFR 101.72(c)(ii)(B), and meet the United States Pharmacopeia (U.S.P.) standards for disintegration and dissolution applicable to their component calcium salts. For dietary supplements for which no U.S.P. standards exist, the dietary supplement must exhibit appropriate assimilability under the conditions of use stated on the product label (21 CFR 101.72(c)(ii)(C).

Qualified Claims About Neural Tube Birth Defects

0.8 mg Folic Acid & Neural Tube Birth Defects

Docket No. 91N-100H
04/03/2001 clarification letter
10/10/2000 enforcement discretion letter

Claim Statement

0.8 mg folic acid in a dietary supplement is more effective in reducing the risk of neural tube defects than a lower amount in foods in common form. FDA does not endorse this claim. Public health authorities recommend that women consume 0.4 mg folic acid daily from fortified foods or dietary supplements or both to reduce the risk of neural tube defects.

Eligible foods

- Dietary supplements containing folic acid

Factors

The disclaimer (i.e., FDA does not endorse this claim...) is placed immediately adjacent to and directly beneath the claim (i.e., 0.8 mg folic acid ...), with no intervening material, in the same size, typeface, and contrast as the claim.

CH 14

The claim meets all 21 CFR 101.14 general health claim requirements, except for the requirements that the claim meet the significant scientific agreement standard and be made in accordance with an authorizing regulation.

Note: there also is a folic acid/neural tube defect health claim authorized by regulation (see 21 CFR 101.79).

CDER-CFSAN Dietary Supplements Agreement

Intercenter Agreement Between the Center for Drug Evaluation and Research and the Center for Food Safety and Applied Nutrition to Assist FDA in Implementing DSHEA Regarding Products that Bear Structure/Function and/or Disease Claims

This document outlines a working agreement between the Center for Food Safety and Applied Nutrition (CFSAN) and the Center for Drug Evaluation and Research (CDER) of the Food and Drug Administration (FDA). The agreement assigns lead Center status for the regulation of certain products that bear structure/function and/or disease claims. It is intended to achieve a more efficient allocation of resources and better coordination of regulatory actions concerning products that purport to be dietary supplements but for which disease claims are made. The agreement does not apply to products purporting to be dietary supplements that are subject to the jurisdiction of other Centers (CBER, CVM, or CDRH).

This agreement is intended to assist FDA in implementing DSHEA and the structure/function rule by clarifying program responsibilities in light of overlapping jurisdiction between CDER and CFSAN. The agreement is entirely procedural in nature and is not intended to affect the Agency's approach to the implementation of the structure/function rule or the regulation of dietary supplements. The agreement does not formally bind FDA and creates no new rights or obligations for FDA or any regulated entities.

Effective Date and Review/Renewal

This agreement takes effect on June 1, 2005. CFSAN and CDER will evaluate this agreement on a tri-annual basis and make appropriate modifications.

Background

CDER is generally the FDA's lead Center for the regulation of human drugs, as defined in Section 201(g) of the Act. CFSAN is the Agency's lead Center for the regulation of human foods, as defined in Section 201(f) of the Act, and dietary supplements, as defined in Section 201(ff) of the Act.

The Dietary Supplement Health and Education Act (DSHEA) added Section 403(r)(6) to the Act. This section provides that the label or labeling of a dietary supplement may bear a claim that, among other things, "describes the role of a nutrient or dietary ingredient intended to affect the structure or function in humans" or that "characterizes the documented mechanism by which a nutrient or a dietary ingredient acts to maintain such structure or function." Such statements

CH
14

are generally referred to as "structure/function" claims. In addition, the definition of a drug in Section 201(g) was amended by DSHEA to establish that a dietary supplement is not a drug solely because the label or labeling makes these structure/function claims.

Accordingly, the label and labeling of dietary supplement products may bear structure/function claims for which no prior FDA review or approval is required. However, DSHEA does not permit any statement in the product's label or labeling that claims to diagnose, mitigate, treat, cure, or prevent a specific disease or class of diseases. These claims are generally referred to as "disease claims" and cause products associated with these claims to be regulated as drugs under Section 201(g)(1)(B) of the Act. Disease claims may be explicit or implied if such claims refer to identifiable characteristics of a disease from which a disease may be inferred. In order to help define the types of claims that are valid structure/function claims under Section 403(r)(6) of the Act, and to distinguish these claims from disease claims, FDA published a final rule on January 6, 2000 (65 FR 1000), known as "the structure/function rule." This MOU will not affect CDER's lead responsibility, as stated in the joint CDER/CFSAN letter of February 29, 2000, for distinguishing between "disease" and "non-disease" states or conditions in implementing the structure/function rule.

CFSAN Designation as Lead Center

Under this agreement, CFSAN is designated as the lead Center for regulatory action for certain products for which the labeling includes disease claims if such products also conform to each of the elements of the dietary supplement definition that appears in Section 201(ff) of the Act. Likewise, CFSAN is designated as the lead Center for regulatory action for certain products for which the labeling includes disease claims, but which do not bear the term "dietary supplements," provided that the products conform to all other elements of the dietary supplements definition that appears in Section 201(ff) of the Act and the products are labeled for marketing purposes as dietary supplements. Furthermore, CFSAN will be the lead Center if the sole reason for the product being subject to the drug requirements is that its labeling includes a disease claim rather than a structure/function or other appropriate dietary supplement claim.

As the lead Center for the products described above, CFSAN will have the authority to include appropriate drug charges (including sections 502 and 505 of the Act) in any regulatory action concerning a product associated with a disease claim. CFSAN agrees to consult with CDER, as appropriate, to ensure consistency when pursuing regulatory action based upon these drug charges.

CDER will retain concurrent jurisdiction to assert drug charges in pursuing regulatory actions against certain types of products for which CFSAN is the lead Center. In these cases, CFSAN will retain the right of first refusal for regulatory action. In these designated areas, CDER may pursue regulatory action for which CFSAN has declined to exercise its authority as lead Center. CDER agrees to consult with CFSAN and provide adequate advance notice before pursuing regulatory action under these circumstances.

CDER's action in these cases will be limited to drug charges and will not include any food charges. The designated areas are for products with disease claims that otherwise conform to each of the elements of Section 201(ff) of the Act, but raise unique issues for which CDER's historical role or medical expertise adds value to the Agency's regulatory action. The designated areas are limited to the following:

- Products containing hormones, including their metabolites and precursors;
- Products that have longstanding use as drugs and are widely recognized as drugs, even though they might be marketed purporting to be dietary supplements; and
- Products for which CDER has identified serious health hazard concerns.

CFSAN will also be the lead Center for regulatory action concerning conventional foods, medical foods, foods for special dietary use, and infant formula, even if disease claims are made for such products.

CDER Designation as Lead Center

The following are the types of products, with disease or structure/function claims, for which CDER will serve as lead Center because the products do not qualify as dietary supplements under Section 201(ff):

1. The product is labeled as an over-the-counter or prescription drug and the product is not labeled as a dietary supplement.

2. The product is not "intended to supplement the diet" under Section 201(ff)(1) of the Act (e.g., street drug alternative products, GHB/GBL).

3. The product does not bear or contain any of the designated "dietary ingredients" under Section 201(ff)(1)(A)-(F) of the Act.

4. The product is not "intended for ingestion" under Section 201(ff)(2)(A)(i) (e.g., topicals, inhalants, suppositories, etc.).

5. The product contains a component, under Section 201(ff)(3)(B)(i), that is an article approved as a new drug that was not marketed as a dietary supplement or a food before such approval (e.g., lovastatin).

6. The product contains a component, under Section 201(ff)(3)(B)(ii), that is an article authorized for investigation as a new drug for which substantial clinical investigations have been instituted and for which the existence of such investigations has been made public, which was not marketed as a dietary supplement before such approval.

CDER will continue to serve as the lead for combination drug and dietary supplement products, such as:

- products that contain a drug and a dietary ingredient in a single product (assuming CDER supports a drug charge);
- products that consist of co-packaged individual drug and dietary supplement products; and
- dual labeled products

CH 14

Chapter 15

Adverse Event Reporting
Guidance

Contains Nonbinding Recommendations
October 2007; Revised June 2009;
Revised September 2013

Guidance for Industry[1]:
Questions and Answers Regarding Adverse Event Reporting and Recordkeeping for Dietary Supplements as Required by the Dietary Supplement and Nonprescription Drug Consumer Protection Act

I. Introduction

This guidance document provides guidance to the dietary supplement industry for complying with the adverse event reporting and recordkeeping requirements prescribed for dietary supplement manufacturers, packers, and distributors by the Dietary Supplement and Nonprescription Drug Consumer Protection Act (Pub. L. 109-462). As required by section 3(d)(3) of this law, FDA (or "we") issued this guidance document to describe the minimum data elements for serious adverse event reports for dietary supplements. This guidance document also provides guidance on (1) how, when, and where to submit a serious adverse event report for a dietary supplement; and (2) records maintenance and access for serious and non-serious adverse event reports and related documents. Further, this guidance document also provides guidance on how to electronically submit a serious adverse event report for a dietary supplement. (We identify recent changes to the guidance document's questions and answers by identifying the date of the most recent change.) We have issued a separate guidance document on the reporting of serious adverse events for over-the-counter (nonprescription) human drug products marketed without an approved application.

FDA's guidance documents, including this guidance, do not establish legally enforceable responsibilities. Instead, guidance documents describe our current thinking on a topic and should

---

1   This guidance has been prepared by the Division of Dietary Supplement Programs, Office of Nutrition, Labeling and Dietary Supplements in the Center for Food Safety and Applied Nutrition at the U.S. Food and Drug Administration.

be viewed only as recommendations, unless specific regulatory or statutory requirements are cited. The use of the word should in FDA guidance documents means that something is suggested or recommended, but not required.

For purposes of this guidance document, "you" refers to the dietary supplement industry.

II. Background

On December 22, 2006, the President signed into law the Dietary Supplement and Nonprescription Drug Consumer Protection Act. This law amended the Federal Food, Drug, and Cosmetic Act (FD&C Act) with respect to adverse event reporting and recordkeeping for dietary supplements and non-prescription drugs marketed without an approved application. This guidance document contains questions and answers relating to the Dietary Supplement and Nonprescription Drug Consumer Protection Act's requirements concerning the mandatory reporting to FDA of serious adverse events for dietary supplements, the minimum data elements to be submitted in such reports, and records of serious and non-serious adverse events reported to a dietary supplement manufacturer, packer, or distributor. This guidance document also provides guidance to the dietary supplement industry on how to submit a serious adverse event report for a dietary supplement via the FDA Safety Reporting Portal (formerly referred to as the MedWatchPlus investment). Electronic submission is voluntary. A manufacturer, packer, or distributor of a dietary supplement who is unable to or chooses not to submit their mandatory serious adverse event report using the FDA Safety Reporting Portal may continue to submit their report by mail on the paper MedWatch form, Form FDA 3500A. For purposes of this guidance document, in several locations, we refer to Form FDA 3500A as the "paper version" and the FDA Safety Reporting Portal as the "electronic version" of the required "MedWatch form" as prescribed by the Dietary Supplement and Nonprescription Drug Consumer Protection Act.

III. Questions and Answers

1. When do the requirements of the Dietary Supplement and Nonprescription Drug Consumer Protection Act become effective?

The effective date for compliance with the requirements of this law was December 22, 2007.

2. What types of foods are covered by the Dietary Supplement and Nonprescription Drug Consumer Protection Act requirements?

The requirements of this law only apply to dietary supplements. No other types of food are covered.

3. What is FDA's definition of a dietary supplement?

Dietary supplements are defined, in part, as products (other than tobacco) intended to supplement the diet that bear or contain one or more of the following dietary ingredients:

a. A vitamin;

b. A mineral;

c. An herb or other botanical;

d. An amino acid;

e. A dietary substance for use by man to supplement the diet by increasing the total dietary intake; or

f. A concentrate, metabolite, constituent, extract, or combination of any ingredient mentioned above.

Further, a dietary supplement must be labeled as such and must be intended for ingestion. A dietary supplement must not be represented for use as a conventional food or as a sole item of a meal or the diet. Finally, the dietary supplement category generally does not include articles approved as new drugs, licensed as biologics, or authorized for clinical investigation under an IND, unless the article was previously marketed as a dietary supplement or as a food. The complete statutory definition can be found in section 201(ff) of the FD&C Act (21 U.S.C. 321(ff)).

4. [Updated September 2013] Does the Dietary Supplement and Nonprescription Drug Consumer Protection Act apply to foods other than dietary supplements, and if not, are there other mandatory reporting requirements for foods other than dietary supplements?

The requirements of the Dietary Supplement and Nonprescription Drug Consumer Protection Act do not apply to foods other than dietary supplements. However, there are other mandatory reporting requirements in section 417 of the FD&C Act that requires a "responsible party" to inform FDA of "reportable food," which is defined as an "article of food (other than infant formula or dietary supplements) for which there is a reasonable probability that the use of, or exposure to, such article of food will cause serious adverse health consequences or death to humans or animals." Also, infant formula manufacturers must comply with notification requirements for violative infant formula under 21 CFR 107.240.

5. What is an "adverse event?"

An "adverse event" is "any health-related event associated with the use of a dietary supplement that is adverse." Section 761(a)(1) of the FD&C Act (21 U.S.C. 379aa-1(a)(1)).

6. What is a "serious adverse event?"

A "serious adverse event" is an adverse event that:

- Results in death, a life-threatening experience, inpatient hospitalization, a persistent or significant disability or incapacity, or a congenital anomaly or birth defect; or

**CH
15**

- Requires, based on a reasonable medical judgment, a medical or surgical intervention to prevent an outcome described above.

Section 761(a)(2) of the FD&C Act (21 U.S.C. 379aa-1(a)(2)).

FDA considers inpatient hospitalization to include initial admission to the hospital on an inpatient basis, even if the patient is released the same day, and prolongation of an existing inpatient hospitalization. Please see the Appendix of this guidance for more information on the criteria for serious adverse events.

7. [Updated September 2013] What is a "serious adverse event report?"

A "serious adverse event report" is a report that must be submitted to FDA using the MedWatch form when a manufacturer, packer, or distributor of a dietary supplement receives any report of a serious adverse event associated with the use of the dietary supplement in the United States. See section 761(a)(3) and (b)(1) of the FD&C Act (21 U.S.C. 379aa-1(a)(3), (b)(1)).

8. Who must submit the serious adverse event report for a dietary supplement to FDA?

The manufacturer, packer, or distributor whose name (pursuant to section 403(e)(1) of the FD&C Act) [2] appears on the label of a dietary supplement marketed in the United States is required to submit to FDA all serious adverse event reports associated with use of the dietary supplement in the United States. Section 761(b)(1) of the FD&C Act (21 U.S.C. 379aa-1(b)(1)).

The Dietary Supplement and Nonprescription Drug Consumer Protection Act usually refers to the entity that is required to submit a serious adverse event report to FDA as the "responsible person." This guidance uses the term "responsible person" as an alternative to "manufacturer, packer, or distributor."

9. Are retailers required to submit serious adverse event reports for dietary supplements to FDA?

Usually not, but the answer could be yes in some situations. Whether a retailer is required to submit a serious adverse event report for a dietary supplement it sells will depend on two things: (1) whether the retailer's name appears on the label of the dietary supplement; and (2) if so, whether the retailer has entered into an agreement with the manufacturer or packer of the dietary supplement transferring responsibility for submitting adverse event reports for the product to the other firm.

A retailer whose name appears on the label of a dietary supplement as its distributor may, by agreement, authorize the manufacturer or packer of the dietary supplement to submit the required adverse event reports for such dietary supplement to the FDA so long as the retailer directs to the manufacturer or packer all adverse events associated with such dietary supplement that are reported to the retailer through the address or

---

2   Under section 403(e)(1) of the FD&C Act (21 U.S.C. 343(e)(1)) and 21 CFR 101.5, dietary supplements and other foods in package form must bear a label containing the name and place of business of the product's manufacturer, packer, or distributor.

telephone number on the label of the dietary supplement. Section 761(b)(2) of the FD&C Act (21 U.S.C. 379aa-1(b)(2)). If such an agreement is in place and the retailer complies with its obligation to forward the dietary supplement adverse event reports it receives to the other party (i.e., the manufacturer or packer), the retailer is under no obligation to report to FDA any serious adverse events for the dietary supplements covered by the agreement. Likewise, if the retailer's name does not appear on the label of a dietary supplement, the retailer is not responsible for reporting any serious adverse events associated with the supplement to FDA.

10. [Updated September 2013] When must reports of serious adverse events be submitted to FDA?

Serious adverse event reports received through the address or phone number on the label of a dietary supplement, as well as all follow-up reports of new medical information received by the responsible person within one year after the initial report, must be submitted to FDA no later than 15 business days after the report is received by the responsible person. Section 761(c)(1)-(2) of the FD&C Act (21 U.S.C. 379aa-1(c)(1)-(2)). For the reasons discussed below, FDA recommends that all other serious adverse event reports received by the responsible person also be submitted to FDA within 15 business days of receipt.

Section 761(c)(1) of the FD&C Act, which contains the 15-day deadline for submitting serious adverse event reports to FDA, expressly applies to serious adverse event reports resulting from information received by the responsible person through the address or telephone number on the product label. Although the FD&C Act does not expressly provide a timeframe for serious adverse event reports that the responsible person receives by other means (such as by e-mail or fax), the reporting of such adverse events is required by the plain language of section 761(b)(1) of the FD&C Act (providing that the responsible person "shall submit . . . any report received of a serious adverse event associated with such dietary supplement when used in the United States . . . ." (emphasis added)), and we recommend that such reports be submitted to FDA within the same timeframe as reports received by phone or mail, i.e., within 15 business days of their receipt by the responsible person.

Prompt submission of serious adverse event reports is important for public health reasons. Delayed reporting of some serious adverse events to FDA solely because of the medium through which the adverse event was reported to the responsible person would lessen the effectiveness of adverse event reporting as an early warning sign of possible safety problems with dietary supplements. Without prompt notification of all serious adverse events associated with dietary supplements, FDA would be unable to investigate and follow up promptly, which in turn could cause delays in alerting the public when safety problems are found. Therefore, we recommend that all serious adverse event reports received by the responsible person should be reported to FDA within 15 business days of receipt, regardless of the means by which the responsible person received the initial report.

CH
15

As soon as all of the minimum data elements (i.e., identifiable patient, initial reporter, identity and contact information of responsible person, suspect dietary supplement, and serious adverse event) are known to the responsible person, the 15-business-day time clock begins to run. That date is Day 0 and should be entered in section G, block 4, on the paper version of the MedWatch form. For the electronic version, this is located on the "Introduction" page as "Enter the date you received the initial report". If the responsible person does not initially receive sufficient data for a serious adverse event report to FDA, but later receives additional information completing the minimum data elements listed in Question 13, then the responsible person should submit the serious adverse event report within 15 business days of the date the additional information was received, with that date entered in section G, block 4, of the paper version of the MedWatch form or on the "Introduction" page for the electronic version as indicated above.

Although the FD&C Act does not expressly require a responsible person to take action in the event that it receives a report of a serious adverse event in which the initial reporter identifies the suspect dietary supplement as one manufactured, packaged, or distributed by another responsible person, we recommend that such reports be promptly forwarded to that other responsible person. In the event that a responsible person receives a report of an adverse event regarding one of its products from another responsible person, the responsible person whose product was involved must submit a serious adverse event report to FDA within the same timeframe applicable to any report received from an initial reporter (i.e., 15 business days from receipt), even if a serious adverse event report has already been submitted to FDA by the first responsible person (see "Suspect Dietary Supplement" discussion in Question 13).

11. [Updated September 2013] How is a serious adverse event report for a dietary supplement submitted to FDA?

A serious adverse event report for a dietary supplement is submitted to FDA on either the paper or electronic version of the MedWatch form (also referred to as Form FDA 3500A for the paper version and the FDA Safety Reporting Portal for the electronic version). The manufacturer, packer, or distributor of a dietary supplement is required by statute to use a MedWatch form when submitting a serious adverse event report to FDA. The statute permits but does not require FDA to modify the MedWatch form for dietary supplement reporting. We initially determined that the paper MedWatch form, Form FDA 3500A, the form used for mandatory reporting of adverse events for other FDA-regulated products, was also the most appropriate MedWatch form available for mandatory reporting of dietary supplement adverse events. As of September 2013, we are making available an electronic option to submit a serious adverse event report for a dietary supplement via the FDA Safety Reporting Portal, the electronic version of the MedWatch form. We encourage industry to use the electronic version of the MedWatch form to submit a serious adverse event report for a dietary supplement because the electronic version will allow for faster processing of reports and may require less follow up by FDA with the responsible person submitting the paper version.

12. [Updated September 2013] Are there any instructions available for filling out the paper and electronic version of the MedWatch Forms to report a serious adverse event for a dietary supplement?

Yes. Instructions for filling out the paper MedWatch form, Form FDA 3500A, for serious adverse event reports for dietary supplements are in the Appendix of this guidance. The electronic MedWatch form, the FDA Safety Reporting Portal, provides the user with detailed navigation instructions to include drop-down menus, lists of values, controlled vocabularies, and mouse over help where possible.

13. [Updated September 2013] What are the minimum data elements that should be included in a serious adverse event report for a dietary supplement, and where should these data elements be entered on the paper and electronic version of the MedWatch Forms?

The five data elements listed in the bullets below should be included in any serious adverse event report for a dietary supplement. These elements, at a minimum, are necessary for FDA to avoid duplication in its adverse event reports database, interpret the significance of adverse events, facilitate follow-up, and detect fraud. The section where each element should be entered on the paper version or electronic version of the MedWatch Forms is given in parentheses at the end of the bullet.

- an identifiable patient (Section A of the paper version/"Problem Summary – Affected Individual Information" of the electronic version);

- an identifiable initial reporter (Section E of the paper version/"Contact Information – Initial Reporter" of the electronic version);

- identity and contact information for the responsible person (i.e., the manufacturer, packer, or distributor submitting the serious adverse event report to FDA) (Section G of the paper version/"Contact Information – Manufacturer, Packer, or Distributor Site Information and Site Point of Contact Information" of the electronic version);

- a suspect dietary supplement (Section C of the paper version/ "Suspect Product(s)" of the electronic version); and

- a serious adverse event or fatal outcome (Section B of the paper version/"Problem Summary – Adverse Event and/or Product Problem Description" of the electronic version).

The responsible person should actively seek information on any minimum data elements that are not initially provided by the reporter and wait to submit a serious adverse event report to FDA until the information is obtained. We do not intend to take enforcement action for failure to report a serious adverse event where, after diligent efforts, the responsible person is unable to obtain all of the five minimum data elements. We recommend that the responsible person document its efforts to obtain the basic elements for a serious adverse event report. As discussed below in the questions and answers about recordkeeping, the responsible person must keep records related to any

CH 15

adverse event report it receives for six years, regardless of whether the event must be reported to FDA. Section 761(e)(1) of the FD&C Act (21 U.S.C. 379aa-1(e)(1)).

During initial contacts with the reporter and subsequent follow-up, the responsible person should make diligent attempts to obtain complete information. To this end, we encourage responsible persons to use trained health care practitioners to elicit information from reporters, computer-assisted interview technology, targeted questionnaires, and/or other appropriate methods that help focus the line of questioning. When the initial report is from a consumer, we recommend that the responsible person seek the patient's permission to contact the health care practitioner(s) familiar with the diagnosis and treatment of the adverse event to obtain further information and relevant medical records, as needed.

Identifiable patient: (Section A - "Patient Information"/"Problem Summary – Affected Individual Information")

To have an identifiable patient means providing enough information to demonstrate that an individual person experienced a serious adverse event. For example, filling in "some consumers" under "Patient Identifier" would not be sufficient; however, a report that listed the patient identifier as "an elderly woman" or "a young man" would be sufficient because there is enough information to assess that a specific person experienced a serious adverse event. One or more of the following automatically qualifies a person as identifiable: age or age category (e.g., adolescent, adult, elderly), gender, initials, date of birth, name, or patient identification number. A report stating that "an elderly woman had anaphylaxis" or "a young man experienced anaphylaxis" would be sufficient. If a report submitted to the responsible person refers to groups of unknown size, such as "some" or "a few" college students got anaphylaxis, the responsible person should follow up to find out the number of patients and then submit a separate report to FDA for each identifiable patient. The responsible person should distinguish each patient so that it is clear that the separate serious adverse event reports are not duplicate reports of a single adverse event.

To protect the privacy of the patient, he or she should not be identified by name or address; instead, the responsible person should assign a code (e.g., the injured person's initials) to each serious adverse event report. The assigned code will permit the responsible person to cross-reference identifying information and contact information for the patient in the event that the responsible person needs to follow up.

Initial Reporter (Section E – "Initial Reporter"/"Contact Information – Initial Reporter")

The initial reporter is the person who first notifies the responsible person about the serious adverse event and can be the patient, a family member, or some other person (e.g., doctor, pharmacist). One or more of the following automatically qualifies a reporter as identifiable: a personal identifier (e.g., name), professional identifier (e.g., doctor, nurse, pharmacist), or contact information (e.g., e-mail address, phone number). In addition to the contact information requested on the form, the initial reporter's e-mail address should also be provided, if available.

CH
15

Individual judgment will be needed at times to decide whether or not a reporter will be considered identifiable for reporting purposes. If the initial reporter is a third party who has only limited information about the serious adverse event (e.g., "my neighbor told me that a friend became seriously ill after taking Product X"), the responsible person should try to obtain contact information (such as a phone number or e-mail address) for someone with personal knowledge of the adverse event. The responsible person should then follow up with that person to obtain enough information to submit a serious adverse event report to FDA (i.e., the five minimum data elements).

If the initial reporter requests that the responsible person not forward the reporter's name and contact information to FDA, the responsible person can submit a report without identifying the reporter, as long as the responsible person keeps the contact information on file so that it may contact the reporter either upon request by FDA or on its own initiative. For these reports, the responsible person should fill in the initial reporter name and address block in section E of the paper version with a statement such as "Requested Anonymity." The same can be entered in the "Initial Reporter" section of the "Contact Information" page on the electronic version.

Responsible Person (Section G - "All Manufacturers"/"Contact Information - Manufacturer, Packer, or Distributor Site Information and Site Point of Contact Information")

This section of the paper and electronic version of the MedWatch forms is for information about the responsible person and the initial report. Per the instructions in Appendix A, blocks 5 and 6 on the paper version are not required for dietary supplement serious adverse event reports. This information is not included on the electronic version.

Suspect Dietary Supplement (Section C - "Suspect Product(s)"/"Suspect Product(s)")

With regard to a *suspect dietary supplement*, provide the complete product name, including brand name, and any other known product attributes. The information provided should be sufficient to uniquely identify the suspect product and distinguish it from other similarly named products. For example, "Vitamin C" or "multi-vitamin" would not be considered complete product names. Examples of information that may be needed to uniquely identify the product include the physical form of the product (e.g., tablet, powder, gelcap, bar); strength (e.g., 120 mg); flavor, if any; and packaging form and size (e.g., 120-tablet bottle).

If a serious adverse event involves multiple dietary supplements that are manufactured, packaged, or distributed by the same responsible person, the responsible person should submit only one serious adverse event report to FDA, listing all suspect products in Section C with the same manufacturer report number in section G, block 9 on the paper version and for the electronic version, listing all "suspect products" where indicated.

If the serious adverse event involves a nonprescription drug product marketed without an approved application and a dietary supplement that is also manufactured, packaged, or distributed by the same responsible person, and the initial reporter views each product as suspect, the responsible person should submit the report about the serious

CH 15

adverse event to both CDER and CFSAN. The report should include information about both suspect products in section C and should use one manufacturer report number.

If a serious adverse event involves multiple suspect dietary supplements that were manufactured, packaged or distributed by more than one responsible person (e.g., manufacturers A and B), and if the event is reported to one of the responsible persons (manufacturer A), then that responsible person (manufacturer A) must submit a serious adverse event report to FDA that identifies both its own product(s) and manufacturer B's product(s) in the Suspect Product section of either the paper or electronic version including a copy of manufacturer A's product label.[3] In such a case, we recommend that manufacturer A also send manufacturer B a copy of the submitted paper version of the report or a copy of the Individual Case Safety Report generated by the electronic version, including manufacturer A's report number. In the event that manufacturer B receives such a report, manufacturer B must then submit its own serious adverse event report, citing manufacturer A's report number in the "Describe Event or Problem" section of the paper version (i.e., section B.5) or the "Problem Summary" section of the electronic version, and including a copy of manufacturer B's product label. Section 761(b)(1) of the FD&C Act (21 U.S.C. 379aa-1(b)(1)).

If a serious adverse event involves a dietary supplement that has been discontinued, the responsible person must still submit a report to FDA. Responsible persons must submit "any report received" of a serious adverse event associated with their products when used in the United States. Section 761(b)(1) of the FD&C Act (21 U.S.C. 379aa-1(b)(1)). Where a product involved in a serious adverse event has been discontinued, the responsible person may make note of this status in Section B.5 of the paper version or in the "Problem Summary" section of the electronic version of the MedWatch forms.

Serious Adverse Event or Fatal Outcome (Section B - "Adverse Event or Product Problem"/"Problem Summary - Adverse Event and/or Product Problem Description")

A *serious adverse event*, as defined in section 761(a)(2) of the FD&C Act (21 U.S.C. 379aa-1(a)(2)), is an adverse event that results in or more of the following patient outcomes or, based on reasonable medical judgment, requires a medical or surgical intervention to prevent one of the following patient outcomes:

- death
- a life-threatening experience

---

3   Section 761(b)(1) of the FD&C Act (21 U.S.C. 379aa-1(b)(1)) requires the manufacturer, packer, or distributor of a dietary supplement to submit to FDA "any report received" of a serious adverse event associated with the dietary supplement when used in the United States. Accordingly, where a report is required, responsible persons must provide FDA with the information about the serious adverse event supplied by the initial reporter. Moreover, section 761(d) of the FD&C Act (21 U.S.C. 379aa-1(d)) requires serious adverse event reports to be submitted using the MedWatch form. The MedWatch form, Form FDA 3500A, in existence when the Dietary Supplement and Nonprescription Drug Consumer Protection Act was adopted, includes Section C, which seeks information about "Suspect Product(s)" known to the responsible person. The electronic version of the MedWatch form available via the FDA Safety Reporting Portal also includes a section for "Suspect Product(s)." Therefore, manufacturer A must report information about manufacturer B's products on the MedWatch form in the example above even though manufacturer A did not manufacture, pack or distribute those products.

- inpatient hospitalization[4]
- a persistent or significant disability or incapacity
- a congenital anomaly or birth defect.

A *serious adverse event* other than death should, at a minimum, be described in terms of signs (including abnormal laboratory findings), symptoms, or disease diagnosis for purposes of reporting. Thus, a report stating that the patient "experienced unspecified injury," "suffered irreparable damages," or "was ill" would not be specific enough. If the initial reporter does not provide any signs, symptoms, or diagnosis, the responsible person should follow up as necessary to obtain more information from that person, the patient, or (with the patient's permission) medical professionals who treated the patient.

A report of a *fatal outcome* (death) meets the minimum description for a serious adverse event even if the events that led to the death are unknown, but such reports should also include any other available information related to the death (e.g., adverse event(s) associated with the death).

14. [Updated September 2013] Can a serious adverse event report be submitted to FDA using the MedWatch voluntary reporting form (Form FDA 3500)?

No. FDA has determined that dietary supplement manufacturers, packers, and distributors must report serious adverse events associated with their products using either the paper MedWatch form, Form FDA 3500A or the FDA Safety Reporting Portal. Section 761(d) of the FD&C Act (21 U.S.C. 379aa-1(d)). However, voluntary reports of adverse events associated with a dietary supplement may be submitted using either the paper MedWatch form, Form FDA 3500 (note the absence of the letter "A"), or the FDA Safety Reporting Portal. Voluntary reports of dietary supplement adverse events would include:

- any adverse event report submitted by a consumer, health care provider, or any other entity that is not a dietary supplement manufacturer, packer, or distributor;
- a report of a non-serious adverse event submitted by a dietary supplement manufacturer, packer, or distributor for one of its products;
- a report of a serious adverse event submitted by a dietary supplement manufacturer, packer, or distributor for one of its products, where the firm is not the "responsible person" who must report the serious adverse event. For example, the manufacturer of a dietary supplement might choose to submit a report of a serious adverse event to FDA even though the distributor was the "responsible person" because the distributor's name appeared on the dietary supplement label. In such a case, FDA would receive both voluntary and mandatory reports of the same serious adverse event.

---

4   See Question 6 and Appendix A for guidance on how FDA interprets the term "inpatient hospitalization" and the other criteria defining a serious adverse event.

CH 15

15. a. [Updated September 2013] Must a copy of the label of the dietary supplement that is the subject of the serious adverse event report be submitted with the report?

Yes. Section 761(b)(1) of the FD&C Act (21 U.S.C. 379aa-1(b)(1)). Wherever possible, responsible persons should submit a copy of the full outer carton/container label and immediate container label from the product the patient used. See 21 U.S.C. 321(k); 21 CFR 1.3(b). Where the patient's product has been specifically identified, but the responsible person does not have a copy of the patient's own label, the responsible person should submit an original or photocopied label that is the same as the label of the product the patient used, or as close as the responsible person can come to that label using all available information.

Where the exact label of the patient's dietary supplement cannot be identified with certainty, such as where a label has changed over time or where the patient's exact product cannot be identified with specificity, the responsible person may submit a copy of the label most likely viewed by the patient, or may submit multiple labels for those products most likely to be associated with the report. In addition, where the label has changed since the time of the adverse event, the responsible person may also submit a copy of the product's current label.

For responsible persons submitting the paper MedWatch form, Form FDA 3500A, this information should be mailed in with the serious adverse event report. For electronic submissions via the FDA Safety Reporting Portal, responsible persons should attach an electronic image of the label in one of the formats listed on the "Attachments" section.

15. b. Should anything other than the product label be submitted along with the serious adverse event report

Yes. As part of the serious adverse event report, we encourage the responsible person to attach the following, as appropriate: (1) hospital discharge summaries, (2) autopsy reports, (3) relevant laboratory data, and (4) other critical clinical data. Please note that this paragraph does not provide an exhaustive list of all the documents or information that may be submitted with the report at the responsible person's option.

16. Does a sample of the dietary supplement that is the subject of the serious adverse event report have to be submitted to FDA?

No. There is no requirement that a sample of the dietary supplement be provided to FDA with the adverse event report, and we do not recommend you submit a sample unless requested to do so.

17. Must new medical information received by the manufacturer, packer, or distributor of a dietary supplement that is related to a previously submitted serious adverse event report also be submitted to FDA?

Yes, any new medical information received within one year of the initial report must be submitted to FDA. Section 761(c)(2) of the FD&C Act (21 U.S.C. 379aa-1(c)(2)). Even if new medical information is received later than one year after the serious adverse event report and therefore does not have to be reported, you must keep it in your file on the serious adverse event for six years because it is a record related to the serious adverse event report. Section 761(e)(1) of the FD&C Act (21 U.S.C. 379aa-1(e)(1)). Although you are not required to submit to FDA any new medical information that is received later than one year after the serious adverse event report, we encourage the voluntary submission of such information so that we obtain a complete report to evaluate.

18. When must the new medical information be submitted to FDA?

This new medical information must be submitted to FDA within 15 business days of being received by the manufacturer, packer, or distributor. Section 761(c)(2) of the FD&C Act (21 U.S.C. 379aa-1(c)(2)).

19. a. [Updated September 2013] How should the new medical information be submitted to FDA? Should another report be filled out and submitted on the MedWatch form, Form FDA 3500A, or using the FDA Safety Reporting Portal, in addition to the initial serious adverse event report originally submitted?

No. A new report does not have to be completed on paper Form FDA 3500A or on the FDA Safety Reporting Portal to submit the new medical information (e.g., medical records). The FDA Safety Reporting Portal allows users to electronically update a serious adverse event report previously submitted via the portal. To submit a follow up report with new medical information, first electronically access the previously submitted report:

- Accessing reports submitted as an account holder: Log in from the homepage of the Safety Reporting Portal. Select the appropriate previously submitted report from the "Submitted Reports Available for Follow-up" list.

- Accessing reports submitted as a guest: From the Safety Reporting Portal homepage, click "Report as Guest." On the "New Guest Report" screen, choose "Follow-up on a report previously submitted as a guest portal user." Enter the appropriate Report Identification Key in the text box that appears.

Once the appropriate report has been chosen for follow up, attach electronic versions of the new medical information on the Attachments section of the follow up report. If the new medical information cannot be condensed into 5 or fewer files of less than 10 MB each (the limitation of the portal) please submit multiple follow up reports to transmit all of the new information.

To submit new medical information related to a serious adverse event report previously submitted to FDA on paper Form FDA 3500A, simply attach a copy of the initial serious adverse event report to a copy of the new medical information in the same form you received it. It is not necessary to re-submit any attachments from the initial serious adverse event report.

CH 15

19. b. [Updated September 2013] Can FDA provide assurance that the new medical information submitted will be consolidated into a single report by FDA?

For submission of new medical information related to reports made using the paper version, when a copy of the initial serious adverse event report on MedWatch Form 3500A is included with the new medical information, we will be able to consolidate the initial submission and the new medical information into a single report. Reports submitted using the electronic version are linked electronically, and the new medical information will be associated with the initial report automatically.

20. [Updated September 2013] Will FDA confirm receipt of serious adverse event reports submitted and provide a tracking number to use for further submissions of new medical information related to the initial report?

If the report is submitted using the FDA Safety Reporting Portal, responsible persons will be provided with a confirmation email containing a time stamped copy of their report upon its submission. This copy also contains an Individual Case Safety Report number to identify the report in any subsequent communications.

If the report is submitted using the paper MedWatch form, Form FDA 3500A, no confirmation of receipt or tracking number is provided to the responsible person at this time. We are working to implement processes that will provide a confirmation of receipt and tracking number to the responsible person when a serious adverse event report for dietary supplements is submitted using the paper version. We will revise this guidance when these processes are implemented.

21. [Updated September 2013] What is the process for getting a copy of MedWatch Form 3500A?

MedWatch Form 3500A is on FDA's Internet web site. If you are unable to access the paper version of the form on-line, request a paper copy of the form by calling 1-800-FDA-1088 or by submitting a written request to:

> MedWatch: The FDA Safety Information and Adverse Event Reporting Program
> Office Of The Center Director
> Center for Drug Evaluation and Research
> 5515 Security Lane
> Suite 5100
> Rockville, MD 20852

22. [Updated September 2013] Where are completed paper versions of serious adverse event reports for dietary supplements to be submitted?

Please mail completed MedWatch form, Form FDA 3500A, along with a copy of the dietary supplement label and any other attachments (see Questions 15a and 15b), to: FDA, Center for Food Safety and Applied Nutrition, Office of Food Defense, Communication and Emergency Response, CAERS Team, HFS-11, 5001 Campus Drive, College Park, MD 20740.

23. [Updated September 2013] What is the process for submitting serious adverse event reports for dietary supplements electronically?

The electronic version of the MedWatch form, the FDA Safety Reporting Portal, is accessible at www.safetyreporting.hhs.gov. A reporter may choose to submit serious adverse event reports as an account holder or as a guest. As noted, the FDA Safety Reporting Portal provides the user with detailed navigation instructions to include drop-down menus, lists of values, controlled vocabularies, and mouse over help where possible.

24. Can the paper version of the MedWatch form, Form FDA 3500A, for a dietary supplement serious adverse event report be submitted to FDA by facsimile?

No. Dietary supplement serious adverse events reported on the paper version of MedWatch form, Form FDA 3500A, along with a copy of the dietary supplement label and any other attachments (see Questions 15a and 15b), should be mailed to FDA (see answer to Question 22 for address). We do not accept these reports by facsimile due to concerns about the quality of this form of transmission (i.e., the clarity and readability of faxed documents).

25. a. How long should records of serious adverse event reports and related medical information be maintained?

The responsible person must maintain all records related to each report of a serious adverse event for a period of 6 years. Section 761(e)(1) of the FD&C Act (21 U.S.C. 379aa-1(e)(1)). These records should include, at a minimum, copies of the following:

- the responsible person's serious adverse event report to FDA, with attachments;
- any new medical information about the serious adverse event received by the responsible person;
- any reports to FDA of new medical information related to the serious adverse event;
- communications and records of communications between the responsible person and
    - the initial reporter
    - any other person(s) who provided information related to the adverse event

25. b. Should records of non-serious adverse events reported to the manufacturer, packer, or distributor of the dietary supplement involved be maintained?

Yes. If you receive a report of a non-serious adverse event associated with a dietary supplement for which you are the manufacturer, packer, or distributor, you must keep the report along with any related records (e.g., records of your communications with the person(s) who reported the adverse event to you, records of your assessment of the event as non-serious). All such records of non-serious adverse events must be kept for six years, just as with records of serious adverse events. Section 761(e)(1) of the FD&C Act (21 U.S.C. 379aa-1(e)(1)).

CH 15

25. c. Can records of serious and non-serious adverse events reported be maintained electronically?

Yes. Electronic records created and maintained to meet the requirements of section 761(e)(1) of the FD&C Act (21 U.S.C. 379aa-1(e)(1)) are subject to the requirements of 21 CFR part 11. Therefore, if you maintain your records electronically, you must comply with the electronic record requirements contained in 21 CFR part 11.

26. Can FDA examine or inspect adverse event report records?

Yes. During an FDA inspection conducted under the authority of section 704 of the FD&C Act (21 U.S.C. 374), we are authorized to have access to all adverse event report records that dietary supplement manufacturers, packers, and distributors are required to maintain. Section 761(e)(2) of the FD&C Act (21 U.S.C. 379aa-1(e)(2)).

27. Is submission to FDA of a serious adverse event report an admission that the dietary supplement involved caused the serious adverse event described in that report?

No. We do not construe submission as an admission that the dietary supplement involved caused or contributed to the adverse event being reported. Any serious adverse event report submitted to FDA, including any new medical information submitted as a follow-up to the initial report, is considered a safety report under section 756 of the FD&C Act (21 U.S.C. 379v) and may be accompanied by a statement, which shall be a part of any report that is released for public disclosure, that denies that the report or the records constitute an admission that the product involved caused or contributed to the serious adverse event. Section 761(f)(1) of the FD&C Act (21 U.S.C. 379aa-1(f)(1)).

Further, we note that both the paper and electronic versions of the MedWatch form contain the statement "Submission of a report does not constitute an admission that medical personnel, user facility, importer, distributor, manufacturer or product caused or contributed to the event."

28. [Updated September 2013] If a serious adverse event involves a dietary supplement that has been discontinued, must the responsible person submit a serious adverse event report to FDA?

Yes. See *Suspect Dietary Supplement* section of Question 13. The responsible person must still submit a report, but may note in Section B.5 of the paper version of the MedWatch form or in the "Problem Summary" section of the electronic version that the product has been discontinued.

IV. Paperwork Reduction Act of 1995

This guidance contains information collection provisions that are subject to review by the Office of Management and Budget (OMB) under the Paperwork Reduction Act of 1995 (44 U.S.C. 3501-3520).

The time required to maintain the dietary supplement adverse event records recommended in this guidance and required by section 761(e)(1) of the FD&C Act is estimated to average 30 minutes per record, including the time to review instructions, search existing data resources, gather the data needed, and complete and review the information collection. Send comments regarding this burden estimate or suggestions for reducing this burden to:

Office of Nutrition, Labeling, and Dietary Supplements, Division of Dietary Supplement Programs, HFS - 810, Center for Food Safety and Applied Nutrition Food and Drug Administration, 5001 Campus Drive, College Park, MD 20740.

This guidance also refers to previously approved collections of information found in the FD&C Act. Submission to FDA of serious adverse event reports for dietary supplements and follow-up reports of new medical information is required by section 761(c)(1)-(2) of the FD&C Act. The electronic submission of dietary supplement adverse event information to us via the FDA Safety Reporting Portal has been approved under OMB Control No. 0910-0645, while submission of dietary supplement adverse event information to us using the original paper forms (Forms FDA 3500 and 3500A) has been approved under OMB Control No. 0910-0291.

An agency may not conduct or sponsor, and a person is not required to respond to, a collection of information unless it displays a currently valid OMB control number. The OMB control number for this information collection is 0910-0635 (expires 3/31/2019).

V. Appendix: Instructions for Completing the paper version of MedWatch Form 3500A to Report a Serious Adverse Event Associated with a Dietary Supplement

Form FDA 3500A (PDF format) is a two-sided form. It is for use by user facilities, distributors, importers, applicants, and manufacturers for "mandatory" reporting of adverse events and product problems associated with drugs, biologics, and devices, as designated in the applicable statutes and FDA regulations. In addition, MedWatch Form 3500A is for use by manufacturers, packers and distributors for "mandatory" reporting of serious adverse events associated with the use of dietary supplements as required by the Dietary Supplement and Nonprescription Drug Consumer Protection Act (Public Law 109-462).

How to Obtain FDA 3500A Forms and Guidance on How to Complete FDA Form 3500A Regarding Serious Adverse Event Reporting for Dietary Supplements

1. Copies of Form FDA 3500A

2. Guidance for Industry: Questions and Answers Regarding Adverse Event Reporting and Recordkeeping for Dietary Supplements as Required by the Dietary Supplement and Non-prescription Drug Consumer Protection Act.

3. Fillable Forms Software

   - If you submit reports frequently, you may download a fillable version of the FDA 3500A form for local installation on your personal computer.

   - This application does not permit electronic submission of reports.

CH
15

4. How to Submit Form FDA 3500A to FDA .

At this time, FDA requires that mandatory reports using MedWatch Form 3500A for serious adverse events associated with the use of dietary supplements be submitted in hard copy by mail only (see #5 for address). FDA does not currently accept dietary supplement serious adverse event reports electronically or by facsimile.

5. Where to Send Mandatory Reporting Forms for Reports of Serious Adverse Events Associated with Dietary Supplements

For Dietary Supplements Only:
Food and Drug Administration
Center for Food Safety and Applied Nutrition
Office of Food Defense, Communication and Emergency Response
CAERS Team (HFS-11)
5001 Campus Drive
College Park, MD 20740

6. Questions About Mandatory Serious Adverse Event Reporting for Dietary Supplements?

Office of Nutrition, Labeling, and Dietary Supplements
Center for Food Safety and Applied Nutrition
Food and Drug Administration
5001 Campus Drive, HFS-800
College Park, MD 20740
(240) 402-2375

General Instructions

- All entries should be typed or printed in a font no smaller than 8 point.

- Complete all sections that apply. If information is unknown, not available or does not apply, the section should be left blank.

- Dates should be entered as mm/dd/yyyy (e.g., June 3, 2005 = 06/03/2005). If exact dates are unknown, provide the best estimate.

- For narrative entries, if the fields do not provide adequate space, attach an additional page(s). The following specific information is to be incorporated:

  - Include the phrase continued at the end of each field of FDA Form 3500A that has additional information continued onto another page

  - Identify all attached pages as Page __ of __

  - Indicate the appropriate section and block number next to the narrative continuation

  - Display the manufacturer, packer or distributor name and report number in the upper right hand corner as applicable

- All submissions must be made in English.

CH 15

Front Page

At the top of the front page

➲ Enter the page number and total number of pages submitted (include attachments in the total) where the words Page __ of __ are indicated.

➲ On the top-right corner of the front page, enter the manufacturer report number, packer report number or distributor report number in the "Mfr Report #" box. Enter all report numbers, if applicable, to cross-reference this report with a report from another source on the same event. The manufacturer, packer, or distributor report number is the unique identifier used by the manufacturer, packer or distributor for this report. The manufacturer, packer or distributor report number is also entered in block G9 on the back of the form.

Section A. Patient Information

A. PATIENT INFORMATION			
1. Patient Identifier	2. Age at Time of Event: or ———— Date of Birth:	3. Sex ☐ Female ☐ Male	4. Weight ———— lbs or ———— kgs
In confidence			

The patient is the person who experienced the adverse event. If more than one person experienced the adverse event, complete a separate form for each patient.

Parent-child/fetus report(s) are those cases in which either a fetus/breast feeding infant or the mother, or both, sustain an adverse event that the initial reporter considers possibly associated with a product administered to the mother during pregnancy. Several general principles are used for filing these reports:

• If there has been no event affecting the child/fetus, the mother is the patient to be described in section A.

• For those cases describing fetal death, miscarriage or abortion, the mother is the patient to be described in section A.

• When ONLY the child/fetus experiences a serious adverse event (other than fetal death, miscarriage or abortion), the child/fetus is the patient to be described in section A. Information concerning the mother, including the name of the product that the mother ingested, if she was the source of exposure to the product, should be provided in section C. Section B5 should describe that the mother ingested the product but the child/fetus experienced the serious adverse event.

• When an infant is found to have a congenital anomaly/birth defect that the initial reporter considers possibly associated with a product administered to the mother during pregnancy, the infant is the patient to be described in section A.

• If both the mother and the child/fetus experience serious adverse events associated with the mother's use of a single product, the responsible person should submit two separate reports to FDA. Each report should be linked to the other using the "Describe

CH 15

Event or Problem" narrative in block B5, which should give the manufacturer report number for the other report.

A1: Patient Identifier

Provide the patient's initials or some other type of identifier that will allow both the responsible person and the initial reporter (if different) to locate the case if contacted for follow-up. Do not use the patient's name or social security number.

The patient's identity is held in strict confidence by FDA and protected to the fullest extent of the law.

A2: Age at Time of Event or Date of Birth

Provide the most precise information available. Enter the patient's birthdate, if known, or the patient's age at the time of event onset. For age, indicate time units used (e.g., years, months, and days).

- If the patient is 3 years or older, use years (e.g., 4 years)
- If the patient is less than 3 years old, use months (e.g., 24 months)
- If the patient is less than 1 month old, use days (e.g., 5 days)
- Provide the best estimate if exact age is unknown

A3: Sex

Enter the patient's gender. If the adverse event is a congenital anomaly or birth defect, report the sex of the child.

A4: Weight

Enter the patient's weight. Indicate whether the weight is in pounds (lbs.) or kilograms (kgs). Make a best estimate if exact weight is unknown.

Section B: Adverse Event or Product Problem

B1: Adverse event and/or Product problem

Choose the appropriate box. For dietary supplements, product problems should be reported to FDA on Form 3500A only if the problem may have caused or contributed to a serious adverse event. In that case, both boxes should be checked. Dietary supplement product problems not associated with a serious adverse event may be reported to FDA on Form FDA 3500 the MedWatch voluntary reporting form.

Adverse event: Any adverse health-related event associated with the use of a dietary supplement. Report only serious adverse events to FDA on Form 3500A. See instructions for block B2, below, for the definition of a serious adverse event.

Product problem (e.g., defects): Any report regarding the quality or safety of any dietary supplement.

B2: Outcomes attributed to adverse event:

Dietary Supplements: Serious adverse events associated with the use of a dietary supplement must be reported to FDA. A serious adverse event, as defined in Section 761(a)(2) of the Federal Food, Drug, and Cosmetic Act, means an adverse event that:

- Results in
    - death;
    - a life-threatening experience;
    - inpatient hospitalization;
    - a persistent or significant disability or incapacity; or
    - a congenital anomaly or birth defect; or
- Requires, based on reasonable medical judgment, a medical or surgical intervention to prevent an outcome described above.

Indicate ALL outcomes that apply to the reported event:

Death: Check if death was an outcome of the adverse event, or if the cause of the death is unknown. Include the date of death, if known.

DO NOT check if:

- The patient died while using a dietary supplement, but there was no suspected association between the death and the use of the product
- A fetus was aborted because of a congenital anomaly, or was miscarried

Life-threatening: Check if it is suspected that:

- The patient was at substantial risk of dying at the time of the serious adverse event.

Hospitalization (initial or prolonged): Check if admission to the hospital or prolongation of hospitalization was a result of the serious adverse event.

DO NOT check if:

- A patient in the hospital took a dietary supplement and subsequently developed an otherwise nonserious adverse event, UNLESS the adverse event prolonged the hospital stay.

CH 15

DO check if:

- The patient was admitted to the hospital for one or more days, even if he or she was released on the same day.
- An emergency room visit resulted in admission to the hospital.

Note: Emergency room visits that do not result in admission to the hospital should be evaluated for one of the other serious outcomes (e.g., death, life-threatening experience, a persistent or significant disability or incapacity, a congenital anomaly or birth defect, or intervention required to prevent one of these outcomes)

Disability or Permanent Damage: Check if the serious adverse event resulted in a substantial disruption of a person's ability to conduct normal life functions (i.e, a persistent or significant disability or incapacity).

Congenital Anomaly/Birth Defect: Check if it is suspected that exposure to a dietary supplement prior to conception or during pregnancy may have resulted in a congenital anomaly or birth defect in the child.

Required Intervention to Prevent Permanent Impairment/Damage (Devices): Not applicable for dietary supplements. This box is for device adverse event reporting only.

Other Serious (Important Medical Events):

Check if, based on reasonable medical judgment, the adverse event required a medical or surgical intervention to prevent one of the following outcomes:

- death;
- a life-threatening experience;
- inpatient hospitalization;
- a significant disability or incapacity; or
- a congenital anomaly or birth defect

B3: Date of Event

Provide the actual date or best estimate of the date of first onset of the serious adverse event. If day is unknown, month and year are acceptable. If day and month are unknown, year is acceptable.

- When a newborn baby is found to have a congenital anomaly, the event onset date is the date of birth of the child.
- When a fetus is aborted because of a congenital anomaly, or other reason, the event onset date is the date pregnancy is terminated.

If information is available as to time during pregnancy when exposure occurred, indicate that information in narrative block B5.

B4: Date of this Report

The date the report is filled out.

CH
15

B5: Describe Event or Problem

For a serious adverse event: Describe the event in detail using the initial reporter's own words, including a description of what happened and a summary of all relevant clinical information (medical status prior to the event; signs and/or symptoms; differential diagnosis for the event in question; clinical course; treatment; outcome, etc.). If available and if relevant, include synopses of any office visit notes or the hospital discharge summary. To save time and space (and if permitted by the institution), attach copies of these records with any confidential information deleted. DO NOT identify any patient, physician, or institution by name. The initial reporter's identity should be provided in full in section E.

Results of relevant tests and laboratory data should be entered in block B6 (see instructions for B6).

Preexisting medical conditions and other relevant history belong in block B7. Be as complete as possible, including the date diagnosed and duration of the preexisting medical condition (see instructions for B7).

B6: Relevant Tests/Laboratory Data, Including Dates:

Provide all appropriate information, including relevant negative test and laboratory findings, in order to most completely convey how the medical work-up/assessment led to strong consideration of dietary supplement-induced disease as etiology for clinical status, as other differential diagnostic considerations were being eliminated.

Include:

- Any relevant baseline laboratory data prior to the administration or use of the dietary supplement
- All laboratory data used in diagnosing the event

If available, include:

- Any pre- and post-event medication levels and dates (if applicable)
- Synopses of any relevant autopsy, pathology, or lab reports

If preferred, copies of any reports may be submitted as attachments, with all confidential information deleted. DO NOT identify any patient, physician or institution by name. The initial reporter's identity should be provided in full in section E.

B7: Other Relevant History, Including Preexisting Medical Conditions:

If available, provide information on:

- Other known conditions in the patient, e.g.,
  - Hypertension
  - Diabetes mellitus
  - Renal/hepatic dysfunction, etc.

CH 15

- Significant history
  - Race
  - Allergies
  - Pregnancy history
  - Smoking and alcohol use
  - Drug abuse, etc.

Section C: Suspect Products

For adverse event reporting, a suspect product is one that the initial reporter suspected was associated with the adverse event. In block C10 enter other concomitant products (other dietary supplements, drugs, biologics, or medical devices) that the patient was using at the time of the event but that are NOT thought by the initial reporter to be involved in the event.

Up to two (2) suspect products may be reported on one form (#1=first suspect product, #2=second suspect product). Attach an additional form if there were more than two suspect products for the reported serious adverse event.

C1: Name:

Use the product or trade name as marketed in the U.S.

C2: Dose, Frequency, and Route Used:

Describe how the product was used by the patient (e.g., one tablet four times a day). For reports involving overdoses, the amount of product used in the overdose should be listed, NOT the amount recommended in the directions on the product label.

C3: Therapy Dates

The therapy dates are the dates during which the dietary supplement was consumed.

Provide the date the patient started taking the dietary supplement (or best estimate) and the date use was stopped (or best estimate). If no dates are known, an estimated duration is acceptable (e.g., 2 years) or, if usage was less than one day, then describe when the dietary supplement was taken (e.g., 1 gelcap at 5 p.m.).

CH
15

C4: Diagnosis for Use

Give the reason(s) why the patient used the product.

C5: Event Abated After Use Stopped or Dose Reduced:

In addition to checking the appropriate box, provide supporting information, lab tests, and dates, if available, in block B6.

C6: Lot #:

If known, include the lot number of the suspect dietary supplement.

C7: Expiration date:

Include the expiration date of the suspect dietary supplement.

C8: Event Reappeared After Reintroduction:

In addition to checking the appropriate box, provide supporting information, lab tests, and dates, if available, in block B6.

C9: NDC # or Unique ID:

If the product has a unique or distinct identification code, such as a Universal Product Code (UPC) number, provide the identification code here.

C10: Concomitant Medical Products and Therapy Dates:

List and provide dates of use for any other dietary supplements, drugs, biologics, or medical devices that the patient was taking or using at the time of the serious adverse event. Do not include products used to treat the serious adverse event.

Section D: Suspect Medical Device is for device adverse reporting only. This section should not be completed by those submitting a serious adverse event report associated with a dietary supplement.

Section E: Initial Reporter

E1: Name, Address & Phone #

Please provide the name, mailing address, and phone number of the person who initially reported the serious adverse event to the dietary supplement manufacturer, packer or distributor, and who can be contacted to provide information on the adverse event if follow-up is necessary. If available, provide the initial reporter's e-mail address and fax number. If the initial reporter has requested that his/her name and contact information not be provided to FDA, enter "Requested Anonymity" in block E1.

CH 15

E2: Health Professional?:

Indicate whether or not the initial reporter is a health professional (e.g., physician, pharmacist, nurse, etc.). If not a health professional, complete block E3 by filling in NA.

E3: Occupation:

Indicate the initial reporter's occupation (type of health professional, if applicable, or "NA" for non-health professionals). For health professionals, include specialty if appropriate.

E4: Initial Reporter Also Sent Report to FDA:

Indicate whether the initial reporter also reported the serious adverse event to FDA.

Back Page

At the top of the back page, enter the page number and total number of pages submitted (include attachments in the total) where the words Page __ of __ are indicated.

Section F: For Use by User Facility/Importer (Devices Only) should not be completed by those submitting a serious adverse event report associated with a dietary supplement.

Section G: All manufacturers

This section is to be filled out by the dietary supplement manufacturer, packer or distributor submitting the serious adverse event report to FDA.

G1: Contact Office - Name/Address:

Enter the full name and address of the manufacturer, packer or distributor reporting site [contact office], including contact name.

G2: Phone Number:

Enter the telephone number of the contact office or a representative knowledgeable about the serious adverse event report.

G3: Report Source:

Check the box(es) that most accurately describe(s) how the manufacturer, packer or distributor [contact office] became aware of the reported serious adverse event or from where the information about the serious adverse event originated.

- Foreign: Foreign sources include foreign governments or foreign affiliates of the manufacturer, packer, or distributor. The country of origin should be included.

- Literature: If the report source is the scientific literature or an unpublished manuscript, a copy of the article or manuscript should be attached. Foreign language articles should be translated into English. Record the date of the article as the date of the event (block B3), and provide a full literature citation in block H10. A separate 3500A form should be completed for each identifiable patient described in the article or manuscript.

- Consumer (including attorneys or family members of the patient): Additional information, whenever possible, should be sought from the treating healthcare provider. A determined effort should be made to obtain additional detailed information from health professionals for all serious adverse events initially reported by consumers.

- Health professional: Physician, pharmacist, nurse, etc.

- Company representative: This check box would be selected if a company representative reported the event to the contact office based on information received from a health professional. The health professional box should also be checked, and the health professional should be listed as the initial reporter in Section E on the front page of the form.

- Distributor: This check box would be selected when the dietary supplement manufacturer or packer who is submitting the serious adverse event report to FDA received the report from a distributor of the product. In this situation, the health professional or other reporter (e.g., patient) who reported the serious adverse event to the distributor should be listed as the initial reporter in Section E on the front page of the form.

- Other: Any source not covered by the previous categories.

G4: Date received by manufacturer:

This means the date when the responsible person (i.e., the manufacturer, packer or distributor whose name is listed on the label of the dietary supplement associated with the serious adverse event) receives the minimum data elements (i.e., identifiable patient, initial reporter, suspect dietary supplement, serious adverse event) to submit a serious adverse event report to FDA.

Blocks G5 and G6 do not have to be completed by those submitting a serious adverse event report associated with a dietary supplement.

G7: Type of Report:

For dietary supplement serious adverse event reports that a manufacturer, packer or distributor is submitting for the first time, check the "15-day" box and the "Initial" box. As specified in Section 761(c)(1) of the Federal Food, Drug, and Cosmetic Act, serious

CH 15

adverse event reports associated with the use of a dietary supplement must be submitted to FDA no later than 15 business days after the report is received through the address or phone number on the label of the product. If the report is received through other means, it should still be submitted to FDA within 15 business days.

Because FDA recommends that follow-up reports of new medical information related to a dietary supplement adverse event report be submitted by attaching a photocopy of the initial serious adverse event report to the new medical information, rather than by completing a new Form 3500A, the "follow-up" box does not apply to dietary supplements.

Block G 8 (Adverse Event Term(s)) should not be completed by those submitting a serious adverse event report associated with a dietary supplement

G9. Manufacturer Report Number

For all manufacturers, packers and distributors:

Enter the Manufacturer, Packer, or Distributor report number exactly as it appears in the "Mfr Report #" field in the upper right corner of the first page.

Section H: Device Manufacturers Only should not be completed by those submitting a serious adverse event report associated with a dietary supplement

Chapter 16

Generally Recognized as Safe (GRAS)
Guidance

Contains Nonbinding Recommendations
October 2016

Guidance for Industry:
Frequently Asked Questions About GRAS for Substances Intended for Use in Human or Animal Food[1]

U.S. Department of Health and Human Services Food and Drug Administration Center for Food Safety and Applied Nutrition Center for Veterinary Medicine

I. Introduction

This list of frequently asked questions (FAQ) is intended to be a convenient place to find answers to common questions about the food substance classification known as "generally recognized as safe" or "GRAS." This FAQ addresses common questions about the regulatory process and regulatory considerations regarding whether the use of a substance in human or animal food is GRAS.

Our Center for Food Safety and Applied Nutrition (CFSAN) provides additional information about GRAS substances intended for use in human food on CFSAN's Web site entitled "Generally Recognized as Safe (GRAS)." Our Center for Veterinary Medicine (CVM) provides additional information about GRAS substances intended for use in animal food on CVM's Web site entitled "Generally Recognized as Safe (GRAS) Notification Program." To contact CFSAN or CVM to obtain more information about whether the intended use of a substance in human food or animal food is GRAS, see section III.

This guidance updates and replaces a previous guidance, entitled "Frequently Asked Questions About GRAS," that CFSAN issued in December 2004. This updated guidance refers to the provisions of a final rule that we published on August 17, 2016 (81 Fed. Reg. 54960) and

---

1   This guidance has been jointly prepared by the Office of Food Additive Safety in the Center for Food Safety and Applied Nutrition and the Division of Animal Feeds in the Office of Surveillance and Compliance in the Center for Veterinary Medicine at the U.S. Food and Drug Administration.

addresses substances used in human food as well as substances used in animal food. This guidance also includes an editorial change, relative to the guidance issued on October 17, 2016, to clarify the response to Question 14.

FDA's guidance documents, including this guidance, do not establish legally enforceable responsibilities. Instead, guidances describe our current thinking on a topic and should be viewed only as recommendations, unless specific regulatory or statutory requirements are cited.

The use of the word should in FDA guidances means that something is suggested or recommended, but not required.

II. Frequently Asked Questions

1. What does "GRAS" mean?

"GRAS" is an acronym for the phrase "Generally Recognized as Safe." Under sections 201(s) and 409 of the Federal Food, Drug, and Cosmetic Act (the FD&C Act), any substance that is intentionally added to food is a food additive, that is subject to premarket review and approval by FDA, unless the substance is generally recognized, among qualified experts, as having been adequately shown to be safe under the conditions of its intended use, or unless the use of the substance is otherwise excepted from the definition of a food additive.[2] Sections 201(s) and 409 were enacted in 1958 as part of the Food Additives Amendment to the FD&C Act. FDA has several lists of substances that are used in food on the basis of the GRAS provision (see Question 15).

2. What are the criteria for eligibility for classification as GRAS?

Under section 201(s) of the FD&C Act, and FDA's implementing regulations in Title 21 of the Code of Federal Regulations (21 CFR), the use of a food substance may be GRAS either through scientific procedures or, for a substance used in food before 1958, through experience based on common use in food. Table 1 provides regulatory citations for key regulations implementing the GRAS provisions of the FD&C Act for substances intended for use in human food. Table 2 provides regulatory citations for key regulations implementing the GRAS provisions of the FD&C Act for substances intended for use in animal food.

---

2   For example, substances whose use meets the definition of a pesticide, a dietary ingredient of a dietary supplement, a color additive, a new animal drug, or a substance used in accordance with a sanction or approval granted prior to September 6, 1958, are excepted from the definition of food additive.

Table 1.—Key Regulatory Text Regarding Whether the Intended Use of a Substance in Human Food is GRAS

Regulatory Citation	Regulatory Text
21 CFR 170.3(f)	Common use in food means a substantial history of consumption of a substance for food use by a significant number of consumers.
21 CFR 170.3(h)	Scientific procedures include the application of scientific data (including, as appropriate, data from human, animal, analytical, or other scientific studies), information, and methods, whether published or unpublished, as well as the application of scientific principles, appropriate to establish the safety of a substance under the conditions of its intended use.
21 CFR 170.30	Eligibility for Classification as Generally Recognized as Safe (GRAS)
21 CFR 170.30(a)	General recognition of safety may be based only on the views of experts qualified by scientific training and experience to evaluate the safety of substances directly or indirectly added to food. The basis of such views may be either (1) scientific procedures or (2) in the case of a substance used in food prior to January 1, 1958, through experience based on common use in food. General recognition of safety requires common knowledge throughout the scientific community knowledgeable about the safety of substances directly or indirectly added to food that there is reasonable certainty that the substance is not harmful under the conditions of its intended use (see § 170.3(i)).
21 CFR 170.30(b)	General recognition of safety based upon scientific procedures shall require the same quantity and quality of scientific evidence as is required to obtain approval of a food additive. General recognition of safety through scientific procedures shall be based upon the application of generally available and accepted scientific data, information, or methods, which ordinarily are published, as well as the application of scientific principles, and may be corroborated by the application of unpublished scientific data, information, or methods.
21 CFR 170.30(c) (1)	(1) General recognition of safety through experience based on common use in food prior to January 1, 1958, may be achieved without the quantity or quality of scientific procedures required for approval of a food additive. General recognition of safety through experience based on common use in food prior to January 1, 1958, shall be based solely on food use of the substance prior to January 1, 1958, and shall ordinarily be based upon generally available data and information. An ingredient not in common use in food prior to January 1, 1958, may achieve general recognition of safety only through scientific procedures.
21 CFR 170.30(c) (2)	(c)(2) A substance used in food prior to January 1, 1958, may be generally recognized as safe through experience based on its common use in food when that use occurred exclusively or primarily outside of the United States if the information about the experience establishes that the substance is safe under the conditions of its intended use within the meaning of section 201(u) of the FD&C Act (see also § 170.3(i)). Common use in food prior to January 1, 1958, that occurred outside of the United States shall be documented by published or other information and shall be corroborated by information from a second, independent source that confirms the history and circumstances of use of the substance. The information used to document and to corroborate the history and circumstances of use of the substance must be generally available; that is, it must be widely available in the country in which the history of use has occurred and readily available to interested qualified experts in the United States. A person who concludes that a use of a substance is GRAS through experience based on its common use in food outside of the United States should notify FDA of that view in accordance with subpart E of this part.

Table 2.—Key Regulatory Text Regarding Whether the Intended Use of a Substance in Food for Animals is GRAS

Regulatory Citation	Regulatory Text
21 CFR 570.3(f)	Common use in food means a substantial history of consumption of a substance by a significant number of animals of the species to which the substance is intended to be fed (and, for food-producing animals fed with such substance, also means a substantial history of consumption by humans consuming human foods derived from those food-producing animals), prior to January 1, 1958.
21 CFR 570.3(h)	Scientific procedures include the application of scientific data (including, as appropriate, data from human, animal, analytical, or other scientific studies), information, and methods, whether published or unpublished, as well as the application of scientific principles, appropriate to establish the safety of a substance under the conditions of its intended use.
21 CFR 570.30	Eligibility for Classification as Generally Recognized as Safe (GRAS)
21 CFR 570.30(a)	General recognition of safety may be based only on the views of experts qualified by scientific training and experience to evaluate the safety of substances directly or indirectly added to food. The basis of such views may be either (1) scientific procedures or (2) in the case of a substance used in food prior to January 1, 1958, through experience based on common use in food. General recognition of safety requires common knowledge throughout the scientific community knowledgeable about the safety of substances directly or indirectly added to food that there is reasonable certainty that the substance is not harmful to either the target animal or to humans consuming human food derived from foodproducing animals under the conditions of its intended use (see § 570.3(i)).
21 CFR 570.30(b)	General recognition of safety based upon scientific procedures shall require the same quantity and quality of scientific evidence as is required to obtain approval of a food additive. General recognition of safety through scientific procedures shall address safety for both the target animal and for humans consuming human food derived from foodproducing animals and shall be based upon the application of generally available and accepted scientific data, information, or methods, which ordinarily are published, as well as the application of scientific principles, and may be corroborated by the application of unpublished scientific data, information, or methods.
21 CFR 570.30(c)(1)	(c)(1) General recognition of safety through experience based on common use in food prior to January 1, 1958, shall address safety for both the target animal and for humans consuming human food derived from food-producing animals and may be achieved without the quantity or quality of scientific procedures required for approval of a food additive. General recognition of safety through experience based on common use in food prior to January 1, 1958, shall be based solely on food use of the substance in the same animal species prior to January 1, 1958, and shall ordinarily be based upon generally available data and information. An ingredient not in common use in food prior to January 1, 1958, may achieve general recognition of safety only through scientific procedures.

Regulatory Citation	Regulatory Text
21 CFR 570.30(c)(2)	(2) A substance used in food prior to January 1, 1958, may be generally recognized as safe through experience based on its common use in food when that use occurred exclusively or primarily outside of the United States if the information about the experience establishes that the substance is safe under the conditions of its intended use within the meaning of section 201(u) of the Federal Food, Drug, and Cosmetic Act (see also § 570.3(i)) for both the target animal and for humans consuming human food derived from food-producing animals. Common use in food prior to January 1, 1958, that occurred outside of the United States shall be documented by published or other information and shall be corroborated by information from a second, independent source that confirms the history and circumstances of use of the substance. The information used to document and to corroborate the history and circumstances of use of the substance must be generally available; that is, it must be widely available in the country in which the history of use has occurred and readily available to interested qualified experts in the United States. A person who concludes that a use of a substance is GRAS through experience based on its common use in food outside of the United States should notify FDA of that view in accordance with subpart E of this part.

3. How are the criteria for eligibility for classification as GRAS similar to the criteria for FDA's approval of a food additive?

Regardless of whether the use of a substance is a food additive use or is GRAS, there must be evidence that the substance is safe under the conditions of its intended use. FDA has defined "safe" (21 CFR 170.3(i) and 21 CFR 570.3(i)) as a reasonable certainty in the minds of competent scientists that the substance is not harmful under the conditions of its intended use. The specific data and information that demonstrate safety depend on the characteristics of the substance, the estimated dietary exposure[3], the population that will consume the substance, and other relevant considerations.

4. How are the criteria for eligibility for classification as GRAS through scientific procedures different from the criteria for FDA's approval of a food additive?

The difference between the criteria for eligibility for classification as GRAS through scientific procedures (21 CFR 170.30(b) and 21 CFR 570.30(b)) and FDA's approval of a food additive (21 CFR 171.1 and 21 CFR 571.1) relates to who has access to the data and information and who has reviewed those data and information. For a substance to be GRAS under the conditions of its intended use, the data and information relied on to establish the safety of the use of the substance must be generally available (e.g., through publication in the scientific literature) and there must be a basis for a person to conclude that the substance is generally recognized, among qualified experts, to be safe under the conditions of its intended use. In contrast, for FDA's approval of a food additive privately held data and information about the substance under the conditions of its intended

---

3   For a substance intended for use in animal food, the data and information address exposure to the target animal and to humans consuming human food derived from food-producing animals.

use are sent by the sponsor to FDA and FDA reviews those data and information to determine whether they demonstrate that the substance is safe under the conditions of its intended use.

5. If an ingredient is GRAS for one use, is it GRAS for all uses?

Not necessarily. Under section 201(s) of the FD&C Act, it is the use of a substance, rather than the substance itself, that is eligible for classification as GRAS (81 Fed. Reg. 54960 at 54963; August 17, 2016). An evaluation of the safety of the use of an ingredient includes information about the characteristics of the substance, the estimated dietary exposure under the intended conditions of use, and the population that will consume the substance. Dietary exposure to a substance depends on the food categories in which it will be used and the level of use in each of those food categories. For information about how CFSAN estimates human dietary exposure to a food substance, see CFSAN's document entitled "Estimating Dietary Intake of Substances in Food" (Ref. 1).

Some uses of a human food substance are intended for a narrowly defined population. For example, some human food substances are intended for consumption by newborn infants who consume infant formula as the sole item of the diet; in such a circumstance, there may be special considerations associated with that population but not with general use of the food substance. Likewise, some substances intended for use in animal food are intended for specific animal species (such as cattle or swine), or for a specific life stage of an animal species; a substance that is safe for use in one animal species may not be safe for use in another species or in the same species at a different stage of life.

6. Is a substance that is used to impart color eligible for classification as GRAS?

The short answer is "No." Under section 201(s) of the FD&C Act, the GRAS provision applies to the definition of a food additive. There is no corresponding provision in the definition (in section 201(t) of the FD&C Act) of a color additive.

However, under section 201(t)(1) and 21 CFR 70.3(f), the term color additive means a material that is a dye, pigment, or other substance made by a process of synthesis or similar artifice, or extracted, isolated, or otherwise derived from a vegetable, animal, mineral, or other source, and that is capable (alone or through reaction with another substance) of imparting color when added or applied to a food; except that such term does not include any material which FDA, by regulation, determines is used (or intended to be used) solely for a purpose or purposes other than coloring. Under 21 CFR 70.3(g), a material that otherwise meets the definition of color additive can be exempt from that definition on the basis that it is used or intended to be used solely for a purpose or purposes other than coloring, as long as the material is used in a way that any color imparted is clearly unimportant insofar as the appearance, value, marketability, or consumer acceptability is concerned. Given the construct of section 201(t)(1) of the Act and 21 CFR 70.3(f) and (g), the use of a substance that is capable of imparting color may constitute use as both a color additive and as a food additive or GRAS substance. For example, betacarotene is both approved for use as a color additive (21 CFR 73.95) and affirmed as GRAS for use as a nutrient in human food (21 CFR 184.1245); in some food products, beta-carotene may be safely and lawfully used for both purposes.

7. Is a substance that is used as a dietary ingredient in a human[4] dietary supplement eligible for classification as GRAS?

Under section 201(s) of the FD&C Act, a substance that is GRAS under the conditions of its intended use is excluded from the definition of a food additive. In addition, under section 201(s) of the FD&C Act the term "food additive" does not include a dietary ingredient[5] used or intended for use in a dietary supplement as defined in section 201(ff) of the FD&C Act. In other words, because dietary ingredients intended for use in dietary supplements are already excepted from the food additive definition, their GRAS status for that use is irrelevant because they are already exempt from the food additive approval requirement. However, some dietary ingredients that may be used in a dietary supplement may also be GRAS for use in a conventional food (e.g., vitamin C; calcium carbonate). In addition, a substance that is not a dietary ingredient as defined in section 201(ff)(1) of the FD&C Act must be approved as a food additive when used in a dietary supplement (e.g., as a coating, filler, or binder) unless the substance is GRAS for that use or otherwise excepted from the definition of a food additive.

8. Must FDA approve GRAS substances?

No. If the use of a food substance is GRAS, it is not subject to FDA's premarket review and approval as a food additive.

9. What is GRAS affirmation?

GRAS affirmation is a process that FDA developed in the 1970s. In response to concerns raised by new information on cyclamate salts, then-President Nixon directed FDA to re-examine the safety of substances considered to be GRAS. FDA announced that the agency would evaluate, by contemporary standards of the time, the available safety information regarding substances considered to be GRAS. If the re-evaluations confirmed that the uses were GRAS, FDA promulgated new GRAS regulations, affirming those findings. FDA also established procedures whereby an individual could voluntarily petition FDA to review the GRAS status of substances that would not have been considered as part of the agency's GRAS review.

In a final rule that FDA published on August 17, 2016 (81 Fed. Reg. 54960), FDA removed that voluntary process from its regulations and replaced it with a voluntary GRAS notification procedure. See Question 10.

---

4   Note that FDA previously published a notice in the Federal Register explaining its conclusion that the Dietary Supplement Health and Education Act of 1994 (which established the exception from the definition of "food additive" in section 201(s) of the FD&C Act for a dietary ingredient of a dietary supplement) does not apply to products intended for use in animals (61 Fed. Reg. 17706; April 22, 1996).

5   "Dietary ingredient" is defined in section 201(ff)(1) of the FD&C Act and generally includes vitamins, minerals, herbs and other botanicals, amino acids, dietary substances, and concentrates, metabolites, constituents, extracts, and combinations of dietary ingredients in the other categories.

10. What is the GRAS notification procedure?

The GRAS notification procedure is a voluntary procedure under which any person may notify FDA of a conclusion that a substance is GRAS under the conditions of its intended use in human food (21 CFR part 170, subpart E) or animal food (21 CFR part 570, subpart E). Although the GRAS notification procedure is voluntary, FDA strongly encourages any person who intends to market a food substance on the basis of the GRAS provision to submit a GRAS notice to FDA.

A GRAS notice has seven required parts as shown in Table 3 for a substance intended for use in human food and as shown in Table 4 for a substance intended for use in animal food.

Table 3.—The Seven Required Parts of a GRAS Notice for a Substance Intended for Use in Human Food

Regulatory Citation	Part of a GRAS Notice	Title
170.225	Part 1	Signed statements and certification
170.230	Part 2	Identity, method of manufacture, specifications, and physical or technical effect
170.235	Part 3	Dietary exposure
170.240	Part 4	Self-limiting levels of use
170.245	Part 5	Experience based on common use in food before 1958
170.250	Part 6	Narrative
170.255	Part 7	List of supporting data and information in your GRAS notice

Table 4.—The Seven Required Parts of a GRAS Notice for a Substance Intended for Use in Animal Food

Regulatory Citation	Part of a GRAS Notice	Title
570.225	Part 1	Signed statements and certification
570.230	Part 2	Identity, method of manufacture, specifications, and physical or technical effect
570.235	Part 3	Target animal and human exposures
570.240	Part 4	Self-limiting levels of use
570.245	Part 5	Experience based on common use in food before 1958
570.250	Part 6	Narrative
570.255	Part 7	List of supporting data and information in your GRAS notice

11. If I choose to submit a GRAS notice, how do I do so?

For a substance intended for use in human food, follow the procedure in 21 CFR part 170, subpart E for submission of a GRAS notice to CFSAN. For a substance intended for use in animal food, follow the procedure in 21 CFR part 570, subpart E for submission of a GRAS notice to CVM.

12. Where do I send my GRAS notice?

For a substance intended for use in human food, send your GRAS notice to the Office of Food Additive Safety (HFS-200), Center for Food Safety and Applied Nutrition, Food and Drug Administration, 5001 Campus Drive, College Park, MD 20740. For electronic submission of your GRAS notice, see Ref. 2.

For a substance intended for use in animal food, send your GRAS notice to the Division of Animal Feeds (HFV- 220), Center for Veterinary Medicine, Food and Drug Administration, 7519 Standish Pl., Rockville, MD 20855. For electronic submission of your GRAS notice, eSubmitter is available for use (http://www.fda.gov/ForIndustry/ FDAeSubmitter/default.htm).

13. If I submit a GRAS notice, how long will it take for me to receive a response from FDA?

The GRAS notification procedure requires that FDA respond to a GRAS notice within 180 days, with an option to extend the 180-day timeframe by 90 days on an as needed basis.

14. If I submit a GRAS notice about a substance intended for use in human or animal food, must I wait until I receive a response from CFSAN or CVM before I market that substance?

No. If you are correct in concluding that a substance is GRAS under the conditions of its intended use, there is no requirement under section 409 of the FD&C Act for FDA review and approval for that use of the substance. Your decision to submit a GRAS notice to CFSAN or CVM is voluntary, and the response to a GRAS notice from CFSAN or CVM is not an approval. You may market a substance that is GRAS under the conditions of its intended use without informing CFSAN or CVM or, if CFSAN or CVM is so informed, while the applicable Center is evaluating your GRAS notice. (See Response 114, 81 Fed. Reg. 54960 at 55022). We recognize, however, that some firms prefer to know that the applicable FDA Center has evaluated a submitted GRAS notice, without raising safety or legal issues, before marketing.

15. Does FDA have a list of substances that are used in food on the basis of the GRAS provision?

FDA's regulations in 21 CFR include several lists of substances that are used in food on the basis of the GRAS provision (see Table 5 and Table 6). Importantly, these lists are not

CH 16

allinclusive. Because the use of a GRAS substance is not subject to premarket review and approval by FDA, it is impracticable to list all substances that are used in food on the basis of the GRAS provision.

CFSAN's Web site entitled "Generally Recognized as Safe (GRAS)," and CVM's Web site entitled "Generally Recognized as Safe (GRAS) Notification Program," each contain a list of substances that have been the subject of a GRAS notice to FDA, whether to CFSAN (for intended use in human food) or to CVM (for intended use in animal food). You can access these lists, along with the response from CFSAN or CVM to the notifier, from CFSAN's Web site and CVM's Web site (Ref. 3 and Ref. 4).

Table 5.—Lists of Substances Intended for Use in Human Food on the Basis of the GRAS Provision

List	Description
21 CFR part 182	Contains the remnants of a list that FDA established in its human food regulations shortly after passage of the 1958 Food Additives Amendment. The list is organized according to the intended use of these substances. As part of CFSAN's comprehensive review of GRAS substances in the 1970s, CFSAN affirmed that the use of some of the ingredients on this original GRAS list are GRAS, and moved the affirmed uses of the substance to 21 CFR Part 184.
21 CFR part 184	Contains a list of substances that CFSAN affirmed as GRAS as direct human food ingredients for general or specific uses. This list derives from CFSAN's 1970s comprehensive review of GRAS substances and from petitions that CFSAN received to affirm the GRAS status of particular uses of some food ingredients.
21 CFR part 186	Contains a list of substances that CFSAN affirmed as GRAS for certain indirect food uses (e.g., in the manufacture of paper and paperboard that contact human food).

Table 6.—Lists of Substances Intended for Use in Animal Food on the Basis of the GRAS Provision

List	Description
21 CFR part 582	Contains the remnants of a list that FDA established in its animal food regulations shortly after passage of the 1958 Food Additives Amendment. The list is organized according to the intended use of these substances.
21 CFR part 584	Contains a list of substances that CVM affirmed as GRAS as direct animal food ingredients for general or specific uses. This list derives from petitions that CVM received to affirm the GRAS status of particular uses of some food ingredients.

16. Can the use of a substance be GRAS even if it is not listed by FDA?

Yes. Because the use of a substance that is GRAS is not subject to premarket review and approval by FDA, it is impracticable to list all substances that are used in food on the basis of the GRAS provision (21 CFR 182.1(a) and 21 CFR 582.1(a)). The use of a substance is GRAS because of widespread knowledge among the community of qualified experts, not because of a listing or other administrative activity.

III. How to Contact FDA With Questions About GRAS

Visit www.fda.gov for the most up-to-date contact information for CFSAN and CVM.

IV. References

1. FDA, "Guidance for Industry: Estimating Dietary Intake of Substances in Food," (http://www.fda.gov/Food/GuidanceRegulation/GuidanceDocumentsRegulatoryInformati on/ucm074725.htm), 2006.

2. FDA, "Guidance for Industry: Providing Regulatory Submissions in Electronic or Paper Format to the Office of Food Additive Safety; Draft Guidance," (http://www.fda.gov/Food/GuidanceRegulation/GuidanceDocumentsRegulatoryInformati on/IngredientsAdditivesGRASPackaging/ucm2021277.htm), 2010.

3. GRAS Notice Inventory, (http://www.fda.gov/Food/IngredientsPackagingLabeling/GRAS/NoticeInventory/default.h tm).

4. Current Animal Food GRAS Notices Inventory, (http://www.fda.gov/AnimalVeterinary/Products/AnimalFoodFeeds/GenerallyRecognized asSafeGRASNotifications/ucm243845.htm)

CH 16

Sample 1

Ozark Country Herbs[1]

March 30, 2018
CMS # 542508

WARNING LETTER
UPS Overnight

Reuben M. Yoder, Owner
Edna M. Yoder, Owner
Ozark Country Herbs
2866 Highway 395 North
Salem, Arkansas 72576

Dear Mr. & Mrs. Yoder

From November 9-13, 2017, the U.S. Food and Drug Administration (FDA) conducted an inspection of your facility located at 2866 Highway, 395 North, Salem, Arkansas 72576. Based on the inspection, a review of your product labels collected during the inspection, and a review of your mail order catalog, we have identified serious violations of the Federal Food, Drug, and Cosmetic Act (the Act) and applicable regulations. You may find the Act and FDA regulations through links on FDA's website at www.fda.gov.

We acknowledge receipt of your undated response to the FDA 483, which was postdated November 22, 2017. We address relevant portions of your response below.

Unapproved New Drugs/Misbranded Drugs

FDA reviewed your product labels and your firm's mail order catalog following the November

---

1   Warning letters issued by the FDA are public information. This and other warning letters are available on the FDA website. https://www.fda.gov/ICECI/EnforcementActions/WarningLetters/default.htm.

9-13, 2017 inspection of your facility. The claims on your product labels and in your mail order catalog establish that your Complete Tissue Syrup, Allergy/Energy Combo, Natural Antibiotic (LDM), Migraine Relief, Pain Relief, Bilbrite Formula, Anti-Yeast, Dental Formula, Heart Tonic, Echinacea-Goldenseal, Lung & Respiratory, Natural Iron, Birth Ease, M.C. Formula, Hormone Health, Ladies Formula, Baby Calm, Rescue Remedy, Eldermint, Diarrhea-X, Nerve & Stress, Kidney & Bladder, Flu & Cold Aid, Cayenne, White Willow, Sinus/Hay Fever, Arthritis Relief, Gripe Water, Concentration Aid, Liver/Gallbladder, Para-Cleanse Package, Wintertime Tea, Teething Oil, Complete Tissue Oil, Deep Tissue Oil, Aloe-Vera Goldenseal Salve, Calendula Salve, Chickweed Salve, Plantain Salve, Congestion Salve, Ear Oil, and Natural Calcium are drugs under Section 201(g)(1)(B) of the Act [21 U.S.C. § 321(g)(1)(B)] because they are intended for use in the cure, mitigation, treatment, or prevention of disease. As explained further below, introducing or delivering these products for introduction into interstate commerce for such uses violates the Act.

Examples of some of the claims on your product labels and your mail order catalog that provide evidence that your products are intended for use as drugs include:

Complete Tissue Syrup:

"This wonderful formula ... has the raw material the body needs to repair bone, flesh, and cartilage. Use for Breaks, Sprains, Wounds, Damaged Nerves, Backache, Arthritis, stiff aching neck, Carpel Tunnel, Tennis Elbow, Gout and much more."

Allergy/Energy Combo:

The word "Allergy" in the product's name.

"May aid in chronic allergies, immune deficiency, cancer, and autoimmune conditions."

"[M]odifies the effects of chemotherapy and radiation therapy."

Natural Antibiotic (LDM):

"It is sometimes called 'Broad Spectrum Plant Antibiotics!' It has proven very effective for any infection or inflammation, and whenever an antibiotic should be used. Use for all respiratory and urinary infections. STAPH, STREP, and Ear infections."

Migraine Relief:

The product's name.

"[R]elieve and prevent migraine headaches"

Pain Relief:

The product's name.

"An effective herbal pain reliever. Use in place of conventional pain relievers. Also beneficial for ... depression, anxiety ... ."

Bilbrite Formula:

"[R]epair damaged vessels"

Anti – Yeast:

"This is a great anti-cancer mix. It ... kills fungi and yeast ... . Also works well for colds and flu."

Dental Formula:

"This formula has been proven to fill in cavities and/or heal tooth pain."

"Get the benefit of being 'dewormed' at the same time!"

Heart Tonic:

"[C]lean the arteries, preventing heart attacks and strokes."

"Regulates blood pressure"

Echinacea – Goldenseal:

"May be beneficial for all viral infections, stomach disorders, inflammation, and skin disorders. It activates white blood cells that help destroy bacteria, fungus, and virus."

Lung & Respiratory:

"This formula is extremely valuable in strengthening and healing the entire respiratory tract, and relieves irritation in the lungs and bronchials. Use for asthma and other lung conditions."

Natural Iron:

"May be beneficial for anemia ... digestive problems, and acne."

Birth Ease:

"Benefits ... include a shorter recovery time with less after-pain ... ."

M.C. Formula:

"May be beneficial as a pregnancy support whenever bleeding or cramping starts."

"It contains herbs that will prevent miscarriage ... ."

Hormone Health:

"Are you or your daughter having those monthly P M S symptoms of ... depression/ anxiety ... ? If so, this formula is for you!"

Ladies Formula:

"This combination of herbs is designed for those who have a problem with infertility ... ."

Baby Calm:

"An all-purpose childhood remedy – from colds and fevers ... ."

Rescue Remedy:

"[U]seful for ... flu, fever, colds, pain ... ."

Eldermint:

"A wonderful remedy for children and adults when trying to avoid the flu or when you already have it."

"[K]eeps fever under control ... also for colds ... ."

Diarrhea -X:

The product's name.

"An excellent remedy to keep on hand for diarrhea."

"Can also be used for colds, flu and fever ... ."

Nerve & Stress:

"May be beneficial to relieve ... depression, anxiety ... ."

Kidney & Bladder:

"This formula has been successfully used for problems with incontinence, bed-wetting, kidney stones, pain in the back caused from kidney infection ... ."

Flu & Cold Aid:

The product's name.

"A great, all around, Flu & Cold remedy!"

Cayenne:

"Wards off diseases"

White Willow:

"[N]atural pain reliever/fever reducer"

Sinus/Hay fever:

The product's name

"Use for sinus congestion, headache, allergies"

Arthritis Relief:

The product's name.

"A time-tested formula for those who suffer with Arthritis/Rheumatism or any joint pain. This combination of herbs that ... relieve pain ... kill fungus and infection ... give wonderful relief."

Gripe Water:

"May aid on occasion your baby's problems with ... cramping ... ."

Concentration Aid (very calming):

"Especially good for children with ADD and ADHD."

Liver/Gallbladder:

"When the liver does not function properly the bile does not excrete freely into the intestinal tract and so it passes off into the bloodstream causing ... reflux and irritable bowel syndrome, headache ... . High blood pressure, heart attack, stroke, diabetes, gallstones ... are directly related to poor liver function. This combination of herbs was formulated to cleanse [,] nourish and support your liver ... ."

Para-Cleanse Package:

"Always start the program about 1 week before Full Moon as parasites are more active around the Full Moon."

Wintertime Tea:

"It will give your immune system the boost it needs to fight off those 'flu bugs'... ."

Teething Oil:

"Directions: Rub on gums as needed to relieve the pain."

Complete Tissue Oil:

"Use for sore, aching joint, sprains, bruises and more."

Deep Tissue Oil:

"Use to break up chest congestion and to speed healing of bruises and sprains."

Aloe-Vera Goldenseal Salve:

"Heals and prevents infection in minor burns, cuts and wounds."

Calendula Salve:

"For varicose veins, fistulas, frostbites, burns, ulcers on the breast, athlete's foot, and wounds."

Chickweed Salve:

"Use for skin rashes, burns, inflammations, impetigo cuts & bruises."

Plantain Salve:

"Good for burns, diaper rash, insect bites and stings, hemorrhoids, varicose veins, open sores and more."

Congestion Salve:

"A great salve when it comes to dealing with chest and head congestion, croup, pneumonia, coughs and earache."

Ear Oil:

"This is very good for ear infections."

"A valuable remedy for earache and inner ear infection. To further aid pain relief or fight infection put a few drops of warm peroxide in the ear before the Ear Oil."

Your mail order catalog also contains evidence of intended use in the form of personal testimonials recommending or describing the use of certain products for the cure, mitigation, treatment, or prevention of disease. Examples of such testimonials include:

Testimonial for Ear Oil/Natural Antibiotic:

"We had to take the baby to the Dr. a number of times with inner ear infection. Now since we use peroxide and Ear Oil and also Natural Antibiotic, we have good success treating it at home … ."

Under the Inner Ear Infection heading:

"[W]e have always been successful in treating inner ear infection using the method described under Ear Oil 3-4 times daily and giving Natural Antibiotic – LDM hourly, until the fever is gone. This method will also work for common earache."

Testimonial for Birth Ease/Natural Calcium:

"Since using Birth Ease and Natural Calcium, the last 5 weeks I have easier labor and birth with very little blood loss and after-pains afterwards."

Testimonial for Rescue Remedy:

"Rescue Remedy seems to work well for the flu. We like to keep it on hand as an all purpose medicine."

Testimonial for Eldermint:

"Our children love Eldermint! They call it candy medicine. I think it works well for cold and flue [sic]."

Testimonial for Natural Antibiotic – LDM:

"Last week our baby was so sick we started for the hospital with her. Before we left I gave her some Natural Antibiotic – LDM and before we got there she was so much better, that we turned around and came back home."

Testimonial for Lung & Respiratory:

"The Lung & Respiratory we had good results with the whooping cough. It actually worsened the cough for a few days [more mucous] but then they got better faster."

Testimonial for Complete Tissue Products:

"The Complete Tissue products have won many compliments in the past year, as more and more people realize the value of this time tested formula in healing Tennis Elbow, Back Pain, leg pain, Carpel Tunnel, Nerve Pain in teeth, sore, aching shoulder & neck & more."

Testimonial for Heart Tonic:

"I had an enlarged heart, which was causing chest pain, and also had high blood pressure. I gave Heart Tonic a try. I used it pretty strong at first. Now my symptoms are good and my blood pressure stays normal."

Testimonial for Kidney & Bladder/Natural Antibiotic:

"I had kidney infection and was sick in bed. I used the Kidney & Bladder formula & Natural Antibiotic every hour the first 2 days and by the 3rd day the fever had left and I was feeling better."

CH
17

Testimonial for Para-Cleanse/Quick Cleanse:

> "Yes, I think this Para-Cleanse and Quick Cleanse did help with our 1 ½ year old. She had the pin worms so bad ... . We wormed her pretty often with other wormer, then decided to try yours, and now she is sleeping a lot better."

Your products are not generally recognized as safe and effective for the above referenced uses and, therefore, these products are new drugs under Section 201(p) of the Act [21 U.S.C § 321(p)]. New drugs may not be legally introduced or delivered for introduction into interstate commerce without prior approval from the FDA, as described in Section 505(a) of the Act [21 U.S.C § 355(a)]; see also Section 301(d) of the Act [21 U.S.C. § 331(d)]. FDA approves a new drug on the basis of scientific data submitted by a drug sponsor to demonstrate that the drug is safe and effective.

A drug is misbranded under Section 502(f)(1) of the Act [21 U.S.C. § 352(f)(1)] if the drug fails to bear adequate directions for its intended use(s). "Adequate directions for use" means directions under which a layperson can use a drug safely and for the purposes for which it is intended (21 CFR 201.5). Prescription drugs, as defined in Section 503(b)(1)(A) of the Act [21 U.S.C. § 353(b)(1) (A)], can only be used safely at the direction, and under the supervision, of a licensed practitioner.

Your Allergy/Energy Combo, Natural Antibiotic (LDM), Pain Relief, Anti-Yeast, Heart Tonic x, Lung & Respiratory, Concentration Aid, Liver/Gallbladder, Hormone Health, Nerve and Stress, Ear Oil, Calendula Salve, Chickweed Salve, and Congestion Salve products are intended for treatment of one or more diseases that are not amenable to self-diagnosis or treatment without the supervision of a licensed practitioner. Therefore, it is impossible to write adequate directions for a layperson to use your products safely for their intended purposes. Accordingly, Allergy/ Energy Combo, Natural Antibiotic (LDM), Pain Relief, Anti-Yeast, Heart Tonic x, Lung & Respiratory, Concentration Aid, Liver/Gallbladder, Hormone Health, Nerve and Stress, Ear Oil, Calendula Salve, Chickweed Salve, and Congestion Salve fail to bear adequate directions for their intended use and, therefore, the products are misbranded under Section 502(f)(1) of the Act [21 U.S.C. § 352(f) (1)]. The introduction or delivery for introduction into interstate commerce of these misbranded drugs violates Section 301(a) of the Act [21 U.S.C. § 331(a)].

We have reviewed your response; however, we are unable to evaluate the sufficiency of your corrective actions, in that it does not address the claims within your mail order catalog. Your response provides a list of products of which your firm plans to change the names but does not provide examples of the actual labeling.

We advise you to review your mail order catalog, product labels, and any other labeling for your products to ensure that the products you offer for sale and the claims you make for your products do not cause them to violate the Act.

Adulterated Dietary Supplements

If your products did not have therapeutic claims which make them unapproved new drugs and/or misbranded drugs, and if the products were properly labeled as dietary supplements, certain of your products[1] would be adulterated dietary supplements within the meaning of Section 402(g) (1) of the Act [21 U.S.C § 342(g)(1)] because the products have been manufactured, packaged, labeled, and/or held under conditions that do not meet the Current Good Manufacturing Practice

(CGMP) regulations for Manufacturing, Packaging, Labeling, or Holding Operations for Dietary Supplements, Title 21, Code of Federal Regulations, Part 111 (21 CFR 111).

During the inspection of your facility, the following significant violations of these CGMP requirements were observed:

1. Your firm failed to establish specifications for any point, step, or stage in the manufacturing process where control is necessary to ensure the quality of the dietary supplement, as required by 21 CFR 111.70(a). Specifically, you have not established any specifications to ensure the quality of your finished products. In establishing the required specifications, you must establish:

   - Specifications for each component that you use in the manufacture of a dietary supplement, as required by 21 CFR 111.70(b);

   - Specifications for the dietary supplement labels (label specifications) and for packaging that may come in contact with the dietary supplements (packaging specifications), as required by 21 CFR 111.70(d);

   - Product specifications for the identity, purity, strength, and composition of finished batch of the dietary supplement and for limits on those types of contamination that may adulterate, or that may lead to adulteration of the finished batch of the dietary supplement, as required by 21 CFR 111.70(e);

   - Specifications for the packaging and labeling of the finished packaged and labeled dietary supplements, including specifications that ensure that you used the specified packaging and that you applied the specified label, as required by 21 CFR 111.70(g).

   We have reviewed your firm's undated response to this observation, which we received on November 27, 2017; however, your response does not identify the specific corrective actions you plan to take. The Agency would recommend you review 21 CFR 111, specifically, Subpart E, Requirements to Establish a Production and Process Control System.

2. You failed to establish and follow written procedures for the responsibilities of the quality control operations, including written procedures for conducting a material review and making a disposition decision, and for approving or rejecting any reprocessing, as required by 21 CFR 111.103. Specifically, you have no written procedures for quality control operations for the manufacturing of your dietary supplement products. You must implement quality control operations into your manufacturing, packaging, labeling, and holding operations of producing dietary supplements, as required by 21 CFR 111.65. Once you have established the required written procedures, your quality control personnel must ensure that your manufacturing, packaging, labeling, and holding operations ensure the quality of the dietary supplements and that the dietary supplements are packaged and labeled as specified in the master manufacturing records, as required by 21 CFR 111.105.

We have reviewed your firm's undated response to this observation, which we received November 27, 2017; however, your response does not identify the specific corrective actions you plan to take. The Agency recommends that you review 21 CFR 111, specifically, Subpart E, Requirement to Establish a Production and Process Control System, and Subpart F, Production and Process Control System, Requirements for Quality Control.

3. You failed to prepare and follow a written master manufacturing record (MMR) for each unique formulation of dietary supplement that you manufacture, and for each batch size, to ensure uniformity in the finished batch from batch to batch, as required by 21 CFR 111.205(a). Specifically, you do not have a written MMR for each unique formulation of dietary supplement that you manufacture, and for each batch size, to ensure uniformity in the finished batch. You must prepare and follow an MMR that identifies specifications for the points, steps, or stages in the manufacturing process where control is necessary to ensure the quality of the dietary supplement and that the dietary supplement is packaged and labeled as specified in the MMR, as required by 21 CFR 111.205(b)(1). In establishing your written MMR, also note that your MMR must satisfy the requirements of 21 CFR 111.210.

We have reviewed your firm's undated response to this observation, which we received November 27, 2017; however, your response does not identify the specific corrective actions you plan to take. The Agency recommends you review 21 CFR 111, specifically, Subpart H, Production and Process Control System: Requirements for the Master Manufacturing Record.

4. You failed to prepare a batch production record every time you manufacture a batch of your dietary supplement products, as required by 21 CFR 111.255(a). Specially, you do not prepare batch production records for any of the dietary supplements you manufacture.

We have reviewed your firm's undated response to this observation, which we received November 27, 2017; however, your response does not identify the specific corrective actions you plan to take. The Agency would recommend you review 21 CFR 111, specifically, Subpart I, Production and Process Control System: Requirements for the Batch Production Record.

5. You failed to establish and follow written procedures to fulfill the requirements related to product complaints, as required by 21 CFR 111.553. Specifically, you have not established any written procedures for product complaints. In establishing your written procedures, you must ensure a qualified person performs all the required steps under 21 CFR 111.560, and you must make and keep a written record of every product complaint, as required by 21 CFR 111.570.

We have reviewed your firm's undated response to this observation, which we received November 27, 2017; however, your response does not identify the specific corrective actions you plan to take. The Agency would recommend you review 21 CFR 111, specifically, Subpart O, Product Complaints.

6. You failed to establish and follow written procedures for holding and distribution operations, as required by 21 CFR 111.453. Specifically, your firm has not established written procedures for holding and distributing operations.

We have reviewed your firm's undated response to this observation, which we received November 27, 2017; however, your response does not identify the specific corrective actions you plan to take. The Agency would recommend you review 21 CFR 111, specifically, Subpart M, Holding and Distributing.

7. You failed to collect and hold reserve samples of reach lot of packaged and labeled dietary supplement that you distribute, as required by 21 CFR 111.83(a). Specifically, your firm does not retain samples of the products you distribute.

We have reviewed your firm's undated response to this observation, which we received November 27, 2017; however, your response does not identify the specific corrective actions you plan to take. The Agency recommends that you review 21 CFR 111, specifically, Subpart E, Requirements to Establish a Production and Process Control System, in particular 21 CFR 111.83, "What are the requirements for reserve samples?"

8. You failed to establish and follow written procedures to fulfill the requirements related to returned dietary supplement, as required by 21 CFR 111.503. Specifically, your firm does not have written procedures regarding the handling of returned dietary supplements.

We have reviewed your firm's undated response to this observation, which we received November 27, 2017; however, your response does not identify the specific corrective actions you plan to take. The Agency would recommend you review 21 CFR 111, specifically, Subpart N, Returned Dietary Supplements.

Misbranded Dietary Supplements

If your products did not have therapeutic claims which make them unapproved new drugs and/ or misbranded drugs, and if the products were properly labeled as dietary supplements, certain products of yours would be misbranded dietary supplements under Section 403 of the Act [21 U.S.C. § 343] because they do not comply with the labeling requirements for dietary supplements as required by 21 CFR 101. Examples of these violations are as follows:

1. Your Harmony, Varicose Relief, Yeast Rid, Joint Support, Sinus & Hayfever, Pain Relief, Heart Tonic, Cough Syrup, Dental Formula, Insure Herbal, Natural Calcium, Lung & Respiratory, Baby Calm, Varicose Relief liquid, Liver-Gallbladder, Billbright Formula, Gripe Water, Bowel Cleanser, Children's Bowel Tonic, Arthritis Relief, Complete Tissue Syrup, Allergy/Energy Combo, Adrenal Aid, Anti-Yeast, Birth Ease, Eldermint, After-Pain Ease, Para-Cleanse, Natural Antibiotic, Natural Iron, Nerve & Stress, Quick Cleanse, Flu and Cold Aid, Migraine Relief, Concentration Aid, M. C. Formula, Rescue Remedy, M.S. Balm, Ladies Formula, Kidney and Bladder, Hormone Health, Echinacea Goldenseal, Fertil-Aid for Women, Lactation Aid, Fertil-Aid for Men, and Diarrhea-X products are misbranded within the meaning of section 403(e)(2) of the Act [21 U.S.C. § 343(e)(2)] because the label fails to declare the net quantity of contents on the principal display

panel as required by 21 CFR 101.7. Specifically, your products do not list the amount of fluid ounces or ounces each product consists of followed by the metric equivalent in parentheses.

2. Your Varicose Relief (capsules and liquid), Gripe Water, Sinus & Hayfever, Eldermint, Anti-Yeast, Insure Herbal, Natural Calcium, Bowel Cleanser, Hormone Health, Lactation Aid, Ladies Formula, Joint Support, and Arthritis Relief products are misbranded within the meaning of section 403(i)(2) of the Act [21 U.S.C. § 343(i)(2)] in that the product label fails to declare the common or usual names of each ingredient used as required by 21 CFR 101.36 and 21 CFR 101.4. Specifically:

   - Your Varicose Relief product labels declare the ingredient stone rt., but this is not the common or usual name for this ingredient;

   - Your Gripe Water product label declares the ingredient soda, but this is not the common or usual name for this ingredient.

   - Your Sinus & Hayfever, Eldermint, Anti-Yeast, and Insure Herbal product labels declare the ingredient Echinacea, your Natural Calcium product label declares the ingredient shavegrass, your Bowel Cleanser product label declares the ingredient turkey rhubarb, your Hormone Health, Lactation Aid, and Ladies Formula product labels declare the ingredient vitex, and your Joint Support and Arthritis Relief product labels declare the ingredient Brigham tea, but these are not the standardized common names noted in the reference Herbs of Commerce;

   - Your Adrenal Aid product label indicates this is a liquid product in that the net contents is stated as "___ fl. oz.," but the product label fails to list the liquid ingredients.

3. Your dietary supplement products are misbranded within the meaning of section 403(q)(1)(A) of the Act [21 U.S.C. § 343(q)(1)(A)] because the labels fail to bear the serving size in accordance with 21 CFR 101.36(b)(1)(i). The terms "serving" or "serving size" for a dietary supplement are defined in 21 CFR 101.9(b) and 101.12, Table 2, as the maximum amount recommended on the label for consumption per eating occasion. Furthermore, common household measures must be followed by the equivalent metric quantity in parentheses.

4. Your Harmony, Varicose Relief capsules, Yeast Rid, Joint Support, Sinus & Hayfever, Pain Relief, Heart Tonic, Cough Syrup, Dental Formula, Insure Herbal, Natural Calcium, Lung & Respiratory, Baby Calm, Varicose Relief liquid, Liver-Gallbladder, Billbright Formula, Gripe Water, Bowel Cleanser, Children's Bowel Tonic, Arthritis Relief, Complete Tissue Syrup, Allergy/Energy Combo, Adrenal Aid, Anti-Yeast, Birth Ease, Eldermint, After-Pain Ease, Para-Cleanse, Natural Antibiotic, Natural Iron, Nerve & Stress, Quick Cleanse, Flu and Cold Aid, Migraine Relief, Concentration Aid, M. C. Formula, Rescue Remedy, M.S. Balm, Ladies Formula, Kidney and Bladder, Hormone Health, Echinacea Goldenseal, Fertil-Aid for Women, Lactation Aid, Fertil-Aid for Men, and Diarrhea-X products are misbranded

within the meaning of section 403(q)(5)(F) of the Act [21 U.S.C. 343 (q)(5)(F)] because the label fails to bear nutrition information ("Supplements Facts") as required by 21 CFR 101.36.

5. Your dietary supplement products are misbranded within the meaning of 403(s)(2)(B) of the Act [21 U.S.C. § 343 (s)(2)(B)] because the label fails to include a statement of identity as a "dietary supplement" as required by 21 CFR 101.3(g).

6. Your dietary supplement products are misbranded within the meaning of section 403(s)(2)(C) of the Act [U.S.C. § 343(s)(2)(C)] in that the labels fail to identify the part of the plant (e.g., root, leaves) from which each botanical dietary ingredient in the product is derived, as required by 21 CFR 101.4(h)(1) and 101.36(d)(1). For example:

- Your Flu and Cold Aid fail to include the part of the plant from which nettle and barberry are derived;

- Your Anti Yeast fails to include the part of the plant from which red clover, pau d'arco, cat's claw, dandelion, nettle, burdock, Echinacea, and butcher's broom are derived;

- Your Heart Tonic fails to include the part of the plant from which gingko, ginger, and gotu kola are derived

The violations cited in this letter are not intended to be an all-inclusive statement of violations that exists in connection with your products. You are responsible for investigating and determining the causes of the violations identified above and for preventing their recurrence or the occurrence of other violations. It is your responsibility to ensure your firm complies with all requirements of federal law, including FDA regulations. You should take prompt action to correct the violations cited in this letter. Failure to promptly correct these violations may result in legal action without further notice, including, without limitation, seizure and/or injunction.

Additionally, we have the following comments:

A copyof 21 CFR 111, Current Good Manufacturing Practice In Manufacturing, Packaging, Labeling, Or Holding Operations For Dietary Supplements, as well as a copy of the Small Entity Compliance Guide: Current Good Manufacturing Practice in Manufacturing, Packaging, Labeling, or Holding Operations for Dietary Supplements December 2010 are included with this letter for your reference.

As a responsible official of a facility that manufactures/processes, packs, re-labels or holds food for human or animal consumption in the United States, you are responsible for ensuring that your overall operation and the products you distribute are in compliance with the law.

Within fifteen (15) working days of receipt of this letter, please notify this office in writing of the specific steps you have taken to correct violations, including an explanation of each step being taken to prevent the recurrence of violations, as well as copies of related documentation. If you cannot complete all corrective actions within fifteen working days, state the reason for the delay and the time within which you will complete the correction.

Section 743 of the Act, 21 U.S.C. § 379j-31, authorizes FDA to assess and collect fees to cover FDA's costs for certain activities, including reinspection-related costs. A reinspection is one or more inspections conducted subsequent to an inspection that identified non-compliance materially related to a food safety requirement of the Act, specifically to determine whether compliance has been achieved. Reinspection-related costs means all expenses, including administrative expenses, incurred in connection with FDA's arranging, conducting, and evaluating the results of the reinspection and assessing and collecting the reinspection fees, 21 U.S.C. § 379j-31(a)(2)(B). For a domestic facility, FDA will assess and collect fees for reinspection-related costs from the responsible party for the domestic facility. The inspection noted in this letter identified non-compliance materially related to a food safety requirement of the Act. Accordingly, FDA may assess fees to cover any reinspection-related costs.

Please submit your response to Paul E. Frazier, Compliance Officer, at the address of 4040 North Central Expressway, Suite 300, Dallas, Texas 75204. If you have any questions, please contact Mr. Frazier at (214) 253-5340.

Sincerely,

/S/

Edmundo Garcia Jr.
District Director
Program Division Director
Office of Human and Animal Food, WD3

[1] Note that not all of your products could meet the definition of "dietary supplement" even if the product labeling did not bear disease claims or even if the products were properly labeled as dietary supplements. For example, products that are not intended for ingestion, such as products that are intended to be rubbed on the body, do not meet the definition of a dietary supplement. See Section 201(ff)(2)(A)(i) of the Act. Also, any products that are represented for use as a conventional food, such as a beverage, do not qualify as dietary supplements. See Section 201(ff)(2)(B) of the Act.

Sample 2

APS BioGroup, Inc
July 6, 2017

WARNING LETTER
VIA UPS
SIGNATURE REQUIRED

Mr. George Stagnitti, President & CEO
APS Biogroup, Inc.
2235 South Central Ave.
Phoenix, AZ 85004-2909

Dear Mr. Stagnitti:

This is to advise you that the Food and Drug Administration (FDA) reviewed your product labels following an inspection of your facility at 2235 South Central Ave, Phoenix, Arizona, from February 6, 2017, to February 16, 2017. Based on our review, we have determined that the therapeutic claims on your "ProGI Soothe Gastrointestinal & Hepatic Support Formula" and "Pathogen Defense" establish that the products are drugs under section 201(g)(1)(B) of the Federal Food, Drug, and Cosmetic Act (the Act) [21 U.S.C. 321(g)(1)(B)] because they are intended for use in the cure, mitigation, treatment, or prevention of disease. Further, even if these products were not unapproved new drugs, they would be misbranded foods under section 403 of the Act [21 U.S.C. 343]. Additionally, based on our review of the labels for your "Children's DiaResQ," "Liver Defend," "Colostrum with Probiotics," and "DPS Throat Spray," we have determined that these products are misbranded under section 403 of the Act [21 U.S.C. 343]. You can find the Act and FDA regulations through links on FDA's home page at www.fda.gov.

Unapproved New Drugs

Examples of some of the label claims that provide evidence that the following products are intended for use as drugs include:

Pathogen Defense

- "Pathogen Defense"

- "[A] combination of natural herbs addressing the overgrowth and infectious potential of various pathogens..."

- "[A]bility to combat viral activity, bacterial colonization and activation of yeast overgrowth..."

ProGI Soothe Gastrointestinal & Hepatic Support Formula

- "N-Acetyl Cysteine has the potential to bind heavy metals such as mercury and cadmium..."

The "Pathogen Defense" and "ProGI Soothe Gastrointestinal & Hepatic Support Formula" products are not generally recognized as safe and effective for the above referenced uses and, therefore, the products are "new drugs" under section 201(p) of the Act [21 U.S.C. 321(p)]. New drugs may not be legally introduced or delivered for introduction into interstate commerce without prior approval from FDA, as described in sections 301(d) and 505(a) of the Act [21 U.S.C. 331(d), 355(a)]. FDA approves a new drug on the basis of scientific data and information demonstrating that the drug is safe and effective.

Misbranding Violations

We reviewed the labeling of your "Children's DiaResQ," "Liver Defend," "Colostrum with Probiotics," and "DPS Throat Spray" products and determined that these products are misbranded under section 403 of the Act [21 U.S.C. 343] for the reasons described below. Additionally, even if your "ProGI Soothe Gastrointestinal & Hepatic Support Formula" and "Pathogen Defense" products did not have therapeutic claims which make them unapproved new drugs, these products would be misbranded foods under section 403 of the Act [21 U.S.C. 343].

1. The "Children's DiaResQ" product is misbranded under section 403(i)(1) of the Act in that the label does not bear an appropriate common or usual name of the food or an appropriately descriptive term, if there is one, or when the nature of the food is obvious, a fanciful name commonly used by the public for such food as required by 21 CFR 101.3(b).

2. The "ProGI Soothe Gastrointestinal & Hepatic Support Formula," "Liver Defend", "Pathogen Defense", and "Colostrum with Probiotics" products are misbranded within the meaning of section 403(i)(2) of the Act [21 U.S.C. 343(i)(2)] in that the product labels fail to declare all the common or usual names of each ingredient used as required by 21 CFR 101.36 and 21 CFR 101.4. For example, the "ProGI Soothe Gastrointestinal & Hepatic Support Formula" lists "Stabilized Flaxseed Complex" and "Aminogen® (patented enzyme blend)" as ingredients which are modified names and not the common and usual names of these ingredients. If these ingredients are multi component ingredients, each sub ingredient must also be declared.

   Also, the "Liver Defend" and "Pathogen Defense" products declare "HPMC (vegetable capsule)" as an "Other Ingredient" but do not list the common or usual name of that ingredient; specifically, HPMC should declared as its scientific name, hydroxypropyl methylcellulose.

   In addition, the "Colostrum with Probiotics" product lists the ingredient "Rice Solubles" which is not the common or usual name of an ingredient.

3. The "Pathogen Defense" product is misbranded within the meaning of section 403(q)(1)(A) of the Act [21 U.S.C. 343(q)(1)(A)] because the serving size declared on the label is incorrect. Serving size for a dietary supplement is the maximum amount consumed per eating

occasion as recommended on the product label as defined in 21 CFR 101.9(b) and 21 CFR 101.12(b) Table 2. The serving size is indicated as 2 capsules; however, the directions indicate "may take up to 3 capsules per day".

4. The "Children's DiaResQ" product is misbranded within the meaning of section 403(q) of the Act [21 U.S.C. 343(q)] in that the nutrition information (e.g. Nutrition Facts Panel) is not in a correct format as required by 21 CFR 101.9. Foods, other than infant formula, represented or purported to be specifically for children 1 through 3 years of age shall bear nutrition labeling for those age groups, as required by 21 CFR 101.9(j)(5). The "Children's DiaResQ" product does not provide nutrition information for children between one (1) year and three (3) years of age. There are specific requirements for children under four (4) years of age and under two (2) years of age in accordance with 21 CFR 101.9(j)(5).

5. Your "DPS Throat Spray" product is misbranded within the meaning of section 403(r)(1)(A) of the Act [21 U.S.C. 343(r)(1)(A)] because the label bears a nutrient content claim, but the product does not meet the requirements to bear the claim. Under section 403(r)(1)(A) of the Act, a claim that characterizes the level of a nutrient which is of the type required to be in the labeling of the food must be made in accordance with a regulation authorizing the use of such a claim. Characterizing the level of a nutrient on the food labeling of a product without complying with the specific requirements pertaining to the nutrient content claim for that nutrient misbrands the product under section 403(r)(1)(A) of the Act.

Specifically, your "DPS Throat Spray" product bears the nutrient content claim "Proline Rich Polypeptides." FDA has issued a regulation specifying criteria for the use of the nutrient content claim "high" in food labeling, which also applies to synonymous claims such as "rich in" [see 21 CFR 101.54(b)(1)]. This regulation requires a food that bears this claim to contain 20 percent or more of the Reference Daily Intake (RDI) or the Daily Reference Value (DRV) of the nutrient per reference amount customarily consumer (RACC). However, this regulation does not authorize the claim "Proline Rich Polypeptides" because there is no RDI or DRV for "proline." Therefore, the use of the term "Proline Rich Polypeptides" to characterize the level of "proline" in your "DPS Throat Spray" product causes your product to be misbranded under section 403(r)(1)(A) of the Act.

6. The "Colostrum with Probiotics" and "DPS Throat Spray" products are misbranded within the meaning of section 403(w) of the Act [21 U.S.C. 343(w)] in that the finished product labels fail to declare the major food allergen "milk" as required by section 403(w)(1) of the Act.

Section 201(qq) of the Act, 21 U.S.C. 321(qq), defines a major food allergen as milk, egg, fish, Crustacean shellfish, tree nuts, wheat, peanuts, and soybeans, as well as any food ingredient that contains protein derived from one of these foods, with certain exceptions, e.g., highly refined oils derived from a major food allergen. A food is misbranded if it is not a raw agricultural commodity and it is, or it contains, an ingredient that bears or contains, a major food allergen, unless either:

- The word "Contains," followed by the name of the food source from which the major food allergen is derived, is printed immediately after or is adjacent to the list of ingredients [section 403(w)(1)(A) of the Act, 21 U.S.C. 343(w)(1)(A)], or

- The common or usual name of the major food allergen in the list of ingredients is followed in parentheses by the name of the food source from which the major food allergen is derived, except that the name of the food source is not required when either the common or usual name of the ingredient uses the name of the food source or the name of the food source appears elsewhere in the ingredient list (unless the name of the food source that appears elsewhere in the ingredient list appears as part of the name of an ingredient that is not a major food allergen) [section 403(w)(1)(B) of the Act, 21 U.S.C. § 343(w)(1)(B)].

  Specifically, "Colostrum with Probiotics" and "DPS Throat Spray" products state "Contains Milk Proteins". "Milk proteins" is not the common or usual name of the food allergen milk.

The violations cited in this letter are not intended to be an all-inclusive statement of violations that exist in connection with your products. You are responsible for investigating and determining the causes of the violations identified above and for preventing their recurrence or the occurrence of other violations. It is your responsibility to ensure that your firm complies with all requirements of federal law, including FDA regulations.

You should take prompt action to correct the violations cited in this letter. Failure to promptly correct these violations may result in enforcement action by FDA without further notice, such as seizure or injunction.

We offer the following comments:

1. The listing of the trademarked name "TRAACS®" within the declared ingredients of the "ProGI Soothe Gastrointestinal & Hepatic Support Formula" product is intervening material in accordance with 21 CFR 101.2(e).

   In addition, the ingredient list and the business name and address on this product are not together in one place without intervening material in accordance with 21 CFR 101.2(e).

2. The "Children's DiaResQ" product's net weight is not declared in the proper format in accordance with 21 CFR 101.7(s). The net wet is declared as "0.74 OZ (21g)" but does not declare the net weight of the individual packets the multiunit retail package consists of.

3. The nutrition information provided on the "ProGI Soothe Gastrointestinal & Hepatic Support Formula" product appears to not be consistent with the requirements under 21 CFR 101.9. For example, the label declares the serving size as 2 scoops (90g) and the directions for use indicate that 90g makes 12 oz of the beverage. The serving size for beverages is 8oz (240ml); therefore, the reference amount for the powder is the amount required to make the reference amount of the prepared form in accordance with 21 CFR 101.12(c). Also, the declaration for the percentages for vitamins and minerals must be expressed to the near-

est 10-percent increments above the 50 percent level. We also note that regulations do not allow for adding nutrients in the Nutrition Facts Label that are not provided under 21 CFR 101.9(c)(8)(ii).

4. The nutrition information provided for the "Children's DiaResQ" product is not consistent with the requirements under 21 CFR 101.9. The declaration for the percentages for vitamins and minerals must be expressed to the nearest 2-percent increments up to and including the 10 percent level.

5. The "Liver Defend" product label bears the following or similar statement: "Percent Daily Values based on a 2,000 calorie diet." This statement is only permitted when the percent of Daily Value (DV) is declared for total fat, saturated fat, total carbohydrate, dietary fiber, or protein as required by 21 CFR 101.9(c) and 21 CFR 101.36(b)(2)(iii)(D).

6. The "DPS Throat Spray" fails to present the nutrition information in accordance with 21 CFR 101.36(e).

7. The following disclaimer "This statement has not been evaluated by the FDA. This product is not intended to diagnose, treat, cure, or prevent any disease" appears on the ProGI Soothe™ product and is not appropriate to be declared on conventional food products. In accordance with 21 CFR 101.93(b), this disclaimer is required when a dietary supplement bears a statement that is provided for by section 403(r)(6) of the Act, and the manufacturer, packer, or distributor wishes to take advantage of the exemption to section 201(g)(1)(C) of the Act that is provided by compliance with section 403(r)(6) of the Act.

8. The "Colostrum with Probiotics" product's declaration of net quantity of contents is not in accordance with 21 CFR 101.7(j)(3).

9. Please note the FDA does not have a regulatory definition for the term "Functional Food" declared on the "ProGI Soothe Gastrointestinal & Hepatic Support Formula" product's label.

Within fifteen working days of receipt of this letter, you should notify this office in writing of the specific steps you have taken to correct the violations noted above. You should include in your response documentation and any other useful information that would assist us in evaluating your corrective actions and an explanation of each step being taken to prevent the recurrence of violations. If you cannot complete corrective actions within fifteen working days, state the reason for the delay and the time within which the corrections will be completed.

Section 743 of the Act [21 U.S.C. 379j-31] authorizes FDA to assess and collect fees to cover FDA's costs for certain activities, including reinspection-related costs. A reinspection is one or more inspections conducted subsequent to an inspection that identified noncompliance materially related to a food safety requirement of the Act, specifically to determine whether compliance has been achieved. Reinspection-related costs means all expenses, including administrative expenses, incurred in connection with FDA's arranging, conducting, and evaluating the results of the reinspection and assessing and collecting the reinspection fees [21 U.S.C. 379j-31(a)(2)(B)]. For a domestic facility, FDA will assess and collect fees for reinspection-related costs from the responsible party for the domestic facility. The inspection noted in this letter identified noncompliance materially related to a food safety requirement of the Act. Accordingly, FDA may assess fees to cover any reinspection-related costs.

If you have any questions regarding this letter, please contact Caroline H. Le, Compliance Officer, at 303-236-3045.

Your written reply should be sent to:

> Caroline H. Le
> Compliance Officer
> US Food & Drug Administration
> P.O. Box 25087
> Denver, CO 80225-0087

Sincerely,

/S/

LaTonya M. Mitchell
District Director, FDA Denver District
Program Division Director
Office of Human and Animal Foods – Division IV West

COMBINED GLOSSARY & INDEX

A

Acceptable daily intake (ADI)	[Guidance NDI] The daily intake of a substance that, during the human lifetime, appears to be without appreciable risk on the basis of all known facts at the time. In the context of an NDI notification, the ADI of an NDI or dietary supplement is calculated as the ratio of the NOAEL to the total safety factor (determined from the studies submitted in the notification).
Act/Act, The	[21CFR§1.377] means the Federal Food, Drug, and Cosmetic Act.
	[21CFR§1.276] means the Federal Food, Drug, and Cosmetic Act
Actual yield	[21CFR§111.3] means the quantity that is actually produced at any appropriate step of manufacture or packaging of a particular dietary supplement.
Adequate	[21CFR§1.500] means that which is needed to accomplish the intended purpose in keeping with good public health practice.
Amino acid	[Guidance NDI] An alpha-amino carboxylic acid used as a constituent of proteins or peptides.
Audit	[21CFR§1.500] means the systematic, independent, and documented examination (through observation, investigation, discussions with employees of the audited entity, records review, and, as appropriate, sampling and laboratory analysis) to assess an audited entity's food safety processes and procedures.
Authorized FDA representative	[21CFR§1.377] means an FDA District Director in whose district the article of food involved is located or an FDA official senior to such director.

B

Batch	[21CFR§111.3] means a specific quantity of a dietary supplement that is uniform, that is intended to meet specifications for identity, purity, strength, and composition, and that is produced during a specified time period according to a single manufacturing record during the same cycle of manufacture.
Batch number, lot number, or control number	[21CFR§111.3] means any distinctive group of letters, numbers, or symbols, or any combination of them, from which the complete history of the manufacturing, packaging, labeling, and/or holding of a batch or lot of dietary supplements can be determined.
Botanical or herbal	[Guidance NDI] A plant, alga, or fungus; a part of a plant, alga, or fungus (e.g., bark, leaves, stems, roots, flowers, fruits, seeds, berries, or parts thereof); or an exudate (secretion) of a plant, alga, or fungus.
Botanical raw material	[Guidance NDI] Whole or physically processed (e.g., cleaned, frozen, dried, or sliced) parts of a single species of plant or a fresh or processed alga or fungus.

C

Calendar day	[21CFR§1.227] [21CFR§1.276] [21CFR§1.377] means every day shown on the calendar.
Chemically altered	[Guidance NDI] See questions IV.B.4 and IV.B.5 for a detailed discussion.
Chronic	[Guidance NDI] Chronic exposure is exposure for more than 3 months. Periods of daily use interspersed with periods of non-use would be considered chronic exposure. In the context of toxicology studies, the term "chronic" generally refers to studies with at least 1 year of repeated dosing. Repeated exposure is divided into 3 categories: subacute, subchronic, and chronic. Subacute exposure refers to repeated exposure to a substance for 1 month or less, subchronic for 1 to 3 months, and chronic for longer than subchronic.
Component	[21CFR§111.3] means any substance intended for use in the manufacture of a dietary supplement, including those that may not appear in the finished batch of the dietary supplement. Component includes dietary ingredients (as described in section 201(ff) of the act) and other ingredients.
	[Guidance NDI] A substance that is part of a mixture. Includes substances that cannot be isolated from the whole, as well as those that can. Once isolated, a component of a mixture is also a constituent (see definition below).
Concentrate	[Guidance NDI] An article in which constituents are more concentrated than in the original. An herbal concentrate is an extract from which all or most of the solvent has been removed, reducing the product to a solid, semi-solid, or syrupy form. The solvent and the process by which the concentrate is made are part of the definition of the concentrate.
Configurational isomer	[Guidance NDI] See Stereoisomers.
Constituent	[Guidance NDI] An article that is a physical part of the whole and can be isolated from the whole.
Contact surface	[21CFR§111.3] means any surface that contacts a component or dietary supplement, and those surfaces from which drainage onto the component or dietary supplement, or onto surfaces that contact the component or dietary supplement, occurs during the normal course of operations. Examples of contact surfaces include containers, utensils, tables, contact surfaces of equipment, and packaging.
Country from which the article is shipped	[21CFR§1.276] means the country in which the article of food is loaded onto the conveyance that brings it to the United States or, in the case of food sent by international mail, the country from which the article is mailed.
Country from which the article originates	[21CFR§1.276] means FDA Country of Production.

D

Dietary ingredient	[Guidance NDI] A dietary ingredient is (A) a vitamin, (B) a mineral, (C) an herb or other botanical, (D) an amino acid, (E) a dietary substance for use by man to supplement the diet by increasing the total dietary intake, or (F) a concentrate, metabolite, constituent, extract, or combination of any ingredient described in (A) through (E).
Dietary substance	Interpreted as a substance that is commonly used as human food or drink; an intentional constituent of food; is not defined in the FD&C Act or by regulation.

Dietary supplement	[21CFR§1.500] has the meaning given in section 201(ff) of the Federal Food, Drug, and Cosmetic Act.
	"[DSHEA] The Definition of Certain Foods as Dietary Supplements.–Section 201 (21 U.S.C. 321) is amended by adding at the end the following: (1) means a product (other than tobacco) intended to supplement the diet that bears or contains one or more of the following dietary ingredients: (A) a vitamin; (B) a mineral; (C) an herb or other botanical; (D) an amino acid; (E) a dietary substance for use by man to supplement the diet by increasing the total dietary intake; or (F) a concentrate, metabolite, constituent, extract, or combination of any ingredient described in clause (A), (B), (C), (D), or (E); (2) means a product that–(A)(i) is intended for ingestion in a form described in section 411(c)(1)(B)(i); or (ii) complies with section 411(c)(1)(B)(ii); (B) is not represented for use as a conventional food or as a sole item of a meal or the diet; and ``(C) is labeled as a dietary supplement; and (3) does–(A) include an article that is approved as a new drug under section 505, certified as an antibiotic under section 507, or licensed as a biologic under section 351 of the Public Health Service Act (42 U.S.C. 262) and was, prior to such approval, certification, or license, marketed as a dietary supplement or as a food unless the Secretary has issued a regulation, after notice and comment, finding that the article, when used as or in a dietary supplement under the conditions of use and dosages set forth in the labeling for such dietary supplement, is unlawful under section 402(f); and (B) not include–(i) an article that is approved as a new drug under section 505, certified as an antibiotic under section 507, or licensed as a biologic under section 351 of the Public Health Service Act (42 U.S.C. 262), or (ii) an article authorized for investigation as a new drug, antibiotic, or biological for which substantial clinical investigations have been instituted and for which the existence of such investigations has been made public, which was not before such approval, certification, licensing, or authorization marketed as a dietary supplement or as a food unless the Secretary, in the Secretary's discretion, has issued a regulation, after notice and comment, finding that the article would be lawful under this Act. Except for purposes of section 201(g), a dietary supplement shall be deemed to be a food within the meaning of this Act."
Dietary supplement component	[21CFR§1.500] means any substance intended for use in the manufacture of a dietary supplement, including those that may not appear in the finished batch of the dietary supplement. Dietary supplement components include dietary ingredients (as described in section 201(ff) of the Federal Food, Drug, and Cosmetic Act) and other ingredients.
Disease or health-related condition	[21CFR§101.14] means damage to an organ, part, structure, or system of the body such that it does not function properly (e.g., cardiovascular disease), or a state of health leading to such dysfunctioning (e.g., hypertension); except that diseases resulting from essential nutrient deficiencies (e.g., scurvy, pellagra) are not included in this definition (claims pertaining to such diseases are thereby not subject to 101.14 or 101.70).
Disqualifying nutrient levels	[21CFR§101.14] means the levels of total fat, saturated fat, cholesterol, or sodium in a food above which the food will be disqualified from making a health claim. These levels are 13.0 grams (g) of fat, 4.0 g of saturated fat, 60 milligrams (mg) of cholesterol, or 480 mg of sodium, per reference amount customarily consumed, per label serving size, and, only for foods with reference amounts customarily consumed of 30 g or less or 2 tablespoons or less, per 50 g. For dehydrated foods that must have water added to them prior to typical consumption, the per 50-g

Disqualifying nutrient levels (cont'd)	criterion refers to the as prepared form. Any one of the levels, on a per reference amount customarily consumed, a per label serving size or, when applicable, a per 50 g basis, will disqualify a food from making a health claim unless an exception is provided in subpart E of this part, except that: (i) The levels for a meal product as defined in 101.13(l) are 26.0 g of fat, 8.0 g of saturated fat, 120 mg of cholesterol, or 960 mg of sodium per label serving size, and (ii) The levels for a main dish product as defined in 101.13(m) are 19.5 g of fat, 6.0 g of saturated fat, 90 mg of cholesterol, or 720 mg of sodium per label serving size.
Domestic facility	[21CFR§1.227] means any facility located in any State or Territory of the United States, the District of Columbia, or the Commonwealth of Puerto Rico that manufactures/processes, packs, or holds food for consumption in the United States.

E

Enantiomers	[Guidance NDI] Mirror-image isomers (optical isomers) that generally have similar chemical and physical properties, but different biological properties in a chiral environment.
Environmental pathogen	[21CFR§1.500] means a pathogen capable of surviving and persisting within the manufacturing, processing, packing, or holding environment such that food may be contaminated and may result in foodborne illness if that food is consumed without treatment to significantly minimize the environmental pathogen. Examples of environmental pathogens for the purposes of this part include Listeria monocytogenes and Salmonella spp. but do not include the spores of pathogenic sporeforming bacteria.
Estimated daily intake (EDI)	[Guidance NDI] For purposes of an NDI notification, the EDI is the highest possible total daily intake level (in mg/day or mg/kg/day) of an NDI, as determined from the proposed conditions of use in the notification and any background exposure from other dietary sources. It is the maximum amount that would be consumed based on the conditions of use proposed in the notification, taking into account cumulative exposure from other dietary sources. The EDI should not be higher than the ADI.
Extract	A product consisting of a solvent (menstruum) combined with a dietary substance or botanical biomass by a process that physically separates constituents from the dietary substance or botanical and dissolves them into the solvent. The extract can be further concentrated through drying to a dry powder or semi-solid form.

F

Facility	[21CFR§1.227] means any establishment, structure, or structures under one ownership at one general physical location, or, in the case of a mobile facility, traveling to multiple locations, that manufactures/processes, packs, or holds food for consumption in the United States. Transport vehicles are not facilities if they hold food only in the usual course of business as carriers. A facility may consist of one or more contiguous structures, and a single building may house more than one distinct facility if the facilities are under separate ownership. The private residence of an individual is not a facility. Nonbottled water drinking water collection and distribution establishments and their structures are not facilities.
Facility	[21CFR§1.500] means a domestic facility or a foreign facility that is required to register under section 415 of the Federal Food, Drug, and Cosmetic Act, in accordance with the requirements of subpart H of this part.

Farm	[21CFR§1.227] means (1) Primary production farm or (2) Seconday activities farm. See primary production farm and secondary activities farm.
	[21CFR§1.328] means: (1) Primary production farm or (2) Secondary activities farm.
	[21CFR§1.500] means farm as defined in 1.227.
Farm mixed-type facility	[21CFR§1.500] means an establishment that is a farm but that also conducts activities outside the farm definition that require the establishment to be registered under section 415 of the Federal Food, Drug, and Cosmetic Act.
FDA Country of Production	[21CFR§1.276] means: (i) For an article of food that is in its natural state, the country where the article of food was grown, including harvested or collected and readied for shipment to the United States. If an article of food is wild fish, including seafood that was caught or harvested outside the waters of the United States by a vessel that is not registered in the United States, the FDA Country of Production is the country in which the vessel is registered. If an article of food that is in its natural state was grown, including harvested or collected and readied for shipment, in a Territory, the FDA Country of Production is the United States. (continued on next page)
FDA Country of Production (cont'd)	(ii) For an article of food that is no longer in its natural state, the country where the article was made; except that, if an article of food is made from wild fish, including seafood, aboard a vessel, the FDA Country of Production is the country in which the vessel is registered. If an article of food that is no longer in its natural state was made in a Territory, the FDA Country of Production is the United States.
Food	[21CFR§1.276] has the meaning given in section 201(f) of the Federal Food, Drug, and Cosmetic Act: (1) Except for purposes of this subpart, it does not include: (i) Food contact substances as defined in section 409(h)(6) of the Federal Food, Drug, and Cosmetic Act; or (ii) Pesticides as defined in 7 U.S.C. 136(u). (2) Examples of food include: Fruits, vegetables, fish, dairy products, eggs, raw agricultural commodities for use as food or as components of food, animal feed (including pet food), food and feed ingredients, food and feed additives, dietary supplements and dietary ingredients, infant formula, beverages (including alcoholic beverages and bottled water), live food animals, bakery goods, snack foods, candy, and canned foods.
	[21CFR§1.227] has the meaning given in section 201(f) of the act, except as provided in paragraph (b)(5)(i) of this section. (i) For purposes of this subpart, food does not include: (A) Food contact substances as defined in section 409(h)(6) of the act (21 U.S.C. 348(h)(6)); or (B) Pesticides as defined in 7 U.S.C. 136(u). (ii) Examples of food include fruits, vegetables, fish, including seafood, dairy products, eggs, raw agricultural commodities for use as food or as components of food, animal feed (including pet food), food and feed ingredients, food and feed additives, dietary supplements and dietary ingredients, infant formula, beverages (including alcoholic beverages and bottled water), live food animals, bakery goods, snack foods, candy, and canned foods.
	[21CFR§1.328] has the meaning given in section 201(f) of the Federal Food, Drug, and Cosmetic Act. Examples of food include, but are not limited to fruits; vegetables; fish; dairy products; eggs; raw agricultural commodities for use as food or as components of food; animal feed, including pet food; food and feed ingredients and additives, including substances that migrate into food from the

GLOSSARY

Food (cont'd)	finished container and other articles that contact food; dietary supplements and dietary ingredients; infant formula; beverages, including alcoholic beverages and bottled water; live food animals; bakery goods; snack foods; candy; and canned foods.
	[21CFR§1.377] has the meaning given in section 201(f) of the act (21 U.S.C. 321(f)). Examples of food include, but are not limited to, fruits, vegetables, fish, dairy products, eggs, raw agricultural commodities for use as food or components of food, animal feed, including pet food, food and feed ingredients and additives, including substances that migrate into food from food packaging and other articles that contact food, dietary supplements and dietary ingredients, infant formula, beverages, including alcoholic beverages and bottled water, live food animals, bakery goods, snack foods, candy, and canned foods.
	[21CFR§1.500] has the meaning given in section 201(f) of the Federal Food, Drug, and Cosmetic Act, except that food does not include pesticides (as defined in 7 U.S.C. 136(u)).
Food allergen	[21CFR§1.500] means a major food allergen as defined in section 201(qq) of the Federal Food, Drug, and Cosmetic Act.
Food product	[21CFR§101.9] means food in any sized package which is manufactured by a single manufacturer or which bears the same brand name, which bears the same statement of identity, and which has similar preparation methods.
Foreign facility	[21CFR§1.227] means a facility other than a domestic facility that manufactures/processes, packs, or holds food for consumption in the United States.
Foreign supplier	[21CFR§1.500] means, for an article of food, the establishment that manufactures/processes the food, raises the animal, or grows the food that is exported to the United States without further manufacturing/processing by another establishment, except for further manufacturing/processing that consists solely of the addition of labeling or any similar activity of a de minimis nature.
Formulation	[Guidance NDI] A formula that (1) lists the identity and quantity of each dietary ingredient and other ingredients (formulation aids) of a dietary supplement, and (2) describes the administered form (e.g., powder, liquid, capsule, etc.).
Full address	[21CFR§1.276] means the facility's street name and number; suite/unit number, as appropriate; city; Province or State as appropriate; mail code as appropriate; and country.
Full-time equivalent employee	[21CFR§1.328] means all individuals employed by the person claiming the exemption. The number of full-time equivalent employees is determined by dividing the total number of hours of salary or wages paid directly to employees of the person and of all of its affiliates by the number of hours of work in 1 year, 2,080 hours (i.e., 40 hours * 52 weeks).
	[21CFR§101.9] means all individuals employed by the person claiming the exemption. This number shall be determined by dividing the total number of hours of salary or wages paid directly to employees of the person and of all of its affiliates by the number of hours of work in a year, 2,080 hours (i.e., 40 hours * 52 weeks).

G

Geometric isomers

[Guidance NDI] Compounds that have the same molecular formula, but differ from each other in the way that the atoms are oriented in space, and therefore have different chemical, physical, and biological properties (unless interconverted in the gut).

Gluten

[21CFR§101.91] means the proteins that naturally occur in a gluten-containing grain and that may cause adverse health effects in persons with celiac disease (e.g., prolamins and glutelins).

Gluten-containing grain

[21CFR§101.91] means any one of the following grains or their crossbred hybrids (e.g., triticale, which is a cross between wheat and rye): (i) Wheat, including any species belonging to the genus Triticum; (ii) Rye, including any species belonging to the genus Secale; or (iii) Barley, including any species belonging to the genus Hordeum.

Gluten-free

[21CFR§101.91] means: (i) That the food bearing the claim in its labeling: (A) Does not contain any one of the following: (1) An ingredient that is a gluten-containing grain (e.g., spelt wheat); (2) An ingredient that is derived from a gluten-containing grain and that has not been processed to remove gluten (e.g., wheat flour); or (3) An ingredient that is derived from a gluten-containing grain and that has been processed to remove gluten (e.g., wheat starch), if the use of that ingredient results in the presence of 20 parts per million (ppm) or more gluten in the food (i.e., 20 milligrams (mg) or more gluten per kilogram (kg) of food); or (B) Inherently does not contain gluten; and (ii) Any unavoidable presence of gluten in the food bearing the claim in its labeling is below 20 ppm gluten (i.e., below 20 mg gluten per kg of food).

Good compliance standing with a foreign food safety authority

[21CFR§1.500] means that the foreign supplier-- (1) Appears on the current version of a list, issued by the food safety authority of the country in which the foreign supplier is located and which has regulatory oversight of the supplier, of food producers that are in good compliance standing with the food safety authority; or (2) Has otherwise been designated by such food safety authority as being in good compliance standing.

Grower

[21CFR§1.276] means a person who engages in growing and harvesting or collecting crops (including botanicals), raising animals (including fish, which includes seafood), or both.

H

Harvesting

[21CFR§1.227] applies to farms and farm mixed-type facilities and means activities that are traditionally performed on farms for the purpose of removing raw agricultural commodities from the place they were grown or raised and preparing them for use as food. Harvesting is limited to activities performed on raw agricultural commodities, or on processed foods created by drying/dehydrating a raw agricultural commodity without additional manufacturing/processing, on a farm. Harvesting does not include activities that transform a raw agricultural commodity into a processed food as defined in section 201(gg) of the Federal Food, Drug, and Cosmetic Act. Examples of harvesting include cutting (or otherwise separating) the edible portion of the raw agricultural commodity from the crop plant and removing or trimming part of the raw agricultural commodity (e.g., foliage, husks, roots or stems). Examples of harvesting also include cooling, field coring, filtering, gathering, hulling, shelling, sifting, threshing, trimming of outer leaves of, and washing raw agricultural commodities grown on a farm.

Harvesting (cont'd)	[21CFR§1.328] applies to farms and farm mixed-type facilities and means activities that are traditionally performed on farms for the purpose of removing raw agricultural commodities from the place they were grown or raised and preparing them for use as food. Harvesting is limited to activities
	[21CFR§1.328] (cont'd) performed on raw agricultural commodities, or on processed foods created by drying/dehydrating a raw agricultural commodity without additional manufacturing/processing, on a farm. Harvesting does not include activities that transform a raw agricultural commodity into a processed food as defined in section 201(gg) of the Federal Food, Drug, and Cosmetic Act. Examples of harvesting include cutting (or otherwise separating) the edible portion of the raw agricultural commodity from the crop plant and removing or trimming part of the raw agricultural commodity (e.g., foliage, husks, roots, or stems). Examples of harvesting also include cooling, field coring, filtering, gathering, hulling, shelling, sifting, threshing, trimming of outer leaves of, and washing raw agricultural commodities grown on a farm.
	[21CFR§1.500] applies to applies to farms and farm mixed-type facilities and means activities that are traditionally performed on farms for the purpose of removing raw agricultural commodities from the place they were grown or raised and preparing them for use as food. Harvesting is limited to activities performed on raw agricultural commodities, or on processed foods created by drying/dehydrating a raw agricultural commodity without additional manufacturing/processing, on a farm. Harvesting does not include activities that transform a raw agricultural commodity into a processed food as defined in section 201(gg) of the Federal Food, Drug, and Cosmetic Act. Examples of harvesting include cutting (or otherwise separating) the edible portion of the raw agricultural commodity from the crop plant and removing or trimming part of the raw agricultural commodity (e.g., foliage, husks, roots, or stems). Examples of harvesting also include cooling, field coring, filtering, gathering, hulling, shelling, sifting, threshing, trimming of outer leaves of, and washing raw agricultural commodities grown on a farm.
Hazard	[21CFR§1.500] means any biological, chemical (including radiological), or physical agent that is reasonably likely to cause illness or injury.
Hazard requiring a control	[21CFR§1.500] means a known or reasonably foreseeable hazard for which a person knowledgeable about the safe manufacturing, processing, packing, or holding of food would, based on the outcome of a hazard analysis (which includes an assessment of the probability that the hazard will occur in the absence of controls or measures and the severity of the illness or injury if the hazard were to occur), establish one or more controls or measures to significantly minimize or prevent the hazard in a food and components to manage those controls or measures (such as monitoring, corrections or corrective actions, verification, and records) as appropriate to the food, the facility, and the nature of the control or measure and its role in the facility's food safety system.
Health claim	[21CFR§101.14] means any claim made on the label or in labeling of a food, including a dietary supplement, that expressly or by implication, including "third party" references, written statements (e.g., a brand name including a term such as "heart"), symbols (e.g., a heart symbol), or vignettes, characterizes the relationship of any substance to a disease or health-related condition. Implied health claims include those statements, symbols, vignettes, or other forms of communication that suggest, within the context in which they are presented, that a relationship exists between the presence or level of a substance in the food and a disease or health-related condition.

Health claim (cont'd)	[21CFR§101.14] means any claim made on the label or in labeling of a food, including a dietary supplement, that expressly or by implication, including "third party" references, written statements (e.g., a brand name including a term such as "heart"), symbols (e.g., a heart symbol), or vignettes, characterizes the relationship of any substance to a disease or health-related condition. Implied health claims include those statements, symbols, vignettes, or other forms of communication that suggest, within the context in which they are presented, that a relationship exists between the presence or level of a substance in the food and a disease or health-related condition.
Holding	[21CFR§1.227] [21CFR§1.328] means storage of food and also includes activities performed incidental to storage of a food (e.g., activities performed for the safe or effective storage of that food, such as fumigating food during storage, and drying/dehydrating raw agricultural commodities when the drying/dehydrating does not create a distinct commodity (such as drying/dehydrating hay or alfalfa)). Holding also includes activities performed as a practical necessity for the distribution of that food (such as blending of the same raw agricultural commodity and breaking down pallets), but does not include activities that transform a raw agricultural commodity into a processed food as defined in section 201(gg) of the Federal Food, Drug, and Cosmetic Act. Holding facilities could include warehouses, cold storage facilities, storage silos, grain elevators, and liquid storage tanks.
	[21CFR§1.500] means storage of food and also includes activities performed incidental to storage of a food (e.g., activities performed for the safe or effective storage of that food, such as fumigating food during storage, and drying/dehydrating raw agricultural commodities when the drying/dehydrating does not create a distinct commodity (such as drying/dehydrating hay or alfalfa)). Holding also includes activities performed as a practical necessity for the distribution of that food (such as blending of the same raw agricultural commodity and breaking down pallets), but does not include activities that transform a raw agricultural commodity into a processed food as defined in section 201(gg) of the Federal Food, Drug, and Cosmetic Act. Holding facilities could include warehouses, cold storage facilities, storage silos, grain elevators, and liquid storage tanks.

I, J

Importer	[21CFR§1.500] means the U.S. owner or consignee of an article of food that is being offered for import into the United States. If there is no U.S. owner or consignee of an article of food at the time of U.S. entry, the importer is the U.S. agent or representative of the foreign owner or consignee at the time of entry, as confirmed in a signed statement of consent to serve as the importer under this subpart.
Ingestion	[Guidance NDI] Taking an article, such as a dietary supplement or other food, into the stomach and gastrointestinal tract by swallowing.
Ingredient	[21CFR§111.3] means any substance that is used in the manufacture of a dietary supplement and that is intended to be present in the finished batch of the dietary supplement. An ingredient includes, but is not necessarily limited to, a dietary ingredient as defined in section 201(ff) of the act.
In-process material	[21CFR§111.3] means any material that is fabricated, compounded, blended, ground, extracted, sifted, sterilized, derived by chemical reaction, or processed in any other way for use in the manufacture of a dietary supplement.

G L O S S A R Y

G L O S S A R Y

International mail	[21CFR§1.276] means foreign national mail services. International mail does not include express consignment operators or carriers or other private delivery services unless such service is operating under contract as an agent or extension of a foreign mail service.

K

Known or reasonably foreseeable hazard	[21CFR§1.500] means a biological, chemical (including radiological), or physical hazard that is known to be, or has the potential to be, associated with a food or the facility in which it is manufactured/processed.

L

Live microbial dietary ingredient	[Guidance NDI] A single-celled prokaryotic or eukaryotic microorganism that is intended to be viable at the point of ingestion.
Lot	[21CFR§1.500] means the food produced during a period of time and identified by an establishment's specific code.
	[21CFR§111.3] means a batch, or a specific identified portion of a batch, that is uniform and that is intended to meet specifications for identity, purity, strength, and composition; or, in the case of a dietary supplement produced by continuous process, a specific identified amount produced in a specified unit of time or quantity in a manner that is uniform and that is intended to meet specifications for identity, purity, strength, and composition.

M

Manufacturer	[21CFR§1.276] means the last facility, as that word is defined in 1.227, that manufactured/processed the food. A facility is considered the last facility even if the food undergoes further manufacturing/processing that consists of adding labeling or any similar activity of a de minimis nature. If the food undergoes further manufacturing/processing that exceeds an activity of a de minimis nature, then the subsequent facility that performed the additional manufacturing/processing is considered the manufacturer.
Manufacturing/ processing	[21CFR§1.227] [21CFR§1.328] means making food from one or more ingredients, or synthesizing, preparing, treating, modifying or manipulating food, including food crops or ingredients. Examples of manufacturing/processing activities include: Baking, boiling, bottling, canning, cooking, cooling, cutting, distilling, drying/dehydrating raw agricultural commodities to create a distinct commodity (such as drying/dehydrating grapes to produce raisins), evaporating, eviscerating, extracting juice, formulating, freezing, grinding, homogenizing, irradiating, labeling, milling, mixing, packaging (including modified atmosphere packaging), pasteurizing, peeling, rendering, treating to manipulate ripening, trimming, washing, or waxing. For farms and farm mixed-type facilities, manufacturing/processing does not include activities that are part of harvesting, packing, or holding.
	[21CFR§1.500] means making food from one or more ingredients, or synthesizing, preparing, treating, modifying, or manipulating food, including food crops or ingredients. Examples of manufacturing/processing activities include: Baking, boiling, bottling, canning, cooking, cooling, cutting, distilling, drying/dehydrating raw agricultural commodities to create a distinct commodity (such as drying/dehydrating grapes to produce raisins), evaporating, eviscerating, extracting juice, extruding (of animal food), formulating, freezing, grinding, homogenizing,

Manufacturing/ processing (cont'd)	irradiating, labeling, milling, mixing, packaging (including modified atmosphere packaging), pasteurizing, peeling, pelleting (of animal food), rendering, treating to manipulate ripening, trimming, washing, or waxing. For farms and farm mixed-type facilities, manufacturing/processing does not include activities that are part of harvesting, packing, or holding.
Margin of safety	[Guidance NDI] A measure of how close the estimated daily intake (EDI) is to the level that has been shown to have no adverse effect in animal or human studies (the NOAEL). It is calculated as the ratio of the NOAEL to the highest total daily intake level (EDI) of the NDI or dietary supplement, as determined from the proposed conditions of use in the NDI notification, and is usually expressed in terms of fold change (e.g., a ten-fold margin of safety).
Marketed	[Guidance NDI] See question IV.A.7.
Master File	[Guidance NDI] In the dietary supplement context, a master file is a file containing manufacturing or other identity information submitted to FDA for use in an NDI notification by the submitter of the master file or by a person designated by the submitter. The submitter may rely on information from the master file in an NDI notification by incorporating it by reference, or may grant written authorization to other parties to incorporate information from the master file by reference in notifications covering the use of the NDI in their own products. A written authorization granting a right of reference to a master file in NDI notifications does not include the right to see or copy the master file unless the submitter of the master file otherwise specifies.
Maximum tolerated dose (MTD)	[Guidance NDI] The highest dose that causes no more than a 10 percent reduction in body weight and does not produce mortality, clinical signs of toxicity, or pathologic lesions that would be predicted to shorten the natural life span of an experimental animal for any reason other than the induction of neoplasms.
Metabolite	[Guidance NDI] A metabolite is a product of metabolism. In the dietary supplement context, a metabolite of a dietary ingredient is a molecular intermediate that incorporates structural elements of the ingested dietary ingredient and whose flux or net production in the human body increases on ingestion of the dietary ingredient. A metabolite can be part of (or an intermediate of) the catabolic or metabolic pathway of a dietary ingredient. FDA considers X to be a metabolite of Y if ingestion of Y by humans results in net production of/increased flux of X, incorporating structural elements of Y.
Microorganisms	[21CFR§1.500] means yeasts, molds, bacteria, viruses, protozoa, and microscopic parasites and includes species that are pathogens.
	[21CFR§111.3] means yeasts, molds, bacteria, viruses, and other similar microscopic organisms having public health or sanitary concern. This definition includes species that: (1) May have public health significance; (2) May cause a component or dietary supplement to decompose; (3) Indicate that the component or dietary supplement is contaminated with filth; or (4) Otherwise may cause the component or dietary supplement to be adulterated.
Mineral	[Guidance NDI] A substance of defined chemical composition which provides a form or source of inorganic elements to the diet. An element is one of a class of substances that cannot be separated into simpler substances by chemical means. Examples: calcium, iodine, and zinc.

Mixed-type facility	[21CFR§1.227] [21CFR§1.328] means an establishment that engages in both activities that are exempt from registration under section 415 of the Federal Food, Drug, and Cosmetic Act and activities that require the establishment to be registered. An example of such a facility is a "farm mixed-type facility," which is an establishment that is a farm, but also conducts activities outside the farm definition that require the establishment to be registered.
Must	[21CFR§111] is used to state a requirement.

N

Nanomaterial, nanotechnology	[Guidance NDI] FDA has not established regulatory definitions of "nanotechnology," "nanomaterial," "nanoscale," or other related terms. In the absence of a formal definition, when considering whether an FDA-regulated product, including dietary ingredients, contains nanomaterials or otherwise involves the application of nanotechnology, FDA intends to ask: (1) Whether a material or end product is engineered to have at least one external dimension, or an internal or surface structure, in the nanoscale range (approximately 1 nm to 100 nm); and (2) Whether a material or end product is engineered to exhibit properties or phenomena, including physical or chemical properties or biological effects, that are attributable to its dimension(s), even if these dimensions fall outside the nanoscale range, up to 1 micrometer (1,000 nm).
New dietary ingredient (NDI)	[Guidance NDI] A dietary ingredient that was not marketed in the U.S. before October 15, 1994.
No longer in its natural state	[21CFR§1.276] means that an article of food has been made from one or more ingredients or synthesized, prepared, treated, modified, or manipulated. Examples of activities that render food no longer in its natural state are cutting, peeling, trimming, washing, waxing, eviscerating, rendering, cooking, baking, freezing, cooling, pasteurizing, homogenizing, mixing, formulating, bottling, milling, grinding, extracting juice, distilling, labeling, or packaging. Crops that have been cleaned (e.g., dusted, washed), trimmed, or cooled attendant to harvest or collection or treated against pests, or polished are still in their natural state for purposes of this subpart. Whole fish headed, eviscerated, or frozen attendant to harvest are still in their natural state for purposes of this subpart.
Nonprofit food establishment	[21CFR§1.227] [21CFR§1.328] means a charitable entity that prepares or serves food directly to the consumer or otherwise provides food or meals for consumption by humans or animals in the United States. The term includes central food banks, soup kitchens, and nonprofit food delivery services. To be considered a nonprofit food establishment, the establishment must meet the terms of section 501(c)(3) of the U.S. Internal Revenue Code (26 U.S.C. 501(c)(3)).
Nontransporter	[21CFR§1.328] means a person who owns food or who holds, manufactures, processes, packs, imports, receives, or distributes food for purposes other than transportation.
Nontransporter immediate previous source	[21CFR§1.328] means a person that last had food before transferring it to another nontransporter.
Nontransporter immediate subsequent recipient	[21CFR§1.328] means a nontransporter that acquires food from another nontransporter.

No-Observable-Effect Level (NOEL)	[Guidance NDI] The highest dose or total daily intake level at which no effects (beneficial, neutral, or adverse) are observed in a properly designed and executed toxicological study.
No-Observed-Adverse-Effect Level (NOAEL)	[Guidance NDI] The highest dose or total daily intake level that did not elicit an adverse effect in a properly designed and executed toxicological study.
Nutritive value	[21CFR§101.14] means a value in sustaining human existence by such processes as promoting growth, replacing loss of essential nutrients, or providing energy.

O, P

Packaging	[21CFR§1.227] (when used as a verb) means placing food into a container that directly contacts the food and that the consumer receives.
Packaging (when used as a noun)	[21CFR§1.328] means the outer packaging of food that bears the label and does not contact the food. Packaging does not include food contact substances as they are defined in section 409(h)(6) of the Federal Food, Drug, and Cosmetic Act.
Packaging (when used as a verb)	[21CFR§1.328] means placing food into a container that directly contacts the food and that the consumer receives.
Packing	[21CFR§1.227] [21CFR§1.328] [21CFR§1.500] means placing food into a container other than packaging the food and also includes re-packing and activities performed incidental to packing or re-packing a food (e.g., activities performed for the safe or effective packing or re-packing of that food (such as sorting, culling, grading, and weighing or conveying incidental to packing or re-packing)), but does not include activities that transform a raw agricultural commodity, as defined in section 201(r) of the Federal Food, Drug, and Cosmetic Act, into a processed food as defined in section 201(gg) of the Federal Food, Drug, and Cosmetic Act.
Pathogen	[21CFR§1.500] means a microorganism of public health significance.
Perishable food	[21CFR§1.377] means food that is not heat-treated; not frozen; and not otherwise preserved in a manner so as to prevent the quality of the food from being adversely affected if held longer than 7 calendar days under normal shipping and storage conditions.
Person	[21CFR§1.328] includes individual, partnership, corporation, and association.
	[21CFR§101.9] means all domestic and foreign affiliates, as defined in 13 CFR 121.401, of the corporation, in the case of a corporation, and all affiliates, as defined in 13 CFR 121.401, of a firm or other entity, when referring to a firm or other entity that is not a corporation.
Pest	[21CFR§111.3] means any objectionable insect or other animal including birds, rodents, flies, mites, and larvae.
Physical plant	[21CFR§111.3] means all or any part of a building or facility used for or in connection with manufacturing, packaging, labeling, or holding a dietary supplement.
Port of arrival	[21CFR§1.276] means the water, air, or land port at which the article of food is imported or offered for import into the United States. For an article of food arriving by water or air, this is the port of unloading. For an article of food arriving by land, this is the port where the article of food first crosses the border into the United States. The port of arrival may be different than the port where consumption or warehouse entry or foreign trade zone admission documentation is presented to the U.S. Customs and Border Protection (CBP).

Port of entry	[21CFR§1.276] means the port of entry as defined in 19 CFR 101.1.
Pre-DSHEA dietary ingredient	[Guidance NDI] A dietary ingredient that was marketed in the U.S. before October 15, 1994.
Primary production farm	[21CFR§1.227] [21CFR§1.328] an operation under one management in one general (but not necessarily contiguous) physical location devoted to the growing of crops, the harvesting of crops, the raising of animals (including seafood), or any combination of these activities. The term "farm" includes operations that, in addition to these activities: (i) Pack or hold raw agricultural commodities; (ii) Pack or hold processed food, provided that all processed food used in such activities is either consumed on that farm or another farm under the same management, or is processed food identified in paragraph (1)(iii)(B)(1) of this definition; and (iii) Manufacture/process food,
	[21CFR§1.227] [21CFR§1.328] (cont'd) provided that: (A) All food used in such activities is consumed on that farm or another farm under the same management; or (B) Any manufacturing/processing of food that is not consumed on that farm or another farm under the same management consists only of: (1) Drying/ dehydrating raw agricultural commodities to create a distinct commodity (such as drying/dehydrating grapes to produce raisins), and packaging and labeling such commodities, without additional manufacturing/processing (an example of additional manufacturing/processing is slicing); (2) Treatment to manipulate the ripening of raw agricultural commodities (such as by treating produce with ethylene gas), and packaging and labeling treated raw agricultural commodities, without additional manufacturing/processing; and (3) Packaging and labeling raw agricultural commodities, when these activities do not involve additional manufacturing/processing (an example of additional manufacturing/processing is irradiation)
Processing	*See* Manufacturing/processing
Product complaint	[21CFR§111.3] means any communication that contains any allegation, written, electronic, or oral, expressing concern, for any reason, with the quality of a dietary supplement, that could be related to current good manufacturing practice. Examples of product complaints are: Foul odor, off taste, illness or injury, disintegration time, color variation, tablet size or size variation, under-filled container, foreign material in a dietary supplement container, improper packaging, mislabeling, or dietary supplements that are superpotent, subpotent, or contain the wrong ingredient, or contain a drug or other contaminant (e.g., bacteria, pesticide, mycotoxin, glass, lead).

Q

Qualified auditor	[21CFR§1.500] means a person who is a qualified individual as defined in this section and has technical expertise obtained through education, training, or experience (or a combination thereof) necessary to perform the auditing function as required by 1.506(e)(1)(i) or 1.511(c)(5)(i)(A). Examples of potential qualified auditors include: (1) A government employee, including a foreign government employee; and (2) An audit agent of a certification body that is accredited in accordance with subpart M of this part.
Qualified individual	[21CFR§1.500] means a person who has the education, training, or experience (or a combination thereof) necessary to perform an activity required under this subpart, and can read and understand the language of any records that the person

Qualified individual (cont'd)	must review in performing this activity. A qualified individual may be, but is not required to be, an employee of the importer. A government employee, including a foreign government employee, may be a qualified individual.
Quality	[21CFR§111.3] means that the dietary supplement consistently meets the established specifications for identity, purity, strength, and composition, and limits on contaminants, and has been manufactured, packaged, labeled, and held under conditions to prevent adulteration under section 402(a)(1), (a)(2), (a)(3), and (a)(4) of the act.
Quality control	[21CFR§111.3] means a planned and systematic operation or procedure for ensuring the quality of a dietary supplement.
Quality control personnel	[21CFR§111.3] means any person, persons, or group, within or outside of your organization, who you designate to be responsible for your quality control operations.
R	
Raw agricultural commodity has the	[21CFR§1.500] meaning given in section 201(r) of the Federal Food, Drug, and Cosmetic Act.
Ready-to-eat food (RTE food)	[21CFR§1.500] means any food that is normally eaten in its raw state or any food, including a processed food, for which it is reasonably foreseeable that the food will be eaten without further processing that would significantly minimize biological hazards.
Receiving facility	[21CFR§1.500] means a facility that is subject to subparts C and G of part 117 of this chapter, or subparts C and E of part 507 of this chapter, and that manufactures/processes a raw material or other ingredient that it receives from a supplier.
Recipe	[21CFR§1.328] means the formula, including ingredients, quantities, and instructions, necessary to manufacture a food product. Because a recipe must have all three elements, a list of the ingredients used to manufacture a product without quantity information and manufacturing instructions is not a recipe.
Registrant	[21CFR§1.227] means the owner, operator, or agent in charge of a facility that manufactures/processes, packs, or holds food for consumption in the United States.
Registration number	[21CFR§1.276] means the registration number assigned to a facility by FDA under section 415 of the act (21 U.S.C. 350d) and subpart H of this part.
Representative sample	[21CFR§111.3] means a sample that consists of an adequate number of units that are drawn based on rational criteria, such as random sampling, and that are intended to ensure that the sample accurately portrays the material being sampled.
Reprocessing	[21CFR§111.3] means using, in the manufacture of a dietary supplement, clean, uncontaminated components or dietary supplements that have been previously removed from manufacturing and that have been made suitable for use in the manufacture of a dietary supplement.
Reserve sample	[21CFR§111.3] means a representative sample of product that is held for a designated period of time.

Restaurant

[21CFR§1.227] means a facility that prepares and sells food directly to consumers for immediate consumption. "Restaurant" does not include facilities that provide food to interstate conveyances, central kitchens, and other similar facilities that do not prepare and serve food directly to consumers. (1) Entities in which food is provided to humans, such as cafeterias, lunchrooms, cafes, bistros, fast food establishments, food stands, saloons, taverns, bars, lounges, catering facilities, hospital kitchens, day care kitchens, and nursing home kitchens are restaurants; and (2) Pet shelters, kennels, and veterinary facilities in which food is provided to animals are restaurants.

[21CFR§1.328] means a facility that prepares and sells food directly to consumers for immediate consumption. "Restaurant" does not include facilities that provide food to interstate conveyances, central kitchens, and other similar facilities that do not prepare and serve food directly toconsumers. (1) Facilities in which food is directly provided to humans, such as cafeterias, lunchrooms, cafes, bistros, fast food establishments, food stands, saloons, taverns, bars, lounges, catering facilities, hospital kitchens, day care kitchens, and nursing home kitchens, are restaurants. (2) Pet shelters, kennels, and veterinary facilities in which food is directly provided to animals are restaurants.

Retail food establishment

[21CFR§1.227] means an establishment that sells food products directly to consumers as its primary function. The term "retail food establishment" includes facilities that manufacture, process, pack, or hold food if the establishment's primary function is to sell from that establishment food, including food that it manufactures, processes, packs, or holds, directly to consumers. A retail food establishment's primary function is to sell food directly to consumers if the annual monetary value of sales of food products directly to consumers exceeds the annual monetary value of sales of food products to all other buyers. The term "consumers" does not include businesses. A "retail food establishment" includes grocery stores, convenience stores, and vending machine locations. A "retail food establishment" also includes certain farm-operated businesses selling food directly to consumers as their primary function. (1) Sale of food directly to consumers from an establishment located on a farm includes sales by that establishment directly to consumers: (i) At a roadside stand (a stand situated on the side of or near a road or thoroughfare at which a farmer sells food from his or her farm directly to consumers) or farmers' market (a location where one or more local farmers assemble to sell food from their farms directly to consumers); (ii) Through a community supported agriculture program. Community supported agriculture (CSA) program means a program under which a farmer or group of farmers grows food for a group of shareholders (or subscribers) who pledge to buy a portion of the farmer's crop(s) for that season. This includes CSA programs in which a group of farmers consolidate their crops at a central location for distribution to shareholders or subscribers; and (iii) At other such direct-to-consumer sales platforms, including door-to-door sales; mail, catalog and Internet order, including online farmers markets and online grocery delivery; religious or other organization bazaars; and State and local fairs. (2) Sale of food directly to consumers by a farm-operated business includes the sale of food by that farm-operated business directly to consumers: (i) At a roadside stand (a stand situated on the side of or near a road or thoroughfare at which a farmer sells food from his or her farm directly to consumers) or farmers' market (a location where one or more local farmers assemble to sell food from their farms directly to consumers); (ii) Through a community supported agriculture program. Community supported

Retail food establishment (cont'd)	agriculture (CSA) program means a program under which a farmer or group of farmers grows food for a group of shareholders (or subscribers) who pledge to buy a portion of the farmer's crop(s) for that season. This includes CSA programs in which a group offarmers consolidate their crops at a central location for distribution to shareholders or subscribers; and (iii) At other such direct-to-consumer sales platforms, including door-to-door sales; mail, catalog and Internet order, including online farmers markets and online grocery delivery; religious or other organization bazaars; and State and local fairs. (3) For the purposes of this definition, "farm-operated business" means a business that is managed by one or more farms and conducts manufacturing/processing not on the farm(s).

S

Safety factor or uncertainty factor	[Guidance NDI] A multiplier used to account for uncertainty about the extent to which data gathered in one context can be used to predict the safety of a substance in other contexts. For example, safety factors attempt to account for differences between animals and humans (uncertainty factor of interspecies variation), differences in sensitivity among humans (uncertainty factor of intraspecies variation), and extrapolation of subchronic to chronic data (uncertainty factor of extrapolated data from subchronic to chronic). Safety factors can be combined multiplicatively to account for multiple sources of uncertainty. Safety factors are used in calculating an acceptable daily intake (ADI) for various FDA-regulated products, including color additives, food additives, and new animal drugs. See questions VI.C.5 and VI.C.7.
Salt of a dietary ingredient	[Guidance NDI] salts are composed of cations (positively charged ions) bound to anions (negatively charged ions). The salt of a dietary ingredient is a neutral compound that is formed by the union of an acid or a base with a counter ion and that dissociates to the starting ingredients after ingestion.
Sanitize	[21CFR§111.3] means to adequately treat cleaned equipment, containers, utensils, or any other cleaned contact surface by a process that is effective in destroying vegetative cells of microorganisms of public health significance, and in substantially reducing numbers of other microorganisms, but without adversely affecting the product or its safety for the consumer.
Secondary activities farm	[21CFR§1.227] [21CFR§1.328] an operation, not located on a primary production farm, devoted to harvesting (such as hulling or shelling), packing, and/or holding of raw agricultural commodities, provided that the primary production farm(s) that grows, harvests, and/or raises the majority of the raw agricultural commodities harvested, packed, and/or held by the secondary activities farm owns, or jointly owns, a majority interest in the secondary activities farm. A secondary activities farm may also conduct those additional activities allowed on a primary production farm as described in paragraphs (1)(ii) and (iii) of this definition.
Shipper	[21CFR§1.276] means the owner or exporter of the article of food who consigns and ships the article from a foreign country or the person who sends an article of food by international mail or express consignment operators or carriers or other private delivery service to the United States.
Stereoisomers	[Guidance NDI] molecules that are identical in atomic composition and bonding, but differ in the three-dimensional arrangement of the atoms.
Subchronic	[Guidance NDI] Refers to toxicological studies that are 1 to 3 months in duration.

Substance	[21CFR§101.14] means a specific food or component of food, regardless of whether the food is in conventional food form or a dietary supplement that includes vitamins, minerals, herbs, or other similar nutritional substances.

T

Target Population	[Guidance NDI] The target population for a dietary supplement means the population group or groups (defined by gender, age, and/or health status) that a manufacturer or distributor identifies (e.g., in product labeling, promotional materials, or in an NDI notification) as those for whom the product is appropriate or recommended. Examples of target populations include adults, children 14 and over, and women going through menopause.
Theoretical yield	[21CFR§111.3] means the quantity that would be produced at any appropriate step of manufacture or packaging of a particular dietary supplement, based upon the quantity of components or packaging to be used, in the absence of any loss or error in actual production.
Tincture	[Guidance NDI] An aqueous alcoholic solution (e.g., an aqueous alcoholic extract of leaves or other plant material). A tincture is characterized by the ratio of the weight of the dried botanical to the volume or weight of the finished product. A 1:5 ratio is 1 part botanical to 5 parts solution.
Trade name	[21CFR§1.227] means the name or names under which the facility conducts business, or additional names by which the facility is known. A trade name is associated with a facility, and a brand name is associated with a product.
Transporter	[21CFR§1.328] means a person who has possession, custody, or control of an article of food in the United States for the sole purpose of transporting the food, whether by road, rail, water, or air. Transporter also includes a foreign person that transports food in the United States, regardless of whether that foreign person has possession, custody, or control of that food for the sole purpose of transporting that food.
Transporter's immediate previous source	[21CFR§1.328] means a person from whom a transporter received food. This source can be either another transporter or a nontransporter.
Transporter's immediate subsequent recipient	[21CFR§1.328] means a person to whom a transporter delivered food. This recipient can be either another transporter or a nontransporter.

U

U.S. agent	[21CFR§1.227] means a person (as defined in section 201(e) of the Federal Food, Drug, and Cosmetic Act (21 U.S.C. 321(e))) residing or maintaining a place of business in the United States whom a foreign facility designates as its agent for purposes of this subpart. A U.S. agent may not be in the form of a mailbox, answering machine or service, or other place where an individual acting as the foreign facility's agent is not physically present. (1) The U.S. agent acts as a communications link between FDA and the foreign facility for both emergency and routine communications. The U.S. agent will be the person FDA contacts when an emergency occurs, unless the registrationspecifies another emergency contact. (2) FDA will treat representations by the U.S. agent as those of the foreign facility, and will consider information or documents provided to the U.S. agent the equivalent of providing the information or documents to the foreign facility. FDA will consider

U.S. agent (cont'd)	[21CFR§1.227] (cont'd) the U.S. agent the equivalent of the registrant for purposes of sharing information and communications. The U.S. agent of a foreign facility may view the information submitted in the foreign facility's registration. (3) Having a single U.S. agent for the purposes of this subpart does not preclude facilities from having multiple agents (such as foreign suppliers) for other business purposes. A firm's commercial business in the United States need not be conducted through the U.S. agent designated for purposes of this subpart.
U.S. owner or consignee	[21CFR§1.500] means the person in the United States who, at the time of U.S. entry, either owns the food, has purchased the food, or has agreed in writing to purchase the food.
Uncertainty factor	[Guidance NDI] See Safety factor.
Unit	[21CFR§101.9] means the packaging or, if there is no packaging, the form in which a food product is offered for sale to consumers.
United States	[21CFR§1.276] means the Customs territory of the United States (i.e., the 50 States, the District of Columbia, and the Commonwealth of Puerto Rico), but not the Territories.

V

Very small importer	[21CFR§1.500] means: (1) With respect to the importation of human food, an importer (including any subsidiaries and affiliates) averaging less than $1 million per year, adjusted for inflation, during the 3-year period preceding the applicable calendar year, in sales of human food combined with the U.S. market value of human food imported, manufactured, processed, packed, or held without sale (e.g., imported for a fee); and (2) With respect to the importation of animal food, an importer (including any subsidiaries and affiliates) averaging less than $2.5 million per year, adjusted for inflation, during the 3-year period preceding the applicable calendar year, in sales of animal food combined with the U.S. market value of animal food imported, manufactured, processed, packed, or held without sale (e.g., imported for a fee).
Vitamin	[Guidance NDI] An organic substance that is a minor component of foods, is essential for normal physiological functions (e.g., maintenance, growth, or development), is normally not produced endogenously (within the body) in amounts adequate to meet normal physiologic needs, and which causes, by its absence or underutilization, a clinically defined deficiency syndrome

W

Water activity (aw)	[21CFR§111.3] is a measure of the free moisture in a component or dietary supplement and is the quotient of the water vapor pressure of the substance divided by the vapor pressure of pure water at the same temperature.
We	[21CFR§1.377] [21CFR§111.3] means the U.S. Food and Drug Administration (FDA).
Working day	[21CFR§1.377] means any day from Monday through Friday, excluding Federal holidays.

X, Y, Z

You

[21CFR§1.227] means the owner, operator, or agent in charge of a facility that manufactures/processes, packs, or holds food for consumption in the United States.

[21CFR§1.276] means the person submitting the prior notice, i.e., the submitter or the transmitter, if any.

[21CFR§1.328] means a person subject to this subpart under 1.326.

[21CFR§1.377] means any person who received the detention order or that person's representative.

[21CFR§1.500] means a person who is subject to some or all of the requirements in this subpart.

[21CFR§111.3] means a person who manufactures, packages, labels, or holds dietary supplements.

INDEX

INDEX

INDEX

INDEX

INDEX

INDEX

INDEX

INDEX

INDEX

INDEX

INDEX

T

INDEX

W

INDEX

X

Y

Z

About the Authors

Dr. Kirstin A. Counts has dedicated over 20 years to patient care, advocacy, and the healthcare industry and is a Board Certified Chiropractic Physician with an additional certification in Functional Medicine Chiropractic Family Practice from the American Chiropractic Association's Council on Diagnosis & Internal Disorders. Focusing on patient care, practice development, compliance strategies, and community outreach, her primary interest is in harmonizing all practical and philosophical approaches to patient care for the unified advancement of the entire healthcare industry.

Having spent many years of her life as a modern dancer, Dr. Counts is no stranger to chronic pain and the sacrifices required to live through it. Her first professional job as a dancer was with the Firethorne Dance Theatre in Tampa, Florida when she was nine years old. She continued to dance professionally at Cypress Gardens, act in public service announcement films for child abuse victims, dance at Carnegie Hall, perform and choreograph with multiple regional dance companies, and perform in Paris through her teenage years and as a young adult. Her choreography and group performance of "Shallow Waters" won the regional competition of the American College Dance Festival representing the University of South Florida.

Initially pursuing a career as a medical doctor following several serious knee injuries and a life-saving hospitalization to treat a systemic infection, she was introduced to chiropractic as a college student by visiting a chiropractor for help with a low back injury. With subsequent treatment, she began to see dramatic changes in her health, including fewer headaches, the elimination of asthma (which she had battled since childhood), and the resolution of chronic knee pain that had been unchanged by surgery.

Her fascination with the human body, its structure, its function and its potential combined with the powerful chiropractic experience she had as a patient led her to pursue a career as a chiropractic physician rather than as a medical doctor, as she had originally planned, after her early career in dance. She built her patient practice on this foundation and with a deep passion for sharing this knowledge and improving the daily lives of patients. During her time in daily practice she discovered that many medical doctors were reluctant to refer their patients to chiropractic specialists and often chose pharmaceutical interventions over manual therapies or dietary supplementation. This realization led her to find alliances within the medical and pharmaceutical communities to build significant bridges between chiropractic and allopathic care and to seek further education in Functional Medicine through the Diplomate of the American Board of Chiropractic Internists (DABCI) program.

During a change in her practice location and management, she became aware of new requirements for small entity compliance to federal law. As a part of the American Recovery and

Reinvestment Act, all public and private healthcare providers and other eligible professionals were required to adopt and demonstrate "meaningful use" of electronic medical records (EMR) in order to maintain their existing Medicaid and Medicare reimbursement levels. While Dr. Counts had spent her career as a physician and private practice owner managing the rigors of insurance participation requirements, changes from ICD 9 to ICD 10, and all of the general standards of practice (including HIPAA), the new regulatory requirements for meaningful use (42 CFR Part 495) were her first entry into formalized federal law changing her practice model and how she needed to think about regulations in a private practice.

In recent years, her focus has been on helping practitioners and manufacturers navigate the regulatory landscape safely to bring well-managed products to patients. She has co-authored published works with a globally renowned pharmaceutical executive and joined a recognized corporate authority on global regulatory compliance for pharmaceutical and dietary supplement manufacturing. Her first audit and inspection of a dietary supplement manufacturer resulted in a multi-company Warning Letter issued by the US Food and Drug Administration (FDA).

She received her doctorate degree from Palmer College of Chiropractic in 2000, graduating magna cum laude. She received her BS in Biology with a minor in Modern Dance from the University of South Florida in Tampa and attended high school and her first year of college at the North Carolina School of the Arts in Winston-Salem where she also majored in Modern Dance.

Mindy Allport-Settle, M.B.A. was born in Beckley and raised in Oak Hill, West Virginia. She moved to North Carolina to attend the N.C. School of the Arts for high school and now lives near Raleigh. Following in the footsteps of Gordon Allport, all of her books are built on a foundation of psychology and sociology with a focus on improving some aspect of industry through research and education.

Her career in healthcare began when she was a teenager working as an emergency medical technician. Since then, she has joined the U.S. Navy's advanced hospital corps, worked in organ and human tissue procurement, specialized in ophthalmology, and moved on to serve as a key executive, board member, and consultant for some of the best companies in the pharmaceutical, medical device, and biotechnology industry. She has provided guidance in regulatory compliance, corporate structuring, restructuring and turnarounds, new drug submissions, research and development and product commercialization strategies, and new business development. Her experience and dedication have resulted in international recognition as the developer of the only FDA-recognized and benchmarked quality systems training and development business methodology.

Her education includes a Bachelor's degree from the University of North Carolina, an MBA in Global Management from the University of Phoenix, and completion of the corporate governance course series in audit committees, compensation committees, and board effectiveness at Harvard Business School.

About PharmaLogika

PharmaLogika is a professional services organization that specializes in the biotechnology industry and offers professional services and products for start-up and emerging organizational growth, discovery and clinical trial navigation, and market entry positioning.

PharmaLogika draws on extensive and diverse experiences in the biotechnology and pharmaceutical industry. Over the years, PharmaLogika team members have led scientific discovery through major research institutions, conducted investigations for various market health authorities (MHAs), developed and implemented regulatory policies as investigators for the Food and Drug Administration (FDA) and the European Medicines Agency (EMEA), sat on boards for major biotechnology organizations, and have led pharmaceutical commercial organizations through new product launches and line extensions.

Pharma
Logika
B o o k s

Need More Copies?

Order now at

www.PharmaLogika.com

or your favorite bookseller

Other titles available from

PharmaLogika Books

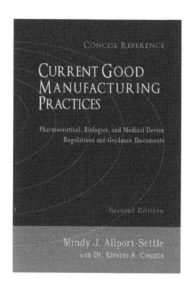

**Current Good Manufacturing Practices:
Pharmaceutical, Biologics, and Medical
Device Regulations and Guidance
Documents,
Concise Reference
Second Edition**

**FDA Establishment Inspections:
Pharmaceutical, Biotechnology, Medical
Device and Food Manufacturing
Concise Reference**

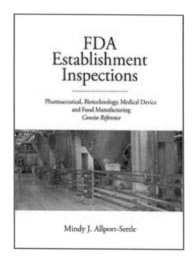

**Federal Food, Drug, and Cosmetic Act:
The United States Federal FD&C Act
Concise Reference**

**Good Clinical Practice:
Pharmaceutical, Biologics, and
Medical Device Regulations and
Guidance Documents
Concise Reference; Volume 1**

**International Conference on
Harmonisation (ICH) Quality Guidelines:
Pharmaceutical, Biologics, and Medical
Device Guidance Documents
Concise Reference**

Visit our website at

www.PharmaLogika.com

for ordering and additional information

Made in the USA
Middletown, DE
13 June 2020